# A Sociological Framework for Patient Care

# A SOCIOLOGICAL FRAMEWORK FOR PATIENT CARE

*Edited by*

**JEANNETTE R. FOLTA,** R.N., Ph.D.

*Co-Director, Research Training Program in Social Psychiatry, School of Nursing, University of California Medical Center*

**EDITH S. DECK,** R.N., M.S.

*Assistant Professor, Coordinator of First-Year Basic Baccalaureate Nursing Program, School of Nursing, University of California Medical Center*

**JOHN WILEY & SONS, INC.** *New York    London    Sydney*

PHOTOGRAPHIC CREDITS

Wynn Bullock: *Title page, Prologue, Part One, Part Seven*
Elaine Mayes: *Part Five*
Phiz Mozesson: *Part Three, Part Four, Part Six (Courtesy of Salvation Army)*
Nathan Zabarsky: *Part Two*

Library of Congress Catalog Card Number: 66–27898

Printed in the United States of America

*To the memory of our first teachers*
*Rev. Leonard Pakulski, O.F.M.C.*
*and*
*John W. Schulze*

# *Foreword*

One of the most exciting developments in the field of nursing education during the past ten years has been our increasing recognition of the importance of the basic sciences in the improvement of nursing care. Students and practitioners are encouraged to identify pertinent concepts, theories, and principles from both the social and natural sciences as the first step in the solution of nursing problems.

This book gives us a sociological framework to serve as one base of departure in that search. It introduces us to the world of patients, families, professionals, and society. The editors pose the thesis that to understand our patients we must understand ourselves and our place in society. To that end they give us initially a clear exposition of a number of common concepts: culture, society, role, status, social class, and others. These are terms that many of us use glibly but inaccurately today in the nursing literature.

Presentations of social movements, the family, and the patient role are included within the book's central theme. We are encouraged to look at ourselves through the social scientists' eyes. Carefully chosen essays and articles by both social scientists and medical professionals serve to support the editors' original contributions. Some of the writers are familiar to all of us; others will be new. All are provocative and challenging. The tone is scholarly but humor also is present. A carefully prepared annotated bibliography provides a bonus for the reader.

A second recent development in nursing also is exemplified in this book. Both of the editors are nurses. They are typical of the nurse scholar of today who has studied in depth in the social sciences and who is able to look at nursing from that broader perspective and to choose essential knowledge, insights, and procedures which both students and practitioners can then apply to patient care.

It is an honor to introduce the reader to this presentation of a sociological framework for patient care.

Katherine J. Hoffman, R.N., Ph.D.
Professor of Nursing
University of Washington

Seattle, Washington
July 1966

# Preface

ανθρωποσ εστι πολιτικον ζωον

*Aristoteles*

Through social life man becomes a human being possessing a self and conducting himself with the use of constructed acts. Group life does not simply consist of associations of reacting organisms or simple response to objects and other stimuli. For as George H. Mead indicates, man possesses a "self" that is a process, not a structure. His action is constructed as he interprets what confronts him, establishes goals, plans activity, and interprets this action to others. He may misinterpret objects or people or use poor judgment, but nevertheless he acts on the basis of his perceptions. Such is the basis of symbolic interaction — the interpretation of others and actions based on this interpretation. The interpretation is made on the basis of values, roles, and norms that exist within a social and cultural structure.

The basis of patient care is the understanding of these symbolic interactions, for it is through this understanding that the health worker may better comprehend human activity. The activities of health workers involve observation, interpretation, and interaction with a variety of persons from many different socioeconomic and cultural backgrounds. Hence the patient and other professionals as well may be seen as persons in social roles, each interpreting their world to themselves and others and acting accordingly. Not only must the professional understand the aspects of behavior that enable the patient to believe and act as he does toward his illness, the hospital, and those responsible for his care, but also the professional must coordinate the action of patients with potential conflicts between institutional and professional priorities. Therefore he needs to study the processes of symbolic interaction and the social structure within which this action is formulated and initiated. Taken together these elements give meaning to the dynamic world and in turn permit the work of the professional and patient to take place despite the complexity and potential confusion or conflict between interpretations and the interpretation and subsequent action.

Even individual illness is a part of the process of symbolic interaction. To understand it fully requires not only notions or theories of its physiological nature but of the processes by which the illness is interpreted and acted upon. Hence the totality of the social variables that influence the individual in his perception of the illness, the anxieties associated with it, the networks of interaction with which he is associated (family, hospital), and the sociocultural definitions of illness and the sick role as normal or deviant behavior must be considered.

To study the patient within this framework, we must examine the concepts, observe and record phenomena, and establish a general theoretical framework of patient care. There is no way to determine the sequence of the study of these phenomena — we may begin with concepts and end with theory or begin with observations and end with concepts and theory. Whatever the starting point, the process is a continual search for the most effective and comprehensive theories and their application. Considering the need for the establishment of theories of patient care and ways of implementing these theories, we have set out to enlarge the systems for understanding and implementing the processes of symbolic interaction as the basis for patient care. Many sociological concepts might be considered relevant to the pursuit of this goal. Because of practical considerations, however, we have chosen to delineate those that have maintained a degree of validity and reliability throughout time. Undoubtedly others would add to or modify these selections we have chosen.

Teachers of nursing and other health disciplines have been finding for many years that their profession is developing with increasing rapidity. They have been forced to take account of recent advances in such diverse fields as physiology, science, psychology, sociology, and research — fields that only a few student generations ago were thought to belong to other disciplines. To some extent new theory and research have helped bring into clearer focus the role and function of all of the health professionals. It is within the province of the health workers (nurse, physician, social worker, etc.) to bring to bear upon patients all relevant factors, from whatever sources and by whatever methods ascertained, that constitute "total" patient care.

With the trend toward integration of all aspects of patient care in the basic curricula, there is a need for a book of readings that will tie together the underlying concepts and principles inherent in comprehensive care. This trend toward integration has led health educators away from the exclusive use of textbooks and increasingly more emphasis has been placed on the use of an extensive variety of readings and bibliographies. Although we do not propose with this book to eliminate the need for textbooks, we have included a representative sample of readings that exemplify the concepts and principles of "total" patient care.

Our aim therefore is to present illustrative selections of the concepts underlying integrated health programs. No claim is made to "cover the whole field" of concepts but rather to choose those we believe will be potentially most useful to teachers and students alike. By a systematic ordering of the most recent and pertinent research and articles by social, behavioral, and health scientists and nurses, it is hoped a basis can be established for a better comprehension of the dynamics and dimensions of patient care.

In addition, we have included an extensive annotated bibliography covering many aspects of health care to supplement the readings and footnotes already included. It is anticipated that these annotations will lead the reader to new ventures in patient care.

This book is a composite of ideas from a variety of sources. Although we have tried to recognize by footnotes, we cannot acknowledge all, for their ideas too are a composite of our "selves" as actors in a social life. To our colleagues and contributors we owe more than symbolic verbal communication can express.

In addition to our contributors, special mention for assistance is due: Mary Rinehart; for tolerance, forbearance, and stimulation of our conceptualizations: Leonard Schatzman and Katherine Hoffman; for secretarial assistance, without which manuscripts cannot gain momentum: Duncan Pierce, Sydney Nance, Steven Tolin, Katherine Lane, Patricia Rodden, and Jean Quinn; not to be forgotten is the staff of Wiley, particularly: Earl Shepherd, Bernard Scheier, and Judith Starnes, who transformed this book of readings from a fantasy to a reality.

To all who have given their time, energy, and thought, we are most grateful.

Jeannette R. Folta
Edith S. Deck

San Francisco, California
July 1966

# Contributors

*Ronald E. Anderson*, M.A.; Department of Sociology, Stanford University, Palo Alto, California

*Ernest A. T. Barth*, Ph.D.; Department of Sociology, University of Washington, Seattle, Washington

*Robert R. Bell*, M.A.; Department of Sociology, Temple University, Philadelphia, Pennsylvania

*Wayne Blanchard*, M.A.; Department of Sociology, University of Washington, Seattle, Washington

*Samuel W. Bloom*, Ph.D.; Department of Sociology and Administration, State University of New York, Downstate Medical Center, Brooklyn, New York

*Peter M. Dean*; Teachers College, Columbia University, New York, New York

*Halbert L. Dunn*, M.D., Ph.D.; Chief of the Office of Vital Statistics, United States Public Health Service, Washington, D.C.

*George L. Engel*, M.D.; Department of Psychiatry, University of Rochester Medical Center, Rochester, New York

*Jeannette R. Folta*, R.N., Ph.D.; University of California Medical Center, San Francisco, California

*Victor J. Freeman*, M.D.; University of Pittsburgh, Pittsburgh, Pennsylvania

*Philip N. Haese*, Ph.D.; Department of Sociology, Psychiatric Institute, School of Medicine, University of Nebraska, Omaha, Nebraska

*Reuben Hill*, Ph.D.; Department of Sociology, University of Minnesota, Minneapolis, Minnesota

*Richard J. Hill*, Ph.D.; Department of Sociology, University of Texas, Austin, Texas

*Gerald A. King*, M.A.; Department of Sociology, Stanford University, Palo Alto, California

*Otto N. Larsen*, Ph.D.; Department of Sociology, University of Washington, Seattle, Washington

*Robert C. Leonard*, Ph.D.; Department of Sociology and Nursing, University of Arizona, Tucson, Arizona

*Lucile Petry Leone*, M.A.; Assistant Surgeon General, United States Public Health Service, Washington, D.C.

*Alfred R. Lindesmith*, Ph.D.; Department of Sociology, Indiana University, Bloomington, Indiana

*George A. Lundberg*, Ph.D.; Department of Sociology, University of Washington, Seattle, Washington

*S. Dale McLemore*, Ph.D.; Department of Sociology, University of Texas, Austin, Texas

*Richard L. Meile*, Ph.D.; Department of Sociology, Psychiatric Institute, School of Medicine, University of Nebraska, Omaha, Nebraska

*Lester C. Mills;* Teachers College, Columbia University, New York, New York

*Horace M. Miner*, Ph.D.; Department of Anthropology and Sociology, University of Michigan, Ann Arbor, Michigan

*S. Frank Miyamoto*, Ph.D.; Department of Sociology, University of Washington, Seattle, Washington

*Louis H. Orzack*, Ph.D.; Department of Sociology and Anthropology, Boston University, Boston, Massachusetts

*Talcott Parsons*, Ph.D.; Department of Social Relations, Harvard University, Cambridge, Massachusetts

*Jeanne C. Quint*, R.N., M.S.; School of Nursing, University of California Medical Center, San Francisco, California

*Leonard Schatzman*, Ph.D.; Sociologist, University of California Medical Center, San Francisco, California

*Clarence C. Schrag*, Ph.D.; Department of Sociology, University of Southern California, Los Angeles, California

*Hans Selye*, M.D.; Institute of Experimental Medicine and Surgery, University of Montreal, Montreal, Canada

*Ozzie G. Simmons*, Ph.D.; Department of Social Anthropology, School of Public Health, Harvard University, Cambridge, Massachusetts

*Dorothy E. Smith*, Ph.D.; Department of Medical Sociology, University of California, Berkeley, California

*Luke M. Smith*, Ph.D.; Department of Sociology, Alfred University, Alfred, New York

*Samuel A. Stouffer*, Ph.D.; Sociologist (Deceased)

*Robert Straus*, Ph.D.; Department of Behavioral Science, University of Kentucky Medical Center, Lexington, Kentucky

*Anselm L. Strauss*, Ph.D.; School of Nursing, University of California Medical Center, San Francisco, California

*Holger R. Stub*, Ph.D.; Department of Sociology, Temple University, Philadelphia, Pennsylvania

*Dorrian Apple Sweetser*, Ph.D.; Sociologist, School of Nursing, Boston University, Boston, Massachusetts

*Richard M. Titmuss*, D.Sc.; Professor of Social Administration, University of London, London, England

*Florence S. Wald*; Dean, School of Nursing, Yale University, New Haven, Connecticut

*Walter B. Watson*, Ph.D.; Department of Social Sciences, University of Alberta, Alberta, Canada

*Leslie A. White*, Ph.D.; Department of Anthropology, University of Michigan, Ann Arbor, Michigan

*Mark Zborowski*, B.S.; Mount Zion Hospital and Research Center, San Francisco California

# Contents

# A Sociological Framework for Patient Care

# Prologue to the Venture

Today's affluent American society manifests concern for social as well as physical survival. Prosperity has made it possible to provide monies for the study of physical ill health, its prevention and cure. As a result, many illnesses have been brought under medical control, and in the process man has become aware that cultural and social factors initiate, influence, or exaggerate illness.

Consequently the public increasingly demands better patient care and the prevention of illness and establishment of ultimate states of health. Just as one who acquires material goods then desires more and more, so as the general health rate improves, the demands for "more" health also increase. Thus industry has been forced by the public and by law to provide increased safety and health measures for employees. Smog devices are required increasingly to help prevent air pollution. And in many communities programs for prevention of illness and for health education have been initiated and continue to grow.

Many of our scientific advances in the control of disease have brought new problems to be solved. Current concern with the effect of such health measures on the structure of the family, health professions, and society at large has focused the desire for a socially as well as physically healthy society. Thus, as each problem is solved, a new challenge arises.

In an attempt to solve some of these dilemmas social medicine is evolving. As Susser and Watson[1] indicate,

social medicine is . . . a complex and difficult branch of medical science in that it attempts to grapple both with the nature of social processes and their complicated relation to health and disease. In consequence, social medicine, if it is to be effective, must draw on the concepts and methods of discipline other than biology and the natural sciences, on epidemiology, demography, sociology, social anthropology, and social psychology.

The significance of the contributions of social science to the field of health and illness is discussed by Dorothy Smith in Part One.

Utilizing the concept of social medicine, we have developed a sociological framework for patient care. Our method has been to conceptualize patient care as an adventurous journey along the roads and pathways of health and illness. To begin the venture it is necessary that we define the concepts to be used throughout. We also explore many of the social factors that influence the beliefs and practices of patients and health workers. Some of these factors create problems for all who are in need of or concerned with effective patient care. We believe that an elucidation of sociocultural influences will expedite the development of more effective treatment modalities.

Man is, after all, a complex of many individualistic attributes and properties or processes. These include age, I.Q., sex, and personality characteristics. On a higher level of variables are those attributes of social position or status that in-

1

clude occupational choice. There are also variables of social structure such as family and social class. Further, there are attributes and processes of culture that include norms, values, and ideals. Taken together, all these variables permit one to answer the question: What makes it possible, or impossible, for persons differentially situated in a social system to want to do and be able to do that which will be in their best interests to do? The contributions of social science enable health workers to relate these specific social factors and processes to particular states of health and illness.

This book considers a number of these social factors and processes that are relevant for patient care. These by no means include all of the relevant factors, but rather our perception of the more salient ones. They include a variety of sociological concepts that are interacting parts of a dynamic social system. No one part is uninfluenced by any other part. They in fact all interact and have influence on each other as well as on the process of patient care as each is modified throughout time and space. The following diagram indicates a sociological framework of such a dynamic social system for patient care:

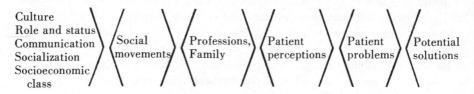

Culture
Role and status
Communication      Social          Professions,   Patient        Patient        Potential
Socialization      movements       Family         perceptions    problems       solutions
Socioeconomic
class

Part One, therefore, concerns the concepts of culture and society, socialization into role and status, communication and perception, and social class. The ways in which man thinks, believes, and acts depend largely on the culture and society in which he dwells. It is within these societal boundaries that his group life and subsequent interpersonal relationships are structured. In these relationships man develops personal goals and aspirations that lead him to action. The more a health worker understands the development and consequences of these relationships, the better he will comprehend patient beliefs and behavior as well as his own.

During his entire life man is being changed and is changing others through the multiplicity of groups to which he belongs or aspires to belong. He selects some group values and rejects others; he learns new roles and avoids others. Socialization is a constant process from birth to death.

As man matures, he decides upon a career choice. If he is to become a health professional, he will undergo not only formal education designed to give him knowledge and ways of applying it but also an informal education to "socialize" him. As he proceeds through the labyrinth on his way to becoming, he will be influenced into new ways of thinking, believing, and acting.

As the following articles will demonstrate, cultural and individual, both patient and professional, perceptions of health and illness are influenced if not determined by the roles played by both groups. The differences among social classes often create different health and social problems and may require different modalities of patient care. The health worker's commitment to his profession, the organization in which he works, or the patients in his care presents potential conflict for himself and his patients, especially if they cannot find a mutual ground for communication. The patient, too, must be socialized into the role of patient. Although the content of socialization may be different for the two groups, as it may be different for the child and the adult, the process is the same.

Part Two explores the paths of some of the major trends and social movements that influence society, patients, and professionals. Although man is born into a particular culture, he personally initiates social action that influences the beliefs and behavior of others. Social movements are important because they provide a basic understanding of the ways in which new norms and values are created and acted upon. They illuminate the dynamics of social change that is part of everyday life and whose impact is felt throughout society.

Trends and social movements within our culture often are created by a desire for change. They begin with a particular ideology justifying the group perspective and end with group action. Such movements may create changes in family structure, the content and process of education, the perceptions, values, and norms of life, and conceptions of health and illness.

Part Three demonstrates that although the health worker needs to be aware of his patients and their families, he also needs to be aware of his own role as a person and professional. He also is an acting, feeling, becoming being who must maintain a life of his own outside his professional and organizational affiliations. Too frequently the health worker becomes so submerged in his professional role that he is unable to maintain a life of his own which is satisfying to himself and his family. Like the patient in his charge, an overpreoccupation and overinvolvement in any one aspect of life can hamper his objective perception of others and their way of life. Whether professional or nonprofessional, an individual must move with the stream of life in order to understand it.

If the professional develops a conception of life that includes but goes beyond his own work, then he can become aware of and knowledgeable about the multiplicity of streams that crisscross every aspect of human endeavor. If he is to stem the tide he must constantly anticipate as well as be aware of social movements, public demands, and governmental preoccupations which have implications for him as both professional and citizen. It is within this overview of society that he can best make his contributions to professional, public, and governmental endeavors. Then he can create intelligent advice regarding policies, programs, and legislation that affect members of his profession, allied professions, and relationships between health and illness.

The advice he gives depends in part on his perception of his function. He may function with purposes in mind that are not related to the immediate needs of any given patient; that is, he may be concerned with efficient care of many patients, involved in research or teaching, or preoccupied with professional and organizational mandates that hinder individualistic care. Such a situation not only may hamper treatment, but also may create role conflict for the professionals. But even so, some type of dialogue between patient and staff is established and patient care does go on.

There are, in addition, many other problems that staff must anticipate in order to prevent possible negative consequences such as language difficulty created by ethnic, cultural, or class differences, or by ignorance and adverse diagnosis or prognosis. Not that patients should be made aware of the latter; rather, that having been made aware of them, the professional is available for a discourse about the consequences for the patient. This in turn requires that the professional be aware of his own basic beliefs, attitudes, and ideology about these adverse conditions. Obviously, if he cannot handle his own anxieties, he will not be able to assist the patient to live or die in dignity.

Part Four deals with the structure of the family, its influences on the individual, and its role in health and illness. Family relationships have enduring significance throughout the life span of the individual. The modes of mate selection and the individual family roles not only influence family members but also have broad implications for health care.

It is often within the family that the individual discovers ways in which to solve everyday stresses and strains. The ways in which he learns to handle these problems influence his ability to withstand more serious emotional and physical stresses that can create or contribute to a variety of illnesses. Similarly this modality of action determines how he can manage the potential and real crises of illness and death throughout the family life cycle.

Not only must the professional be concerned with the individual patient who has sought or been brought to his care, he must consider the family constellation and the mutual relationship of patient to family. Information regarding diagnosis, progress, and prognosis should be communicated to both the individual and his immediate family or significant others. In many instances the family, whose members are of crucial importance in the patient's care, rehabilitation, and resocialization into society, is the last to be consulted or informed by health professionals. Not only is this important but in many instances the care and cure of the patient requires the involvement of both the individual and his family in the decisions regarding his fate.

In some instances, particularly in communicable diseases and in psychiatric disorders, it may be necessary to involve the entire family in the treatment process. For as Opler and Singer[2] point out, the family constellation which is related to ethnic background plays an important role in the manifestations of certain psychiatric disorders. This also implies that the treatment must be different. For example, Opler and Singer[3] demonstrate that the schizophrenic males of Irish and Italian descent present different sets of symptoms. The Irish, who are dominated by their mothers and viewed by them as "forever boys and burdens," are sexually repressed, fantasy rather than action oriented, and suffer from alcoholism and feelings of sin and guilt. On the other hand, Italians, dominated by their fathers who sanction free expression of emotion, exhibit more overt homosexuality, behavioral disorders, and hostility toward authority. This is only one of many examples of the need for family involvement in total patient care.

Total patient care depends not only on family involvement but on perceptions of health and illness. Part Five directs us along the path to a definition of these

states. It discusses the incidence and prevalence of disease and the societal definitions that contribute to decisions regarding this problem. It is here that the
health worker gets a glimpse of the ways in which individuals decide whether
they are ill and, if so, whether they will seek help. Perceptions vary in regard
to what constitutes illness and requires assistance. Some will immediately seek
professional medical help; for others lay or quasi-professionals are selected to
help solve the health problem. If the health professional is aware of some of the
sociocultural dynamics of individual action, ways may be found for prevention
of serious hazards or at least earlier treatment and care. For man's behavior is
based on what he takes into account of his own goals, others' expectations of
him, and his image of what his action will mean to himself and others. This
action may be centered around a particular event or around a series of social
situations. If ill, he may accept without question any information given by those
who are close to him, or he may accept information only from particular categories of health workers. He may seek general information or solely that which
is specific to his perceived problem. Once engaged in treatment he may question
the treatment modality, intervene in the treatment plan, or manage his own care.

Each individual has his own comprehension of illness, health, and the professionals and agencies that provide care. Everyone has his own terminology
for defining illness and care which may or may not coincide with that of
health workers. The following are possible perceptions and actions of particular individuals:

1. Understands the health problem but modifies it to fit his own life style.
2. Understands the health problem but rejects it.
3. Understands the health problem and accepts professional treatment.
4. Does not understand the health problem but seeks help for its solution.
5. May neither understand the health problem nor seek help for its solution.

The individual's action depends largely on his understanding of the situation.
The following diagram illustrates the several factors that may be involved:

Depending on his original perceptions, the patient may or may not seek information or assistance. If he does and his expectations of illness, professionals, and
agencies coincide with what he finds, he will not need to modify these perceptions. What usually occurs, however, is that he constantly has to revise his expectations. In any event he develops one or more strategies to enable him to
handle the situation. He may avoid it, confront it, seek outside assistance, utilize
magic ("If I don't know what it is, it will go away!"), or seek the help of other
intermediaries between himself and his caretakers such as to ask the nurse to ask
his doctor to explain his illness to him.

Part Six explores the path of patienthood. If the individual becomes ill and decides to seek medical care, he is confronted with a variety of new situations and problems. He does not become a patient simply by becoming ill or being hospitalized; rather, he learns this new role. Both he and the health workers are then faced with problems of stress, anxiety, pain, fear, and possible death. The implications of these problems may vary depending on the cultural and social backgrounds of those involved in the care process. Differences in perception of these problems may facilitate or hamper the patient's ability to adapt to his new situation and participate in his treatment and care along the way to, rehabilitation.

On the road back to health, the ill develop their own criteria for progress. Decrease in pain and medication, more and different kinds of food, increased ambulation, type of unit or ward assigned, and a definite date set for discharge are frequently used as indicators of progress. Using this observable data, the patient makes the assumption either that he will reach a state of health or become more ill. This may or may not be the case. Frequently the inadequate or inaccurate information that health workers transmit causes misconceptions.

The professional has a responsibility both to help the patient and to strive to understand clearly what he is expressing. This implies that all communication must transpire on the patient's level which in turn depends on the social variables that impinge upon the patient's perception. The health worker must also endeavor to become aware of the factors lying beneath the surface of the verbal notations. These include psychosocial problems such as the patient's shifting roles and changes in self-concept and in family demands.

The professional must be cognizant of the fact that patients try to maintain a self-image and life style unchanged by disease. The patient often tends to see himself as unaltered by disease even though he may have made many changes in his way of living. The extensive adjustments he makes to his illness are determined by his sense of what is adequate for himself. Such adjustments include initially making his own diagnosis and instituting his own care based on previous or readily available experience. The health worker thus has an additional responsibility to disseminate accurate information to a public audience. Today scientific knowledge is undergoing constant revision. Health and research teams from many disciplines are solving many of the mysteries of life. New ways are being developed for the testing and application of this new knowledge to better patient care. But new problems continue to arise. Research findings are not static; they require constant retesting. New research is and should be designed to develop useful theories for health and health care.

How can the health professional handle the complexity of problems that arise or are inherent in the process of patient care? Part Seven provides some suggestions through the use of problem solving and research, theory development and computer dissemination of information. These methods are by no means the only available or useful modes of solution; instead, they are discussed as the potentially most useful at this time in history.

Problem-solving techniques, if properly used, allow the health worker to deal with everyday individualistic contingencies that confront him. This technique is not sufficient, however, for the development of a theory of health care and practice which is essential for coping with health problems on a larger scope. These problems belong to the realm of research. The utilization of mechanized computers allows us to conduct research and analyze data on a much larger scale than ever before possible. This is not the only use for computers. They may also be utilized to perform many of the tasks that take health workers' time away from the patient. In addition, they can function as convenient and rapid sources of stored knowledge about the latest discoveries in the area of patient care.

---

1. M. W. Susser and W. Watson, *Sociology in Medicine*, London: Oxford University Press, 1962, p. viii.

2. Marvin K. Opler and J. L. Singer, "Ethnic Differences in Behavior in Psychopathology," *International Journal of Social Psychiatry*, **2**, 1956, 11–22.

3. *Ibid.*

# PART ONE

## *The Venture: Sociological Concepts*

Man is essentially a thinking, feeling, and creative animal. Although he may not be rational in every aspect of his life, he strives to incorporate his behavior and beliefs into a meaningful whole. He positions within a hierarchy of ideals and desires all the complex variables that confront him in every cognitive and affective decision. Thus over the centuries he has been able to solve many of the mysteries of the world. Struggling with a vast number of findings and theories, and in the face of innumerable setbacks, man has managed to wrest some kind of rational order from his existence. In so doing he has progressed slowly from the realm of folklore and superstition to one in which scientific methods have given him meaningful ways of learning about himself and the life around him.

Many of yesterday's truths have become today's fictions, whereas many "science fiction" and primitive absurdities of yesterday are seen as the facts and truths of today. The Indian witch doctor's "sweat teepee" used for high fevers and the disease now known as pneumonia has become the "steam room" in the sterile and scientific hospital of the twentieth century. Man has learned to control aspects of the earth, his environment, and interstellar space. Control of disease and the development of birth delivery processes have increased his life expectancy beyond the imagination of primitive man. Unfortunately, however, all our technological advances have not brought with them a comparable conquest of the problems involved in man's relationship to man.

In the contemporary health arena, illness has been thrown to the hospital where biological and psychological heroes and heroines valiantly attempt rescue — sometimes succeeding, sometimes failing. Ill health is not as simple as the germ theory. We must venture beyond this theory in order to create innovations within the sphere of life known as patient care. It is no longer sufficient for the biologist to state that $x$ causes $y$ and for nurse and doctor to set about curing $y$ disease in Mr. John. Scientific studies of the causes of illness now show us that the disease known as $y$ is influenced, if not in fact caused, by a multiplicity of variables and not by a single causative agent. Similarly, "cure" is becoming secondary to "care," and a multidisciplinary approach is necessary to care successfully for Mr. John.

The determination of Mr. John's state of health or illness, as well as his reaction to his condition, depends not only on the intensity of his state but also on a set of variables that may antecede or intervene between the onset of the symptoms and the recognition of the illness, and between the recognition and the action taken, if any. These variables may be *biological* in nature; that is, they may involve a pathological state within the body. They may be *psychological* involving factors such as anxiety, stress, and fear regarding the potential consequences of the disease. Other variables may include those of a *cultural* nature;

9

that is, they may involve ways in which health and illness are affected by learning. Still other variables may involve the *social* situation, including the place and surroundings in which the illness occurs, the accessibility and availability of assistance, and knowledge of the necessity for treatment or the types of care available. As Parsons indicates, the surroundings in which illness occurs influence the ability to obtain release from obligations to family, friends, job, or even the social order itself. The manner of response, and hence the probability of receiving care of any sort, is a complex of these biological, psychological, cultural, and social variables. As indicated in the Prologue, the concepts of culture and society must be defined if these variables are to be in any way significant in the relationships of health workers and patients, man to man.

The behavior of mankind has regular and recurrent patterns. The fundamental events of birth, marriage, and death, the details of toothbrushing, bathing, use of the lavatory, and even behavior in public places, all follow discernible patterns. The focus on individual idiosyncrasies, however, often leads us to overlook the similarities and repetitiveness of behavior. To account for these regularities, the concepts of culture and society have been developed by social science.

## CULTURE AND SOCIETY

Formerly anthropologists agreed on the definition of culture, but this is no longer true. We will use White's definition: "Culture is a class of things and events that consist of, or are dependent upon, symboling, considered in an extrasomatic context." Not that culture is extrasomatic, but rather that it is interpreted within an extrasomatic context. That is, people *have* a culture; they do not constitute a culture. Culture is, after all, composed of ways; society is composed of people.

Culture, then, refers to patterns of social interaction, normative and behavioral systems, and products of these systems. It is not a single way of acting and believing; rather it provides defined alternatives within the boundaries of prescription and taboo.

All cultures have some common elements, but it is the configuration of traits within each culture that is unique. These configurations comprise a series of folkways, mores, and norms that determine the limits of behavior and the symbols and material goods that are both the products and enhancers of the culture. The folkways consist of typical ways of conduct and action which are common to a group. They have been handed down from generation to generation and are acted upon without much thought. Examples include throwing rice at a wedding, and shaking hands or rubbing noses in greeting. Mores, on the other hand, although they also are unquestioned ways of acting, carry with them the notion of a sense of "proper," moral, or virtuous behavior. Examples include delivering one's baby in a hospital and not challenging the word of one's physician. Norms are sets of rules with strict sanctions that act as guides to conduct and tend to produce conformity. Examples include the patient's following the advice of health workers and the professional conforming to the procedure manual of the hospital.

Man is not born with a culture, he is born into one. He apprehends this complex of social products through communication. Although he is born with biological needs for food, sex, and the like, he learns through culture how to satisfy them. There are prescriptions and taboos regarding the kinds of food to be eaten and the method of preparation: raw rattlesnake for the jungle man, seaweed-fried octopus for the Oriental, broiled steak for the Texan. Alternatives within any cultural system are available within the boundaries dictated by the culture: to boil, broil or bake; to become a carpenter, farmer, or physician; to self-diagnose and self-treat illness, or to seek and use the skills of trained professionals for such services.

No one person manifests all elements of his culture. Cultural beliefs become incorporated into language which in turn affects these beliefs by providing, as Brown[1] notes, names for the concepts by which man deals with his world. To the extent that the individual is exposed to a language system, his perception of his culture is expanded. Not all cultural alternatives, however, are learned by every-one in a certain culture, for some normative requirements are specific only to members of various groups as determined by age, sex, role, or geographic area.

## COMMUNICATION AND PERCEPTION

Symbolic interaction (communication) constitutes, as Lundberg, Schrag, and Larsen state, the basic process of human social life. It is through communication that culture is transmitted. For communication is concerned largely with norms, statuses, values, and reciprocal relationships and operates on the premise that be-havior is an interplay between self and the expected or actual behavior of others. Man, unlike other animals, creates and uses symbols and hence does not depend entirely on his immediate experience and environment. Rather, symbols allow him to perceive, to organize these perceptions, and to abstract aspects of reality. Symbols, then, are any acts, objects, or events that stand for something else (referent). They are not just shortcuts for communicating experience; they are the heart of communication.

Every word is a symbol; every idea a complex of symbols. Language is a sys-tematic arrangement of these complexes organized in such fashion that direct experience can be communicated to as well as learned from others. The reliable representation of human experience requires that the symbols used be both accurate and adequate; that is, they should bear a rational relationship to ex-perience, and they should exhaust the symbolic possibilities of experience. For example, one may say, "My patient is a Caucasian, male, age 42, who has Hodgkins disease." Although this may be accurate, it may not be adequate for planning his care and treatment in that he may well feel his condition is not serious and therefore does not require professional help. The ways in which we perceive and even the things that we see are significantly and consistently affected by the symbols we use during the perceiving process, whether or not we are aware of our use of them. We "see" by the use of symbols, and the accuracy of our per-ception depends on the accuracy and adequacy of these symbols.

There are many characteristic ways of seeing. We can see a tree from many perspectives: poetically, botanically, militarily, or commercially. We can write poems about trees, observe the size, shape, and structure of the tree, think of the tree as a weapon, a place to hide, potential food, or as an economic investment. Hence the dynamic process of perception depends on a number of interlocking variables, the relative importance of which depends on the situation at hand. The botanist chooses his variables and symbols for the experience of a tree quite differently than the starving man alone in the forest.

In order to see, we have to participate in a discourse within a world of belief and knowledge. As Brown[2] indicates, the process of naming objects is part of the development of language and behavior. New language adds new perspective; new experiences require new words; this makes possible new kinds of behavior that are dynamic and expansive, not static and ritualized. To perceive, we must create a framework in which words are tied together into a meaningful whole; that is, there is no concept of illness without a concept of medicine, no concept of vitamin without a concept of diet, no concept of patient without a concept of health.

The language of social science is both difficult and deceptively simple. Concepts of class and culture, for example, often give the mistaken impression that these groupings of persons respond identically or very similarly, which is not, in fact, the truth. It is no more true to assume that all members of the Nacirema culture described by Miner act alike than it is to assume that each member of the lower socioeconomic class advocates crime. Perception, to a large extent, is learned. Although the individual is born with certain organs that enable him to perceive, he *learns* the elements that constitute for him a framework within which to place his experiences. Obviously, if the individual lacks one or more of his senses of sight, sound, smell, taste, touch, or pain, he will have difficulty in perceiving in certain ways. As Helen Keller has demonstrated, however, the blind can learn to "see" through the development and perfection of other senses.

The culture, society, and class into which one is born structure, in part, the kinds of perception that are possible. The Chinese, for example, are much more perceptive of minute physical differences among individual Orientals than are Caucasians; artists are more perceptive of slight changes in color and hue than nonartists; some ethnic groups discriminate more finely than others among the varieties of pain. Perceptions comprise not only designations of experience but also attitudes toward it. The child who looks at a red, white, and blue object, calls it a flag, and then puts it in the mud and stomps on it has the right designation, flag, but an incorrect attitude; the child who makes a mud pie and eats it has the wrong designation, food, but the correct attitude. Similarly some cultural groups identify and react to certain experiences as pain but do not hold the attitude that professional help should be sought for its alleviation.

## SOCIALIZATION

Each individual is born into one of many large subcultural groups, all of which make up society as a whole. If these groups are to survive, the members of each group must be able to perceive its structure correctly and be motivated to conform to its norms and requirements. Although man's biological nature makes it possible for him to perceive and conform, it also necessitates that he learn to use language, for it is through symbolic interaction that he becomes a social being.

The process by which culture and its norms are transmitted is known as social-ization. It is, as Merton[3] points out, the means by which individuals learn the values, attitudes, interests, skills, and knowledge of their cultural group. Through this process the individual acquires discipline, aspirations, and ambitions, assumes new and different roles, and learns the skills required in these roles. Also it teaches him to delay gratification by aspiring to "greater things." Social control is taught both to develop the social individual and to strengthen the group.

Socialization is a dynamic process that has a beginning but never an end. The newborn enters the process as a member of what Cooley[4] defines as the primary group — that small, intimate, relatively permanent group with which he will con-tinue to have frequent contact throughout his life. His entrance into the family is his first contact not only with intimacy but also with authority figures. From them he learns, through imitation and interaction, the norms, requirements, and satisfactions of social life. Later, through interaction with his peer groups, he will learn still other folkways and informal aspects of societal living.

One is not born with a consciousness of *self* — it develops through interaction with others; in this way one also develops a *social* consciousness. One's concept of self grows as communication skills develop on both verbal and nonverbal levels. According to Cooley,[5] the essential nature of self is its reflective character, known as the "looking-glass self." The individual temporarily looks at himself through the eyes of others; his perception of how they view him influences what his actual self becomes. Early in life he starts learning to control his destiny by continually reevaluating others' reactions to him. This process is not smooth and uniform, since people may respond to him differently from his expectations or he may be unwilling or unable to perceive their responses correctly.

The individual's perception of others' judgment of him influences both his judgment of himself and his subsequent behavior. As he reflects some of these perceptions to himself, he develops a concept of "real self." In addition, this process gives rise to a notion of "ideal self" or what he would like to be. To the extent that his "real" and "ideal" selves are the same, personal conflict and stress is minimized.

Early in this process of evaluation and reevaluation, the individual begins thinking of self in terms of "I" as well as developing a sense of group identifica-tion. The extent of socialization through learning values and skills will determine which group or groups he will consider outsiders. The outsiders are, by and large, the secondary group — that large, impersonal, constantly changing group of people not included in his immediate and intimate world of other persons.

As an adult the reference groups from which the individual selects his ambi-tions, aspirations, gratifications, and rewards continually reshape his self. This process of adult socialization is one of learning new roles that provide blueprints for anticipated as well as actual socialization. By this time, as Lindesmith and Strauss indicate, he has learned to "take the role of others." That is, he not only plays roles, he learns to anticipate and "feel" what it is like to be in many given role positions. Obviously the roles he is learning are not entirely consciously or deliberately learned. They emerge from informal as well as formal interaction with others, for role is a composite not only of formal mandates but also of informal anticipations and expectations of behavior within and beyond the given role.

Society is after all a network of relationships among individuals who are members of a complex array of cultures and social groups. The notions of role, position, and status provide links between the elements of such a network. Role is the fundamental unit of social structure. The concept of role is linked to what a person *should* do, as well as to what a person *does* do. Role is also the dynamic component within the behavioral system. As Lundberg, Schrag, and Larsen[6] point out, a behavioral system comprises norms that include role requirements in the nature of formal prescriptions and informal expectations which are attached to positions and result in action. The position or location of a person within a set of roles is the static component. The role requirements describe how he should act according to the norms of the group. Some of the formal requirements may be stipulated by law, as are some norms governing the role of physicians, whereas others may be stipulated by the organization in which the role occupier works. For example, some states allow licensed practical nurses to give drugs, but some hospitals within those states still do not allow this practice. On the other hand many informal expectations are also placed on the role incumbent by families and peer groups. As Linton[7] points out, an individual may occupy several roles or positions simultaneously, but he does not exercise them at the same time. For example, a physician may also be a father, husband, and brother, but when he interacts with a patient he acts only the role of physician. In the same way that a person learns the norms and behavior appropriate to the role he occupies, he also learns to establish a hierarchy within the multiple roles he plays. This allows him to act one role at a time and thereby minimize the potential for conflict.

To the extent that there is agreement among the role requirements, and between these requirements and the individual's anticipated acts, role conflict is again minimized. Contradictory or ambiguous requirements make it impossible for the incumbent to act as his role indicates he should and hence decrease the predictability of role performance. Similarly, as Mechanic[8] states, in order for two individuals to establish a workable relationship, it is necessary that each be aware of the other's role expectations. In a therapeutic setting the communication of unambiguous expectations is necessary for the process of therapy to take place. When communication becomes unclear, role distortions or conflict may occur.

## *SOCIAL CLASS*

Stratification or division of a population by relatively homogeneous statuses (positions within the prestige system of a society) constitutes a "social class" system. Although culture determines the general thoughtways and behavioral patterns of all members within a given society, social class accounts for differences in obligations, restrictions, privileges, and rewards among different groups within that society. The social class to which one belongs influences one's perception and behavior. Hence the fact that society is segmented by social class also provides a framework for understanding common values among these large groupings.

In a stratified society there are differences in status among those who interact within that society. These differences usually include occupation, residence, income, and education as well as differences in value systems and styles of living. The upper class with its emphasis on family background and gracious living, the middle class with its emphasis on career achievement and respectability, and the lower class's emphasis on "getting by" provide examples of some overall differences among the classes. These distinctions in turn create differences within the opportunity and reward structure as well as in the interaction patterns. For, as Simmons points out, the differential distribution of disease entities between classes, the consequent evaluation of appropriate foci of public-health activity, and the interpersonal relations between the health team and members of various class systems all demonstrate the implications of social-class values and opportunities for health needs and services.

---

1. Roger Brown, "How Shall a Thing Be Called?," *Psychological Review*, **65**, 1958, 267 276.

2. *Ibid.*

3. Robert K. Merton, *Social Theory and Social Structure*, Glencoe, Ill.: Free Press, 1959. See especially Part II.

4. Charles H. Cooley, *The Two Major Works of Charles H. Cooley: Social Organization; and Human Nature and the Social Order*, Glencoe, Ill.: Free Press, 1956.

5. *Ibid.*

6. George A. Lundberg, Clarence Schrag, and Otto Larsen, *Sociology*, 3rd ed., New York: Harper and Row, 1963. See especially pp. 11–14.

7. Ralph Linton, *The Cultural Background of Personality*, New York: Appleton-Century, 1945.

8. David Mechanic, "Role Expectations and Communication in the Therapist-Patient Relationship," *The Journal of Health and Human Behavior*, **2**, 1961, 190–198.

# 1. THE CONCEPT OF CULTURE

## *Leslie A. White*

Much of the discussion of the concept of culture in recent years has been concerned with a distinction between culture and human behavior. For a long time many anthropologists were quite content to define culture as behavior, peculiar to the human species, acquired by learning, and transmitted from one individual, group, or generation to another by mechanisms of social inheritance. But eventually some began to object to this and to make the point that culture is not itself behavior, but is an abstraction from behavior. Culture, say Kroeber and Kluckhohn,[1] "is an abstraction from concrete human behavior, but it is not itself behavior." Beals and Hoijer[2] and others take the same view.

Those who define culture as an abstraction do not tell us what they mean by this term. They appear to take it for granted (1) that they themselves know what they mean by "abstraction," and (2) that others, also, will understand. We believe that neither of these suppositions is well founded; we shall return to a consideration of this concept later in this essay. But whatever an abstraction in general may be to these anthropologists, when culture becomes an "abstraction" it becomes imperceptible, imponderable, and not wholly real. According to Linton,[3] "culture itself is intangible and cannot be directly apprehended even by the individuals who participate in it." Herskovits[4] also calls culture "intangible." Anthropologists in the imaginary symposium reported by Kluckhohn and Kelly[5] argue that "one can see" such things as individuals and their actions and interactions, but "has anyone ever seen 'culture'?" Beals and Hoijer[6] say that "the anthropologist cannot observe culture directly; ...."

Thus when culture becomes an abstraction it not only becomes invisible and imponderable: it virtually ceases to exist. It would be difficult to construct a less adequate conception of culture. Why, then, have prominent and influential anthropologists turned to the "abstraction" conception of culture?

The reasoning is simple and direct: if culture is behavior, then (1) culture becomes the subject matter of psychology, since behavior is the proper subject matter of psychology; culture would then become the property of psychologists and "psychologizing sociologists"; and (2) nonbiological anthropology would be left without a subject matter. The danger was real and imminent; the situation, critical. What was to be done?

The solution proposed by Kroeber and Kluckhohn was neat and simple: let the psychologists have behavior; anthropologists will keep for themselves abstractions from behavior. These abstractions become and constitute *culture*.

The present writer is no more inclined to surrender culture to the psychologists than are Kroeber and Kluckhohn; indeed few anthropologists have taken

Excerpted by permission of the author and the American Anthropological Association, from the *American Anthropologist*, Vol. 61, 1959, pp. 227–252.

greater pains to distinguish psychological problems from culturological problems than he has. But he does not wish to exchange the hard substance of culture for its wraith either. No science can have a subject matter that consists of intangible, invisible, imponderable, ontologically unreal "abstractions"; a science must have real stars, real mammals, foxes, crystals, cells, phonemes, gamma rays, and culture traits to work with. We believe that we can offer an analysis of the situation that will distinguish between psychology, the scientific study of behavior on the one hand, and culturology, the scientific study of culture, on the other, and at the same time give a real, substantial subject matter to each.

The first step in scientific procedure is to observe, or more generally to experience, the external world in a sensory manner. The next step — after precepts have been translated into concepts — is the classification of things and events perceived or experienced. Things and events of the external world are thus divided into classes of various kinds: acids, metals, stones, liquids, mammals, stars, atoms, corpuscles, and so on. Now it turns out that there is a class of phenomena, one of enormous importance in the study of man, for which science has yet no name: this is the class of things and events consisting of or dependent upon symboling. It is one of the most remarkable facts in the recent history of science that this important class has no name, but the fact remains that it does not. And the reason why it does not is because these things and events have always been considered and designated, not merely and simply as the things and events that they are, in and of themselves, but always as things and events in a particular context.

A thing is what it is; "a rose is a rose is a rose." Acts are not first of all ethical acts or economic acts or erotic acts. An act is an act. An act becomes an ethical datum or an economic datum or an erotic datum when — and only when — it is considered in an ethical, economic, or erotic context. Is a Chinese porcelain vase a scientific specimen, an object of art, an article of commerce, or an exhibit in a lawsuit? The answer is obvious. Actually, of course, to call it a "Chinese porcelain vase" is already to put it into a particular context; it would be better first of all to say "a glazed form of fired clay is a glazed form of fired clay." As a Chinese porcelain vase, it becomes an object of art, a scientific specimen, or an article of merchandise when, and only when, it is considered in an esthetic, scientific, or commercial context.

Let us return now to the class of things and events that consist of or are dependent upon symboling: a spoken word, a stone axe, a fetich, avoiding one's mother-in-law, loathing milk, saying a prayer, sprinkling holy water, a pottery bowl, casting a vote, remembering the sabbath to keep it holy — "and any other capabilities and habits [and things] acquired by man as a member of [human] society" (Tylor).[7] They are what they are: things and acts dependent upon symboling.

We may consider these things-and-events-dependent-upon-symboling in a number of contexts: astronomical, physical, chemical, anatomical, physiological, psychological, and culturological, and consequently they became astronomic, physical, chemical, anatomical, physiological, psychological, and culturological phenomena in turn. All things and events dependent upon symboling are dependent also upon solar energy which sustains all life on this planet; this is the astronomic context. These things and events may be considered and interpreted in terms of the anatomical, neurological, and physiological processes of the human beings who exhibit them. They may be considered and interpreted also in terms of their relationship to human organisms, i.e., in a somatic context. And they may be considered in an extrasomatic context, i.e., in terms of their relationship to other like things and events rather than in relationship to human organisms.

When things and events dependent upon symboling are considered and interpreted in terms of their relationship to human organisms, i.e., in a somatic context, they may properly be called *human behavior*, and the science, *psychology*. When things and events dependent upon symboling are considered and interpreted in an extrasomatic context, i.e., in terms of their relationships to one another rather than to human organisms, we may call them *culture*, and the science, *culturology*.

A thing or event dependent upon symboling — a symbolate — is just what it is, but it may become significant in any one of a number of contexts. As we have already seen, it may be significant in an astronomic context: the performance of a ritual requires the expenditure of energy which has come from the sun. But within the sciences of man we may distinguish two significant contexts: the somatic and the extrasomatic. Symbolates may be considered and interpreted in terms of their relationship to the human organism, or they may be considered in terms of their relationships to one another, quite apart from their relationship to the human organism. Let us illustrate with some examples.

I smoke a cigarette, cast a vote, decorate a pottery bowl, avoid my mother-in-law, say a prayer, or chip an arrowhead. Each one of these acts is dependent upon the process of symboling; each therefore is a symbolate. As a scientist I may consider these acts (events) in terms of their relationships to me, to my organism; or I may treat them in terms of their relationships to one another, to other symbolates, quite apart from their relationship to my organism.

In the first type of interpretation I consider the symbolate in terms of its relationship to my bodily structure: the structure and functions of my hand, for example; or to my stereoscopic, chromatic vision; or to my needs, desires, hopes, fears, imagination, habit formation, overt reactions, satisfactions, and so forth. How do I feel when I avoid my mother-in-law or cast a ballot? What is my attitude toward the act? What is my conception of it? Is the act accompanied by heightened emotional tone, or do I perform it in a mechanical, perfunctory manner? And so on. We may call these acts *human behavior*; our concern is *psychological*.

What we have said of acts (events) will apply to objects (things) also. What is my conception of a pottery bowl, a ground axe, a crucifix, roast pork, whisky, holy water, cement? What is my attitude and how do I react toward each of these things? In short, what is the nature of the relationship between each of these things and my own organism? We do not customarily call these things human behavior, but they are the embodiments of human behavior; the difference between a nodule of flint and a stone axe is the factor of human labor. An axe, bowl, crucifix — or a haircut — is congealed human labor. We have then a class of objects dependent upon symboling that have a significance in terms of their relationship to the human organism. The scientific consideration and interpretation of this relationship is *psychology*.

But we may treat symbolates in terms of their relationships to one another, quite apart from their relationship to the human organism. Thus, in the case of the avoidance of a mother-in-law, we would consider it in terms of its relationship to other symbolates, or symbolate clusters, such as customs of marriage — monogamy, polygyny, polyandry — place of residence of a couple after marriage, division of labor between the sexes, mode of subsistence, domestic architecture, degree of cultural development, and so on. Or if we are concerned with voting we would consider it in terms of forms of political organization (tribal, state), kind of government (democratic, monarchical, fascist); age, sex, or property qualifications; political parties and so on. In this context our symbolates become *culture* — culture traits or trait clusters, i.e., institutions, customs, codes, etc., and the scientific concern in *culturology*.

*Culture, then, is a class of things and events, dependent upon symboling, considered in an extrasomatic context.* This definition rescues cultural anthropology from intangible, imperceptible, and ontologically unreal abstractions and provides it with a real, substantial, observable subject matter. And it distinguishes sharply between behavior — behaving organisms — and culture; between the science of psychology and the science of culture.

## THE LOCUS OF CULTURE

If we define culture as consisting of real things and events observable, directly or indirectly, in the external world, where do these things and events exist and have their being? What is the locus of culture? The answer is: the things and events that comprise culture have their existence, in space and time, (1) within human organisms, i.e., concepts, beliefs, emotions, attitudes; (2) within processes of social interaction among human beings; and (3) within material objects (axes, factories, railroads, pottery bowls) lying outside human organisms but within the patterns of social interaction among them. The locus of culture is thus intraorganismal, interorganismal, and extraorganismal.

But, someone might object, you have said that culture consists of extrasomatic phenomena and now you tell me that culture exists, in part, within human organisms. Is this not a contradiction? The answer is: No, it is not a contradiction; it is a misunderstanding. We did not say that culture consists of extrasomatic things and events, i.e., phenomena whose locus is outside human organisms. What we said is that culture consists of things and events considered within an extrasomatic context. This is quite a different thing.

Every cultural element has two aspects: subjective and objective. It might appear that stone axes are "objective," and ideas and attitudes are "subjective." But this is a superficial and inadequate view. An axe has a subjective component; it would be meaningless without a concept and an attitude. On the other hand, a concept or an attiude would be meaningless without overt expression, in behavior or speech (which is a form of behavior). Every cultural element, every culture trait, therefore, has a subjective and an objective aspect. But conceptions, attitudes, and sentiments — phenomena that have their locus within the human organism — may be considered for purposes of scientific interpretation in an extrasomatic context, i.e., in terms of their relation to other symboled things and events rather than in terms of their relationship to the human organism. Thus we may consider the subjective aspect of the mother-in-law taboo, i.e., the conceptions and attitudes involved, in terms of their relationship, not to the human organism, but to other symbolates such as forms of marriage and the family, place of residence after marriage, and so on. On the other hand, we may consider the axe in terms of its relationship to the human organism — its meaning; the person's conception of it; his attitude toward it — rather than to other symboled things and events such as arrows, hoes, and customs regulating the division of labor in society.

Of course culture does not and could not exist independently of people. But, as we have pointed out earlier, cultural processes can be explained without taking human organisms into account; a consideration of human organisms is irrelevent to the solution of certain problems of culture. Whether the practice of mummification in pre-Columbian Peru was indigenous or the result of Egyptian influence is an example of a kind of problem that does not require a consideration of human organisms. To be sure the practice of mummification, its invention in Peru, or its diffusion from Egypt to the Andean highlands, could not have taken place without the action of real, flesh-and-blood human beings. Neither could Einstein have worked out the theory of relativity without breathing, but we do not need to take his respiration into account when we trace the history, or explain the development, of this theory.

Those who argue that it is people, not culture, that do this or that mistake a description of what they see for an explanation of these events. Seated in the Senate gallery they see men making laws; in the shipyards men are building freighters; in the laboratory human beings are isolating enzymes; in the fields they are planting corn; and so on. And, for them, a description of these events, as they observe them, is a simple explanation of them: it is people who pass laws, build freighters, plant corn, and isolate enzymes. This is a simple and naïve form of anthropocentrism.

A scientific explanation is more sophisticated. If a person speaks Chinese, or avoids his mother-in-law, loathes milk, observes matrilocal residence, places the bodies of the dead on scaffolds, writes symphonies, or isolates enzymes, it is because he has been born into, or least reared within, an extrasomatic tradition that we call culture which contains these elements. A people's behavior is a response to, a function of, its culture. The culture is the independent, the behavior the dependent, variable; as the culture varies so will the behavior. This is, of course, a commonplace that is usually expounded and demonstrated during the first two weeks of an introductory course in anthropology. It is indeed people who treat disease with prayers and charms or with vaccines and antibiotics. But the question, "Why does one people use charms while another uses vaccines?" is not explained by saying that "this people does this, that people does that." It is precisely this proposition that needs to be explained: why do they do what they do? The scientific explanation does not take the people into account at all. And as for the question, "Why does one extrasomatic tradition use charms while another uses vaccines?" this also is one to which a consideration of people, of human organism, is irrelevant; it is answered culturologically: culture, as Lowie has observed, is to be explained in terms of culture.

## "IT TAKES TWO OR MORE TO MAKE A CULTURE"

There is a conception, not uncommon in ethnological theory, that whether a phenomenon is an element of culture or not depends upon whether it is expressed by one, two, or "several" individuals. Thus Linton[8] says that "any item of behavior . . . which is peculiar to a single individual in a society is not to be considered as a part of the society's culture. . . . Thus a new technique for weaving baskets would not be classed as a part of culture as long as it was known only to one person." Wissler,[9] Osgood,[10] Malinowski,[11] Durkheim,[12] and others have subscribed to this view.

Two objections may be raised against this conception of culture: (1) if plurality of expression of learned behavior be the significant distinction between culture and not-culture, then the chimpanzees described by Wolfgang Köhler in *The Mentality of Apes* had culture, for innovations made by a single individual were often quickly adopted by the whole group. Other subhuman species also would have culture according to this criterion. (2) The second objection is: if expression by one person is not enough to qualify an act as a cultural element, how many persons will be required? Linton[13] says that "as soon as this new thing has been transmitted to and is shared by even one other individual in the society, it must be reckoned as a part of culture." Osgood[14] requires "two or more." Durkheim[15]

needs "several individuals", at the very least." Wissler[16] says that an item does not rise to the level of a culture trait until a standardized procedure is established in the group. And Malinowski[17] states that a "cultural fact starts when an individual interest becomes transformed into public, common, and transferable systems of organized endeavor."

Obviously such a conception does not meet the requirements of science. What agreement could one find on the point at which an "individual interest becomes transformed into public, common, and transferable systems of organized endeavor"? Or suppose an ornithologist said that if there were but one specimen of a kind of bird it could not be a carrier pigeon or a whooping crane, but that if there were an indefinite number then they could be pigeons or cranes. Or suppose a physicist said that if there were but one atom of a certain element that it could not be copper, but if there were "a lot of such atoms" then it might properly be called copper. One wants a definition that says that item $x$ belongs to class $y$ or it does not, regardless of how many items of $x$ there may be (and a class, in logic, may have only one member, or even none).

Our definition meets the requirements of a scientific definition: an item — a conception or belief, an act, or an object — is to be reckoned an element of culture (1) if it is dependent upon symboling, and (2) when it is considered in an extrasomatic context. To be sure, all cultural elements exist in a social context; but so do such nonhuman (not dependent upon symboling) traits as grooming, suckling, and mating exist in a social matrix. But it is not sociality, duality, or plurality that distinguishes a human, or cultural, phenomenon from a nonhuman or noncultural phenomenon. The distinguishing characteristic is symboling. Second, whether a thing or an event can be considered in an extrasomatic context does not depend upon whether there is only one such thing or event, or two, or "several." A thing or event may be properly considered an element of culture even if it is the only member of its class, just as an atom of copper would still be an atom of copper even if it were the only one of its kind in the cosmos.

And, of course, we might have pointed out in the first place that the notion that an act or an idea in human society might be wholly the work of a single individual is an illusion, another one of the sorry pitfalls of anthropocentrism. Every member of human society is of course always subjected to sociocultural stimulation from the members of his group. Whatever a man does as a human being, and much of what he does as a mere animal, is a function of his group as well as of his organism. Any human act, even in its first expression in the person of a single individual, is a group product to begin with.

1. A. L. Kroeber and C. Kluckhohn, "Culture, A Critical Review of Concepts and Definitions," *Papers of the Peabody Museum of American Archaeology and Ethnology*, Cambridge, Mass.: Harvard University Press, 1952, p. 155.

2. Ralph L. Beals and Harry Hoijer, *An Introduction to Anthropology*, New York: Macmillan, 1953, pp. 210, 219.

3. R. Linton, *The Study of Man*, New York: Appleton-Century, 1936, pp. 288–289.

4. M. J. Herskovits, "The Processes of Cultural Change," in Ralph Linton (Ed.), *The Science of Man in the World Crisis*, New York: Columbia University Press, 1945, p. 150.

5. C. Kluckhohn and W. H. Kelly, "The Concept of Culture," in Ralph Linton (Ed.), *The Science of Man in the World Crises*, New York: Columbia University Press, 1945, pp. 79, 81.

6. Beals, *op. cit.*, p. 210.

7. Edward B. Tylor, *Primitive Culture*, 5th ed., London: Murray, 1913, p. 1.

8. R. Linton, *The Cultural Background of Personality*, New York: Appleton-Century, 1945, p. 35.

9. Clark Wissler, *Introduction to Social Anthropology*, New York: Holt, 1929, p. 358.

10. Cornelius Osgood, "Culture: Its Empirical and Non-Empirical Character," *Southwestern Journal of Anthropology*, 1951, pp. 207, 208.

11. B. Malinowski, "Man's Culture and Man's Behavior," *Sigma Xi Quarterly*, 1941, p. 73.

12. E. Durkheim, in George Catlin (Ed.), *The Rules of Sociological Method*, Chicago: University of Chicago Press, 1938, p. lvi.

13. Linton, *The Study of Man, op. cit.*, p. 274.

14. Osgood, *op. cit.*, p. 208.

15. Durkheim, *loc. cit.*

16. Wissler, *loc. cit.*

17. Malinowski, *loc. cit.*

# 2. ELEMENTS OF COMMUNICATION

*George A. Lundberg, Clarence C. Schrag,*
*and Otto N. Larsen*

Communication is the process through which a set of meanings embodied in a message is conveyed to a person or persons in such a way that the meanings received are equivalent to those which the initiator(s) of the message intended.[1] The essential elements of any communication system include the following:

Source of communication: The creator of an idea or the developer and/or sender of a message.

Message: The information, ideas, content, or subject matter to be communicated.

Form of communication: Spoken or written language, Morse Code, semaphore signals, smoke signals, music, painting, gestures, etc.

Channel or medium of communication: Printed texts, graphic displays, phonographic recordings, films, radio, television, newspapers, etc.

Destination of communication: The receiver, receivers, or audience of a message, real or potential.

Context of communication: The physical, psychological, or sociocultural conditions or circumstances under which communication takes place.

Goal of communication: The purpose to be achieved by the message, the anticipated results.

Effects of communication: The accomplishment or the outcomes of communication, the uses to which the messages are put.

Communication models employing these elements have taken several forms. Some, such as those dealing with "information theory," are highly mathematical types.[2] Others use words and graphic devices to portray the intricate processes of the communicative act. All these are fairly comprehensive. Some emphasize *roles* that develop in communication.[3] Others focus on the *stages* through which a message passes.[4] Still others tend to emphasize the *continuity* of the sensory process from the stimulus to the elicited response.[5]

These models identify and interrelate the essential parts of any system of communication and specify the functions that these parts perform. The major points may be summarized as follows:

1. Communication means that information is passed from one place to another. To communicate is to attempt to establish a "commonness" between two points. Communication has been achieved when there has been a transfer of meaning.

2. Every communicative act is a reciprocal (interactive) process. This means that a given source also serves

as a destination, and a given destination also serves as a source.

3. In achieving communication, both the source and the destination will at varying times:

(a) *transmit* (encode the message)

(b) *evaluate* (the mediatory responses of what happens to the message within the system).

(c) *receive* (decode the message).

4. There are three main sources of stimulation for the source and the destination as they perform the above functions:

(a) They react to stimuli from each other.

(b) They react to stimuli within themselves (past experience).

(c) They react to stimuli from objects or events in the external common environment.

5. The "feedback" that a source gets from his own message and from a response of the destination becomes the corrective basis for achieving a greater degree of communication.

6. The source encodes, and the destination decodes, in terms of the experiences each has had. If there is no common experience, then there will be no transfer of meaning. Through "feedback" the source can try to encode again in such a way as to relate the message to parts of his experience which are more like those of the destination.

7. Any communication system has a maximum *capacity* for handling experience. One of the important skills of communication lies in knowing how near capacity to operate a channel. In human communication systems this may be influenced by the structure of the language. The sequence of words and sounds that make up every language are governed by certain probabilities. English is about 50 per cent redundant

(redundance here means the percentage of the message which is not open to free choice in encoding. For example, once you choose the letter *j* there is no word in English in which that letter of the alphabet is followed by *b, c, d, f, g, j, k, l, q, r, t, v, w, x,* or *z*).[6]

8. Any communication system is subject to distortion and filtering ("noise"). In human terms distortion can develop under the following conditions:

(a) If the source does not have adequate or clear information.

(b) If the message is not encoded fully, accurately, effectively in transmittable symbols.

(c) If the symbols are not transmitted fast enough and accurately enough, despite interference and competition, to the desired receiver.

(d) If the message is not decoded in a pattern that corresponds to the encoding.

(e) If the destination is unable to handle the message so as to produce the desired response.[7]

This identification of elements and processes in communication systems clarifies the meaning of communication for sociological purposes. Communication begins with contact between persons, but contact does not necessarily result in communication. There must be a transmission of meanings before communication has taken place. This is achieved through alternate and reciprocal stimulation and response among persons. The tools of communication and the habits of their use are acquired through social interaction.

When persons interact, they are engaged in communication. They achieve communication by identifying with each other's situations. The communicative act means "getting on common ground," "seeing the other person's point of view," and "knowing how he feels." The black marks on white paper in this book are designed to transmit certain knowledge, experiences, and attitudes about a subject matter to enable the reader to understand the sociological point of view. Student success in a quiz based on the text might be some index of successful communication. There has to be "feedback" or response to a message before there can be any estimate of the degree of communication that has taken place. In writing, as in other formal modes of communication, feedback is not immediate. Sometimes it never occurs at all. How long a response is delayed, or if it occurs at all, depends principally on how well the writer can predict the probable response of his reader when he formulates and assembles the black marks. If the writer can correctly "imagine" the reader's response — if he knows intimately the language conditioning of his reader — he has achieved the primary basis of communication.

Any act of communication is then, first of all, an *interact*. Even where media of mass communication, such as television, are employed, there must be some form of interaction between the communicator and his absentee audience before the degree of communication can be assessed. In fact, the success of the communication of mass media content is measured by the "feedback" from the audience through such compliance behavior as subscriptions, fan mail, or purchase of a sponsor's product. Such responses affect future media content. However, it is in person-to-person speech communication that participant behavior and the interaction process is most evident.

Person-to-person speech as an act of communication is a two-way process involving the telling and hearing of messages. How, in general, do a teller and hearer come into communication? The communicative process is initiated when the teller utters sounds which symbolize his experiences. To the extent that the hearer has had similar experiences, and has been conditioned to associate the given sounds with those experiences, communication is possible. Often, when the teller indicates what he understands, the hearer verbalizes his own activity or suggests changes in the teller's statements until each person reproduces in his own estimation the other's experiences. This is the general give-and-take process of communication regardless of whether the message has to do with the instigation of a riot, the change to another brand of toothpaste, the appreciation of a sunset, the learning of a mathematical formula, or the description of a burial practice. The act of communication is thus a reciprocal and alternate *taking of roles*, a process of symbolically putting oneself in the place of another, and behaving as if one were subject to the stimuli, experience, and associations which affect the other person.

To most people language means talk, or speech, or conversation. Technically, language is not restricted to pure vocal expression but includes any standardized and conventionalized system of symbols. Lindesmith and Strauss note this distinction and also add an indispensable behavioral dimension to the definition of language:

We should not . . . make the mistake of thinking of language merely as a system of words, as a combination of phonemes, or as the contents of a dictionary. Language is, first of all, a form of behavior. *It is not merely a system of sym-*

*bols, but is the activity of using and interpreting symbols.* Speech is often said to be the most primitive and ancient form of language behavior, but speech is meaningless unless it is addressed to an understanding listener. Hence we may say that conversation is the essential and original form of language, noting not only that language behavior originates in cooperative social action but that it is such action. That is why parrots are not given credit for language behavior, even though they may produce words.[8]

On a more readily understood level, linguists have compiled an impressive body of data marking the boundaries of "speech communities." Everyone recognizes that, while Americans speak English, there are distinct regional patterns of language expression. Regional variations in expressions reflect the influence of factors such as colonial settlements, geographical barriers, transport facilities, and social stratification on localizing or disseminating linguistic usages. These studies also throw light on migrations within the country and raise questions about the influence of "leveling forces," such as schools, radio, and the printed page. Will our local and regional dialects eventually be smoothed out to a standard American English? In noting that the leveling forces are not quite powerful among the folk as one might suppose, one linguist says:

. . . Local and regional expressions are not likely to disappear entirely from our language. Many of them survive because they stand for local or regional phenomena. It is very doubtful, for example, that we shall ever have a nationally accepted term for griddlecakes made of corn meal. For one thing, they are rarely served in the Wheat Belt. It is difficult to detect any trend toward a national name for them: they are still known by a wide variety of expressions, such as johnnycakes, johnnikins, corn cakes, corn dodgers, hoe cakes, ash cakes. A similar situation exists with regard to wheat cakes. The term pancakes is generally known throughout the Eastern states, but in eastern New England they are almost always called griddlecakes, around Philadelphia hot cakes, west of Philadelphia flannel cakes and south of the Potomac battercakes or batty cakes.[9]

Regional variations in the terms that denote the same items can be important factors in communication. For example, if nationwide information campaigns are to have any chance of success they have to take these regional variations into account. But more significant is the wide range of communicative skills that have been observed within a given speech community. For example, in a study probing into individual accounts of a disaster experience, members of lower and middle social classes (categorized by income and education) exhibited striking differences in the way in which they handled the following four basic communicative skills:

1. *The number and kinds of perspectives utilized. Lower-class respondents* gave straight, direct descriptions of events only as *they* saw and experienced them, whereas middle-class respondents also included in their descriptions the perspective of another person, a class of persons, an organization, an organizational role, or even the whole town.

2. *The ability to take the listener's role.* The lower-class respondent rarely explained or qualified an utterance. He took for granted that his perceptions represented reality and were shared by all who were present. The middle-class respondent qualified, summarized, and set the stage with rich introductory material, expanded themes, used illustrations, anticipated disbelief, and meticulously located and identified places and persons. He depended less on saying "You know," and insisted on pursuing explanations when he realized that a point lacked plausibility.

3. *The handling of classifications.* Lower-class respondents made references mainly to the acts or particular people. They did not talk about relationships or

about categories of people or acts. Middle-class speech was organized around classifications, around broad categories of persons and acts.

4. *The framework and stylistic devices which order and implement the communication.* Lower-class respondents did not give well-organized accounts of what happened to them in the disaster, but presented a recollection of single incidents joined together, if at all, by crude chronological notations such as "then . . . and then." Middle-class respondents organized their accounts around frames emphasizing sequence, human drama, or one stressing interlocking classes of civic acts. Middle-class respondents had the ability to depart from a theme while yet holding it in mind. Because they incorporated multiple perspectives, they could add long asides, discuss the parallel acts of other persons in relation to themselves, make varied comparisons for the enrichment of detail and comprehension—*and then return to the original point and proceed from there.*[10]

There is a close relationship, then, between language and the mind and milieu of those who speak it, whether they be individuals, a people, or a social class. We need only to leaf through a dictionary of the Livonian language to determine that the Livonians are pre-eminently a people of fishermen and sailors, and that, in contrast to the Estonians, neither agriculture nor urban life plays an important part in their existence. The same holds true for the well-known abundance of vocabulary among the Arabs and the Laplanders concerning, respectively, different kinds of camels and reindeer.[11]

Language *stands* for things that human beings experience. To a large degree it also *determines* what they will experience. Men's notions of honesty sometimes depend on the word they use. A European "finds" a lost object and seeks to return it to its first possessor, who is, in his eyes, its true owner. For

the Vietnamese, on the contrary, the true owner is not the one who loses but the one who finds, because in his language, in effect, "to find something," expressed by *du'o'c*, means "to obtain in a manner to own."[12]

What is perceived is organized by various interests, needs, and capacities expressed through the symbols we command. If a person intends to buy a new suit, he observes suit styles and colors as he walks down the street. If he is thirsty, he may particularly notice Coca-Cola or beer signs. Here, also, may be observed how symbols organize perception. Actually, class representatives, not unnamed isolated objects, are "seen." That is, action toward objects is in accordance with classification of them. Perceiving thus involves linguistic distinctions. Objects cannot be perceived as belonging to a category unless the language has already designated categories, or enables the construction of new classes.

Past experience, interests of the moment, and the condition of the organism, whether fatigued, hungry, excited, or depressed, all are capable of providing the motivational impetus to perceiving selectively. To further verify this statement, it is only necessary to spend a few minutes reading the classified advertisements in a newspaper. After reading hundreds of such items, it will be noticed that the only items recalled are those that relate to the reader's own particular bodily, mental, or social situation. Unnoticed may be the very ads that would have been noticed by another member of the family, or even by oneself at another time.

When people are faced with data so sketchy or so poorly structured as to fit no available frame of reference, they tend to create new material or revise the old in such a manner that meaning is satisfied. In satisfying meaning, perceiving is most likely to follow the line of familiarity and expectation. That is, persons tend to see what they are looking for, or what they have seen in the past.

In communication, as in all social living, man imposes organization on the discrete elements of his experience. The observation that human beings tend to organize perceptions into orderly, comprehensive, and stable patterns suggests three important hypotheses: (*a*) *that symbols tending to disorganize experience will not be perceived*; (*b*) *that any symbolic experience that reinforces a preexisting pattern is almost certain to be perceived*; and (*c*) *that symbols that make meaningful a previously confused pattern will tend to be perceived*.

It is clear that messages do not have an absolute stimulating value. The bases of perception are built through the ongoing processes of socialization. However complex these processes may be in the initial organization of perception, as they are established they are extremely influential in directing subsequent experience. Since without communication of some kind group life is not possible, the individual is required to learn to perceive objects and events as his fellows do in order to communicate with them about his experiences and to understand theirs.

If society and its constituent organizations were a brick house, communication would be the mortar that makes the building of the structure possible and holds it together as a unified whole. Just as a brick house is only as secure as its mortar, so with society and its mortar, communication. In either case, let the mortar crumble and the house will fall.[14]

---

1. Joel Smith, Robert C. Bealer, and Francis M. Sim, "Communication and the 'Consequences' of Communication," *Sociological Inquiry*, Winter 1962, p. 12.

2. Claude E. Shannon and Warren Weaver, *The Mathematical Theory of Communication*, Urbana, Ill.: University of Illinois Press, 1949.

3. B. H. Westley and M. S. MacLean, Jr., "A Conceptual Model for Communications Research," *Journalism Quarterly*, Winter 1957, pp. 31–38; and T. M. Newcomb, "An Approach to the Study of Communicative Acts," *Psychological Review*, November 1953, pp. 393–404.

4. Wendell Johnson, "The Fateful Process of Mr. A Talking to Mr. B," *Harvard Business Review*, January-February 1953.

5. Jurgen Ruesch, "The Observer and the Observed: Human Communication Theory," in R. R. Grinker, *Toward a Unified Theory of Human Behavior*, New York: Basic Books, 1956, pp. 36–54.

6. Shannon and Weaver, *op. cit.*, p. 102.

7. Some of these eight points have been adapted from Wilbur Schramm, *The Process and Effects of Mass Communication*, Urbana, Ill.: University of Illinois Press, pp. 3–26.

8. A. R. Lindesmith and A. L. Strauss, *Social Psychology*, New York: Dryden, 1956, pp. 56–57.

9. Hans Kurath, "The American Languages," *Scientific American*, January 1950, p. 50. For a discussion of the potent factors operating against stability and uniformity in the language via the processes of pronunciation, see Jotham Johnson, "The Changing American Language," *Scientific American*, August 1955, pp. 78–83.

10. Leonard Schatzman and Anselm Strauss, "Social Class and Modes of Com-

munication," *American Journal of Sociology*, January 1955, pp. 329–338.

11. Andrus Saareste, "Language and National Character," *The American Behavioral Scientist*, December 1960, p. 39.

12. *Ibid.*

13. Paul F. Lazarsfeld, Bernard Berelson, and Hazel Gaudet, *The People's Choice*, New York: Columbia University Press, 1948.

14. Eugene Walton, *A Magnetic Theory of Organizational Communication*, U.S. Naval Ordnance Test Station Publication 111, January 1962, p. 1.

# 3. SOCIALIZATION

### Alfred R. Lindesmith and Anselm L. Strauss

G. H. Mead has described graphically how children playfully imitate the roles of elders or associates and thus gradually develop an ability to see objects, other persons, and themselves from a nonegocentric standpoint. Mead emphasizes what Piaget merely noted in passing, namely, that language is basic in the development of the ability to play roles.

[There are] countless forms of play in which the child assumes the roles of the adults about him. The very universal habit of playing with dolls indicates how ready for expressing, in the child, is the parental attitude or, perhaps one should say, certain of the parental attitudes. The long period of dependence of the human infant during which his interest centers in his relations to those who care for him gives a remarkable opportunity for the play back and forth of this sort of taking of the roles of others. . . . In the play of young children, even when they play together, there is abundant evidence of the child's taking different roles in the process; and a solitary child will keep up the process of stimulating himself by his vocal gestures [spoken words] to act in different roles almost indefinitely . . . . A child plays at being a mother, at being a teacher, at being a policeman; that is, it is taking different roles . . . . We have something that suggests this in what we call the play of animals: a cat will play with her kittens, and dogs with each other . . . . But we do not have in such a situation the . . . taking (of) a definite role in the sense that a child deliberately takes the role of another. . . . He plays that he is, for instance, offering himself something, and he buys it; he gives a letter to himself and takes it away; he addresses himself as a parent, as a teacher; he arrests himself as a policeman. He has a set of stimuli which call out in himself the sort of responses they call out in others. He takes this group of responses and organizes them into a certain whole. Such is the simplest form of being another to one's self. It involves a temporal situation. The child says something in one character and then his responding in another character is a stimulus to himself in the first character, and so the conversation goes on. . . . In that early stage (of childhood) he passes from one role to another just as a whim takes him.[1]

The child's playing at being persons other than himself is paralleled in actual life by the playing of the real roles in which he is involved with parents and playmates. One of the theories of play is that it is a preparation for later adult activity wherein the individual applies the skills that he has acquired. Thus the standards of fair play and the proper attitude toward defeat in competition are often said to be learned on the gridiron or on the "playing fields of Eton." No doubt it is from considerations of this kind that the widespread absorption of children (and adults) in comic strips

Excerpted by permission of the authors and publishers, from *Social Psychology*, 2nd ed., New York: Dryden, 1956, pp. 391–397. Copyright 1956 by Holt, Rinehart and Winston, Inc. (All quotes of George H. Mead are reprinted from *Mind, Self, and Society* by permission of the University of Chicago Press. Copyright 1934, University of Chicago Press.)

and comic books concerns and alarms some who feel that constant identifications with comic-strip characters of doubtful virtue may lead the children to emulate these fictional "heroes." Without accepting this position one may recognize that this kind of play activity and fantasying gives the child a repertoire of roles and practice in switching from one to the other.

The initial role taking of the young child is simple and limited, involving only limited and brief fragments of behavior and the imitation of a few specific persons. As the child's circle of acquaintanceship is enlarged, as his mastery of communication develops, and as his real roles multiply in number and become more complex, the role-taking processes become more complicated, as we shall see.

## THE GENERALIZED OTHER AS AN ORGANIZATION OF OTHER'S ROLES

When the child has developed the ability to grasp the role of one other person at a time, he is on the road to becoming a social being. However, before he can participate in organized adult activity, the child must be able to conceive his own role from the standpoint of all other participants. An illustration will help to make this clear.

Suppose that a group of Air Force men is on a bombing mission. Each man has a definite, assigned general role which involves certain duties and obligations. Each man has a clear conception of his general role as he imagines it from the points of view of all the others. He also has a clear picture of how his own role fits with the roles of each of the other men.

By contrast, the very young child is able to take the role of only one other person at a time. From this simple kind of role taking the child eventually develops the ability: (1) to take the roles of others in the situation; (2) to organize these roles into an integrated whole; and (3) to view his own behavior from this standpoint. Mead's suggestion of how this learning occurs is as follows:

If we contrast play with . . . an organized game, we note the essential difference that the child who plays in a game must be ready to take the attitude of everyone else involved in that game, and that these different roles must have a definite relationship to each other. . . . In a game where a number of individuals are involved . . . the child taking one role must be ready to take the role of everyone else. If he gets in a ball nine he must have the responses of each position involved in his own position. He must know what everyone else is going to do in order to carry out his own play. He has to take all of these roles. They do not all have to be present in consciousness at the same time, but at some moments he has to have three or four individuals present in his own attitude, such as the one who is going to throw the ball, the one who is going to catch it, and so on. . . . The attitudes of the other players which the participant assumes organize into a sort of unit, and it is that organization which controls the response of the individual. . . . Each of his own acts is determined by his assumption of the action of the others who are playing the game . . . he has to have an organization of these roles; otherwise he cannot play the game.[2]

Through his participation in organized games, in play, and in other activities, the child learns to take the role of the participants and grasps the fact that the roles of others are intertwined. At the same time he comes to see how his own activity within the situation looks from the standpoint of the others. He sees his own actions as part of a whole pattern of group activity.

Mead has coined a term for this organization of others' roles; he calls it the "generalized other." He uses this expression because it means that one is taking the related roles of all the other participants rather than the role of just one other person. This concept of the generalized other applies to the organized roles of the participants within any defined situation.

The term "generalized other" does not refer to an actual group of people; but rather to a conception or an interpretation which a person derives from his experiences. He then regulates his behavior in terms of these supposed opinions and attitudes of others. He imagines what "people" would say "if they knew" or what they will say "when they know." The term "people" may not have any specific reference to actual persons, but may merely represent his conception of abstract moral standards. These standards widen as role playing becomes more generalized.

## CONCEPT DEVELOPMENT AND THE ORGANIZATION OF PERSPECTIVES

The child, like the adult, discriminates between persons, acts, and things in terms of concepts; but the content of his classifications is different from what it will be as he grows more knowledgeable. As new classifications are learned and discovered, old ones change, are revised and qualified. As the child's conceptual-

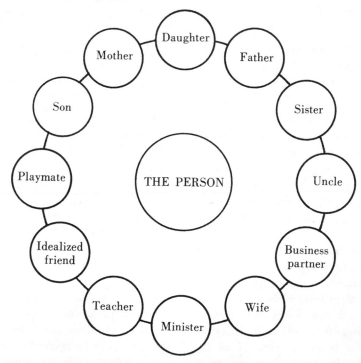

A person learns to look upon his own behavior from the points of view of all these people. He learns their various points of view at different periods in his life, and they have varying importance for the organization of his behavior.

izing ability approaches the adult standard his concepts become more numerous and their interrelationships more complex. His ability to play roles and to understand the actions and motives of others develops in a parallel course.

The earlier role conceptions of children are, from the adults' viewpoint, rather curious and often amusing, although in their own way they represent a primitive if incorrect systemization of role. Thus very young children know there are storekeepers and customers, but they think that the customer buys goods and both he and the storekeeper pay each other. Only the customer buys goods, the storekeeper never does. Monetary activity is confined to buying and selling. Although one storekeeper may help another sell, the distinction between owner and employer is unclear and is not involved in the buying-selling transactions. There are no other roles such as that of manufacturer.[3]

Hartley and his associates[4] have pointed out, in a study of some oddities of children's role conceptions, how the young child is unable to organize certain perspectives properly. Thus a young child conceives of a mother only from one perspective, and denies that mothers can play other roles (that of saleslady, for example). Older children widen the positions from which role players are viewed until they are able to conceive of any individual as momentarily or permanently playing one role but potentially capable of playing many others. The inflexibility of the very young child, who like Gertrude Stein insists that a mother is a mother is a mother is a mother, represents an inability to slide in imagination from perspective to perspective or to organize perspectives into a more inclusive whole.

Hartley's discussion is deficient in that it does not bring out the fact that the young child who cannot conceive of his mother as a saleswoman nevertheless can conceive of her as a daughter of his grandmother. He can do this because in his immature systematization of role concepts, certain roles seem compatible with each other while others do not.

At one step of his concept development the child will deny that two roles are compatible, but later, having grasped their relationship, will agree that they go together. Thus he will early deny that a teacher can be a storekeeper or vice versa because each belongs to a different world. Later the child agrees that a teacher could be a storekeeper "after school," but still denies that a storekeeper can be a customer. Still later he sees that a storekeeper can buy in a store and still in a general sense be a storekeeper, but does not yet perceive that the storekeeper must be a customer of manufacturers.

Much of the child's early learning about role relationships occurs in concrete situations where the roles are played out before his eyes. However, most role relationships are rather abstract. Even those relationships that seem most concrete and visible, for example those between a teacher and a pupil, involve much more than is visible on the surface. Greater maturity and breadth of experience are necessary before the child can be expected to understand the subtler aspects of such relationships.

1. George Herbert Mead, *Mind, Self, and Society*, Chicago: University of Chicago Press, 1934, pp. 364–365 and 150–151.

2. *Ibid.*, pp. 151–152, 154.

3. Anselm L. Strauss, "The Development and Transformation of Monetary Meanings in the Child," *American Sociological Review*, 17, 1952, 278.

4. E. Hartley, M. Rosenbaum, and S. Schwartz, "Children's Perceptions of Ethnic Group Membership," *Journal of Psychology*, 26, 1948, 387–398.

# 4. IMPLICATIONS OF SOCIAL CLASS FOR PUBLIC HEALTH

## Ozzie G. Simmons

This paper[1] will consider three areas in which social class and status have important implications for public health: (1) the differential distribution of disease and consequent evaluations of appropriate foci of public-health interest and activity; (2) the functioning of interpersonal relations within the health team and between team and public; (3) the congruence between public-health precepts and felt needs of the public at whom these precepts are directed.

For present purposes "status" and "class" will be employed as generic terms, the former to refer simply to rank, or relative position in a status hierarchy, and the latter to refer to a group of individuals who occupy a broadly similar position in a status hierarchy. When the term "class status" is used it refers to membership in a given stratum of a status hierarchy, whether this stratum be a statistical aggregate or a real group. When class-value differences are discussed in terms of middle class and lower class, the reference is to modal types which higher- and lower-status people may manifest in different degrees; it does not necessarily follow that all higher-status people adhere to the middle-class modal type, and all lower-status people to the other. Presumably many members of both these strata may not incorporate the corresponding class values and may deviate from the modal type in other respects. It may be noted that the character of modal types is determined by common economic and power situations and cultural experiences, which offer more or less similar life chances or opportunities. In discussing interpersonal relations the primary focus will be on the ways in which orientations to relative status affect the functioning of a given relationship. In discussing congruence and divergence between public-health precepts and felt needs of the public, the primary focus will be on modal subcultural types.

## THE DIFFERENTIAL DISTRIBUTION OF DISEASE

Like the social welfare movement, the public-health movement has been conceived and implemented primarily by middle-class people, and directed primarily at lower-class people. As in most social movements the public-health movement was mainly activated by motives of social uplift and self-protection. The conclusion, in 1830, that if cholera were not stamped out it might move from the slums to within the middle-class gates led to a sudden increase in interest in public health both in Europe and the United States. According to Shryock, "Fear now combined with humanitarianism to demand

Reprinted by permission of the Society for Applied Anthropology, from *Human Organization*, Vol. 16, 1957, pp. 7–10.

investigations, cleanups, and general sanitary reform."[2]

Public health traditionally has focused on the control of the mass diseases which, by and large, have had their greatest incidence and prevalence among the lower classes, as for example, smallpox, typhus, typhoid, the nutritional-deficiency disorders, and tuberculosis. With increasing control of these diseases, new mass diseases, such as the cardiovascular disorders and poliomyelitis, have claimed not only the attention of public health personnel but have excited great public interest among our higher-status groups as well, as currently reflected in the great annual fund-raising drives.[3] Taking as a specific case the contrast between polio and tuberculosis, we find that when the treatments for the latter were developed, professional interest far exceeded public interest; yet when the Salk polio vaccine was developed, public interest far exceeded professional, and Salk became a national hero. There is an inverse correlation between degree of public interest and incidences connected with these two diseases. Polio rates are relatively low compared to those of other mass diseases, and tuberculosis rates continue relatively high.[4]

This striking difference between polio and tuberculosis may be regarded in large part as a function of class distributions and perceptions of disease.[5] Tuberculosis, like many of the older mass diseases, is primarily identified with lack of personal and environmental hygiene, poverty, overcrowding, and malnutrition, but in the case of polio, as in that of the cardiovascular ailments, no such identification has been established. In fact, there is some evidence to indicate that higher polio rates are to be found among those who enjoy quite the opposite set of conditions.[6] Tuberculosis and polio are both public threats, but the crucial difference here seems to be that tuberculosis is pretty well confined to our lower-status groups, while polio is within the middle-class gates.

## THE FUNCTIONING OF INTERPERSONAL RELATIONS

The practice of public health is carried on within two main interpersonal relations systems, the intrateam and team-public systems. Participants in either system may be members of the same or different societies, but in either case, class, as it refers to subcultural differences, may add an important dimension. Although there has been some research on interpersonal relations in the practice of clinical medicine and psychiatry, investigations in the public-health field have scarcely yet gone beyond impressions and casual observations. We will consider here only a few of the possibilities in intrateam relations in the intercultural situation, and in team-public relations in the intracultural situation.

The most common instance of public-health teams where members belong to different societies is to be found in technical assistance programs in "underdeveloped" countries. In this intercultural situation, class considerations can minimize or enhance major cultural differences that obtain between team members. With regard to class factors that serve to reduce cultural differences, it has been noted that class cultures tend to go beyond societal boundaries. As Saunders has pointed out, an upper-class Mexican American may feel more at ease with an upper-status Anglo American than with a lower-class Mexican

American in a situation involving some degree of intimacy, since their awareness of cultural group distinctions is minimized, even though it may not be entirely superseded, by their social-class identification.[7] In Latin America, upperclass groups in different countries, due to similar positions of dominance, possession of power and wealth, and the common experience of travel and education in Europe and America, tend to have value systems which not only approximate those of higher-status Americans, but are more similar to each other than to those of lower-class Latin Americans in their respective countries.

With regard to the role of class factors in enhancing cultural differences among team members, it may be that, despite the cross-societal bond, tensions will be engendered, for example, between Americans and their local collaborators because of failure of the American to understand and acknowledge what may often be substantial differences in status between the two relative to their own class hierarchies. Thus, in contrast to the American, who will only in the rare case be descended from a top status family and have held a high-level position in his own country, local collaborators are likely to be members of ruling class families and to occupy high-ranking positions in their government's ministry of health. Americans, by virtue of their tendency to play down class differences, as well as of pronounced ethnocentric tendencies, are not likely to manifest overtly the degree of respect for their collaborators which the latter may expect as their due. For the same reasons, they are likely to reject or ignore the subordinating and deference devices traditionally used by upperclass people in conducting their relations with lower-status people in those countries where status differences are generally explicitly acknowledged and taken for granted. One of the most pervasive grievances nursed by upperclass people abroad with respect to Americans concerns the latter's treatment of servants as near-equals by giving them the same food, paying them "too much," and so on.

Ideally, the doctor's role in the therapeutic relationship focuses on his performance of a technical specialty, on his impartially serving the patient's health needs independently of whether he likes the patient as a person, and on his obligation to give priority to the patient's well-being over his own personal interests. This ideal seems to hold across the board in most Western societies, although it may not always hold in nonWestern societies.[8] This role definition is calculated to inspire trust, respect, and confidence between doctor and patient, and thus ensure cooperation. In practice, however, it seems that the ideal is seldom approximated in professionalpatient relationships, and that it is precisely in the doctor-patient relationship where it is least likely to be achieved.

Studies in intracultural situations, both here and in other societies, indicate a tendency for class considerations to overshadow therapeutic considerations in the professional-patient relationship. It appears that the degree to which the qualities ideally defined as essential to the therapeutic relationship, namely mutual trust, respect, and cooperation, will be present in a given professionalpatient relationship varies inversely with the amount of social distance. Conversely, the greater the social distance, the less likely that participants will perceive each other in terms of the ideal type roles of professional and patient, and the more likely that they will perceive each other in terms of their social-class status in the larger society.

The therapeutic relationship should function at its optimum where professional and patient are of the same class status. Studies of the psychotherapeutic relationship in this country indicate that the patients who most nearly approach the therapist's status are accorded the best treatment and the most sympathy.[9] In the public-health context, it is possible that, although the professional may deem it easier to relate to patients who are of the same class status, higher-status patients may reject the health worker not because of his class status as such but because they perceive his attempts to serve them at all as identifying them with the lower-status people typically served by public health, and thus regard him as a threat to their social position. In a Peruvian village an auxiliary health worker was rejected by higher-status people because "she was perceived as equating them with the unwashed and uneducated poor."[10] In Chile nurses in a health center were extremely reluctant to approach middle-class families in their sectors because they anticipated a poor reception.[11]

In public health, where the typical case is that of higher-status professional and lower-status patient, the available evidence indicates that doctors and patients do not "get along" as well as do nurses and patients, but this need not mean that the respective class statuses of doctor, nurse, and patient are the sole or even principal factors in determining the difference in quality of doctor-patient and nurse-patient relations. Such factors as differences in professional training and expected role performances must also be weighed.[12]

In attempting to specify the varying roles that class perceptions and values may play in the functioning of professional-patient relations, it would be worthwhile to investigate whether status considerations loom larger for the professional or for the patient. In Regionville, for example, there was considerable feeling on the part of lower-status people that physicians did not want them as patients.[13] On the other side, some of the factors that influence professionals to inject status considerations into their relations with patients may be related to the professional's orientations to upward mobility. In Colombia, for example, the cities have been flooded by rural immigrants who no longer classify themselves according to the traditional status system. As a result of the competition to rise socially, individuals with some small position of authority press their weight on others to force a recognition of their status. Thus doctors and nurses in the Colombian government health centers are often overbearing in their treatment of the public.[14]

## PUBLIC-HEALTH PRECEPTS AND NEEDS OF PUBLIC

To the extent that it may be characterized as a social movement, public health has inevitably incorporated the dominant middle-class values of our society, primarily those that stem from the "Protestant ethic" core.[15] It follows that public-health precepts are formulated in terms of these values, and applied on the assumption that they are universally meaningful and desirable. However, class differences may set substantial limits to the degree of congruence possible between these precepts and the felt needs of a lower-class public.[16] We may ask: (1) To what extent do public-health workers apply their middle-class norms in working with lower-status groups? (2) Are lower-class norms significantly different in those areas where middle-class norms are imposed? (3) If there are such points of difference, how relevant are they for the effective functioning of public-health activities?

Lower-status families are beset by greater economic insecurity than higher-status families, and their "scientific" knowledge about modern medicine is apparently less extensive than that of higher-status people, but beyond these reality factors classes also vary in their behavioral characteristics and value orientations.

In view of the prominent public-health emphasis on personal and environmental hygiene, possible class differences in the importance attached to cleanliness is an area that readily comes to mind. For middle-class people cleanliness is not simply a matter of keeping clean but also an index to the morals and virtues of the individual. It has been frequently observed that middle-class valuations of cleanliness approach compulsive proportions, and that lower-status people are much more casual in this matter. It is possible that the stress placed on cleanliness in health education and other public-health activities far overshoots any felt needs in this area on the part of lower-status people.

Middle-class norms place great emphasis on the ability to defer gratifications in the interest of long-run goals. Readiness to sacrifice the present for some possible gain in the future may not be nearly so pervasive a pattern among lower-status people, who may accord priority to immediate rewards. This suggests some questions with regard to the public-health emphasis on prevention. Is acceptance of the value of prevention contingent upon ability to defer gratification, and, if so, do lower-class norms in this area set limits to such acceptance? Are lower-status people as willing, as higher-status people may be, to inconvenience themselves by adoption now of practices aimed at avoiding possible consequences in the future?

Middle-class norms accord high value to rationality, as it refers to use of foresight, deliberate planning, and allocation of resources in the most efficient way.[17] This again places an emphasis on future time orientations that may not be particularly meaningful to lower-status people. However, public-health teachings assume that this value does hold for lower-status people when they emphasize the development of regular health habits and the expenditure of the domestic budget in ways best calculated to ensure a balanced diet for the family.

Middle-class norms prescribe a strong sense of individual responsibility, which sets a high premium on resourcefulness and self-reliance. This value is frequently built into public-health goals. For example, the principal objective of health education is often expressed as the "inculcation in each individual of a sense of responsibility for his own health." This ideal pattern of individual responsibility can be contrasted with one of reciprocity, particularly within the family, that seems more characteristic of lower-class norms. The lower-status individual may be much less likely to think that responsibility for his well-being rests solely with himself, and more likely to think that if something does happen, the kin group will see him through.

An individual's definitions of and responses to health and illness have import for a wide range of public-health problems, and these are usually class linked. Throughout Latin America, for example, lower-status groups adhere to a vigorously functioning medical tradition which health workers and other medical people do not share.[18] The gulf is in part maintained by the health worker's rejection of this folk medicine tradition as "superstition," and in part by the fact that lower-status people reserve for folk medicine a wide variety of illnesses defined as inaccessible to scientific medicine because doctors do not "know" them and therefore cannot cure them.

Finally, we may briefly consider class differences in child-training patterns as these are relevant for public health. Middle-class socialization patterns tend to be consistently organized in accordance with the middle-class emphases on effort and achievement, which are thought to be good in themselves or good because they are instrumental to long-run goals, and as a consequence the middle-class child is subjected to considerable close supervision and control.[19] On the other hand, lower-class socialization patterns are relatively easy-going, and allow the child much more latitude with respect to eating, sleeping, cleanliness, dress, work, school, and play. Lower-status parents may be much more rigid about obedience, but the imposition of authority is usually arbitrary and inconsistent. Maternal and child-health programs are considered to be one of the most crucial in any large-scale public-health effort, and the mother is generally regarded as the most strategic person to reach in health education. Much of the education of lower-status mothers seems to be based on the premise that the latter are as motivated in controlling and molding their children as are higher-status mothers, and if this is not actually the case, it would mean that these teachings stand relatively less chance of being implemented.

Moreover, if lower-class socialization is so likely to be governed by the child's own inclinations, his parents' convenience, and fortuitous circumstances, it is probable that the health worker must cope with much greater variation in practices than he may be aware of.

## CONCLUSION

This discussion has considered three areas in which social class has important implications for public health. Social-class differences are associated with the differential distribution of disease and consequent definitions of appropriate foci of public-health interest and activity, with variations in quality of inter-personal relations and the health team and between the team and the public it serves, and with divergences in goals and perceptions between the health worker and his client.

By virtue of the fact that the situation of action in the public-health field typically involves the higher-status practitioner and lower-status patient, class differences in realistic conditions, value orientations, and behavioral characteristics may have a substantial role to play in determining the outcome of public-health programs. Acceptance or rejection of the goods and services that public health has to offer in large part depends upon how these are perceived by the recipient. Such perceptions vary with one's class membership, and attempts to change them are likely to collide with the individual's investment in his group affiliations. A social class constitutes a membership group, and promoting and maintaining one's acceptance by the group calls for conformity with the perceptions and behavior demed correct and desirable by the group, whether it be in relation to health and illness or anything else.

1. Revised version of a paper read at the 1955 annual meeting of the American Anthropological Association, Boston, Mass.

2. R. H. Shryock, *The Development of Modern Medicine: An Interpretation of the Social and Scientific Factors Involved*, New York: Knopf, 1947.

3. The writer is indebted to Dr. Edward Wellin for suggesting this instance of class differentials in disease, and in particular for bringing out the significance of the contrast between tuberculosis and polio.

4. National figures for three sample years are as follows (from the Massachusetts Bureau of Health Information):

| | Poliomyelitis | | Tuberculosis | |
|------|-------|--------|---------|--------|
| Year | Cases | Deaths | Cases | Deaths |
| 1940 | 9,804 | 1,026 | 102,984 | 60,428 |
| 1945 | 13,624 | 1,186 | 114,931 | 52,916 |
| 1950 | 33,330 | 1,686 | 121,742 | 33,633 |

5. The role of class factors in these contrasting public reactions seems clear, but obviously there are always other variables associated with specific diseases that play some part as well. In the case of tuberculosis and polio, there may be, e.g., differences in dramatic impact and publicity. Polio has physically visible aftereffects, although this must be compared with the social visibility associated with tuberculosis. Also, any disease, like polio, that tends to victimize children in disproportionately large numbers seems to excite more public reaction. However, in view of the great overlap in age between those who contract the two diseases, it is difficult to say what part this factor may actually play in dermining public attitudes. Although comparable information for tuberculosis is lacking, the importance of class factors in evaluating polio is borne out by Deasy's findings regarding participation in the 1954 polio-vaccine field trials, namely that upper-status mothers were much more likely to have taken previous precautions against the disease, knew more about the trials, and demonstrated a higher awareness of the disease entity itself. See Leila C. Deasy, "Socioeconomic Status and Participation in the Poliomyelitis Vaccine Trial," *American Sociological Review*, 21, 1956, 185–191.

6. Paffenbarger and Watt, in their epidemiological study of polio in South Texas, report that "groups of individuals living under better economic circumstances with the many associated 'advantages' of greater personal cleanliness, less crowding, better food, and less association with verminous insects may suffer a significantly higher attack rate to the paralytic disease and suggests that . . . for the United States [this] is somehow related to an improved standard of living." Ralph S. Paffenbarger, Jr., and James Watt, "Poliomyelitis in Hidalgo County, Texas, 1948: Epidemiological Observations," *American Journal of Hygiene*, 58, 1953, 269–287.

7. Lyle Saunders, *Cultural Difference and Medical Care*, New York: Russell Sage Foundation, 1954.

8. Cf. McKim Marriott, "Western Medicine in a Village of Northern India," in Benjamin D. Paul (Ed.), *Health, Culture, and Community: Case Studies of Public Reactions to Health Programs*, New York: Russell Sage Foundation, 1955, pp. 239–268.

9. Cf. Alan Grey, "Relationships between Social Status and Psychological Characteristics of Psychiatric Patients," unpublished Ph.D. thesis, University of Chicago, 1949. See also F. C. Redlich, A. B. Hollingshead, and Elizabeth Bellis, "Social Class Differences in Attitudes toward Psychiatry," *American Journal of Orthopsychiatry*, 25, 1955, 60–70.

10. Edward Wellin, "Water Boiling in a Peruvian Town," in Paul, *op. cit.*, pp. 71–103.

11. Ozzie G. Simmons, *The Health Center of San Miguel: An Analysis of a Public Health Program in Chile*, Santiago: Institute of Inter-American Affairs, 1953.

12. See Ozzie G. Simmons, "The Clinical Team in a Chilean Health Center," in Paul, *op. cit.*, pp. 325–348.

13. Earl L. Koos, *The Health of Regionville*, New York: Columbia University Press, 1954.

14. Charles J. Erasmus, "Changing Folk Beliefs and the Relativity of Empirical Knowledge," *Southwestern Journal of Anthropology*, 8, 1952, 411–428.

15. This refers to public health not only in the United States but in all areas that have been importantly influenced by the British and American varieties of public health.

16. In the preparation of this section, the writer is indebted for suggestions to an address by Dr. Walter B. Miller entitled "Social Class: Its Influence on Health Behavior," delivered at the October 1955 meeting of the Massachusetts Public Health Association.

17. This and the following formulation of middle-class norms were suggested by a summary description of middle-class standards in Albert Cohen, *Delinquent Boys: The Culture of the Gang*, Glencoe, Ill.: Free Press, 1955, pp. 89–90.

18. See Erasmus, *loc. cit.*; George M. Foster, "Relationships between Theoretical and Applied Anthropology: A Public Health Program Analysis," *Human Organization*, 11, 1952, 5–16; and Ozzie G. Simmons, "Popular and Modern Medicine in Mestizo Communities of Coastal Peru and Chile," *Journal of American Folklore*, 68, 1955, 57–71.

19. Cf. Arnold W. Green, "The Middle-Class Male Child and Neurosis," *American Sociological Review*, 11, 1946, 31–41.

# Epilogue to Part One

Though health workers know some of the social characteristics of their patients —
for example, age, sex, and class — many are not really aware of the significance
of these variables in health care. Often they assume that although patients differ
because they come from different ethnic backgrounds, they, the health professions,
somehow are exempt from such influences. Yet very often problems associated
with care and treatment of the ill are related to the fact that health workers and
patients come from different socioeconomic and subcultural groups. Thus patient
and professional differ considerably in their definitions and perceptions of health
and illness and their conceptions of causation and treatment. It is essential that
the professional be constantly aware of the similarities and dissimilarities between
himself and his client in order to facilitate the most comprehensive health care.

Communication is basic to any beneficial patient-staff relationship. To a large
extent the two groups speak to one another in a foreign tongue. As a consequence
some system for reaching consensus must be established on both verbal and nonverbal levels. The status structure through which the two groups are linked influences the development of such a system.

In order to develop the most effective communication, it is necessary that the
communicator of health information (whether to the general public or to specific
patients) send messages that are both adequate and accurate. That is, the communicator must have a comprehension of the audience to whom the information
is directed. One of the problems of initiating preventive or treatment programs is
a lack of congruence. It often actually happens that recipients of health communication receive adequate but not accurate information. Frequently the folkways of a group provide ways of judging what constitutes adequate information
regarding the interpretation of illness and even its treatment. Unfortunately this
information is not always accurate. The notion, for example, of rubbing the chest
of a child who has a severe cold with "goose grease" is adequate for that particular situation. But the inaccuracy of the notion that "goose grease" "cures" the
cold may lead in fact to a potential endangering of the child's life, especially if
the "cold" turns out to be pneumonia. In contrast, although it is accurate to
prescribe a specific diet for a diabetic, it may not be accompanied by adequate
information regarding the dangers inherent in not following the diet. To the
extent that the communicator of health information provides the client with
accurate and adequate information, the possibility of optimal care is enhanced.

To be effective the information communicated not only must be adequate and
accurate, but also must be relevant and acceptable to the patient's mores. If the
health worker is concerned with involving the patient in his own care, it is not
helpful to give him information about other patients and other illnesses. Furthermore, even though the patient or his family may understand how to give an
insulin injection, this does not mean that they agree with the health worker about

its importance or necessity. As a matter of fact, in some cultural groups, although the afflicted individuals may be able to perform the treatment procedures involved, the customs of the group may dictate that it is prayer that heals, not drugs.

The conception of communication that we have just given is focused largely on differences in cultural and class orientations between patient and health worker. But differences in role expectations between the two also affect communication. The ill are "supposed" to act as patients, desire to recover, and assiduously follow the mandates of the professionals. The professional is "supposed" to have all the relevant knowledge at his fingertips, convey this information, and ultimately cure the patient. When this is not the case, for either patient or professional, role conflict may arise. For example, when professionals either do not have the necessary curative knowledge or when treatment is virtually experimental, role conflict for self, or between self and others, may become evident. This dilemma can be alleviated through a more comprehensive understanding of the sociocultural characteristics of the clients and the practice of more effective communication.

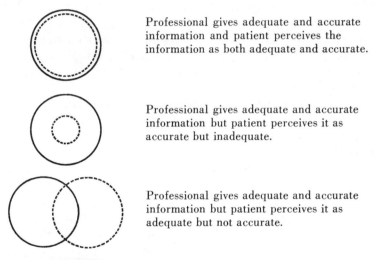

Professional gives adequate and accurate information and patient perceives the information as both adequate and accurate.

Professional gives adequate and accurate information but patient perceives it as accurate but inadequate.

Professional gives adequate and accurate information but patient perceives it as adequate but not accurate.

FIGURE I. Adequate and accurate communication.

There are, of course, many other combinations that the reader may identify. These simply serve as examples.

The establishment of effective communication between health workers and patients requires consideration by the former of the verbal and nonverbal forms in which messages are sent and received. The language used and the channels through which it is sent must be adapted to the person(s) for whom it is intended. If the receiver is a lower-class member, simple sentences and concrete concepts will be more meaningful rather than complex sentences or abstract concepts. Facial expressions, body posture, and the use of hands may also help the patient to understand the message. The use of language is a form of behavior, and any communication involves the process of "taking the role of the other." For understanding to occur, the health worker needs to picture himself in the role of his patient. This process will give him clues to follow in tailoring his language and gestures in the most expedient and comprehensive fashion. A variety of stimuli (verbal and nonverbal) are constantly impinging upon individuals. From this complex array of stimuli the individual selectively perceives only those that are meaningful for him. He cannot incorporate *all* the communication that is directed toward him. In addition, there are many other potential barriers to effective communication. Messages may be sent and received, but either not understood or misinterpreted, or the words may be interpreted literally without any consideration of the nonverbal feelings underlying the message. It is essential that the communicator establish a means whereby he can obtain feedback and thereby evaluate the effect of his message.

The effectiveness of communication may be evaluated in many ways. The health worker can observe the behavior of his patient to determine whether any change has taken place. He can engage the patient in a dialogue that may include specific questions that require answers other than a simple "yes" or "no." The most important aspect of this dialogue is the listening process. Many patients, especially those of the lower class and certain subcultural groups, may not be able to express themselves; but if the health worker really listens he may be able to assist the patient by using the process called reflection, in which the patient makes a statement and the professional "reflects" the statement for clarification. This feedback can then be utilized, not only for evaluating effectiveness, but also for determining patient needs and planning future care.

# PART TWO

## *The Roads: Trends and Social Movements*

Modern society is a complex of norms, values, and behaviors. Technological changes throughout man's history have modified his personal orientations — thoughts, beliefs, and other forms of behavior — and his social organizations. Communication and transportation systems have enabled him to traverse the millions of miles his predecessors never believed existed. This geographic mobility has resulted in the breakdown of extended families and concentration on nuclear families; specialization and new career possibilities have resulted in a much greater social mobility. These inventions and changes also have challenged traditional beliefs and values and often have created forces of unrest and collective behavior.

Social change in many ways has not kept up with the gigantic advances in technology. Stresses have occurred because behavior patterns have not altered at the same rate of speed as the technological changes. Because of this cultural lag man is plagued with problems of population control, war, rapid economic fluctuations, social diseases, institutional decay, and ambiguous norms. Medical advances have brought problems as well as solutions. Keeping more people alive through better obstetrical techniques, earlier diagnosis and treatment, antibiotics and sanitation has also produced the specter of an overpopulated world.

The health professions and their ideologies are potentially affected by the public, that ever-growing group of people who regard themselves as affected by all events and activities and who are vocal about their concern. Though a public may be widely dispersed geographically, it still has great influence that must be taken into account. For within its ranks collective behavior occurs and is sustained. This collective behavior is important, for it gives rise to new norms, values, and action. It seeks to produce social change, to modify the established patterns of relationships between men.

Out of collective behavior, social movements occur if one or more of three conditions arise:[1] (1) the absence or weakness of social forms, for example, given a new situation one does not know how to act; (2) the basis for a decision is ambiguous, for example, an issue such as fluoridation arises, and it is the individuals in society who must decide on a course of action; or (3) perspectives and values change, for example, family planning is seen as necessary in order to provide adequate education for offspring.

A social movement, then, is a voluntary association of people engaged in a concerted effort to change the attitudes, behavior, and/or social relationships in a larger society. From this perspective any group activity may be viewed in a sense as collective behavior or a social movement when groups of individuals act together with a division of labor and establish lines of individual conduct. A social movement survives only if it adjusts effectively to the current social

47

situation. The National Polio Foundation provides a good illustration. The advent of the Salk vaccine, its widespread acceptance, and the subsequent decrease in the number of polio cases required the Foundation either to terminate or to extend its services beyond that single disease entity. The agency met the challenge by choosing the latter course and now provides services for birth defects as well as for polio.

Three main types of social movements are: (1) value oriented—focused on change and the promise of societal betterment, for example, the planned parenthood movement and the many groups working for the mentally ill; (2) power oriented—focused on control of man, for example, political revolutions; (3) separatist oriented—focused on isolation through a break with the larger society, for example, the Amish community or the Doukhobors. For purposes of a sociological framework of patient care, this chapter will focus primarily on value-oriented types of social movements.

A value-oriented social movement that predominated until the late 1940's was known as the Protestant Ethic.[2] The basic philosophy of the Protestant Ethic involved fixed roles for women and men and strict discipline for children, including rigid feeding patterns. The general orientation to life included hard work, little personal pleasure, little leisure time, rigid value systems, and fixed attitudes and beliefs. Gratification and satisfaction came from "a job well done," as jobs were not viewed as occupation or profession but as "callings," and education was focused on training people drawn from a particular life situation for a specific job that was expected to remain the same. In the educational system the teachers were the authority, the learner was not expected to contribute in the learning process.

To be ill was viewed as the result of the individual's inadequacies, sins, or lack of willpower. Only illness of a *physical* nature was acknowledged; what is now called mental illness was viewed as the possession of the person by demons. The ill were expected to accept sickness as retribution. After assuming the patient role, a person was expected to let others make decisions to which he would submit without complaint or question. He was allowed no part in decisions regarding his treatment or care. In general, care consisted of removing the patient from his home environment, placing him in an institution, curing him of his ills, and sending him back home. Since acute physical illnesses were the concern of this period, treatment centered around taking care of the pathological condition in the body. This was related to the general orientation to life expressed in the statement: "A healthy body produces more physical labor."

The organization of the hospital was similar to that of the family; the power structure was also reminiscent of the family. The hospital was a rather simple organization with the roles of each of the health workers clearly defined. The physician (male) made the decisions about the care of the patient; the nurse (female) followed the physician's orders. The doctor focused on disease entities; the nurse nurtured and comforted by maintaining a clean environment, feeding, clothing, and bathing the patient. Both the physician and the nurse responded to their calling by working long hours, being "dedicated" and sacrificial. To attend the sick was a charitable duty.

In terms of the physician's relationship to the patient, the latter was subordinate;

but because medicine was perceived as a calling rather than an economic enterprise or occupation, the patient was allowed to pay the physician with whatever goods he had available, whether pickles, pigs, or pennies.

The next social movement affecting the role of the sick and the role of the health professional was the Freudian Ethic.[3] This orientation to life included permissive feeding patterns and lack of discipline for the child. The male and female became concerned with understanding each other's motives and behavior. The roles of parent and companion and those of employee and employer became less strictly defined. The general orientation to work was to be kind, permissive, and understanding of self and others. Family ties became less strong and less influential.

The sick appeared less deviant as all people began to examine their *psyche* in relation to their *soma*. Health workers became preoccupied with the psychological aspects of illness. New types of illness (psychosomatic disorders) were identified, and all illnesses were believed to have a psychic component. Thus the concept of "total patient care" was introduced.

The role of the patient changed. He was now expected to express his feelings, talk about himself, and assist in his entire treatment. With the concept of "total patient care" arose a change in hospital organization, structure, and power. The hospital began to be viewed not as the only place to care for the sick, but as one of many health agencies in the community to assist people. Since prevention of illness was also an important element of this movement, the hospital had to become more concerned with the patients' families and the role of hospitals as educational institutions. Many new disciplines and specialties emerged to meet the psychophysical needs of patients. The simple male-female-child (physician-nurse-patient) relationship dissolved and was replaced by a more complex interdisciplinary structure.

Recently a new social movement has developed which requires reorganization of contemporary society. For lack of a better term, we call it the "experiential living" movement; its primary emphasis is on social health and welfare. Its general orientation to life involves religious, political, and educational reform. The emphasis is on change in all aspects of life—*status quo* has yielded the stage to *social change*. Through the mass media we are daily made aware of the multiplicity of specialized change movements—antiwar, antipoverty, anti-illness, antisocial class, antiracial and ethnic differences, all adding up to the development of the "great society." Problem solving and scientific research represent the ways to bring about this new rational world.

The family, the primary social institution, of course has been greatly affected by this movement. Although the divorce rate has increased, so has the marriage rate. This does not reflect a disorganization of family structure, but rather a change in the functions and roles within this social institution. The role relationship of parents and children has taken new form. A composite of social groups has taken responsibility for child behavior. The child, both of his parents, educational and legal organizations, and society at large are held accountable for the total socialization of the child. Peer groups have increased in importance in developing standards of behavior, role performance, and gratification.

The aims of this movement necessitate viewing one's occupation as an aspiring for professional status. Emphasis is on career achievement through formal education as opposed to apprenticeships. The "dropout" is viewed as intolerable. The educational systems focus on individual development, but within specified limitations.

The concept of the individual as a total thinking, believing, being, and becoming person permeates everything. Yet the accumulation of vast storehouses of knowledge has led to specialization, and division of labor within professional groups has become more clearly delineated. The concepts of specialization and of the total individual are more often than not in conflict, even though both may be found in all professional groups.

To exponents of the experiential movement, illness is often viewed as a defect in societal functioning. The ill are considered as a composite of *socio*psychophysiological components. After assuming the patient role, an individual is expected to fully participate in all aspects of his treatment and care and to be responsible for some aspects of his movement toward health. This is true whether he is treated by a private physician or in a hospital.

Hospitals are becoming secondary to other agencies that were and are being established for social medicine. Mental-health centers that provide partial care in the patient's own community are emerging. No longer are they called hospitals but rather community centers for treatment. Now hospitals are designated as health centers; health professionals as health workers. More and more other community organizations like Synanon and public-health agencies are expected to assume the traditonal functions and services of hospitals. The return of the patient to his home and community is gaining in impetus. Medical care is making the full cycle back to the home.

As part of the experiential movement, individuals are seeking new, unique experiences. Adolescents and young adults are "experimenting" with narcotics, pep pills, and the "utopiates" such as LSD, peyote, and marijuana in a search for self. Other media being explored in an attempt to find life's meaning are extrasensory perception, hypnosis, "happenings," nonverbal and expressive parties, and dance movements.

Such developments have resulted in a reevaluation of medical and social ills. The government, for example, has imposed new laws regarding the dispensing and use of drugs such as LSD. Other forms of behavior, including sexual expression and its consequences, are currently being reviewed by legislators. On the other hand, religious and other organizational groups concerned with social welfare are attempting to influence the government in order to change laws which they view as controlling social and moral behavior.

The government's influence has spread into other aspects of health and welfare. It now subsidizes programs for the study and treatment of special diseases, training of various professional groups, building of new facilities, and financing research programs in the health field. More and more federal funds are being appropriated for health care. From 1961 to 1964 more health legislation was enacted than during any other four-year period in American history. Some of this legislation included monies appropriated for the study of environmental health, mental health, prevention and treatment of mental retardation, cause, prevention and treatment of cancer and heart disease, and a community-based approach to health problems — for example, the poverty program and care of the aged.

The allocation and withholding of federal and state funds has wide implications for health care and planning. The medicare program is an example. In 1965 an amendment to the Social Security Act was passed establishing a broad program of health coverage for people over 65 years of age. This program includes two types of federal health insurance: hospital and medical. The former covers hospitalization, out-patient diagnostic services, posthospital extended care, and posthospital home care services. The latter covers physician and surgeon services, home health visits, diagnostic tests, artificial limbs, and so on.

Many of the types of care provided for in this bill are now virtually nonexistent. This is one example of cultural lag in the health fields. Although the social movement is toward community health, most health workers are neither trained nor oriented in this direction. Medicare also calls for trained quasi-nursing personnel who are not currently available.

Not only do new discoveries, private agencies, and governmental programs within these trends and movements affect health and care, but also they create new problems to be solved. As Dorothy Smith states, the trend toward a utilization of sociological concepts raises several issues. Among them is the question of the patient as an unknown quantity. That is, many health professionals no longer know the patient as a member of an ethnic and social-class group, but rather as a diagnosed illness. Smith indicates the problems inherent in treating the patient as a "whole person" in view of the complexity of current medical organizations.

Freeman reminds us that we must move beyond the germ theory of illness and consider the human (social) aspects of health and illness. Although the germ theory allows us to cure the patient, it offers no solutions to the effective *care* of the ill. To effect such a care requires a consideration of the sociopsychological and cultural manifestations that impinge upon the patient.

On the other hand, medicine has become institutionalized, as Miyamoto indicates. It, like any other form of human endeavor, is subject to fads and fashions. These in turn produce new and different forms or structures within which the process of patient care transpires.

A number of major social trends affect the professionalization of patient care. Bureaucratization, changes in technology, standards of living, division of labor with specialization, and values conflicts, all have implications, as Leonard's article demonstrates. New roles are created and new problems must be solved.

The question that remains is succinctly posed by Leone in her report to the Surgeon General's office. That is: Is the profession ready for action in the care of some of the major contemporary health problems? Will the solution of these problems remain as another cultural lag in the process of patient care? The future-oriented health worker can answer these problems.

---

1. Ralph H. Turner and Lewis Killian, *Collective Behavior*, Englewood Cliffs, N.J.: Prentice-Hall, 1957.

2. Max Weber, *The Protestant Ethic and the Spirit of Capitalism*, London: Allan & Unwin, 1930.

The term Protestant Ethic is hereby used as described and refers to Weber's treatment of the Ethic. It does not mean to imply the Protestant religions, but rather the value system that was derived from Protestantism. This "ethic" is by no means extinct, but is no longer predominant in American culture.

3. Richard LaPiere, *The Freudian Ethic*, New York: Duell, Sloan, 1959.

The term Freudian Ethic is used only as described and refers to LaPiere's notion of the Ethic. It does not mean to imply Freud but rather the value system that was derived from the theories of Freud. This ethic also is not extinct, but is no longer as predominant in American culture.

# 5. THE ROLE OF SOCIOLOGY IN MEDICINE

*Dorothy E. Smith*

When societies were a good deal smaller and simpler than they are today, people could acquire through their ordinary daily encounters what they needed to know about social relationships and the varieties of human personality. But as societies increase in size and complexity and as the roles that people play in them become more specialized, the disjunction between the individual's experience of society and society as it is becomes unmanageably large. The situation in which the individual acts and through which he learns directly about human relationships is only a very small part of a total complex of such situations. The circumstances of his life may be influenced directly or indirectly by the doings and decisions of others with whom he has no contact, whom he has no means of influencing directly, and whose beliefs and values may be very different from his. The personal milieu within which he experiences society directly no longer coincides with the boundaries of the social structure that must be taken into account.

This growth in the size and complexity of society has had its own particular reflection in the development of medical institutions. In the last few decades scientific and technological advances have radically altered the structure of medical action. The gross increase in population and the emergence of great urban concentrations also have altered the demands made on medical services. The medicine institutions of modern society are a vast network of interdependent organizations. The crucial interpersonal dyad, the physician and patient relationship, has not lost its importance but it is now only part of a complex which has profoundly altered the basis of the relationship.

In the classic and probably idealized image of the physician-patient relationship, the general practitioner encountered his patients not only in a medical setting and in relation to specifically medical goals, but also in their homes, with their families, and in other settings in the community. The physician's knowledge of human relations and the varieties of the human condition was gained in the course of his practice and in his daily experience of a definite community. His clientele was ordinarily drawn from a limited locale. He knew his people, their way of life, their prejudices, their virtues, and their failings. In spite of differences in education and generally in social class, he could enter into their culture and values as a member of the same community. Today, of course, the physician rarely visits the home. There has been a change too in the social matrix linking physician to patient outside the medical setting. Changes in the size and structure of communities mean that most patients and physicians inhabit different segments of a single large community. The physician himself will be

---

This paper was prepared especially as an original contribution to this book.

at home in only one of these, but his patients may be drawn from others of which he has little or no direct experience. They may have different educational backgrounds, live under different socioeconomic conditions, or come from different ethnic groups.

A hundred years ago the boundaries separating medicine from the moral and religious aspects of society were far from clear. The physician's role defined him as an authority with respect to the patient's emotional and social difficulties as well as to his organic problems. The startling scientific advances in medicine have been in the biological and physical sciences. This is reflected today in an approach of physician to patient which is more exclusively organic, more exclusively technical and specific than it was in the past. Thus the scope of the physician's focus upon the person of the patient is markedly contracted as compared with that of earlier times.

The enormously expanded market for medical services combined with scientific and technological changes have stimulated differentiation and specialization of medical roles and agencies. Within the profession itself it is no longer possible for one individual to be fully competent in all fields of medicine. Subspecializations within the profession have proliferated rapidly and the proportion of general practitioners has declined markedly. But medical roles here refer also to other occupational roles that contribute to the total medical service to patients. Nursing has transformed what was once largely the province of the amateur into a highly skilled and specialized profession. Many aspects of diagnosis and treatment require technical skills for which people must be specially trained. There has

been a general proliferation of additional related occupational roles such as laboratory and X-ray technicians, physiotherapists, and many more. The complexities of hospital management have led to the emergence of the professionally trained nonmedical hospital administrator. There is specialization also among organized agencies and departments contributing to the total structure of medical action. Hospitals provide diagnosis, care, and treatment on an in-patient basis. Public-health departments are responsible for administering policies concerned with environmental health. Voluntary organizations accumulate funds and organize and distribute special services. Drug companies, pharmacists, and insurance companies are among the other organizations and professions that play an important part in the total medical structure of action characteristic of modern society.

Sociology as a discipline has emerged largely in response to the challenge of developing a systematic understanding of the complexities of human relations in contemporary society. It has accumulated a body of knowledge of theoretical concepts and formulations and an established repertoire of research procedures which make possible an increasingly sophisticated and refined comprehension of social organization and the processes of interpersonal relations. Sociological research in industry, government, the field of corrections, and many other areas feeds back into sociology and becomes available as a source of new insights and information. A major part of the sociologist's contribution to any specific field is his professional access to knowledge of human relationships built up from many such fields.

This opportunity for drawing upon a systematically formulated general experience of society is particularly relevant to unanticipated consequences of specialization and differentiation within medicine. The perspective of the individual in an occupational role tends to become limited to those aspects of experience that are immediately relevant to his special skills and objectives. As occupational roles become parts of more complex structures and as they become more specialized, personal experience becomes increasingly inadequate as a reliable source of information about social relationships. The complex structures within which the individual operates cannot be grasped by any straightforward rule-of-thumb approach. Specialization of roles is accompanied by a narrowing of focus and fragmentation of the total perspective among different individuals with different skills and objectives. For example, a physical therapist whose objective is to reactivate a patient's atrophied leg muscle has necessarily a different perspective on medicine than a pharmacist whose objectives include marketing cosmetics to customers and servicing medical prescriptions for physicians. At the same time the structures that need to be understood become harder to grasp directly. The perspectives of sociology as a discipline incorporate procedures that enable the sociologist to look at these structures *as if* he were not an actor in them. At the most general level it is the sociological perspective that is his most important potential contribution to medicine, or indeed to any other major institution in modern society.

The ways in which sociology is particularly relevant to medicine will be summarized under three main headings: (1) the patient as an unknown quantity; (2) the problem of the whole person; and (3) the complex of medical organizations.

## THE PATIENT AS AN UNKNOWN QUANTITY

### In the Community

One consequence of the developments just discussed is that the patient has become a largely unknown quantity. Specialization has narrowed the bases of contact between medical practitioner and patient, and the two parties to the medical transaction may inhabit very different cultural worlds. In the field of psychiatry it has been found that major difficulties occur in establishing a psychotherapeutic relationship between the middle-class psychiatrist and his working-class patient.[1] The working-class patient finds it hard to believe in "talking" as a means of treatment. He also is ordinarily less skilled verbally than most middle-class patients. Moreover he is likely to expect the psychiatrist to act in an authoritative manner, to give him advice and tell him what to do. The psychiatrist with a patient from this background cannot take for granted that he will share the assumptions upon which the psychotherapeutic relationship is based.

Such differences in culture are relevant beyond the psychiatric situation. In a study of a community in New York City, Suchman[2] found major variations among ethnic subgroups with respect to their knowledge of disease and its prevention. He found, for example, that Puerto Ricans understood and shared the objectives and methods of modern medicine much less than white Protestants and Jews. This finding may help to explain why some ethnic minorities are harder to reach in public health and medical care than others.

Suchman's study also showed that ethnic groups differed in degree of parochialism. Relationships within some ethnic groups were tightly knit and the general orientation was more traditional and authoritarian. More cosmopolitan groups were characterized by loosely knit relationships and less traditional attitudes. These differences were associated with widely different orientations toward medical practice. Suchman suggests that parochial groups are more at home with the personal type of medical care provided by private practice and do not easily accept the impersonality of large-scale health plans and out-patient clinics.

Since medical relationships are generally initiated by the patient rather than the physician or other health specialist, the level of knowledge about medicine clearly is important if preventive medicine is to be effective. The symptoms that patients recognize as pointing to the need for medical treatment are important to the early diagnosis and treatment of disease. Koos[3] has shown in a study of illness in "Regionville" that members of different social-class groupings tend to recognize different symptoms as cues to seek treatment. Respondents in the study were asked which of a list of symptoms—ranging from loss of appetite to excessive vaginal bleeding—would indicate a need for medical attention. Respondents in the lowest social class were markedly indifferent to many symptoms. By contrast 75 per cent of those in the highest social class indicated that they would seek medical treatment for all the symptoms listed except loss of appetite and backache.

*In Hospital*

Although an organizational structure brings people together in direct and indirect contact with one another, it also interposes barriers to communication. The role of the patient in a hospital may lead to neglect of his human needs because no adequate channel exists through which the patient can communicate his personal concerns and feelings. Sociological studies of mental hospitals have made practitioners in that field more aware of the kind of interpersonal milieu found on the ward to which the hospitalized patient is exposed.[4] Studies in general hospitals have shown some of the varieties of meaning that the patient's hospital experience may have for him.[5] Renee Fox's[6] study of the patients' attitudes toward the risks of experimental medication and technique shows how meaning and dignity is given to their experience through their integration into a culture of participation with the research physicians. Other studies have drawn attention to sources of misunderstanding between patients and staff. Julius Roth[7] in his work on tuberculosis sanatoriums shows that the timetable of the patient's progress through the hospital has a very different meaning for patients than it does for members of the medical staff. The latter schedules tests, operations, and the award of privileges according to clinical imperatives. The patients, on the other hand, in an effort to establish a stable perspective on their uncertain progress, set up timetables based in part on how other patients fare and in part on the informal culture of the group. These timetables constitute norms in terms of which patients come to view tentative privileges as definite rights, due them following the lapse of an appropriate period of time. Departures from the timetable were treated as breaches of an implicit contract between themselves and the hospital.

These are some of the ways in which the patient may be made known to persons working in the health field through the use of sociological methods and perspectives.

## THE PROBLEM OF THE WHOLE PERSON

The human being is more than an organic entity. He is an organism, a psyche, and a social actor. These various aspects are assigned to different scientific jurisdictions and yet are part of an indivisible whole. Although we do not as yet understand how these different dimensions work together in the resulting observable behavior of the individual, it is clear that they are all there and in some sense interacting in any behavioral process. Medical science is a practice as well as a field of research. As a science that addresses itself to that complex of human responses known as sickness, it must take into account that sickness is a behavior of the whole person. Insofar as the individual's behavior arises out of organic, social, and psychological processes, we need systematic knowledge of how the latter enter into sickness behavior and the etiology of disease.

## THE SOCIAL PATTERNING OF SICKNESS BEHAVIOR

Being a patient is a specific role in a definite institutional setting. Being sick is also a socially patterned role though more general and less specifically defined with respect to others than the role of patient. The behaviors appropriate to this role, the patterns of sickness behavior, are not simply a function of the individual's organic state, but include patterns that are learned and socially relevant. When the health specialist encounters the patient, he does not encounter a *tabula rasa* but a person with a history of encounters with health personnel, a person who in his childhood experiences and through informal training has learned patterns of action relevant to these relationships. He may have learned, for example, to assign a special meaning and patterns of action to the experience of pain.[8] He may have learned to pay attention to certain kinds of symptoms rather than others. He may even have learned to be sick in certain ways.

The idea of the sick role draws attention to the fact that the organic state of sickness and the social patterning of sickness do not necessarily coincide. For reasons not necessarily connected with his physiological state the individual may want to avoid being defined as sick when he is sick or, in situations of stress, to take advantage of his physiological state to secure the release from obligations to which being sick entitles him.[9] Most diseases moreover do not have a defined terminal point and stages of convalescence are in part socially defined. The patient's personal situation may influence his willingness to leave the sick role and resume normal functioning. The termination of sickness is a social process of negotiation between patient and medical practitioner. The termination of sickness in death is also a social process and the ways in which the medical setting shapes the individual's experience of dying is only beginning to be studied.

*Social Factors in the*
*Etiology of Disease*

There are many ways in which social factors may enter into the etiology of disease. One factor that affects a wide range of health relevant variables is social class. The individual's socioeconomic position affects his access to some of the minimal conditions of health—adequate food, pure water and air, reasonable housing conditions, as well as the general quality of medical care received. Conditions of health also may be directly influenced by the culture of a group. Beliefs and values transmitted in a particular group or subgroup of a society may influence practices relevant to health. Cultural restrictions on food may produce deficiency diseases even when foods that could supply the deficiency are available. There is the hypothesis too that the lower incidence of cancer of the cervix among Jewish women is linked with the practice of circumcizing Jewish males. Certain occupations also are associated with definite hazards; some, like mining, by exposing the individual to disease-producing agents, and others by subjecting the individual to stress that results in disease.

The social structure clearly influences the transmission of contagious disease. Diseases that are transmitted by direct contact between persons travel in structures that pattern the encounters between persons. The social patterning of sexual encounters influences the spread of venereal disease. Diseases that are transmitted through a mediating agent (fleas, for example) are also influenced by aspects of social structure that facilitate the movement of the mediating agent. And it is clear that the rise of urbanism and the expansion of trade between different countries and cities is directly related to the history of epidemics in Western Europe. Advances in medical technology, however, have resulted in the diminished significance of contagious diseases while chronic diseases have become of greater relative importance.

In many of the chronic diseases, social psychological factors causing stress appear to be etiologically significant. For example, a number of studies have suggested a relationship between psychological conflicts and essential hypertension.[10] A recent study in a region of North Dakota found that subjects who were socially mobile, either geographically or occupationally, had a higher ratio of observed to expected cases of coronary heart disease than more stable men.[11] It is also believed that social psychological factors may contribute to other diseases, including arthritis and peptic ulcers.

Social psychological factors creating stress may influence the individual's general susceptibility to illness as well as contribute to specific diseases. Hinkle and Wolff[12] in their study of illness among employees of a corporation found not only that some individuals tended to have many more illnesses than others but also that illnesses tended to cluster in periods rather than being more or less randomly distributed over the years. Their study suggests two main ways in which the individual's social situation influences his susceptibility to illness. First, the periods of greatest illness frequency were found to correspond to periods of stress in the individual's life. Second, they found that individuals who were more frequently ill than others were also more likely to have grown up in families characterized by conflict. This suggests that interpersonal relations in childhood may influence the individual's general susceptibility to stress and hence to illness in later life.

Sickness behavior may thus be influenced in a number of ways by social factors. The individual's basic personality structure and his major life goals are shaped in the interpersonal experiences of childhood. Social factors shape his adult occupational experience and his general life situation. Viewing illness as a total response of the individual to his life situation means taking into account the social dimensions of behavior which are the special province of the sociologist.

## THE COMPLEX OF MEDICAL ORGANIZATIONS

The medical service that the patient receives is the end product of complex organizational activities in which many individuals interact. The patient himself is a participant and himself contributes in interaction with others to the objectives of his own health. Even the private practitioner and his patients can be viewed as a special kind of organizational structure. The medical services that the patient receives depend on the type of hospitals in the community, his physician's relationship to them, the pharmacists, and others. The physician's role coordinates and mobilizes the services of other agencies and facilities as well as his own skills and knowledge in the patient's service. The type of medical service provided and its quality are determined in large part by the effectiveness of these cooperative processes.

The structure of organized cooperative action is defined first of all by the formally specified roles of participants. Roles are patterned ways of breaking down organizational tasks into parts for which different individuals can be made responsible. The physician is responsible for diagnosis, for prescribing and supervising treatment procedures; the patient's role involves being there to be treated and cooperating with the physician and the nurse in treatment procedures; the nurse is responsible for technical aspects of his care and for assisting the physician in many diagnostic and treatment procedures, for keeping records on the patient, and for the general standards of ward care and housekeeping. The different roles intermesh and the final performance depends on the contribution of each.

An organization such as a hospital or medical school is a complex of such roles. Each particular set of cooperative activities takes place therefore in a context created by the actions and beliefs of others and is influenced by the total structure of organizational action. For example, hospitals have characteristically multiple lines of authority, an administrative structure running from trustees to clerical workers and domestic employees, and a second line of authority in the professional medical structure. If the hospital is large the latter may be divided further into a number of departments. Nursing services may also constitute a quasi-independent structure of authority. Each of these may have competing interests and different conceptions of their own role in the hospital and what its goals should be. Improving nursing services to the community may conflict with the development of research. Sources of conflict may influence interpersonal contacts at various levels and hence the effectiveness of cooperative action between individuals in the different roles.

The formal definitions of roles do not fully specify how individuals should act.

Indeed there is generally a need for improvisation, particularly when different aspects of a task come into conflict with one another. The nurse in a mental hospital may have to make her own balance between her obligations to keep order on the ward and a therapeutic emphasis on encouraging patients to interact freely with one another. An organization is capable of flexibility only because individuals do improvise in roles, because they do step outside the formal definitions to meet specific conditions and particular needs. Moreover people enter into personal relations of friendship or enmity which influence their attitude toward their work and the kinds of norms that guide their behavior. It has been found that the informal work norms of friendship groups in an organization are in many ways important in determining how individuals do their work. If members of informal groups share an interest in their work the individual's efforts are supported by group norms and rewarded by the responses and interest of others who are personally important to him. Informal groups, however, may develop values that diverge from those of the organization. When this happens they may present substantial sources of resistance to conformity with the formal requirements of their role.

These aspects of the informal structure of an organization can also make a great deal of difference to its success. For example, education consists of much more than the content of courses, the program of study, the results of tests, and so on. The relations between faculty and students, the informal relationships that develop among students, and the total organizational context of the medical school influence the motivation of the student to study, how he decides what is important, how he comes to choose what

to specialize in.[13] Similar factors may influence the quality of care provided by a hospital. When colleague group relations are personally satisfying and professionally lively, the performance of individuals is at a higher standard. Studies have shown that the type of intellectual and professional climate maintained by a group of colleagues in a hospital or clinic setting is important in determining the general standard of medical care.[14] Similar patterns are important too in maintaining quality of medical care in private practice. Studies show that practitioners in some form of group practice generally provide better care than those in individual practice.[15] The implication of such studies is that opportunities for contact with professional colleagues is of considerable importance in maintaining commitment to professional standards.

A different level of understanding is involved in confronting the total structure of medical action in a society. In addition to the medical profession itself and other health professions, insurance companies, drug companies, volunteer organizations, trade unions, legislative bodies, as well as hospitals and public-health departments all contribute to the total picture. These structures and their relationships differ from society to society. Each total system provides a characteristic form of medical service with its distinctive advantages and disadvantages. The structure of American medicine is made up of a large number of independent agencies. It is pluralistic in conformity with the general preference for avoiding centralized regulatory agencies. It has been extremely successful in institutionalizing technological and scientific advances. It has been less successful, however, in providing an equitable distribution of medical care to different segments of the population. In particular, there are gaps in the provision of adequate medical care to the economically underprivileged members of the society. This perspective on the totality of medical institutions is one to which sociologists might make major contributions. It is as yet, unfortunately, relatively underdeveloped.

## CONCLUSION

These are some of the ways in which sociologists contribute to medicine. In recent years their contributions have increased both in quantity and significance. In many ways, however, the full power of sociological theory and research methodology has yet to be deployed in medicine. How rapidly this comes about depends on the opportunities for research in medicine made available to sociologists and their freedom to define their problems sociologically. The issue sometimes raised is how far sociologists should work on medically defined problems (as in epidemiological studies) and how far on problems that have primarily sociological relevance. If medical problems are defined as exclusively or largely organic, then the use of sociological concepts and methods cannot be more than adjunctive. If, however, the medical frame of reference shifts toward the concept of the "whole person," sociological concepts and formulations will become a basic element in the medical perspective.

---

1. For example, L. Schaffer and J. K. Myers, "Psychotherapy and Social Stratification: An Empirical Study of Practice in Psychiatric Out-Patient Clinic," *Psychiatry,* 17, 1954. 83–93.

2. E. A. Suchman, "Socio-medical Variations among Ethnic Groups," *American Journal of Sociology,* LXX, 1964, 319–331.

3. E. L. Koos, *The Health of Regionville,* New York: Columbia University Press, 1954, pp. 30–38 in particular.

4. For example, A. H. Stanton and M. S. Schwartz, *The Mental Hospital, A Study of Institutional Participation in Psychiatric Illness and Treatment,* New York: Basic Books, 1954; and W. Caudill, *The Psychiatric Hospital as a Small Society,* Cambridge, Mass.: Harvard University Press, 1958.

5. For example, R. L. Coser, *Life in the Ward,* East Lansing, Mich.: Michigan State University Press, 1962.

6. R. Fox, *Experiment Perilous, Physicians and Patients Facing the Unknown,* Glencoe, Ill.: The Free Press, 1959.

7. J. Roth, *Timetables, Structuring the Passage of Time in Hospital Treatment*

*and Other Careers,* New York: Bobbs-Merrill, 1963.

8. M. Zborowski, "Cultural Components in Responses to Pain," *Journal of Social Issues,* 8, 1952, 16–30.

9. For example, see David Mechanic and E. A. Volkart, "Stress, Illness Behavior, and the Sick Role," *American Sociological Review,* 26, 1961, 51–58.

10. N. A. Scotch and H. J. Geiger, "The Epidemiology of Essential Hypertension: A Review with Special Attention to Psychological and Socio-cultural Factors. II: Psychological and Socio-cultural Factors in Etiology," *Journal of Chronic Diseases,* 16, 1963, 1183–1213.

11. S. L. Syme, M. M. Hyman, and P. E. Enterline, "Some Social and Cultural Factors Associated with the Occurrence of Coronary Heart Disease," *Journal of Chronic Diseases,* 17, 1964, 277–289.

12. E. Hinkle, Jr., and H. G. Wolff, "Health and the Social Environment," in A. H. Leighton, J. A. Clausen, and R. N. Wilson (Eds.), *Explorations in Social Psychiatry,* New York: Basic Books, 1957.

13. For example, R. K. Merton, G. G.

Reader, and P. L. Kendall (Eds.), *The Student-Physician, Introductory Studies in the Sociology of Medical Education*, Cambridge, Mass.: Harvard University Press, 1957; H. S. Becker, B. Geer, E. C. Hughes, and A. L. Strauss, *Boys in White, Student Culture in a Medical School*, Chicago, Ill.: University of Chicago Press, 1961.

14. For example, I. Belknap and J. G. Steinle, *The Community and Its Hospitals*, Syracuse, N.Y.: Syracuse University Press, 1963; M. Seeman and J. Evans, "Stratification and Hospital Care," *American Sociological Review*, Part I: **26**, 1961, 67–79; Part II: **26**, 1961, 193–203; and R. W. Revans, *Standards for Moral, Cause and Effect in Hospitals*, London: Oxford University Press, 1964.

15. For example, Osler L. Peterson, Leon P. Andrews, Robert S. Spain, and Bernard G. Greenberg, "An Analytical Study of North Carolina General Practice, 1953-54," *The Journal of Medical Education*, **31**, 1956, Part 2.

# 6. SOCIAL MOVEMENTS IN THE FIELD OF MEDICINE

## S. Frank Miyamoto

Medicine like all other fields of science is institutionalized. Institutions arise in the functional areas, such as the giving and seeking of medical service, in which there is need for an enduring orderly relationship among diverse people performing different roles. By organizing behavior into stable and predictable patterns, institutions serve the function of routinizing collective action and of minimizing the confusion and conflict that otherwise would arise. The requisite condition for institutional stability is a relatively widespread and stable consensus among the participants on: (1) the values emphasized; (2) the ideas and beliefs that constitute the cognitive bases of action; and (3) a social structure that defines the patterns of relations expected of the participants.

But what if the consensual foundation of an institution is brought seriously into question or becomes severely disorganized for any reason? The processes of collective action will then be disturbed, and it is predictable that those affected will attempt to reorganize relations so that a smooth coordination of action is again possible. The scope and vigor of the reorganizational effort will vary, of course, with the range and severity of the disruption, but where any large number of persons are affected, the potential exists for the appearance of a persistent collective effort to reorder the situation.

Such collective enterprises often are called social movements.[1]

A social movement is defined as "a collectivity acting with some continuity to promote a change or resist a change in the society or group of which it is a part."[2] The study of social movements thus is a study of change, but its perspective on change is unique. In contrast to the investigations of change by trend analysis, by tracing the development of an idea or technique, by analyzing the role of innovators and other leaders, or by comparing the state of affairs at two points in time, the present approach considers the role of people as a collectivity in effecting change.

In a short essay the nature of social movements may be clarified most easily by an illustration. In the history of antisepsis we are told that crude but effective ideas on the antiseptic treatment of wounds were introduced as early as the fourteenth century by Theodoric and Henri de Mondeville, but that a storm of opposition caused their suggestions to become buried and lost for six hundred years.[3] The long and difficult struggles in the nineteenth century of Holmes, Semmelweiss, Lister, and others in seeking to establish antiseptic procedures have also been vividly reported, and the dependence of Lister's ultimate success on Pasteur's germ theory has been noted.[4] In short, according to the typical

---

This paper was prepared especially as an original contribution to this book.

history of medicine, changes in medicine result from the scientific and rational cogency of the ideas and techniques offered, the repeated demonstration of their effectiveness, the persistence of innovators in insisting on changes, and the existence of general conditions favoring the change.

The student of social movements, however, wishes to analyze in detail the conditions in the time of Theodoric and de Mondeville which maintained the traditional medical institution, and thereby disposed both the medical profession and its clientele to reject the innovation. He would seek to understand the persistence of these conditions into the time of Holmes and Semmelweiss, but in the latter would inquire also into the historic changes that were undermining the structure of traditional medicine and preparing the way for radical alterations of medicine. In particular he would examine the tactics of the leaders, both among the protagonists and antagonists of antisepsis, in mobilizing support for their respective views, and attempt to understand how by organized effort the supporters of antisepsis overcame the opposition.

Thus change viewed from the standpoint of social movements focuses attention on the decay of institutional controls, trends of popular disposition, the rise of innovators and leaders, the role of small cohesive clusters of supporters, the mobilization of a larger following, and the struggle of the innovating group and the opposition for power and control. Social change is seen not merely as the product of impersonal forces, but as the consequence of events and men so influencing other men's views and patterns of relations as to make an innovation assimilable by the group or society.[5]

Actually, scientific medicine is not a field in which social movements abound, as they do in politics, religion, and social reform. The reason is that in medicine the values sought as well as the criteria for judging the validity of new ideas (the scientific canons) are widely understood and accepted, as they are not in the other fields, and these conditions support strong movements toward institutional stability. Moreover the influential workers in the field are professionals; that is, the patterns of relations are well structured and conduct is restrained by code and creed. Nevertheless few would deny that medicine is still both science and art, and to the extent that it remains an art the field is subject to fashion movements as are all forms of art. Moreover medicine has its political and social-reform aspects, as witness the recent controversy over Medicare, and on these problems the medical professions and their clientele engage in social movements no less than do political and social reformers.

Although the fashion movement usually is not considered a typical form of social movement because of its importance in fields of science, some attention will first be given to it before taking up the more general case.

## FASHION MOVEMENTS

"Fashion" is a term commonly reserved for trends in dress styles, but technically speaking it refers also to a type of gradual change often found in art, philosophy, literature, music, and, as Schroedinger points out, even in physics and other related sciences.[6] Its distinguishing characteristic is the appearance among members of a group or society of a widespread tendency to accept, on the basis of subjective rather than objective criteria of choice, a course of action in one direction rather than any other. Unlike the transitoriness of fads, however, fashions evolve slowly and follow a characteristically cyclical path.[7] The gradual shift of emphasis in psychiatry from biological to psychic and again to biological theories of mental disorder has the essential features of a fashion movement.

Fashion movements occur in a particular kind of setting. The basic requirement is a changing environment; the more extensive and rapid the changes, the more dynamic is the fashion tendency. Unlike actions that are guided by rational or utilitarian considerations, fashions occur where the criteria of action are vague, uncertain, and not defined by widely accepted standards. Thus the technique of smallpox vaccination, which has had demonstrable success in immunizing against the disease, has scarcely varied over many decades, but the techniques for treating allergies have shown notable variations. Finally, fashion occurs when there emerges a collective disposition, a simultaneous subjective tendency of many, to prefer one line of action over others.

The notion of a collective disposition requires special discussion. Collective dispositions are basically shaped by those conditions of life that significantly affect the experiences of people. For example, in an affluent society whose members experience much comfort and ease of living, it is predictable that medical workers will be disposed to give, and patients to expect, a good deal of attention to problems of minimizing the latter's discomfort and pain; but rather different attitudes would be expected if societal experiences were continuously harsh. The foregoing illustrates only a minor influence on disposition. More fundamental and general effects in our society stem from urbanization, scientific and technological developments, industrialization, increased speed and scope of communication and transportation, increased specialization, modifications of training, and consequent alterations in typical relations among people. Dispositions also are shaped by satiation with a prevailing mode.

How such changes may orient the collective disposition in a specific direction is not well understood. Nevertheless it seems obvious that the components of collective disposition, such as values, attitudes, beliefs, interests, awareness, taste, and inclinations generally, are noticeably affected. The point deserving emphasis here is that people occupying a given sector of society tend to be uniformly affected and therefore to develop the same dispositions. Once a collective disposition develops, it directs attention to certain facets of the world and closes the mind to others.[8] Thus the dramatic demonstration of the relationship between microorganisms and diseases directed attention to sanitation problems, immunization techniques, and pharmaceutical means of controlling diseases, but perhaps delayed advances in tissue study. The development of ever more powerful microscopes in turn may have drawn attention to tissue study, but perhaps have deterred studies of body chemistry.

Collective dispositions and the resulting fashion movements have at least a threefold effect on medicine: (1) where objective criteria for judging the preferability of one line of action over another are lacking, judgments are likely to be influenced, for good or ill, by the prevailing fashion mode; (2) because of the prevailing wind, so to speak, advances of medical science are likely to be wafted along certain courses to the neglect of other equally valid courses; (3) in general those who attempt to move against the prevailing fashion stream face not only contrary prejudices but also an unfavorable climate for developing their own ideas.

A brief note should be added about fads in medicine. Unlike fashions, which have a historical sweep about them, fads are transitory and lack historical continuity, are more contagious if less enduring, affect fewer people, and tend toward excesses. Like fashions, however, a fad is a collective action guided by a subjective rather than objective determination of the action, and prompted by a strong collective disposition to accept a given type of innovation.[9] Hence fads are most prevalent among persons highly sensitive to certain types of novel ideas, who are not firmly controlled by established principles and conventions, and who interact intensely with others of similar inclination.[10]

Medicine is particularly susceptible to fads because of the insistent demand of the clientele for cures and palliatives. It is doubtless difficult for physicians, confronted by demands for relief by patients and families, to await full validation of new drugs and techniques. The aggressive activity of pharmaceutical and medical supply firms adds to the pressure. There is also the danger of being charged with practicing conservative medicine, while on the other hand the line between progressive and faddistic medicine is not always a clear one. Finally, what may be seen as a rational extension of established principles to those schooled in one point of view may be regarded as utter faddism by those holding a dissimilar view. Fads in medicine are probably inevitable, but the worst examples of them may be eliminated by controlling the conditions that induce fads.[11]

## SOCIAL MOVEMENTS

The mental-hygiene movement, which was organized by Clifford Beers in 1908 to protect the mental health of the public and improve the standard of care of the mentally ill, is not a typical movement in the medical field. Nevertheless it is useful for illustration here because it reflects features characteristic of movements generally and clarifies problems unique to professional movements. Also it has been reported in particularly full detail.[12]

Almost all social movements begin as an attack on an existing institutional system. Beers' autobiographical classic, _The Mind That Found Itself_,[13] vividly related the brutality that he experienced while a patient in three mental hospitals, and the resolution that grew in him to work toward ridding hospitals of their inhumane practices. But the problem lay, as Beers recognized, less in the characters of the staff personnel than in the current inadequacies in the state of psychiatric knowledge, the financing of care, the physical and organizational arrangements for care, and the public understanding of mental illness. Present-day studies make it clear that when workers in a hospital understand only physically coercive methods of controlling their patients, the institutional structure becomes geared to this mode of control, and efforts to eliminate the traditional controls require wholesale restructuring of certain key institutional features.[14] It was this organized system supporting the traditional ideas that Beers' movement sought to overcome.

In the background of such a specific

movement, there is invariably a *general social movement*, an unorganized and intermittent but nevertheless perceptible stirring among segments of the populace in the direction of the ultimate specific form. Long before Beers, men like Pinel, Esquirol, and Tukes demonstrated the effectiveness of a humane approach in the treatment of the mentally ill, and in this country there appeared no less distinguished personages, including Benjamin Rush, Thomas Kirkbride, and Dorothea Dix, who crusaded to improve the treatment of mental patients. But the movement in this phase tended to have the characteristic that Blumer attributes to the general movement:

Such a movement is episodic in its career, with very scattered manifestations of activity. It may show considerable enthusiasm at one point and reluctance and inertia at another; it may experience success in one area, and abortive effort in another. In general, it may be said that its progress is very uneven, with setbacks, reverses, and frequent retreading of the same ground.[15]

The number of successes during the nineteenth century were actually quite substantial, considering the widespread ignorance about mental disorders which then prevailed. The Hartford Retreat and asylums like McLean and Bloomingdale became model hospitals of their day; Dorothea Dix, more than any other single individual, contributed to the removal of the mentally ill from jails and almshouses to hospitals of the insane; and the professionalization of psychiatrists and neurologists was begun. But there were abortive efforts as well. The "Cult of Curability" of the mid-nineteenth century, which made extravagant claims for the curability of mental patients under proper hospital care and aroused widespread enthusiasm, was demolished by hard facts that exploded the claims. New buildings for the care of patients were erected, but the methods of patient care maintained within the walls were scarcely advanced over those known a half century earlier.[16]

Although the nineteenth century produced no sustained collective effort to humanize the care of mental patients, it forged a collective disposition on which a successful mental-hygiene movement might be founded. A literature grew that provided a permanent source of stimulation to those who wished to emulate Pinel, Tukes, and Dorothea Dix. Leadership emerged from among reformers, educators, publicists, and philanthropists who, at least individually, added their weight to the program for improving the hospitals. Professionalization of the workers in the field—the psychiatrists, neurologists, nurses, and social workers—gradually developed and laid the basis for a sustained drive to improve the standard of patient care. And the American public emerged out of the nineteenth century with a far greater conscience about social problems than might have been deemed possible at the beginning of the century.

Because of the nature of the medical field, a social movement in this area often moves along two channels—changes among the professionals and changes among the lay public and the clientele—and some attention should be given to this dual process. The two are related, of course, but their developments occur at different times and accelerate at different rates. Professionals, as previously suggested, are more thoroughly organized than the public, and in a social sense are more stable and thereby more conservative, but they are also more sensitive to the advances of science. That is, their changes tend to be undertaken through their organized structure, both formal and informal, and their resistances to change arise when the structure is threatened. Indeed in the latter case the structure itself is the chief weapon against change.

Changes in the psychiatric profession during the nineteenth century thus were notably related to changes in their organization. Two dates may be selected to mark points of change. In 1844 the Association of Medical Superintendents of American Institutions for the Insane and the Prevention of Insanity, the early forerunner of the American Psychiatric Association, was organized by a talented group of physicians who have come to be known as The Original Thirteen. The formation of the association was an important step in the professionalization of American psychiatry, and through its meetings and national journal it established a means for exchanging ideas and elevating the standards of asylums; but its concerns were primarily administrative and its membership policy was narrow and exclusive.[17]

In 1892 when the name of the association was changed to the American Medico-Psychological Association, the change reflected a basic shift that was occurring in the psychiatric field. As a consequence of neurological experience gained during the Civil War, a small but vigorous group of neurologists appeared in the last quarter of the century who, in company with noninstitutional psychiatrists and social workers, launched a bitter attack on the institutional psychiatrists for their reactionary methods of patient care, isolation from noninstitutional contacts, and lack of interest in research. This group formed the National Association for the Protection of the Insane and the Prevention of Insanity (1880), an abortive movement with a program similar to that later promulgated by Beers, which began auspiciously but foundered a few years later mainly because of its divisive attack on the institutional physicians. The conflicts of this period aroused intense antagonism, but it had the ultimate effect of opening the association to broader membership (signified by the change of name), and of leading to a greater stress on the study and treatment of mental disease.[18] In the background of these last events was the enormous boost to rational medicine that came with the acceptance of Pasteur's germ theory.

The case is interesting because it illustrates a characteristic of social movements: they often emerge from a background of conflict and a rash of earlier movements. At the heart of the process is a struggle for power by which each group seeks ascendency for its own view.

Space does not permit an equally detailed account of the changes in public attitudes. It suffices to say that the efforts of the nineteenth-century crusaders were directed largely at arousing the moral conscience of the nation, and that the changes in the public were more related to other reform efforts current in America than in the case of the professionals.

Beers' Mental Hygiene Movement, organized in 1908, thus appeared under most favorable circumstances and enjoyed unusual success.[19] We can touch on only a few of the conditions that contributed to its success. Beers' remarkable book was a vital factor in arousing the spontaneous support that greeted his initial organizational effort. Because a social movement is an enterprise of a collectivity, it always is faced with the problem of drawing collective attention to the issues and of provoking sufficient consensus and commitment to enable the mobilization of action. The book did just that. It attracted wide interest; it had the ring of truth; it vivified the needs; it aroused sympathy; and it offered a symbol about which to mobilize the movement.

Successful movements since the time of Christ and his disciples have started with a nuclear group, and Beers had such a group that was admirably selected for the respect and range of influence that the members commanded. Two of them, Adolph Meyers and William James, were his closest allies and advisors, and Beers could not have placed himself in better hands. By winning the support of some of the most eminent and respected men of his time, both within as well as outside the medical profession, he assured the legitimacy of his movement, and the latter fact as well as the appeal of his book helped assure financial support. Clifford Beers himself was an ideal agent to lead such a movement. He had the single-mindedness of purpose typical of all great movement leaders, he was utterly devoted to his cause, and he was untiring in the pursuit of his goals.

Social movements generally are conflict groups, for they usually face the hostile resistance of the institutions that they seek to renovate, and also must vie with competing reform groups. In this respect the Mental Hygiene Movement was atypical, for little conflict is reported in its history. Several factors seem to account for this condition. First, the appearance of the movement was timely, for both the public attitude toward mental illness and the medical views regarding the treatment and care of patients were changing, and the climate was favorable for change. Second, the professionals and the public were joined, not only at the level of leadership but also in the trend of attitudes; and the movement also worked closely with professional organizations. Third, the movement advanced slowly and carefully on problems, and its changes were made palatable to the existing institutions. Its earliest efforts were fact-gathering activities, a distinct service considering the poor compilation of statistics and other data hitherto. Legislative reforms were undertaken readily because of the obvious inadequacies in the existing law. Hospital surveys, undertaken "only at the request of the institution or some other responsible organization," became an effective basis of the movement's major work of seeking improvements in patient care.

A carefully programmed movement, however, gives no assurance of avoiding conflict, for it then is likely that reform groups restive over the slow pace may seek to displace the slower-moving organization and install its more radical program. The Mental Hygiene Movement had the unusual quality of absorbing the work of other related groups or of integrating its activities with those of others.

Clearly this chapter has been too brief to give a genuine understanding of social movements in medicine. It is hoped, however, that it has succeeded in conveying the central concern of the approach: to analyze how a collectivity that seeks to displace an established pattern of behavior may, through an interactive process and mobilization of groups, overcome resistance and dissension and thereby institute coordinated action at a new level.

1. Herbert Blumer, "Social Movements," in A. M. Lee (Ed.), *New Outline of the Principles of Sociology*, New York: Barnes & Noble, 1946, pp. 199–220.

2. Ralph H. Turner and Lewis M. Killian, *Collective Behavior*, Englewood Cliffs, N. J.: Prentice-Hall, 1957, p. 308.

3. Bernhard F. Stern, *Society and Medical Progress*, Princeton, N. J.: Princeton University Press, 1941, pp. 190–191.

4. *Ibid.*, pp. 191–202.

5. The best examples of sociological studies of movements are found in studies of revolutions. See: Crane Brinton, *The Anatomy of Revolution*, rev. ed., Englewood Cliffs, N.J.: Prentice-Hall, 1952; and Philip Selznick, *The Organizational Weapon*, New York: McGraw-Hill, 1952.

6. Erwin C. Schroedinger, *Science, Theory, and Man*, New York: Dover, 1957, pp. 81–132.

7. Kurt and Gladys E. Lang, *Collective Dynamics*, New York: Crowell, 1961, pp. 465–488.

8. Neil H. Borden, "The Economic Effects of Advertising," in Wilbur Schramm (Ed.), *Mass Communications*, Urbana, Ill.: University of Illinois Press, 1949, pp. 186–190.

9. Neil J. Smelser, *Theory of Collective Behavior*, New York: Free Press of Glencoe, 1963, pp. 170–221.

10. Herbert Menzel and Elihu Katz, "Social Relations and Innovation in the Medical Profession: The Epidemiology of a New Drug," *The Public Opinion Quarterly*, XIX, Winter 1955-1956, pp. 337–352.

11. Louis Lasagna, *The Doctor's Dilemma*, New York: Harper, 1962.

12. Albert Deutsch, *The Mentally Ill in America*, 2nd ed., New York: Columbia University Press, 1952. Also, *One Hundred Years of American Psychiatry*, New York: Columbia University Press, 1944.

13. Clifford W. Beers, *The Mind That Found Itself*, 7th ed., New York: Doubleday, 1960.

14. John and Elaine Cumming, "Social Equilibrium and Social Change in the Large Mental Hospital," in Milton Greenblatt et al. (Eds.), *The Patient and the Mental Hospital*, Glencoe, Ill.: Free Press, 1957, pp. 49–72.

15. Blumer, *op. cit.*, p. 201.

16. Deutsch, *op. cit.*, pp. 88–299.

17. *Ibid.*, pp. 186–212.

18. *Ibid.*, pp. 272–299. Also, W. R. Russell, "From Asylum to Hospital," *American Journal of Psychiatry*, 100, 1944, 87–97.

19. Nina Ridenour, *Mental Health in the United States*, Cambridge, Mass.: Harvard University Press, 1961.

# 7. THE IMPACT OF SOCIAL TRENDS ON THE PROFESSIONALIZATION OF PATIENT CARE

## Robert C. Leonard

### INTRODUCTION

The doctor, administrator, and patient all define the nurse role in ways convenient to their own roles. The physician has a well-established claim on the nurse as his assistant, but in carrying out the doctor's prescriptions the nurse may come in conflict with the patient's expectations or with hospital policy. She may also find the prescription in conflict with her own professional judgment about what is best for the patient. Who does the nurse respond to — the doctor, the hospital, the patient, or her profession?

To complicate it further, the nursing profession itself does not speak with one voice. Ideally, all are working toward the same goal. But there is enough lack of coordination in the system so that a great deal of "role conflict" is created for the nurse. This is one of the best-worn topics in the sociology of nursing literature, and it may seem redundant to confront it once again. But it appears to me that continued discussion is inevitable as long as the conflicting expectations remain. Of special interest to me are the patient's expectations. And, viewing the problem from the perspective of the patient role, I especially want to examine some implications of professionalizing the patient-care seg-

ment of current nursing role definitions.

I should make clear at the outset that what I shall present here is mainly a sociological diagnosis of the problem — not a prescription for the nursing profession. A final solution must be sought through the regular political processes of the health professions, because what the nurse's role *should be* is basically a policy question, not a question of fact. There are questions of fact surrounding this issue, however. And for some of these factual questions sociological theory and research may be able to suggest possible answers.[1] For one thing there has been research into the various performances expected of the nurse, and the existence of role conflict has been well documented. Of more interest here, however, is what appears to me to be a matter of agreement among doctors, administrators, patients, and nurses. There appears to be considerable agreement in expecting the nurse to provide what can be called the "expressive function" in the patient care-and-cure system. This "expressive function" is roughly equivalent to what has been called the "mother-surrogate" and "bedside psychologist" roles. We are probably talking about somewhat the same thing when we speak of "tender loving care." Certainly nurses have an historic claim

Revision of keynote address to Annual Educational Institute, California Board of Nursing Education and Nurse Registration, Asilomar (October 1965). In addition to those persons specifically cited, this paper draws heavily on previous collaboration with former colleagues at the Yale School of Nursing, Florence S. Wald, Dean.

to this role, but whether or not they choose to keep it in the face of rising pressures for other roles, the agreement on the desirability of the expressive role suggests its performance will continue to be problematic until it is established professionally with status equal to that of the other roles in the system.

But to put our questions bluntly: does becoming "professional" mean getting "hard-boiled" and giving up "tender loving care"? Further, does the demand of the modern hospital for "efficiency" require impersonal, routine, bureaucratic care of patients? I want to answer in the negative. In fact, performing patient care through impersonal, bureaucratic, policy-centered routines may actually result in less efficient use of hospital resources. We often hear the question, can we afford to spend valuable nursing time in talking with patients? The answer may be that a few minutes spent at certain points in the patient's course through the hospital can result in saving many minutes later on — for example, extra time spent on admission or in introducing some treatment or care procedure may prevent time-consuming misunderstandings later and ineffective use of personnel. As the old aphorism goes: "A stitch in time saves nine." Furthermore, I will argue, a genuinely professional level of skill may be required for effective performance of the expressive role in the patient care-and-cure system.

I believe it is important to recognize some aspects of the larger social context of this problem. Much of what is involved here is beyond the control of any one profession. And conceiving of the problem too narrowly may unnecessarily limit the range of possible solutions or even prevent reaching a solution at all.

To begin, consider that we are dealing with a care-and-cure social system — a network of social relations in which a number of professional roles are involved in both the care and the cure of the customer who is in a role called "patient." The hospital is one such system.[2] In considering the dilemmas of the nursing role in this system, we can learn something by first considering some of the dilemmas of the system. Consider the conflict between on the one hand, bureaucratization and on the other hand professionalization of patient care and cure. Consider also the pervasive impact of technological change. All this is happening at the same time that population and cultural changes have produced a rapid increase in demand for health services and forced a redistribution of functions among the health professionals. I also would like to include for consideration the possibility of an imbalance in the importance assigned the care-and-cure goals of the system. (Behind this lies the imbalance between development and application of the biophysical and social sciences.) The problems created by conflicting definitions of the nurse role are intensified and often may actually be the consequence of these major trends.

## BUREAUCRATIZATION AND PROFESSIONALIZATION

The first of these trends is bureaucratization. Increasingly the production of goods and the distribution of services has been centralized in larger and larger organizations such as hospitals. And these organizations have been increasingly bureaucratized. In western civilization in general, work of all kinds has been absorbed into these formal work organizations in which there is a striving for a clearly defined hierarchy of authority in which each position in the organization has clearly delimited responsibilities. One of the dilemmas of our modern age is that the expected benefits from these large organizations often seem to be offset by a diversion of resources from service to the customer to maintenance and expansion of the organization. Whether we are talking about a school system, a chain department store, an insurance company, government agency, or hospital, a frequent complaint is the impersonality and lack of concern that the customer experiences. But that is just the beginning of the problem in the case of the health organizations. The original aim in forming these bureaucratic organizations is to increase efficiency and effectiveness through specialization of tasks. But increased division of the work among specialties requires increased coordination. This in turn requires an administrative structure. It is at this point that bureaucratization of work comes in conflict with another major trend in our society — the professionalization of work.

In becoming a salaried employee of an organization, the "professional" becomes a "bureaucrat." And in the process another conflict occurs. In addition to that between the bureaucracy and the customer, there is now conflict between the bureaucracy and the profession.[3] The professions conceive of their members as workers who exercise individual judgment based on a special body of knowledge unique to the profession. The professionalization of work is a trend toward creating workers who are expected to exercise a great deal of initiative in dealing with each client as an individual. The authority for the professional is his profession's special body of knowledge. An axiom of the professions is that only other qualified members are competent to evaluate the professional's performance. On the other hand, the bureaucracy stresses predictable behavior on the part of its employees based on preset, established policies. The role of the bureaucrat is to apply the organization's rule book. And authority in a bureaucracy is assigned according to position within the administrative hierarchy, not according to competence within a profession. The irony of this for nursing is that at the same time that nurses have been increasing their efforts to professionalize, their work has increasingly come under the direction of bureaucratic authority structures. During the First World War period, approximately 75 per cent of all nurses in the United States were employed in private fee-for-service practice. In 1930, 55 per cent were in private practice, but a much larger proportion were employees. Today over 75 per cent of nurses are the hired hands of health bureaucracies.[4]

## TECHNOLOGY

Consider another major trend in our society: technological change. The impact of technological change is felt throughout our occupational structure. The health professions, however, have not felt the brunt of it yet to the extent that have specialties where unemployment exists. Technologically induced changes in the occupational structure eliminate whole sets of jobs, so that we have large groups of people who are chronically unemployed because they are unemployable. They have no skills for which there is a demand. The likelihood of this becomes greater of course as there is greater and greater specialization of the work. And the risk is greatest among those workers whose education has not been general enough to make them adaptable to major shifts in technology. This has clearly recognizable implications for nursing education. It is sufficient to note here that one of the justifications for a liberal-arts background in the basic nursing curriculum is this anticipation that greater flexibility based on broader education will help promote continued professional usefulness. Such a shift in the educational scheme seems to have major implications for the profession's definition of the nurse role. But the role conflicts engendered by these professional redefinitions appear unavoidable in the face of technological change.

## POPULATION AND LEVELS AND STANDARDS OF LIVING

In addition to all this, the hospitals are faced with rising demand for their services. This is due to a combination of factors, but a main one is population change. Other factors of course are an increase in the ability to pay (level of living) and a rise in expectation level (standards). People today expect to be healthy. Definitions of illness have changed, and this is due in part of course to the efforts of the health professions themselves. They have increased the demand for their own services. And hospitalization plans have rationalized the methods of payment to make possible increased demand. Change in our population structure so that we have greater proportions of people in the dependent ages, the young and old, is a major contributor to this disparity between demand and supply.

## DIVISION OF LABOR AND STRATIFICATION

The distribution of this increasing amount of health work, of increasing technical complexity, is complicated by the conflict over supervision of the work between the bureaucracy and the professions. It is also complicated by another process that sociologists have identified as another major social trend —increasing division of labor. Population size (commonly discussed in the health professions as a problem of "manpower") is a factor behind changes in division of labor. Nursing has been feeling the impact of these social processes in an increasing pressure to extend and amplify the "doctor's assistant" definition of the nurse role. The nursing profession's problems have thus been compounded by increasing and changing delegation of tasks formerly assumed by the physician. Behind this lies a demographic fact: for the past century there has been a steady decline in the per capita number of medical doctors in the United States, and for at least the past fifty years there has been an extremely sharp rise in the per capita number of active graduate nurses.[5] Add to this the process identified by sociologists as "stratification" of the various positions in the occupational division of labor. Authority and prestige become distributed according to the occupational rankings that emerge. In this case assignment of high prestige and authority to these tasks formerly part of the physician's role may explain the nursing profession's acceptance of them—just as low prestige and authority given direct patient-care tasks encourages willingness to turn them over to "subprofessional" aides and clerks. Any proposal to professionalize patient-care tasks is, consequently, a proposal to change the existing stratification system. And this brings us to a consideration of the system's value structure.

## VALUE CONFLICT

Many services formerly provided by hospitals have been removed so we now have something approaching a homogeneous set of problems to be handled by the organization. But there remains one important source of value conflict that has been intensified by the trend for the doctor's work to be moved out of the home and out of the office and into the hospital. The hospital has become a place to put the expensive diagnostic and treatment equipment that no single doctor could afford to purchase by himself. So in addition to being a place to take care of the sick the hospital has also become a workshop for the doctor.[6] And the organization necessary for facilitating the doctor's work may not be sufficient to provide for patient care. Care routines and diagnostic and cure procedures are not necessarily congruent with each other. More typically, in fact, the medical diagnostic and treatment functions subordinate the care routines. It seems fair to say that in most hospitals today patient care takes a poor second place to patient cure. This is seen in budget decisions where expensive, esoteric pieces of equipment are given priority over, for example, hiring enough nurses to perform such functions as the admission procedures which are instead performed by lower-paid, lower-skilled personnel. The decision is to get the high-priced, even if rarely used, very prestigious treatment installation—and the care function loses out.

## EXPRESSIVE, INSTRUMENTAL, AND BUREAUCRATIC ROLES

In summary, the nurse stands in a highly transient vortex of changes over which she has little control and which appear to be pushing the profession in several different directions at once. Is there no common thread of agreement in these differing definitions of the nurse's role? And is there to be no continuity with the past? I suggest that there is at least one common thread running through all of these conflicting sets of expectations. This is performance of the patient-care function, the "expressive function" in the care-and-cure system. Now what do we mean by "patient care"? Particularly crucial in this concept is the patient's feeling of trust, that "people here *care* what happens to me." More generally, it is a matter of maintaining the cohesion of this social system we call a hospital. And cohesion requires the motivation of the members to participate. Particularly important is the *patient's* motivation. The patient's motivation is particularly important, but also probably the most neglected aspect of the system. Among professionals and staff there is a tendency toward a "take it or leave it" attitude. It seems assumed that the patient will do what he is told to do without question "because it is for his own good." What is forgotten is that he cannot do it if he does not understand what he is being told. It is also often forgotten that trust and confidence must be earned by the nurse and doctor. Or at the very least, the patient's initial trust and confidence can be lost through neglect. A few years ago Miriam Johnson and Harry Martin identified as a "social system" the three-role group of physician-patient-nurse.[7] They applied two sociological principles: (1) continuance of a social system requires both goal achievement and maintenance of system cohesion; (2) role differentiation often tends to occur in which two specialists emerge—one for goal achievement and the other for system maintenance. These have been called the "instrumental" and "expressive" roles. And both roles are equally important for the system. Johnson and Martin suggested that perhaps the instrumental function (cure of the patient) might be the specialty of the physician, whereas the expressive function might be the nurse's specialty.

But several observers have concluded that nursing in the generic sense of this expressive "care" function is disappearing from the nursing profession. This is the conclusion reached by Sam Schulman who wrote:

Nurses and nursing may be going along divergent paths. . . . Affect in patient relationships . . . will still continue. It is too basic a characteristic to change. But this aspect of patient needs will be met by others . . . nursing . . . will still be nursing, but it will be carried on by persons of other occupational affiliations, not the professional nurse.[8]

If this prediction comes true, then resolution of the nurse's role conflicts will be by assumption of the "healer" role as a medical technician or "assistant doctor" in performance of the cure function. As we have already seen, it may actually be that the hospital bureaucrat role will dominate. As Rushing concludes:

It may be true that the profession of nurse originated in response to the needs of sick people; but the nurse's function in hospitals today is being determined more and more by the organizational need to plan, organize, supervise, and coordinate. . . .[9]

In either case, assumption of the independent professional role is not developing, and patient care is decreasingly being performed by nurses. It is not necessary here to be concerned about the implications for the nursing profession. Rather, our main interest is in consequences for the total patient care-and-cure system. One important consequence that I surmise is that the care function is simply not being performed. Certainly this conclusion is not contradicted by the evidence from interviews with patients.[10] With regard to the patient's perceptions of the nurse, the big question that stands out in the patient's mind is "do these nurses really care about what happens to me?" The patients do value friendliness, personal attention, and fast response by the nurse. But they express a *great* concern about mistakes. They also believe that hospitals are understaffed and nurses are overworked. This of course contributes to the patient's concern about safety. In sum, the patient's foremost concern was interest and attention—that is, whether the nurse "cared" about him—and second was a concern about safety. These two are not unrelated since the patient quite reasonably could not expect to be safe in the hands of overworked, rushed nurses who do not really care anyway. This coincides with the patient's major complaint about his stay in the hospital: people don't tell him anything. This lack of communication from the staff, combined with the perception that the staff does not care, may lead to a kind of temporary patient paranoia which can, I think, have very serious consequences for the patient's career through the hospital. The main question to ask at this point is "is it possible to give effective patient care without convincing the patient that he is in a place where people do care what happens to him?"

A number of years ago an article characterized the nurse role as an instrumental one concerned solely with making the patient well. According to this argument the patient is regarded by the nurse simply as a case to be cured and not as a person who needs help. It was not within this conception of the nurse role to become involved with what the patient is thinking or feeling about his treatment.[11] This description of the nurse role was based on observation of actual behavior of nurses. But when Skipper asked student nurses to define the nurse role, he found their conception of the role to be much closer to that of providing the expressive function in which the patients would be treated as persons rather than cases. Warm, cordial nurse-patient relationships are approved.[12] To summarize, both patients and nurses expect the nurse to perform this expressive, supportive function. It is reasonable to expect that doctors also think of this as an important part of the nurses' role.[13] Yet the fact seems to be that the nurse does not perform as expected. How does this happen? The explanation lies in those dilemmas of the care-and-cure system that have been reviewed here. Of these dilemmas of the system, I want to add particular emphasis to one that appears to me most amenable to deliberate change: the conflict in value given the care-and-cure functions of the system. This brings me to some research on the consequences of providing the "expressive" function. If verified by sufficient repetitions, then this beginning research underlines the importance of expressive patient care—importance not only in more satisfied patients, but also in less patient-staff friction. And less friction results in more efficient

and effective patient care. Perhaps most important is the impact on effectiveness of prescribed medical treatment, that is, the consequences of effective patient care for patient cure.

## PATIENT-CARE RESEARCH

Relatively speaking, there has been very little research testing the effects of performance of the expressive function in the patient care-and-cure social system. There has been a lot of debate about "psychological support" and "interpersonal relations" in the hospital, but the amount and quality of the research has not compared favorably with that done in other institutional spheres, such as industry. (I suspect there is still a strong tendency in the medical culture to view these skills as part of the "art" of professional practice, and thus not open to scientific research.) I want to briefly review some experiments that indicate one kind of research that can help provide a foundation for professionalization of patient care. Whether this professionalization of patient care is to be done by the nursing profession, by psychiatrists, or by some new profession as yet unidentified is not my concern. But whoever is to attempt to professionalize this psychological support—the social-emotional, expressive elements in patient care—their efforts will be greatly facilitated by this kind of social research.

The experimental design consists of subjecting a random half of a set of patients to an experimental nursing approach, and comparing the outcome of those nurse-patient interactions with the other half of the patients—the "control group." The experimental treatment consists of a patient-centered "expressive" nursing, in this case provided by experienced graduate nurses who have also had special graduate-school instruction in interpersonal relations. The experimental nurse focuses on how the patient is defining his situation —what he is thinking and feeling about his hospital experience. The general prediction is that this kind of interaction with the nurse can reduce patient distresses, confusion, and misunderstanding, and that this can produce desired consequences in patient's medical condition as well as in patient satisfaction and cooperativeness.

Consider one patient-care situation— admission to the hospital. The first experiment was in the emergency room. One of the routines in this emergency room was to take patient blood pressure on admission. For the experiment we also retook blood pressure after the admission procedure. The experimental nurse took every other "true emergency" and the control patients went through the routine provided by the regular staff. There is reason to expect elevated blood pressures as a result of distress. Then the experimental effect would be revealed in lowered blood pressures. This prediction was verified: on the average the experimental patients' systolic blood pressure dropped 15 points. The control group, in contrast, showed an average *rise* of 3 points. Knowing the kind of experiences that are likely to be confronted by a patient in the emergency room of a large urban teaching hospital, we can guess why their blood pressure went up. (Probably, as a matter of fact, going on duty there makes the staff members' pressure go up also. It is just one of those high-pressure places in a hospital. It would make an interesting study to map the blood pressures in all the various parts of the hospital.) A

state mental hospital is another place where you can expect people to arrive under a fair amount of distress—some enter under custody of a policeman, others in straightjackets, and many take the emergency-room route from general hospitals around the state. A second experiment was conducted in this setting and the results were comparable to those in the emergency room, although the differences between control and experimental groups were not as large.[14]

Three more experiments with scheduled surgical admissions followed. The first was in the "clinic" university service side of the hospital, where many of the patients could not remember ever having seen the surgeon, and often as a matter of fact did not see one during their whole surgical experience. As before in the emergency room and mental hospital, the experimental patients showed signs of reduced distress, whereas the control patients did not. The other two experiments were with "private" patients. Again the experimental patients' blood pressures dropped, but the control patients showed a similar drop. They did not receive the experimental nursing, yet their blood pressures went down. What happened in these last two experiments to produce the different results? For one thing we have a different category of patient. The "private" patient was from a different kind of background and in general probably has greater competence for coping with stressful situations. In addition, they probably received more preparation from their physicians. Furthermore the contrast between the private and clinic side of the hospital is like night and day. Things are quieter, probably everyone's stress level—staff as well as patient—is lower. The new patient receives fewer insults from the social environment. The experimental nurse *was* reducing distress on admission, but the control patients were having their distress relieved in other ways. This explanation was documented by postexperimental interviews. In the interview the patients would say, "Yes, I was kind of tense when I came in." And then, "Well, I felt better after a while." When asked why they felt better, the experimental patients usually identified the admitting nurse. They did not know she was an experimental nurse, but they identified her as the one who helped them relax. The control patients identified various other sources of help: maybe the doctor came, or the head nurse, or another patient. Somehow or other they all adjusted and began to feel more comfortable.[15]

One of the implications of these admission experiments could be that in certain places—such as emergency admissions—it is important to have skilled professional people in order to take care of patients in high stress and to prepare them for those high-tension situations in the hospital that patients are sometimes thrust into. In other places—such as private scheduled surgical admissions—perhaps admission tasks could be delegated to less-skilled personnel. This is a possible indication from these experiments. But I suspect that there is more to it than that. That is, it is worth entertaining the possibility that admission is much more crucial than in just relieving immediate distress (as indicated by elevated blood pressures).

This possibility is illustrated by the fifth admission experiment. The experimental nurse's hypothesis was that she could admit patients to the hospital in such a way that their whole stay in the hospital would be more comfortable and more effective. That is, their adjustment to the hospital, their whole course through the hospitalization, would be smoother than it would be if they did not receive the kind of induction to the setting which she would provide on admission. This experiment was with private patients and there were no differences between control and experimental groups with regard to changes in immediate distress—as indicated by such measures as blood pressure. But we also measured "ward adjustment" in two ways: a questionnaire filled out by staff nurses, and a predischarge interview with the patients. What were the results? The head nurses on the average reported the experimental patients to be less demanding and less impatient.[16] In general, they were "good," "cooperative" patients. But this was not bought at the price of passivity or martyrdom. The admitting nurse did not just scare the patients into keeping quiet in order to make the staff happy. The experimental patients were also rated by the head nurses as more often asking questions, more often making requests, and more often initiating conversations. These patients were active in going after what they needed, yet at the same time managed to do so without appearing demanding or "impatient." This relationship, from the nurse's point of view, is summarized by the answers to another question: would you say the patient's use of nursing personnel was extremely good, very good, moderately good, . . . etc.? The experimental patients averaged "extremely" to "very" good ratings whereas the control patients were rated "fairly good" to "poor" in their "use of nursing personnel." Interviews with the patients show complementary differences. All of the experimental patients said that the nurse "always stayed" to answer questions, whereas the control patients less often reported this to be the case. Experimental patients also more often said the nurse explained what was going to happen, and that the nurses more often answered the light promptly. The social process involved here was one of mutual withdrawal and conflict between patient and staff in the one case, and cooperation and liking in the other. If you have a demanding, uncooperative, difficult patient, the staff withdraws, and the more they withdraw from the patient, the more demanding he gets: a vicious cycle is set up. Perhaps the experimental admission began the opposite process, leading to mutual satisfaction for both patient and staff.[17]

One final point: are the implications of such experiments practical? Can these results be put into practice? One frequently mentioned barrier is time. Can we afford to have nurses spending valuable time talking to patients? Our answer may ultimately be that we cannot afford to *not* have them spend the time. This is suggested by an experiment on the administration of a nursing procedure. As is reported in detail elsewhere, the finding was that time spent introducing the predelivery enema resulted in a more effective procedure.[18] The point to stress here, however, is that the same amount of time was spent by both experimental and control approaches, but it distributed differently. The experimental nurse spent a good deal more time before she ever got around to the procedure. She concentrated on the job, but she regarded talking to the patient as part of her job and was particularly intent on getting the patient's acceptance of this procedure before she went ahead

with it. The time spent in talking with the patient was made up by much faster outcome of the procedure itself, whereas the control nurse spent her time fighting the patient and the procedure itself took longer. The same amount of time is spent, but it is spent in a different activity and the control nurses were less effective. So if you want to talk about efficiency, spending the same amount of time—or even more—with a greater result can add up to greater efficiency for the expressive approach.[19]

I should emphasize that all of these studies should be regarded as just the beginning—pilot studies testing possible avenues for future research. I do not suggest that anyone go out and change any hospital on the basis of these beginning studies. But I strongly urge anyone who is concerned with this kind of patient-care problem to support research of this kind so that eventually there will be sufficiently precise and specfic evidence to guide major changes in practice.

These results alone are of interest. But there is a hint of even further significance. It appears possible that the patient's satisfaction with the doctor is affected. The patient's care experience in the hospital influences his evaluation of the medical cure. In the last admission experiment, in response to the question: "How successful do you think your surgery was?" the experimental patients more often thought their surgery to be successful than did the control patients. Of course this opinion was not based in fact—or was it? The patient is probably not a very good judge of surgical results. But perhaps there were real differences in the outcome of the surgery. This could be the consequence of greater psychological distress which in turn, we have seen, appears to result from the different social processes surrounding those patients not receiving the experimental admission process. Further research may well reveal a direct impact of "expressive" patient care on the final outcome of the cure procedures.

We have, in fact, other studies that suggest such an impact: in postoperative complications from gynecological surgery, posthospital complications of children's tonsil and adenoid surgery, and complications during labor.[20] There is no time to review all these other studies here, but perhaps this brief review of the admissions experiments suggests to you at least the possibility of patient-care research which may eventually provide guidelines for professionalizing patient care, and precisely specify the impact of the patient-care social process on patient cure.

1. Margaret D. Ellison, Donna Diers, and Robert C. Leonard, "The Uses of Behavioral Sciences in Nursing," *Nursing Research*, 14, 1965, 71–72.

2. On this care-cure distinction, see Hans O. Mauksch, "The Nurse: Coordinator of Patient Care," in James K. Skipper and Robert C. Leonard (Eds.), *Social Interaction and Patient Care*, Philadelphia: Lippincott, 1965. All the other major concepts used here are current in sociological theory, and can be found in most introductory textbooks.

3. Ronald G. Corwin, "The Professional Employee: A Study in Conflict in Nursing Roles," *American Journal of Sociology*, 66, 1961, 604–615, also reprinted in Skipper and Leonard, *op. cit.*; Harvey L. Smith, "Two Lines of Authority: The Hospital's Dilemma," *The Modern Hospital*, March 1955, reprinted in E. Gartley Jaco (Ed.), *Patients, Physicians, and Illness*, Glencoe, Ill.: Free Press, 1958; Robert N. Wilson, "The Social Structure of a General Hospital," *The Annals*, 346, 1963, 67–76, also reprinted in Skipper and Leonard, *op. cit.*; C. Wright Mills, *White Collar*, New York: Oxford University Press, 1959, p. 113; Harold L. Wilensky and Charles N. Lebaux, *Industrial Society and Social Welfare*, New York: Russell Sage Foundation, 1958, Chaps. X and XI; Robert Dubin, *The World of Work*, Englewood Cliffs, N.J.: Prentice-Hall, 1958, pp. 114–115.

4. Esther Lucile Brown, *Nursing as a Profession*, New York: Russell Sage Foundation, 1936, p. 74; William A. Rushing, "The Hospital Nurse as Mother Surrogate and Bedside Psychologist," *Mental Hygiene*, 50:1, January 1966, n.p.; American Nurses Association, *Facts about Nursing*, 1962–1963 edition, p. 11 and (1957) p. 8.

5. Leo F. Schnore, "Statistical Indicators of Medical Care: An Historical Note," *Journal of Health and Human Behavior*, 3, 1962, pp. 133–135; Brown, *op. cit.*, p. 20.

6. Hans O. Mauksch, "It Defies All Logic—But a Hospital Does Function," *The Modern Hospital*, October 1960, 67–70.

7. "A Sociological Analysis of the Nurse Role," *American Journal of Nursing*, 58 1958, 373–377.

8. "Basic Functional Roles in Nursing: Mother Surrogate and Healer," in Jaco, *op. cit.*

9. Rushing, *op. cit.*

10. James K. Skipper, Jr., "Communication and the Hospitalized Patient," and Daisy L. Tagliacozzo, "The Nurse from the Patient's Point of View," both in Skipper and Leonard, *op. cit.*

11. Isadore Thorner, "Nursing: The Functional Significance of an Institutional Pattern," *American Sociological Review*, 20, 1955, 531.

12. James K. Skipper, "The Role of the Hospital Nurse: Instrumental or Expressive?," in Skipper and Leonard, *op. cit.*

13. George Devereaux and Florence R. Weinter, "The Occupational Status of

Nurses," *American Sociological Review*, **15**, 1950, 631.

14. On the experimental nursing process, see Hilda Mertz, "Nurse Actions That Reduce Stress in Patients," *American Nurses Association Monograph No. 1*, 1962; and Barbara J. Anderson and R. C. Leonard, "Individualizing the Admission Process in a Psychiatric Hospital," *American Journal of Psychiatry*, **120**, 1964, 890–893. For a fuller report of the experimental design and results, see Barbara J. Anderson, Hilda Mertz, and R. C. Leonard, "Two Experimental Tests of a Patient-Centered Admission Process," *Nursing Research*, **14**:2, Spring 1965.

15. For a summary of these first four experiments, relevant references, and details of the fourth experiment, see Roslyn R. Elms and R. C. Leonard, "Effects of Nursing Approaches during Admission," *Nursing Research*, forthcoming.

16. These items were adapted from a very useful guide to patient satisfaction studies published by the U. S. Public Health Service, *Patients and Personnel Speak*.

17. Flora A. Vigliotti, "The Effects of Two Nursing Admissions Approaches on Patients' Distress and Ward Adjustment: A Clinical Experiment," unpublished master's thesis, Yale Medical Library, 1964.

18. Phyllis A. Tryon and R. C. Leonard, "Giving the Patient an Active Role," in Skipper and Leonard, *op. cit.*; and "A Clinical Test of Patient-Centered Nursing," *Journal of Health and Human Behavior*, forthcoming.

19. Thelma Thornton and R. C. Leonard, "The Efficiency and Effectiveness of Three Nursing Approaches," *Nursing Research*, **13**, Spring 1964.

20. Rhetaugh G. Dumas et al., "The Importance of the Expressive Function in Preoperative Preparation," in Skipper and Leonard, *op. cit.*; Patricia A. Moran, "An Experimental Study of Pediatric Admissions," unpublished master's thesis, Yale Medical Library, 1963, and "Parents in Pediatrics," *Nursing Forum*, **8**:3, 1963; Perry R. Mahaffy, "The Effects of Hospitalization on Children Admitted for Tonsillectomy and Adenoidectomy," *Nursing Research*, **14**:1, Winter 1965; Barbara L. Bender, "An Experimental Study of the Relationship of Nursing Care and the Incidence of Vomiting during Labor," unpublished master's thesis, Yale Medical Library, June 1963.

# 8. HUMAN ASPECTS OF HEALTH AND ILLNESS: BEYOND THE GERM THEORY

## Victor J. Freeman

The need for social knowledge in the field of medicine may be seen in the human aspects of health and illness, which can be understood only as we understand the nature of man-environment relationships. For this reason the present concern is with the nature of these relationships as they influence health, illness, and medicine; and the consideration of these relationships may include: (1) an outline of some key concepts; (2) an analysis of health and illness in the man-environment frame of reference; and (3) a note on a rational approach to health and illness which involves the basic principles of psychodynamics.

## KEY CONCEPTS

### Human Aspects of "Health"

It is rather fashionable today in public-health circles to talk of promoting "health." However, since an adequate definition of "health" is hard to come by, a more realistic approach would be to emphasize that about which we already know a great deal—namely, how to prevent disease.

It might be sobering to our utopian enthusiasm if we reflect on a current shift of emphasis in the field of nutrition. The commercial pressure to consume relatively large quantities of whole milk, butter, and eggs in the name of robust health has become what might be labeled a "cultural value" in our American life. But now current researchers around the country, and even the daily press, suggest that if we wish to avoid a fatal coronary illness we must go to the extreme of avoiding most of the dairy delights which have been fostered by the milk, butter, and egg industry.[1]

A moral to be gained from this example involves a principle that ought to be basic to any aspect of health education. Instead of attempting to promote such intangibles as "health" or "mental health," we would be better off helping people deal more rationally and responsibly with the facts we already know about illness. We can advise people as to the consequences of certain kinds of excesses or deficiencies in behavior, but it is probably unwise for us to attempt "health promotion" by placing the value judgment "healthy" on any particular behavioral pattern. For example, it might be well for health educators to advise people that they can avoid certain forms of malnutrition by the consumption of dairy products, but that excessive use of the latter may contribute to such problems as obesity and atherosclerosis. They should not go so far as to proclaim that dairy products are always healthy for everyone.

Reprinted by permission of the author and publisher, from the *Journal of Health and Human Behavior*, Vol. 1, 1960, pp. 8–13.

*Human Aspects of "Illness"*

"Illness" is easy to determine in the extremes of disease. But when a person is in an ambulatory, occupationally productive state, the problem of defining "illness" may be very difficult. This is particularly the situation in the noninfectious group of diseases. In this nonmicrobiologic area, we tend to include chronic diseases such as coronary heart disease, peptic ulcer, schizophrenia, rheumatoid arthritis, and a host of others.

In his book *Beyond the Germ Theory*, Iago Galdston underscores disease causation by dividing the sources of morbidity into three groups. From his point of view,

. . . The germ theory of disease which highlights the morbid effects produced by external noxious agents, germs, toxins, and the like, has long absorbed most of the thought and concern of clinicians and public-health workers. However, to be fully effective, public health, as well as clinical medicine, must be concerned not only with the exogenous noxious agents, but also, and even more, with the deprivational and stress sources of morbidity.[2]

But we do not have to go "beyond the germ theory" in order to deal with "the deprivational and stress sources of morbidity." The man-environment frame of reference utilized in epidemiology to deal with the "germ" theory is a highly useful working hypothesis for dealing with the noninfectious as well as the infectious diseases.

## MAN-ENVIRONMENT RELATIONS

Man lives in a highly complicated environment. And it gets more complicated as he gets more ingenious. For purposes of academic convenience, we divide the environment into physical, biologic, and social areas. In the area of the physical we contend daily with the "elements." Light and dark, humidity and temperature, and various aspects of atmospheric pressure and content are physical factors of environment with which we are in constant interaction.

In the biologic area, microorganisms loom large as environmental factors with which man has to contend. As Galdston has emphasized, this aspect has received its due attention. However, this is only in respect to "illness." There is much to be said about microorganisms in regard to man's "health." The other major areas of consideration in the biologic environment are the sources of food and clothing, namely the plant and animal kingdoms.

In the third area of our environment, the social, we include those factors embraced by the terms "society" and "culture." Just as we interact with the "elements," with plants, animals, and microorganisms, so do we find ourselves in constant interaction with the culture around us. We are exposed to this aspect of our environment via many avenues of communication, such as song and story, literature, the arts, community custom, press, radio, and now television. Our interaction with our culture and its effects on our state of "health" or "illness" is just beginning to be appreciated. In addition to the broader aspects of cultural influence, we find that we are in constant interaction with that part of our social environment known as "people." It is this segment of our total man-environment relationship which comprises the most significant part of our emotional life. Just as the biologic environmental area provides the major source for physiologic growth and development, so the social segment of our environment is our major source for psychologic growth and development.

### Stress and Strain as Related to "Health" and "Illness"

It is now appropriate to analyze the factors in the man-environment relationship which affect "health" and "illness" and to consider the way in which these factors interact.

### "Illness" and Man-Environment Relationships

It should be apparent from this discussion of the physical, biologic, and social phases that all aspects of environment are ever with us as constant sources of stimulation for our individual psychophysiologic energy systems. Absolutely or relatively we find that environment has its "constructive" as well as "destructive" effects on us, and that in the "destructive" phase, phenomena of deprivation, excess, "virulence," and idiosyncrasy or deviance all may represent "stress" on a particular individual or group under specific conditions.

The term "stress" is rapidly gaining new connotations, with the result that there is semantic confusion. However, when employed in its more traditional engineering "stress-strain" context, it is a useful concept. Used thus, *stress* "is any force that would injure the body if the latter did not bring appropriate counterforce to bear."[3] *Strain* "is the result of 'stress' and manifests itself in the form of (tissue) injury, or compensating body mechanisms."[4] Thus we see that the consequence of environmental "stress" is body response, or a series of responses, which results in a spectrum of psychophysiologic reactions varying from the maintenance of equilibrium to states of disequilibrium, with

establishment of altered conditions of equilibria, which latter we call "disease" or "illness."

### A Preliminary Paradigm

To illustrate this frame of reference, Table 8-1, though it suffers from the usual disadvantages of oversimplification and arbitrary classification, nevertheless should suggest a logical man-environment approach to human disease. In this chart the environmental sources of human "stress" are associated with the consequent "strains." Thus, for example, the stress of "drought," or the lack of water in the physical environment, may lead to the human strain of pathologic thirst, with death as a possible consequence. There are other ways in which the stress "drought" may alter man's equilibrium. For example, drought can lead to crop and livestock destruction, and thereby indirectly result in the additional stress of food deficiency with its consequent strain of starvation. Obviously the boxes in this chart are not intended to be finite boundaries, but rather to be foci which may enable us to obtain an overall, ecologic perspective. The examples given are for the purposes of illustration, and are in no way intended to be inclusive.

In many instances it will be noted that specific diseases seem to be the result of several types of "strain," which latter are the consequence of "stresses" of different environmental origins. For example, coronary heart disease is listed as being associated with the stress of "excessive cold" or snow shoveling, and "excessive interpersonal conflicts." If we can presume for the moment that this is a reasonable assumption, it is then obvious that a series of stresses and strains are involved in a sequential

## TABLE 8-1

### Environmental Sources of Human "Stresses" and Associated "Strains"

| "Stress" categories | Inorganic environment (physical) | | Organic nonhuman environment (biologic) | | Organic human environment (social) | |
|---|---|---|---|---|---|---|
| | "Stresses" | "Strains" | "Stresses" | "Strains" | "Stresses" | "Strains" |
| Deprivation | Lack of water, e.g., as in a desert experience, drought | Pathologic thirst | Vitamin deficiency | Beriberi, scurvy | "Sensory" deprivation | Marooned and solitary confinement syndromes |
| | Oxygen deprivation | Asphyxiation | Food deficiency | Inanition, starvation | Interpersonal deprivation | Grief, clinical depression peptic ulcer? tuberculosis? |
| | | | | | Loss of role and status Cultural deprivation | Suicide? anomie? Crime? delinquency? |
| Excess | Excessive cold | Freezing | Vitamin and drug excess | Poisonings, addictions | Excessive interpersonal conflict | Neuroses? rheumatoid arthritis? |
| | Excessive snow shoveling | Coronary heart disease? | Food excess | Obesity, atherosclerosis | | tuberculosis? psychoses? "accidents"? coronary heart disease? alcoholism? |
| | Atmospheric polution, radioactivity | Cancer, congenital deformity? | | | | |
| Turbulent and virulent change | Inorganic turbulence: floods, tornadoes, earthquakes, volcanoes, etc. | Various kinds of shocks traumas | Virulent microbes, epidemics | Smallpox, diphtheria, tuberculosis, typhoid, polio | Turbulent social change Rapid disruption of norms and functions | Wars, pathologic leaders, e.g., Hitler, Napoleon Lawless behavior, suicide? |
| Intolerance-deviance | Intolerance of sunlight, cold | Exhaustion, shock | Of allergens Of fermented products | Hayfever, food allergies Some types of alcoholism? | In interpersonal relations | Some types of schizophrenia and other psychoses? |

association. The excessive consumption of animal fats tends in some of the population to result in an unduly high level of serum cholesterol and $\beta$-lipoproteins, which in turn presumably results in the pathologic state known as "atherosclerosis." Then if the coronary arteries are involved in this process of "atherosclerosis," and the heart is exposed to excessive stress as it may be, either from the physical effort of shoveling snow or the emotional effort of controlling one's impulses as a result of stimulation from excessive interpersonal conflicts, the resultant strain well may be the pathologic "illness" known as "coronary heart disease."

The principal value of this particular frame of reference is the opportunity it provides to examine, at one time, a number of the multiple factors that may be associated with a particular disease entity, and thereby more readily to plan a program of control and prevention. Thus this reference frame is a potential epidemiologic tool. The frame of reference also permits common epidemiologic principles to be applied more readily to almost all disease categories.

### "Health" and Man-Environment Relationships

For the most part this dicussion of man-environment relationships, "strain" has been dealt with in regard to "illness." In the foregoing definition of "strain," it is noted that one manifestation could be a "compensating body mechanism." It is necessary to recognize that such "compensating body mechanisms" need not necessarily be associated with disease, and in fact may result in a more stable state of "health." Employing the term "strain" in this "constructive" connotation may be jarring to one's semantic composure; but its use in this way can lead to a better appreciation of "normal" behavior, whether in the "medically healthy" or "medically unhealthy."[5] An example in the nonpsychologic realm is the mechanism of antibody formation following exposure to microbial stress. Antibodies are "compensating mechanisms" which the body produces in response to the stress of invasion by bacteria and other microorganisms. It is because of our success in public health in artificially promoting such types of "strain" that we have enabled our population to withstand the dread scourges of the past and participate in prolongation of life.

Another example from the field of microbiology is the tuberculin test. A "positive" reaction may have opposite interpretations. At one time it may be indicative of a state of progressive disease. At another it may be the sign of a state of "healthy" resistance. But in both instances, it is a "strain" resulting from "stress."

Similar phenomena occur in the area of interpersonal behavior. "Defense mechanisms" may be signs of "healthy" adjustment or they may be the first indications of progressive mental disease. In the sense that the tuberculin response is evidence of an interaction, but not necessarily a "disease" state, we need to recognize that with behavioral "compensating mechanisms," a man-environment interaction is occurring which may be "healthy" or "unhealthy," depending on other factors.

Behavioral mechanisms of adaptation which go to make up our personality patterns—"defense mechanisms" such as "displacement" and "reaction formation"—are as universal as fingerprints. We all have them, even though each pattern may be uniquely different. Like our respiration, pulse, and body temperature, these behavioral mechanisms serve an essential purpose. However, also like our physiologic apparatus, our psychologic system can get involved in marked variations, which in the extreme may involve "disease." But just as increased respiration and the fast pulse that follow a run upstairs are signs of "health" rather than "sickness," so it is that the increased use of specific behavioral mechanisms also may be a sign of "health." In the behavioral field we should think not only of "the psychopathology of everyday life," but also of the "psychophysiology" in everyday living.

## CONSTRUCTIVE EFFECTS OF OUR ENVIRONMENT

It is trite to observe that we are part of our environment. However, it is worthy of emphasis to note that in order to grow, develop, reproduce, and mature, not only as individuals but also as families, social groups, and nations, we must continuously assimilate parts of our environment. In this respect our environment is a constant source of supplies essential to our survival and general health and welfare. Without such environmental supplies, we could not maintain an adequate state of equilibrium in order to withstand the daily stresses of living, let alone the more severe types of stress which occur during crisis. To the extent that our environment enables us to maintain such states of equilibria, it is "health promoting." It is obvious that the provision of such essentials as water, food, and vitamins is critical to anybody's state of "health." Less obvious in the list of "healthful" environmental elements are the nonpathogenic microbes. As any farmer knows, either intui-

tively or intellectually, the bacteria of the soil are essential to the adequate growth and development of his crops.

Least obvious as environmental requirements important to living are the social factors. Social scientists remind us that our culture is what distinguishes us from other animals. And this environmental element must be in constant supply if man is going to continue his development along the path of civilization. In addition to the culture whichs sets our pattern for living, we must have people who relate to us in specific ways, available to us throughout life in order that we may be effectively motivated in our life work. We are only just beginning to recognize the importance of such "human supplies" in the daily task of maintaining that "satisfactory" state of equilibrium which we call "health."

As indicated in discussing the example on nutrition, so in the behavioral area of man-environment relations we should not attempt to "promote health" by asserting our value judgements through dogmatic statements of what we believe to be desirable kinds of behavioral man-environment relationships. Rather we would be on sounder ground if we spent our efforts enlightening people as to the dangers of behavioral extremes, at the same time as we emphasize that there is plenty of latitude in between. Whether we whip our child or deprive him of candy as a means of discipline is not critical; nor is the method by which we reward him. What is important is that we not err in the direction of excessive punishment beyond realistic limits on the one hand, or unrealistic permissiveness on the other. Also we need to be reasonably consistent in all situations involving reward and punishment.

## RATIONAL APROACH TO "HEALTH AND ILLNESS"

The problem of introducing a greater measure of rationality in man's behavior toward "health and illness" involves the application of basic principles of psychodynamics. However, the scientific approach to "human relations" is not always acceptable. An example of such resistance recently appeared in the popular press when a Harvard professor of business protested that we have been fed too much "human ralations."[6] Equally undesirable is excessive enthusiam for academic self-knowledge. This is exemplified by a national biostatistician's plea that we teach people to "know themselves and thus become better balanced and able to meet their daily problems more adequately."[7] We must neither decry nor overemphasize the potential value of applying present-day knowledge in the field of psychodynamics to all areas of "health and illness." Present knowledge in the psychosocial field is sufficiently well developed to aid in reducing much human suffering and misery. With the beginning of the development of a more scientific approach in consultation,[8] perhaps the realization of the effective application of this knowledge is not too distant.

Utilizing the "ecologic" man-environment frame of reference would appear to be helpful in considering specific disease entities and in attaining an over-all view of "health-illness." Seen from this perspective we can approach most disease threats via a two-pronged attack: the environmental and the individual approach.

### Environmental Approach

As we make the environmental approach we may reduce, alter, or otherwise control the agents of "stress" directly, or control them indirectly through their avenues of movement. Such measures have been highly sucessful in the physical and biologic areas of environment. They have yet to be effectively implemented in the social areas.

### Individual Approach

In the approach to the individual we may increase his ability to handle "stress" by providing adequate environmental supplies; and also by helping him to establish "healthy" types of "strain"; for example, the "conditional" learning of "healthy" behavioral responses, such as antibody production in immunization, or the reflex caution exercised in crossing traffic or swimming in deep water. Teaching people how to handle the "stresses" of interpersonal conflict is a skill we have hardly begun to develop.

Are we really "beyond the germ theory"?

1. Robert E. Olson, "Prevention and Control of Chronic Disease: Cardiovascular Disease — with Particular Attention to Atherosclerosis," *American Journal of Public Health*, 49, 1959, 1120–1128.

2. Iago Galdston, *Beyond the Germ Theory*, New York: Health Education Council, 1954.

3. H. Belding, *Lecture Notes*, Course PH 203, Graduate School of Public Health, University of Pittsburgh, 1958.

4. *Ibid.*

5. "Medically" is used here in the sense of tissue involvement.

6. M. P. McNair, "Too Much Human Relations," *Look*, 22, October 28, 1958.

7. H. L. Dunn, "High-Level Wellness for Man and Society," *American Journal of Public Health*, 49, 1959, 286–292.

8. Gerald Caplan, *Concepts of Mental Health and Consultation*, Washington: U.S. Department of Health, Education, and Welfare, Children's Bureau, 1959, pp. 181–211.

# 9. IS NURSING READY?

## Lucile Petry Leone

*A National Program to Conquer Heart Disease, Cancer, and Stroke* is the title of the report of a commission appointed by President Johnson in February 1964. The commission presented this report to the President in December 1964.

Like the report *Action for Mental Health*, January 1961, and the several recent publications on mental retardation, for example, this document brings forth the needs for health services of specific kinds on the part of the people of the United States. The first implication for nursing in these reports is the obligation of nurses to be informed about the nature and magnitude of the nation's major health problems and the movements toward their solutions, which are suggested by experts in the respective fields.

Nurses caring for patients in hospitals, physicians' offices, clinics, patients' homes, nursing homes, schools, or occupational health programs know that heart disease, cancer, and stroke account for a high number of their patients and are the major killers. Sickness and death rates vary with age, sex, geographic location, and many other factors. The dimensions of the problem are seen in the following startling figures from the commission's report.

In 1963 nearly a million people in the United States died of cardio-vascular-renal diseases. One fifth of these died from stroke. These deaths accounted for more than half of those which occured in this country that year. In 1900 these causes accounted for only one death in seven. About 15 million people suffer from definite heart disease and about as many more from suspected heart disease.

If the quarter million people aged 25 to 64 who died of heart disease in 1963 had lived one more productive year, they would have added $2 billion worth of output to our nation's economy.

At least two million people now alive in the United States have suffered stroke. Eight of 10 stroke victims survive the first attack, usually in a seriously disabled condition.

In 1963 more than one quarter million Americans died of cancer, 45 per cent of them under 65 years of age. The number of people under treatment for cancer in 1964 was estimated at 830,000. Of these, 540,000 were estimated to be new cases. Cancer is either the first or the second cause of deaths reported for children between the ages of 1 and 14 years.

The economic loss to the country through these diseases is tremendous. Add costs of care to loss of productivity due to premature death and disability, and the figure reaches $31.5 billion per year. By far the larger part of this is

Reprinted by the permission of the author and publisher, from the *American Journal of Nursing*, Vol. 65, 1965, pp. 68–72. (U.S. President's Commission on Heart Disease, Cancer, and Stroke, *Report to the President*, Washington, D.C.: U.S. Government Printing Office, 1964, Vol. 1.)

due to loss of productivity. No money value can be placed on the suffering, the loss of dignity, and the misery accumulated from these causes. More investment of effort, knowledge, and money in prevention and care can decrease loss from disability and early death and the unmeasured costs of human suffering.

The conquest of these diseases through laboratory and clinical research is more promising than ever before. Think of the blue babies who, no longer blue, now live. Think of the patients with synthetic heart valves, arteries, and pacemakers who are at work. Think, too, of the patients for whom surgery on blood vessels prevented strokes; the stroke patients who having had early and thorough rehabilitative measures, are self-sufficient; and the patients whose hypertension is controlled by drugs. These are only a few of the recent advances in therapy and prevention of these diseases.

## SLOW FOLLOW-THROUGH

But new health knowledge in the form of life-giving service reaches people too slowly. Many who need service are not reached at all. Many remain unmotivated to seek the potential benefits of old and new scientific discoveries.

The lag between discovery and application must be reduced. And discovery must and will march forward even more rapidly, challenging health workers to strive still more efficiently to reduce the lag between it and service.

The report points out that in 1930, 25 per cent of people with a diagnosis of cancer were alive five years later and, in 1950, 30 per cent with such a diagnosis lived at least five years. It is estimated that we have knowledge now

to increase that figure to 50 per cent. Nearly half the women with cervical cancer are salvaged. If early detection methods at our command now were fully utilized, the salvage rate could exceed 90 per cent.

For every breakthrough, says the report, there must be follow-through. Follow-through requires facilities for patient care and research, community services, educated health manpower, and effective leadership and organization. Follow-through calls for even a stronger alliance of private, public, and voluntary effort. It calls for wise decisions on issues of public policy. The report states that (1) the federal government shares responsibility for assuring these patients' ready access to the best of services; (2) it has major responsibility to support research to generate new knowledge; and (3) it has major responsibility for direct, diversified support of education to produce the health manpower on which control of heart disease, cancer, and stroke depends.

## NETWORK OF CENTERS

The commission recommends a national network of regional heart disease, cancer, and stroke centers for research, teaching, and patient care; rehabilitation centers; diagnostic and treatment stations; medical complexes; and additional centers of excellence in medical education and research. It urges communitywide planning and action, more research and demonstrations in community services, and coordinated statewide laboratory facilities. It recommends a national cervical-cancer-detection program, and a national program of continuing education of health personnel. It recommends federal investment in communications talent for information to the public on these diseases. It recommends ways to give greater support of research, support of education of medical and supporting professions, and technicians, including specialists in library and audiovisual aids; strengthening of medical libraries and other means of disseminating information to professions and to the public; and improved systems for collecting and interpreting statistics essential for understanding and controlling these diseases. This is, indeed, a comprehensive program.

The report emphasizes the importance of coordination of actions at every level —community, state, regional, and national. Every person—professional and concerned layman—has a job to do in this exciting new mobilization of effort toward the conquest of heart disease, cancer, and stroke.

A commission composed of experts in cardiovascular diseases, cancer, and stroke, combined with other influential leaders, has given us this comprehensive program to reduce the human and economic waste caused by these diseases. Already certain phases of the program are before the U.S. Congress in the form of legislative proposals. Hearings have been held on several. Some of the programs recommended in the commission's report can be carried out without legislation.

## QUESTIONS FOR NURSING

Let us look at the meaning for nursing, assuming that an all-out effort is made to carry out the recommendations. Are we ready? Can we fulfill our responsibilities in this action? What must we do?

For every nurse caring for patients in hospitals, nursing homes, schools, industries, out-patient departments, and patients' homes, there is new knowledge to master for use in her own position. Each will encounter patients with heart disease, cancer, and stroke in varying numbers. The numbers will be larger than before, because the case-finding techniques will bring them to attention. Some nurses will become specialists, because some patients will be nursed in units devoted solely to their care or in situations where these patients are in high proportion. All nurses will be expected to help promote the preventive programs, some in special ways. Many nurses who care for these patients will also take part in clinical research. Some nurses will be collaborative or independent investigators in nursing and related research. Some nurses will help with areawide planning and designing of community services. Some will be on advisory committees on the establishment of services. Some will supervise care of stroke patients in nursing homes. Some will be consultants in this and the other fields named.

There will be new kinds of activity for nurses, too—helping to make films; programming instruction; inventing and adapting equipment. Other activities include writing the literature of nursing in this field; guiding the making of abstracts, indexes, and all the other means of organizing and communicating information for professionals and for patients, families, and the public; and studying the motivation of people to seek and use help.

The network of facilities providing the specialized services of the kinds recommended by the commission's report would require large numbers of additional staff nurses, head nurses, and supervisors, all qualified to assist in

The parallels between Negroes and the mentally retarded may be worth investigation for learning from either group about the treatment and the prospects of the other. After all, categorical assessments of the individual, institutionalized deprivation, and the loss of hope seem to be weapons common to society's attack on both groups. Discriminatory practices, neglect, and the like may in fact have positive consequences for those who practice them, whether directed at racial groups or at the mentally retarded. The residential institutions for the retarded, and the schools, welfare agencies, courts, and other screening and treating facilities may depend in part on systematic techniques for discrimination against the mentally retarded which are sanctioned and supported by a complex body of traditions.

The change of programming by the centers and institutions undoubtedly will be vast; the shift in role-patterned duties of professionals and others will be extensive; and additional numbers of personnel required will be large. It remains to be seen whether this kind of challange can be met through planning or through enhanced educational and training programs, or whether entirely new facilities may have to come into being.

Dr. Leonard Duhl has recently been quoted as suggesting "a whole new concept of institutional and semi-institutional care." He proposes the establishment of whole communities dedicated to the care, education, and training of persons such as the retarded. A most interesting part of Senator Kennedy's summary on this, which appeared in the October-November 1965 *Children's Limited*, is the obvious extensive reliance on the vast resources of selected towns and cities restructured as service communities. The senator referred to all employers, bus drivers, salesgirls, policemen and housewives, teachers and students, as potential contributors to the large effort described.

For this and other changes to come about, we may possibly find our problem magnified, but its solution a simple one, and I prefer to put it this way: more people with more varied skills may work with the retarded in the future. Following Duhl's point, their contacts will be closer to the usual round of their day's labor and leisure than at present, with less separation and isolation of the retarded from the community at large. Increased professionalization and standardization of services with improved levels of care, treatment, and rehabilitation will be necessary to provide a greater integration of work roles than exists today.

---

1. The 135 public residential institutions for the mentally retarded in the United States in 1965 housed approximately 192,000 individuals. American Association on Mental Deficiency, *Directory of Residential Facilities for the Mentally Retarded*, Willimantic, Conn., 1965, p. lv.

2. William J. Goode, "Encroachment, Charlatanism, and the Emerging Profession: Psychology, Sociology, and Medicine," *American Sociological Review*, **25**, 1960, 902–914.

3. Gunnar Dybwad, *Challenges in Mental Retardation*, New York: Columbia University Press, 1964; and Leo Kanner, *A History of the Care and Study of the Mentally Retarded*, Springfield, Ill.: Thomas, 1964.

4. Harold Wilensky, "The Profession-

alization of Everyone?," *American Journal of Sociology*, **LXX**, 1964, 137–158; and Kenneth S. Lynn (Ed.), *The Professions in America*, Boston: Houghton Mifflin, 1965.

5. Edward Gross, *Work and Society*, New York: Crowell, 1958.

6. James W. Dykens, Robert W. Hyde, Louis H. Orzack, and Richard H. York, *Strategies of Mental Hospital Change*, Boston: Massachusetts Department of Mental Health, 1964.

7. Ewan Clague, "Economic Manpower and Social Welfare," presented at Symposium on Manpower for Social Welfare: Goals for 1975, University of Chicago, April 1965.

8. Louis H. Orzack, "Social Change, Social Policy, and Manpower: A Social Welfare Fantasy," in Edward L. Schwartz (Ed.), *Research Approaches to Manpower Problems*, New York: National Association of Social Workers, forthcoming 1966; and Louis H. Orzack, "The Function of Sociological Research for Planning Treatment Programs for the Residential Retarded," New York: National Association for Retarded Children, mimeographed, 1965.

9. Stephen A. Richardson, Norman Goodman, Albert H. Hastorf, and Sanford Dornbusch, "Cultural Uniformity in Reaction to Physical Disabilities," *American Sociological Review*, **26**, 1961, 241–247.

# 11. ROLE CHANGE AND SOCIALIZATION IN NURSING

## S. Dale McLemore and Richard J. Hill

During the last decade, sociologists have become increasingly concerned with processes and problems of adult socialization. In a review of current socialization theory and research, Sewell calls special attention to this emphasis but notes that "... what is known on adult socialization is rather scant ... in comparison with what is known on childhood and adolescence."[1] Promising beginnings have been made in the study of how occupational and professional roles are transmitted.[2] Considerable attention has been devoted to socialization within the medical and allied professions with nursing receiving a share of this consideration.[3] In the context of professional socialization, this paper relates certain changes in the role of the nurse to factors which are expected to influence acceptance of such changes.

## ROLE CHANGE IN NURSING

There is increasing consensus about major dimensions along which the role of the nurse has been and is changing. This role is seen by various observers as increasingly (1) technical,[4] (2) specialized,[5] (3) bureaucratic,[6] and (4) managerial.[7] Nursing has become more technical partly because functions once reserved to physicians have been transferred to the nurse. This increased technical emphasis has been accompanied by greater specialization of nursing functions[8] and of clinical divisions within the large modern hospital.[9] As modern hospitals have become centers of both scientific knowledge and technical apparatus, certain changes in hospital organization also have occurred. Of basic importance has been the increasingly bureaucratic nature of hospitals. Given the significance of hospitals as work locations for nurses, this trend in hospital organization has introduced fundamental shifts in the nurse's occupational role.[10]

One principal consequence of the increasingly hierarchical organization of hospitals has been the assumption by the professional nurse of a variety of managerial duties.[11] The technical-managerial role which has emerged in nursing contains features requiring scientific preparation and full professional status.[12] The evolution of this new concept of the professional nurse has brought about, and been associated with, substantial changes in philosophies and practices of nursing education.[13] Among the important changes in

Reprinted by permission of the publisher, from the *Pacific Sociological Review*, Vol. 8, 1965, pp. 21–27. (This paper is based on portions of a study supported by the U.S. Department of Health, Education, and Welfare, Bureau of State Services, Division of Nursing, Research Grants Branch, Grant No. NU 00065-03. The authors wish to express thanks to Charles M. Bonjean for several useful criticisms of an earlier draft of this manuscript.)

nursing education designed to assist nurses in coping with the new technical-managerial definition of the nursing role are (1) a great increase in number and influence of collegiate programs, (2) emphasis on liberal and democratic educational philosophies, and (3) rapid expansion of a variety of training procedures drawing on social-science concepts and findings. A particularly important point for purposes of this paper is that the model of management generally advocated by those favoring the above changes has been the "human-relations" approach.[14] The special attractiveness for professional nurses of this managerial model is that it is:

... most efficient for dealing with events which are not uniform ... and with occupations emphasizing social skills as technical aspects of this job ....[15]

Advocates of this approach hope that the human-relations model will delineate in social-scientific terms a unique, professional function for nurses.

What elements of the human-relations approach to management are thought to be especially relevant for supervisory nurses? The general principle underlying the human-relations approach is that leaders should possess specific attitudes and promote types of interaction which "... convey to the individual a feeling of support and recognition for his importance and worth as a person."[16] In this way, leaders may, it is argued, obtain "... the full potential of every major motive which can be constructively harnessed in a working situation."[17]

Among specific attitudes which are consistent with the human-relations principle, and which are especially pertinent to the managerial function of nurses, are the following:

1. The effective leader is *democratic*. She gains commitment of each member of the work group to the task at hand through discussion of task-relevant problems. She encourages subordinates to participate in the decision-making process.

2. The effective leader is aware of the importance of hierarchical arrangements of statuses as an organizational requirement; however, she views status differences in *functional* rather than traditional terms. The traditional patterns of deference, especially toward physicians, that exist in hospitals are vestiges of an earlier period and frequently interfere with the provision of optimal patient care.[18]

3. The effective leader is *considerate* in that she is responsive to the ideas of her subordinates, appreciative of their skills, and sensitive to their prerogatives. She recognizes the relevance for job performance of the individual's personal characteristics and feelings.

Another attitude which is sometimes alleged to be characteristic of the nurse who adopts the human-relations model of group leadership is "willingness to initiate work activity";[19] however, there is disagreement in the human-relations literature concerning this attitude. Some writers use "initiatory" to describe an authoritarian, dominative, task-oriented, or arbitrary style of leadership. In this view the considerate leader and the initiatory leader are opposing types.[20] Other observers, however, use the term to convey the idea that the leader may be firm in assisting, supporting, and directing subordinates without being dictatorial or threatening. When used in this way, "initiates action" implies firm and decisive leadership which is nonetheless considerate.[21]

The interest and disagreement among these writers suggests that the concept "initiates action" is an important element of the human-relations approach but that either initiating or failing to initiate action may reasonably be interpreted as being consistent with the human-relations principle. These interpretations support the general view that:

4. In striving to direct subordinates in a democratic, functional and considerate way, the effective leader must regulate the extent to which she *initiates action* although it is not completely clear whether such regulation implies increase or decrease.

In summary, then, from the perspective of human-relations theorists, the professional nurse as a technical-manager is expected to be (1) *democratic* in her orientation toward the work group, (2) *functionally oriented*, as opposed to traditionally oriented, toward the hospital social structure, (3) *considerate* of her coworkers, and (4) alert to efforts on work-group performance of *initiating action*.[22]

## SOCIALIZATION OF NURSES

The transition in role definition described above is still under way and has not been uniformly accepted by nurses. Students of change in nursing have noted recently, for example, that "probably no other profession is undergoing so dynamic a reconsideration of itself and its social role . . ."[23] and that "there are many points of confusion and conflict in the current definition of the social role of the professional nurse."[24] As pointed out earlier, the general changes which are occurring in nursing have stimulated profound modifications in nursing education, and thereby have increased the probability that certain categories of nurses will have been exposed to and will exhibit to a greater degree attitudes which are consonant with the human-relations model. Furthermore, the process of socialization does not terminate with graduation from a training program. Conflicts in definitions of the nursing role may be brought even more sharply into focus as the neophyte commences her professional career and moves through various stages in it, generating a continuous potential for attitude formation and change. Given this assumption of continuous differential exposure and acceptance, four basic hypotheses concerning adult socialization of nurses can be generated.

First, since educational change has been most prominent in collegiate programs, nurses holding college degrees should be characterized by a greater acceptance of human-relations attitudes than those not having a college degree.

Second, given the relatively recent exposure of nurses to the human-relations model, acceptance of human-relations attitudes should be more characteristic of recent graduates of nurse training programs than of earlier graduates.

Third, the trends toward increasing technical complexity and bureaucratic structure described earlier have been most pronounced in larger hospitals where problems of coordinating highly specialized personnel are most acute. It is reasonable to assume, therefore, that the steadily increasing influence of the human-relations philosophy of management has had its greatest impact on nurse managers in large hospitals.

Fourth, the forces which differentially affect supervisory nurses in large hospitals also impinge unequally upon those of high and low authority, independently of hospital size. Nurses in high authority positions are more likely to be concerned with coordination of hospital-wide functions, problems of general management, and development of organizational solutions to management problems. As a consequence the nurse with considerable responsibility might be expected to be more concerned with general models of administration than the nurse who is responsible for a particular work unit.

It should be noted, finally, that the four general hypotheses actually are composed of four specific hypothetical relationships. The independent variables are expected to be related in a specified direction to three of the four dependent variables. Nurses who are recent graduates possessing college degrees, and who occupy high positions of authority within large hospitals, are expected to be more democratic, functional, and considerate. The four independent variables are expected to be related consistently, but in an unspecified direction, to willingness to initiate action.

## PROCEDURES

The findings reported below are based on information gathered from hospital nurses holding positions of head nurse or above. Questionnaires were administered during 1962 and 1963 to all participants in a large management-training workshop program for supervisory nurses. Of the 803 participants, 697 possessed the characteristics pertinent to the present investigation.

Measures of the four independent variables were based on background items included in the questionnaires.

The instruments also contained scales designed so measure the four dependent attitudinal variables. The extent of nurses "democratic" orientation to their work groups was measured by the ten-item democracy scale developed by Henry Riecken.[25]

"Functional orientation" toward hospital social structure was measured by a ten-item revision of a scale originally devised by Melvin Seeman and John W. Evans.[26] The responses of nurses in management positions to the original Seeman-Evans items were factor analyzed to determine their relative contributions to common dimensions. On the basis of the factor loadings obtained, the ten items with highest positive contributions on a single basic dimension were selected for use in this study.

The measurement of both willingness to "initiate action" and "consideration" is based upon the work of Edwin Fleishman and his associates.[27] Again, nurses' responses to Fleishman's original items were factor analyzed. Two basic dimensions resulted and were identified as "consideration" and willingness to "initiate action." In this case, two criteria were employed in the final selection of items. Every item selected had both a positive loading on one factor and a loading approaching zero on the second. The resulting scales provided a ten-item measure of "consideration" and a thirteen-item measure of willingness to "initiate action."

## FINDINGS

The basic data used in testing the hypotheses are summarized in Tables 11-1 through 11-4. "Possession of a college degree" is related significantly to all four dependent variables, and the relationships to "democracy," "functional orientation," and "consideration" are in the predicted direction. (See Table 11-1.) "Possession of a college degree" is seen to be related to willingness to "initiate action" such that those possessing degrees are *less* willing to "initiate action" than others.

TABLE 11-1

MEAN ATTITUDE SCORES OF NURSE MANAGERS
BY POSSESSION OF A COLLEGE DEGREE

| Attitudes of nurse managers | Possesses a college degree | | Level of significance of difference between means |
|---|---|---|---|
| | Yes | No | |
| Democratic orientation* | 7.34 | 9.75 | .001 |
| Functional orientation† | 32.11 | 34.96 | .001 |
| Consideration‡ | 30.40 | 29.65 | .05 |
| Willingness to initiate action§ | 32.63 | 35.38 | .001 |
| Number of cases | 156 | 541 | |

*Democratic orientation scores can assume values ranging from −30.00 (most democratic) to +30.00 (least democratic).

†Functional orientation scores can assume values ranging from 10.00 (highest functional orientation) to 50.00 (lowest functional orientation).

‡Consideration scores can assume values ranging from 10.00 (lowest consideration) to 50.00 (highest consideration).

§Willingness to initiate action scores can assume values ranging from 13.00 (lowest willingness to initiate action) to 65.00 (highest willingness to initiate action). Since direction of difference was not predicted with respect to willingness to initiate action, a two-tailed test of significance was employed.

TABLE 11-2

MEAN ATTITUDE SCORES OF NURSE MANAGERS
BY RECENCY OF GRADUATION

| Attitudes of nurse managers* | Recency of graduation | | Level of significance of difference between means |
|---|---|---|---|
| | 1950 or later | Prior to 1950 | |
| Democratic orientation | 8.03 | 10.07 | .001 |
| Functional orientation | 33.38 | 35.00 | .001 |
| Consideration | 30.20 | 29.55 | .02 |
| Willingness to initiate action | 34.37 | 35.04 | n.s. |
| Number of cases | 292 | 405 | |

*See notes to Table 11-1.

A pattern of relationships similar to that observed for "possesses a college degree" is also seen with respect to the variable "recency of graduation." (See Table 11-2.) The relationship between "recency of graduation" and "willingness to initiate action" is in the same direction as in the analysis presented in Table 11-1, with recent graduates being *less* willing to "initiate action"; but the difference is not sufficiently large to be considered statistically significant.

"Hospital size" is related significantly to "democracy," "functional orientation," and willingness to "initiate action"; but the relation of this

nurses in lower positions (see Table 11-4); however, the probability of chance occurrence of the observed difference is slightly larger than that conventionally employed in determining statistical significance. With respect to "functional orientation" and "consideration," only very slight differences were observed. Willingness to "initiate action," on the other hand, is significantly related to "authority level"; and, again, the direction is consistent with previous analyses.

In the above analyses, certain similarities appear. The independent variables tend to be related to "democracy," "functional orientation," and

TABLE 11-3

MEAN ATTITUDE SCORES OF NURSE MANAGERS
BY HOSPITAL SIZE

| Attitudes of nurse managers* | Hospital size† | | Level of significance of difference between means |
| --- | --- | --- | --- |
| | Large | Small | |
| Democratic orientation | 7.13 | 9.82 | .001 |
| Functional orientation | 32.39 | 34.89 | .001 |
| Consideration | 30.09 | 29.74 | n.s. |
| Willingness to initiate action | 33.81 | 35.04 | .02 |
| Number of cases | 158 | 539 | |

*See notes to Table 11-1.
†Large hospitals are those having 600 or more beds.

variable to "consideration" is not significant. (See Table 11-3.) The pattern of relationships seen in Table 11-3 is similar to the patterns of Table 11-1 and 11-2. All three predicted differences arc in the expected direction, and nurses from large hospitals are *less* willing to "initiate action" than others.

Finally, corresponding to expectations, nurses in higher positions of authority are more "democratic" than

"consideration" in the expected direction with eight of the twelve comparisons being statistically significant. Willingness to "initiate action," also as expected, demonstrates a tendency to be related consistently to the independent variables with three of these four relationships achieving statistical significance. The direction of relationship is such that those who are recent graduates possessing college degrees, and who

TABLE 11-4

MEAN ATTITUDE SCORES OF NURSE MANAGERS
BY HOSPITAL AUTHORITY LEVEL

| Attitudes of nurse managers* | Hospital authority level† | | Level of significance of difference between means |
|---|---|---|---|
| | High | Low | |
| Democratic orientation | 8.69 | 9.73 | .06 |
| Functional orientation | 34.28 | 34.36 | n.s. |
| Consideration | 29.98 | 29.67 | n.s. |
| Willingness to initiate action | 34.18 | 35.34 | .01 |
| Number of cases | 347 | 350 | |

*See notes to Table 11-1.

†High authority level refers to all nurse managers above head nurse. Low authority level refers to head nurses only.

are in positions of high authority within large hospitals, are *less* likely to "initiate action" than others.

Interpreting the above findings is difficult because without further analysis there is no way to know whether the independent variables assessed are equally important in accounting for attitude differences or to know the extent to which explanation could be improved by various combinations of the independent variables. This problem—combination of the independent variables—may be handled in different ways. The analytic strategy utilized here was, first, to construct extreme "types" of nurses defined by the presence or absence of all four independent variables; and, second, to compare the constructed types on each of the dependent variables.[28] No attempt was made to infer the independent causal importance of the four factors.[29] This strategy led to a comparison of two "types" of nurses. The Type X nurse is in a position of high authority, is a recent graduate holding a college degree, and is employed by a large hospital.

The Type Y nurse is in a lower position of authority, is an early graduate not holding a degree, and is employed by a small hospital. Following the reasoning from which the previously stated hypotheses were generated, Type X nurses were expected to be *more* (*a*) "democratic," (*b*) "functionally oriented," and (*c*) "considerate" than Type Y nurses. Again, Type X nurses were expected to be different, in an unspecified way, with respect to willingness to "initiate action."

Two further problems of interpretation exist. First, the independent variables do not operate in isolation from one another. For example, "authority level" and "recency of graduation" are related such that those in positions of high authority are less likely to be recent graduates.[30] Second, the dependent variables are also intercorrelated to some extent. Perhaps the scales employed tap a common dimension as well as specific ones. However, the correlations between the scales are sufficiently low to permit the assumption that four different but interrelated dimensions of the human-relations complex are being measured.[31]

Data pertinent to the comparison of the constructed types are summarized in Table 11-5. The contrasting types differ significantly with respect to all of the dependent variables. In all four cases, the level of statistical significance surpasses the .02 level. In addition, the magnitudes of the differences involved are larger than those occurring in the analyses of the individual independent factors. These results suggest that this *combination* of the independent variables differentiates more sharply nurse orientations than do the independent factors considered singly.

Tendencies toward consistency among the observed relationships were noted previously. The findings with respect to the typology give further support to the suggested pattern. The observed differences between the types are in the direction expected for "democracy," "functional orientation," and "consideration." The difference with respect to willingness to "initiate action" is similar to that seen in Tables 11-1 through 11-4.

## CONCLUSION

After reviewing contemporary nursing trends, this paper examined the extent to which elements of the human-relations philosophy are characteristic of hospital nurses in management positions. Analysis of nursing's professional context led to selection of four statuses which are related to the process of professional socialization in nursing and which were expected to influence status occupants' reactions to specific elements of the human-relations model. Four general hypotheses were formulated stating the anticipated relationships between the variables. Testing the hypotheses revealed a pattern of relationships in which each of the four independent variables tended to be related consistently to all four dependent variables. Observation of these relationships led to the construction of two nurse manager "types." These types were constituted by combining those extremes of the independent variables leading to similar predictions. This procedure resulted in the following typology:

### TABLE 11-5

MEAN ATTITUDE SCORES OF CONTRASTING
TYPES OF NURSE MANAGERS

| Attitudes of nurse managers* | Types of nurse managers | | Level of significance of difference between means |
|---|---|---|---|
| | Type X | Type Y | |
| Democratic orientation | 6.13 | 12.42 | .001 |
| Functional orientation | 30.33 | 35.82 | .001 |
| Consideration | 30.73 | 28.78 | .02 |
| Willingness to initiate action | 32.33 | 36.11 | .01 |
| Number of cases | 15 | 130 | |

*See notes to Table 11-1.

1. *Type X Nurses*—Those nurses in positions of high authority, who are recent graduates holding college degrees, and who are employed by large hospitals.

2. *Type Y Nurses*—Those in lower positions of authority, who are earlier graduates not holding a degree, and who are employed by small hospitals.

Comparison of these types on each of the dependent variables resulted in the observation of significant differences in all cases; furthermore, the pattern of interrelationships emerging from the earlier analyses became increasingly distinct.

These findings show that attitudes which are related to elements of the human-relations philosophy are exhibited differentially by nurse managers. In the terminology of this paper, Type X nurses were found to evidence greater degrees of "democracy," "functional orientation," and "consideration," and less willingness to "initiate action" than Type Y nurses. Since examination of changes in the nursing role and its supporting patterns of professional socialization led, in every case, to correct predictions concerning the existence of relationships between the independent and dependent variables and, in the three instances where direction was specified, to correct predictions concerning the direction of relationships, we interpret the findings to mean that the human-relations philosophy of management has been employed increasingly as a source of professional norms in nursing.

While the above interpretation is consistent with the data, it is not dictated by them. It may be the case, for example, that the requirements of various roles within nursing systematically favor the selection of certain types of people over others; and that, therefore, the pattern of relationships we have described may have arisen partially or wholly through selection. It might be argued that not only may processes of professional socialization in nursing operate to inculcate the human-relations philosophy, but that those who for any reason tend to display the attitudes of Type X nurses are more likely to be selected for specific roles within nursing than those displaying attitudes of the Type Y nurse.

This argument, that both selection and socialization may produce the results reported here, may not be dismissed lightly; however, the weight of available evidence on this point suggests that socialization is substantially the more powerful process. In a recent summary of relevant findings, Corwin and Taves state with reference to selection that "... the ideologies of prospective nurses are similar to those of the general population";[32] and that:

In the past, nursing apparently attracted highly dedicated women committed to the ideal of service to humanity, but today it recruits a heterogeneous group who selects nursing for a variety of reasons.[33]

Although comparisons of student nurses with recruits in other fields indicate that some degree of selection is operative, and while determining the exact role of selection is an important research task in its own right, there is at present little evidence to suggest that the types of selection which occur can account for the findings of the present study.[34]

Another problem of interpretation of results deserving mention concerns magnitudes of differences reported, particularly those in Tables 11-1 through

11-4. Even though the differences in most cases are statistically significant, they are generally fairly small. Nevertheless, the prediction of reliable differences within an occupational group is theoretically suggestive. We would expect to find somewhat larger differences than reported here to exist between nurses and similar professionals, for example, school teachers or social workers. Even larger differences would be expected in comparisons of nurses and members of occupations which are composed of both sexes or of men only and which are not of the "helping" variety.

An implication of the two lines of criticism considered here—selection as an alternative explanation and emphasis placed upon small differences—is that the argument presented in this paper might fruitfully be checked across occupational lines. The same kinds of differences existing among nurses may exist also for occupations which have not been exposed in a direct way to the human-relations philosophy and which employ quite different procedures of training. Such findings could not well be interpreted in the terms presented in this paper.

In conclusion, this paper suggests one way in which changes in the nursing role have affected the content of the nurse's professional training and experience. Increasingly technical, specialized, bureaucratized, and managerial role requirements have stimulated the search for a new rationale or definition of nursing as a profession. It has been argued that the human-relations model of management is advocated as such a rationale; that structural features of the nursing profession, through various channels of socialization, create inequalities in the distribution of ideas; and that, consequently, there is predictable, differential exposure to and acceptance of the human-relations model among nurses.

---

1. William H. Sewell, "Some Recent Developments in Socialization Theory and Research," *The Annals of the American Academy of Political and Social Science,* **349,** 1963, 163–181.

2. *Ibid.* Sewell cites several of the principal studies covering such diverse groups as medical students, lawyers, nursing students, symphony musicians, life insurance salesmen, psychiatric attendants, legislators, and rabbis indicating that numerous points of departure already exist. For further citations, see also Samuel W. Bloom, "The Process of Becoming a Physician," *The Annals of the American Academy of Political and Social Science,* **346,** 1963, 77–87; and Melvin Seeman and John W. Evans, "Apprenticeship and Attitude Change," *American Journal of Sociology,* **67,** 1962, 365–378.

3. See, for example, Howard S. Becker and Blanche Geer, "Medical Education," in Howard E. Freeman, Sol Levine, and Leo G. Reeder (Eds.), *Handbook of Medical Sociology,* Englewood Cliffs, N.J.: Prentice-Hall, 1963, pp. 169–186; Bloom, *loc. cit.*; Rue Bucher and Anselm Strauss, "Professions in Process," *American Journal of Sociology,* **66,** 1961, 325–344; Temple Burling, Edith M. Lentz, and Robert N. Wilson, *The Give and Take in Hospitals,* New York: Putnam, 1956, pp. 95–107; Ronald Corwin and Marvin J. Taves, "Nursing and Other Health Professions," in Freeman, Levine, and Reeder, *op. cit.,* pp. 187–212; Hans O. Mauksch, "Becoming a Nurse: A Selective View," *The Annals of the American Academy of Political and Social Science,* **346,** 1963, 88–98.

4. Margaret Bridgman, *Collegiate Education for Nursing,* Philadelphia: Russell Sage Foundation, 1953, pp. 27–28.

5. Everett C. Hughes, Helen MacGill

Hughes, and Irwin Deutscher, *Twenty Thousand Nurses Tell Their Story*, Philadelphia: Lippincott, 1958, pp. 82–83.

6. Leonard Reissman and John Rohrer (Eds.), *Change and Dilemma in the Nursing Profession*, New York: Putnam, 1957, p. 13.

7. Burling, Lentz, and Wilson, *op. cit.*, p. 109.

8. Bridgman, *op. cit.*, p. 27.

9. Hughes, Hughes, and Deutscher, *op. cit.*, pp. 82–83.

10. Reissman and Rohrer, *loc. cit.*

11. Robert K. Merton, "Status-Orientations in Nursing," *American Journal of Nursing*, **62**, 1962, 72.

12. Robert W. Habenstein and Edwin A. Christ, *Professionalizer, Traditionalizer, and Utilizer*, Columbia, Mo.: University of Missouri Press, 1955, p. 2.

13. Bridgman, *op. cit.*, p. 179.

14. For a general discussion of this model, see Chris Argyris, *Personality and Organization*, New York: Harper, 1957; Keith Davis and William G. Scott (Eds.), *Readings in Human Relations*, New York: McGraw-Hill, 1959; Robert C. Day and Robert L. Hamblin, "Some Effects of Close and Punitive Styles of Supervision," *American Journal of Sociology*, **69**, 1964, 499–510; Rensis Likert, *New Patterns of Management*, New York: McGraw-Hill, 1961; Eugene Litwak, "Models of Bureaucracy Which Permit Conflict," *American Journal of Sociology*, **67**, 1961, 177–184; and William F. Whyte, "Human Relations—A Progress Report," in Amitai Etzioni (Ed.), *Complex Organizations*, New York: Holt, Rinehart, and Winston, 1961, pp. 100–112. For the influence of this model on nursing, see for example, Faye G. Abdellah et al., *Patient-Centered Approaches to Nursing*, New York: Macmillan, 1960; Bridgman, *loc. cit.*; and Esther Lucile Brown, *Newer Dimensions of Patient Care*, Part 2, New York: Russell Sage Foundation, 1962.

15. Litwak, *op. cit.*, p. 177.

16. Likert, *op. cit.*, p. 102.

17. *Ibid.*, p. 103.

18. Brigman, *op. cit.*, p. 36, states: "In the opinion of some observers a prime essential for the improvement of the health services is the elimination of the common rigid hierarchical system. At times it seems as though the professional personnel...are less concerned with the total harmonious effort than with their own pride of place. Attitudes of superiority, on the one hand, and resentment on the other, create needless internal and external conflict. ... The only remedy seems to be a sharp reversal of traditional attitudes. ... The nursing profession is making a great effort to do at least its share in this direction."

19. Mary Tschudin, Helen Belcher, and Leo Nedelsky, *Evaluation in Basic Nursing Education*, New York: Putnam, 1958, p. 122.

20. Bernard Berelson and Gary A. Steiner, *Human Behavior: An Inventory of Scientific Findings*, New York: Harcourt, Brace and World, 1964, p. 374.

21. Likert, *op. cit.*, p. 101.

22. For convenience, these four characteristics are hereinafter referred to in terms of the key words denoting them.

23. Esther Lucile Brown, in Foreword to Bridgman, *op. cit.*, p. 7.

24. Kenneth D. Benne and Warren Bennis, "Role Confusion and Conflict in Nursing: The Role of the Professional Nurse," *American Journal of Nursing*, **59**, 1959, 196. Also see Ronald G. Corwin, "The Professional Employee: A Study of Conflict in Nursing Roles," *American Journal of Sociology*, **66**, 1961, 604–615.

25. Henry W. Riecken, *The Volunteer Work Camp: A Psychological Evaluation*, Cambridge, Mass.: Addison-Wesley, 1952, p. 34. Illustrative items from the democracy scale are: (1) "Almost any job that can be done by a committee can be done better by having one individual responsible for it"; (2) "Sometimes one can be too open-minded about the possible solutions to a problem that faces a group"; (3) "Discipline should be the responsibility of the leader of a group."

26. Melvin Seeman and John W. Evans, "Stratification and Hospital Care, "*American Sociological Review*, **26**, 1961, Part I: 67–69, Part II: 193–203. Illustrative items from the functional orientation scale are: (1) "An intern should not presume to disagree with the medical judgment of the attending staff physician"; (2) "The head nurse should avoid becoming very friendly with the nurses and

aides working under her"; (3) "Respect for, and deference to, one's superior is absolutely essential in the hospital."

27. Edwin Fleishman, Edwin F. Harris, and Harold E. Burtt, *Leadership and Supervision in Industry*, Columbus, O.: Ohio State University Press, 1955. Illustrative items from the initiates action scale are: "In my position as a leader in nursing, I think I should . . . (1) Emphasize getting things done on time; (2) Stress being ahead of competing work groups; (3) Decide in detail what shall be done and how it shall be done by the work group." Illustrative items from the consideration scale are: "In my position as a leader in nursing, I think I should . . . (1) Be slow to accept new ideas; (2) Refuse to compromise on a point; (3) Change the duties of people in my work group without first talking it over with them."

28. A multivariate analysis of these data was performed, revealing the existence of interaction effects. Theoretically, an analysis of variance model could have been employed at this point in an attempt to estimate the magnitude of such interaction. However, the restrictions and assumptions of analysis of variance make it inappropriate in the present instance. For example, the subclass N's are for the most part unequal and disproportionate, and the subclass distributions make the assumption of homogeneity of variance untenable. The basic table reporting the 64 means resulting from the multivariate approach is available from the authors.

29. H. M. Blalock, "Evaluating the Relative Importance of Variables," *American Sociological Review*, **26**, 1961, 866–874; and D. Gold, "Independent Causation in Multivariate Analysis: The Case of Political Alienation and Attitude Toward a School Bond Issue," *American Sociological Review*, **27**, 1962, 85–87.

30. Gamma = .23.

31. Intercorrelations among the scales ranged from −.13 to +.33.

32. Corwin and Taves, *op. cit.*, p. 195.

33. *Ibid.*, p. 197.

34. *Ibid.*, pp. 197–200.

# 12. THE PROCESS OF BECOMING A PHYSICIAN

## Samuel W. Bloom

Within the general field of the sociology of the professions, recent research has been directed to the consideration of how individuals are prepared to fill the professional role.[1] The problem is not so much how students acquire the requisite technical knowledge and skill but mainly how they acquire professional attitudes and values. In more technical terms it is the study of the processes of socialization through which individuals acquire professional roles. In this paper we will be interested in questions which are general to the sociology of the professions as they apply to the study of how individuals learn the physician's role. We will not attempt to review all of the studies of this problem.[2] Rather it will be our goal to classify the range of perspectives which have guided studies of the socialization of the physician, to interpret their theoretical roots, and, with selected results, to illustrate the major directions of inquiry which appear to be emerging.

## SOCIALIZATION: A DEFINITION

Socialization, as that term is used here, designates "... the processes by which people selectively acquire the values and attitudes, the interests, skills, and knowledge—in short, the culture— current in the groups of which they are or seek to become a member."[3] It is important to distinguish this concept from its quite different meaning in economic and political usage. The latter, loosely speaking, refers to the "nationalization" of industry, business, or professional services. It is this sense of the word which is implied by the phrase "the socialization of medicine." Socialization, as used in sociology and psychology, is a descriptive concept concerned with "social maturation," or how individuals are shaped into members of groups.

For much of its early history, research in socialization was confined to the early years of the human life cycle. More recently, attention has been directed to how individuals acquire the attitudes and values, the skills and behavior patterns of various social roles as these processes occur throughout the life cycle. In other words, "adult socialization" has emerged as a focus of study.

The medical school, of course, is only one part of the total institutional complex which makes up modern medicine. It is, however, the agency most responsible for transmitting the culture of medicine.[4] Thus the studies of how the recruits to medicine learn to think, feel, and act "like a doctor" are found, by and large, to focus upon the medical school.

Reprinted by permission of the author and publisher, from the *Annals of the American Academy of Political and Social Science*, Vol. 346, 1963, pp. 77–87.

## CONCEPTUAL FRAMEWORK

At the level of theory, published studies separate into two general categories. There are those investigations which are concerned with the study of the medical school as a whole environment or social system, and there are studies which focus upon the social psychology of specific attitudes. The former are based upon theory which asserts that any particular attitude or behavior is interdependent in a patterned way with related attitudes and behavior and that socialization can only be understood in its full social context. In contrast, the second type of study is directed principally toward identifying the attributes of individuals which qualify them to become good physicians.

The first approach is best represented by the research of Robert Merton and his associates from the Columbia University Bureau of Applied Social Research[5] and by Everett C. Hughes and his associates from the University of Chicago.[6] Although these two studies are quite different in their details, they share a perspective which is distinctly limited to the sociology of learning centering upon the social and cultural environments which facilitate or hamper the learning of the professional role.

The studies of Leonard Eron may be chosen to exemplify the second approach.[7] Eron has attempted to identify the attitudes of medical students on a scale of cynicism-humanitarianism, to compare them with other groups, to document the patterns of attitude change which might occur in association with stages of the medical student's career, and to find out whether certain psychological correlates may be associated with attitudes according to predictions based on psychological theory.

Beyond this very general classification of perspective, the description of this area of research grows more complicated, as illustrated by the work of Kenneth R. Hammond and Fred Kern, Jr. at Colorado[8] and George Reader and Mary Goss at Cornell.[9]

In each of these settings a long-range experimental study was conducted of attitudinal and other effects of a specific educational program. At Colorado successive senior classes were divided randomly into an experimental group and a control group — the one assigned to the General Medical Clinic program, where they were taught comprehensive care; the other assigned to the traditional curriculum. At Cornell a similar procedure was followed in connection with the Comprehensive Care and Teaching Program. In spite of these basic similarities of method and purpose, appraisal of the two studies reveals a difference of perspective which fits the twofold classification described above. The Colorado group is clearly more oriented toward the psychology of learning; at Cornell the data on individual response are consistently interpreted within the framework of the school conceived as a social system. The difference, however, is only in emphasis. There is much overlap in the approaches of these two studies.

Further consideration of the problem of conceptualizing the process of becoming a physician will emerge from a review of the findings of selected studies, according to the stages in the career of the medical student.

### The Prospective Student

More attention appears to have been given to the study of medical students before they begin the study of medicine than at any time thereafter. To a large extent, however, this research has been directed at the cataloguing of the attributes of medical students.[10]

Thus we know that a relatively high proportion of medical students are recruited from families of the professional and managerial class; moreover, a significant minority have fathers who are physicians. On the other hand, it is equally evident that there has been a consistent trend for more than half a century in the United States to the democratization of recruitment, with increasing proportions of physicians tending to come from lower ranks in the social structure.

At the same time careful documentation of such variables as intelligence and college grades has indicated what many medical educators have interpreted as a downward trend in the quality of medical recruits. To be sure, the median intelligence-test score of medical students is slightly higher than that for graduate students in selected fields, but it is lower than in the fields of physics and mathematics, chemistry, and English.[11] Moreover, the proportion of freshman medical students with a grade average of A decreased from 40 per cent in 1950–1951 to 16 per cent in 1955–1956. Equally alarming to many has been the steady reduction in the ratio of applicants to available places in medical schools.

The question remains: what do such data tell us about the processes of career choice among recruits or their impact upon the profession? It is all too easy to link democratization trends with the apparent reduction of intellectual quality. Moreover on the commonly held assumption that specific attributes, such as intelligence, college grades, and family background, add up to the composite "ideal medical student," the interpretation of these data has indeed tended

to be anxious and pessimistic among medical educators.

The limitation of such studies of the prospective student, whether they are primarily descriptive or designed for the prediction of later performance and behavior, is that they assume a direct relationship between discrete traits or combinations of traits and patterns of behavior. The influence of situational and social factors is not included. Moreover, they do not allow sufficiently for the evolutionary character of the process of career decision. As one author proposes:

When a career is seen as a dynamic expression of the interplay of . . . ability, interests, motives, temperament, training, and especially opportunity, it becomes much more appropriate to conceive of the *evolution* of a career rather than the choice of a career.[12]

The decision to enter a career begins with the generation of an ambition. A fundamental aspect of ambition is the structuring of present conduct in the interest of a future goal. Medicine, because it is characterized by long periods of training and probation and by a long delay in rewards, obviously requires a great deal of ambition which is tough enough to survive a long period of the postponement of gratifications.[13]

There are two distinct ways of conceiving such an ambition. The first and most common sees it as primarily a subjective matter, generated in private and internalized as a drive. The second conceives of ambitions as "social" in character. The former approach is well known. It asserts a type of person who, out of inner needs, desires, and abilities, is attracted to a career which fits his personal equation. The latter view emphasizes the importance of groups for both the genesis and nourishment of career ambitions. The medical ambition particularly, it has been proposed, is too demanding to survive a social setting which does not generously support it. The reason so many recruits to medicine come from the families of the higher socioeconomic strata, this view continues, is that such families possess the mechanisms for generating and nurturing the medical ambition.

These two views are not mutually exclusive. The more satisfactory explanation of how the medical career decision generates will combine the two approaches, as suggested by the research of Natalie Rogoff.[14]

Rogoff, studying six successive classes at one medical school, found that a majority report that they considered medicine as a career very early. Fully 51 per cent say they first considered entering medicine at age thirteen or younger. Students whose fathers were doctors characteristically took this first step very early. However, the same was true for students who came from lower-status, mobile families.

The age when a definite career choice was made presents quite a different picture. "For the modal student," Rogoff writes,

the definite career choice is keyed to the institutional requirements of the educational system. He does not prolong his choice much beyond the point when he must select courses appropriate to medical school prerequisites, nor does he arrive at the decision before the socially prescribed time.

Unlike the wide dispersion in the age at which medicine is first considered, "the age at making the definite decision shows a marked concentration, occurring during the 16 to 20 year age period."

There are, indeed, some youthful deciders. About 18 per cent of Rogoff's 741 subjects had already made up their minds to become doctors when they were no more than fifteen years old. The sons of physicians, however, although among the first to think of a medical career, are not typically among the first to decide. On the contrary, it is apparently not uncommon for physicians' sons to experience a prolonged delay in reaching a final decision. As Rogoff suggests, this delay lends credence to anecdotal accounts about difficult conflicts experienced by the sons of strong and accomplished fathers as they work through questions of their own ego identity.

The contribution of Rogoff's research is important in several different respects. On the one hand, it documents the general hypothesis that a medical career may be conceived as a set of more or less successful adjustments to a network of institutions, formal organizations, and informal relationships, and supports Hall's more specific explanation of the role of the family in the initial step toward the career. On the other hand, it raises intriguing questions about the connecting links between the processes of career selection and the processes of social and emotional maturation, such as are described by Eli Ginzberg.[15]

Rogoff raises another important question for research in her assertion that different types of decision making appear to be associated with different attitudes toward medicine as a career. In other words, the student who decides early and is nurtured and supported in a career aspiration may bring very different feelings about the profession with him into the professional school than a classmate who decided early but was required to "go it alone" or to sustain his interest in the face of discouraging environmental circumstances. The profession may have a quite different meaning to one who is forced to compete and prove himself at every step of the way than for one who, though no more able, has the course marked for him securely at every step of the way. That such factors may pervade one's attitudes toward himself as a doctor or toward patients is a reasonable hypothesis.

## THE DOORWAY TO MEDICINE

The curriculum which has been typical of medical schools in the United States for at least fifty years is divided into two halves. The first two years are the "basic science" or "preclinical" years: they present the student with an intensive experience confined mainly to the laboratory and lecture hall. The second two years are spent in the hospital, learning by actual experience with both hospitalized in-patients and with ambulatory out-patients.

Recent years have witnessed much experimentation with this curriculum. Its fundamentals, however, remain essentially unchanged. Western Reserve, for example, has designed methods for giving the student experience with patients from the very beginning of medical school, thus deliberately attempting to break down the separation which the more standard curriculum places between so-called basic and clinical studies. Nevertheless, the fundamental order of presentation remains the same as before; that is, the student begins his medical studies with gross anatomy and continues in an order which recapitulates the history of the development of the medical sciences. The dissection of the gross tissues is combined with microscopic studies; the study of structure (anatomy) leads into the study of function (physiology) and biochemistry,

thus completing the first year of the curriculum. The second year is dominated by the study of pathology; all of the approaches taken in the first year are repeated, but now for purposes of studying the human organism when it goes wrong. Capping the preclinical studies is pharmacology, in which the student is taught methods of intervention which are designed to help and correct pathological processes.

However, although this basic curriculum has not changed, medical educators have become deeply concerned about the possibility that it contains implicit, unintended consequences for the attitudes of medical students toward patients. Taking the study of anatomy as an example, let us explore to see how this might be possible.

*Attitudinal development.* For centuries the study of gross anatomy has been the first step of the medical career. This important position in the medical curriculum is said to have been earned four centuries ago when anatomy became "the science which rescued medicine from witchcraft."[16] It continues in this position, however, on more than traditional grounds. One must learn the structure of the human organism, it is argued, before one can fully understand its functions and behavior.

There is much to suggest, however, that for the student anatomy provides a learning opportunity which involves more than basic knowledge and technical skill. For example, an anatomy professor annually points out in his opening lecture that "the greatness of Vesalius was that he did not accept the dead hand of authority."[17] This professor goes on, in different ways, to challenge his students to be critical of the "dead hand of authority." This inherent "skepticism," he makes clear, is even more important for the advancement of science than the details of knowledge and dissection skills.

This kind of attitude, however, is still in the realm of what we would call direct methods of teaching. It is obviously the conscious intention of this anatomy professor to impart to his students the importance of an attitude that he includes within the content of his course. Other attitudes are taught indirectly. "Anatomy," continues the same professor, "is the first door through which students enter school, and it is in anatomy that they form an impression that is going to be fundamental for their whole tour of the school."

Other medical educators are more explicit about the effects upon student attitudes of anatomy and the other basic sciences. For example, it has been one interpretation that the student's experience in the basic sciences has a harmful effect upon his attitudes toward his future patients. The very essentials of a scientific approach, as defined in our example above, become in this latter argument the source of dehumanization, of the creation of an "emotional callous." "To be really scientific," one educator observed, "it became necessary for the doctor to impose an instrument of some sort between himself and the patient. The patient was ignored in order to obtain a coned-down view of a single part. . . ."[18] This is postulated as an unintended effect upon attitudes toward patients as human beings which derives from the nature of the learning experience.

Another similar view about the unintended attitudinal effects of the student experiences in the basic sciences goes further. Not only are attitudes created; other attitudes are destroyed. Moreover,

in this view "good" attitudes are destroyed and "bad" ones are created. Medical students, it is said, grow "cynical" about people and lose their humanitarianism. This is the substance of the conclusions reached in the attitude studies by Leonard Eron, and other studies have produced confirming data concerning the course of attitudinal development during medical school.[19]

*Detached concern.* Medical educators, however, are not simply for humanitarianism and opposed to cynicism as one might be for godliness and opposed to evil. Their specific concern is about behavior toward patients. The focal question, therefore, is whether the cynicism which has been observed to develop during medical school does, in fact, indicate a loss of concern for patients which interferes with effective performance as a physician. This question is anticipated in the theoretical writings of Talcott Parsons,[20] and it is the main subject of inquiry in the studies by Renee Fox of what she calls "training in detached concern."[21]

It is well known in medicine that a physician must be sufficiently detached or objective in his attitude toward the patient to exercise sound judgment and keep his equanimity. At the same time he must also have enough concern for the patient to give him sensitive, understanding care. It is this combination of attitudes which Renee Fox calls "detached concern." Taken separately these two attitudes appear to be contradictory. The medical situation, however, joins them into a single pattern of variation.

Thus the service orientation, which is a major aspect of the social organization of medicine as a profession, when translated into behavior, leads to more than a simple humanitarianism. It requires, to be sure, a deep empathic concern for human beings, but not without the controlling influence of a measure of detachment. Moreover, both Parsons and Fox assert that the profession does not rely on the recruitment and self-selection of applicants who have a personality type which includes detached concern; the profession trains its members in this ability and is organized to help them maintain it. Lief and Fox describe the anatomy laboratory as an example of the complex training process which occurs in training for detached concern.[22]

Exploring, examining, and cutting into the human body and being confronted with death itself are included by Lief and Fox among the cardinal professional experiences of the physician. To acquire greater detachment in the face of these emotion-laden experiences, they state, is one of the primary problems for the medical student during his first two years.

Even though students prepare themselves for human dissection in various ways before entering medical school, it is generally true that students do not have a "real acquaintanceship with death" when they first arrive in medical school. Nevertheless, the emotional feelings which students at first experience toward dissecting the cadaver, at least on the conscious level, seem to be short-lived. Lief and Fox write:

By the end of their first day in the anatomy laboratory, some students have become so absorbed in the work of dissection that they have begun to forget their emotional response and to feel more casual about what they are doing. Here is the first instance in which the vast amount of intellectual work necessary in medical school serves as a protective device against intensive emotions. The anxiety involved in learning the material sufficiently well so that they can pass examinations becomes a "psychic counterirritant" for students.

Other evidence is presented, however, to show that, although students work in the anatomy laboratory without too much conscious anxiety, they continue to react with emotion on less conscious levels. Lief and Fox describe a variety of mechanisms of control and defense which are commonly utilized both to develop detachment and to control emotionality. One of the most important motivations to behave with composure in the laboratory is to secure the approval and respect of classmates.

Thus we are presented with two ever-present aspects of any educational experience, the intellectual work itself and the association with fellow students, and told how, in the case of the medical student, they appear to serve a particular function in the training in detached concern. In this explanation, studying hard and defining the task at hand in scientific terms is the most useful method the student has of defending himself against the anxiety which is implicit in the nature of the task itself. As the student successfully adjusts to a task at one level of anxiety, the preclinical curriculum seems to increase the intensity of the challenge. The human cadaver represents a more difficult emotional hurdle than the dead laboratory animal; the live animal of the physiology laboratory is emotionally harder to work on than the cadaver; it is more difficult to work on live dogs than with live cats. In the opinion of Lief and Fox: "Students regard each of these events as 'one step closer to being doctors.'"

What, if any, relationship is there between the training in detachment, as described in these studies, and the cynicism which has been the subject of so much worry to medical educators? One cannot fail to note their similarities. A thin line separates "objective scientific attitudes" from cynicism or loss of humanitarianism. However, there is a black-or-white connotation to the studies of cynicism-humanitarianism that is not shared in the kind of analysis presented by Lief and Fox. They described the danger not as one type of attitude as opposed to another but as

a pathological process of overdetachment . . . which may lead them, as mature physicians, to perceive and treat patients mechanistically . . . [and] may go on to the unconscious fantasy that the best patient is one who is completely passive and submissive and that the most cooperative patient is inert, anesthetized, or even dead.

## KANSAS STUDY OF STUDENT CULTURE

In the Kansas study,[23] one finds many similarities, both in method and findings, to the Columbia research in general and to the papers by Fox in particular. In the interpretation of findings, however, the Kansas study separates itself very distinctly from the Columbia group.

The Kansas study agrees in general with other studies of "the fate of idealism" among medical students. They question the meaning, however, of what appears to be a drift toward cynicism. Is this truly cynicism, they ask, or is it more a "veneer of cynicism"? The initial idealism of medical students, they assert, is a rather naive stereotyped motivation to help people. As these students develop more specific conceptions of the doctor's role, their so-called idealism becomes less stereotyped. In general, it is concluded, the education of medical students leads away from stereotypes and toward a greater specificity

of perspectives. The processes by which this is accomplished include prominently the same "mechanisms" described by Lief and Fox: namely, the intellectual work itself and the association with fellow students. Indeed, up to this point, the two accounts seem very alike, but in the interpretation of how these aspects of the educational experience function, they separate.

The Kansas study asserts that medical students run into a kind of unexpected wall as they enter the professional school. It is an academic obstacle course, similar to the one just completed in premedical studies but bewildering in the totality of its demands for work. Moreover, the student does not find the special kind of "medical" relief which his naive idealism had led him to hope for. Medical school, in other words, is more school than medical. The student adjusts by focusing down his attention to the problem of passing.

In solving this problem, the student adapts, according to the Kansas study, by cutting back his earlier willingness to put forth almost any effort that might be required and replacing it with a preoccupation for the most economical ways of learning.

In this adaptation, the individual student finds that it is most helpful to join hands with classmates. "Students," writes Becker, "find a collective solution to their common pressing problem — the fact that there is more to learn than they have time for in the time available."

In general, the student culture, as described in the Kansas study, is distinctly separate and, to some extent, secret from the faculty. Students present one face to their masters, acquiescence and cooperation, in the interests of academic survival; in their own culture, they are more independent and critical.

In this respect the Kansas study presents a picture of the medical school which has interesting comparisons with other types of "total institutions."[24] Most particularly, the description of the small groups of the clinical years is reminiscent of well-known sociological descriptions of work groups in factories.[25] Such groups typically set work norms, and both help the slow worker — student — and restrain the fast.

The Kansas "boys in white" are separate from "men in white" by a wide status gap similar to that between a child and adult. Their development is in contest with authority. They learn from their teachers but not with them. The lines between student and faculty are sharply demarcated, almost like battle lines. Students, therefore, form an interest group which is analogous to adolescent culture, especially in its sense of separation from the "establishment," or, in this case, the faculty. Communication between these two groups is, at least implicitly, a form of bargaining between interest groups. Power is its mediating force.

The interpretation of the Columbia research group is almost directly opposite; they propose that the medical student is "a student-physician" who develops in concert with his faculty. This is a relationship between adults in which common purpose exist from the start, and learning is a process of collaboration.

Even in their interpretations of the fate of idealism, the two studies reflect a basic difference of view. Both agree that the development of cynicism is more apparent than real. For the Kansas group, however, this is explained by the change from naive stereotypes about medicine to more specific conception of the realities. Fox, on the other hand, describes the process as a kind of temporary disenchantment caused by the delicate adjustments which students are forced to make between the complex and sometimes conflicting requirements of the doctor's role.

In explanation of these differences of interpretation, the different types of medical schools which were studied must be noted. The Kansas group studied a midwestern state-university school; the Columbia group studied most intensively two eastern so-called prestige schools from Ivy League universities and a third school which was in the middle of far-reaching curriculum reform. It is possible that these differences of region, type of support, and general professional status are the basis of the differences between findings of the two studies. The final word, of course, must await further research.

## DISCUSSION

One senses a special urgency in the concern of medical educators about the attitudes toward humanity of its future physicians. Perhaps a combination of "empathy" and "sympathy" describes better than "humanitarian" what medical educators have in mind as a positive force in physicians; "cynicism" is probably a good word for the negative.

Because of the importance of this problem, it is not surprising that so much of the research on medical-student attitudes has attempted to find out something about how medical students feel about other human beings and, particularly, their attitudes toward patients. That these attitudes change during medical school is strongly indicated by the available evidence. Exactly what these attitudes are, however, is still subject to interpretation. That some form of disenchantment occurs is too universally reported to ignore. But whether this disenchantment is permanent, whether it is a factor which interferes with or facilitates behavior as a physician, whether it is indeed more accurately called maturation rather than disenchantment — these questions remain unanswered. They are questions, however, which recently have been and continue to be the subject of intense investigation.

It is important to add that the training of the professional does not end with medical school. There is much reason to believe that the internship and residency contribute more to the socialization of the professional than any other experiences. This is the crucial period when the values to which the individual has been exposed in the medical school and the hospital are most likely to find their final internalized form and become the basis upon which the new physician begins to make decisions for himself.

From the standpoint of sociology, these investigations lend general support to the proposition that adult socialization is important in the career of the professional. Earlier research on the attitudes of medical students assumed, to a large extent, that these attitudes were determined prior to the medical-school experience mainly by factors in the personality. From this latter point of view, the medical-school experience did not really count, except as a kind of mold into which students either fit or did not. The sociologist enters this area of research with a quite different conception of the importance of the medical school; above all, he credits the school environment with being a vitally important influence upon the development of the student into a professional.

1. One of the best-known examples is Robert K. Merton, George G. Reader, and Patricia L. Kendall, *The Student-Physician, Introductory Studies in the Sociology of Medical Education*, Cambridge, Mass.: Harvard University Press, 1957. In the first essay of this volume, "Some Preliminaries to a Sociology of Medical Education," Merton reviews the development of the sociological study of the professions, citing as the main originators Robert E. Park, in his work of the 1920's, followed by his colleague at the University of Chicago, Everett C. Hughes. Also cited are two reviews: Ernest O. Smigel, "Trends in Occupational Sociology in the United States: A Survey of Postwar Research," *American Sociological Review*, 19, 1954, 398–404; and Theodore Caplow, *The Sociology of Work*, Minneapolis: University of Minnesota Press, 1954.

2. See Howard S. Becker and Blanche Geer, "Medical Education," in Howard E. Freeman, Leo G. Reeder, and Sol Levine (Eds.), *The Handbook of Medical Sociology*, New York: Prentice-Hall, 1963.

3. Merton et al., *op. cit.*, p. 287.

4. *Ibid.*, p. 5.

5. *Ibid.*, see especially Part I, pp. 3–104.

6. The major publication of this study is the book by Howard S. Becker, Blanche Geer, Everett C. Hughes, and Anselm L. Strauss, *Boys in White, Student Culture in Medical School*, Chicago: University of Chicago Press, 1961.

7. Leonard D. Eron, "The Effect of Medical Education on Attitudes: A Follow-up Study," in Helen Hofer Gee and Robert J. Glaser (Eds.), *The Ecology of the Medical Student*, Evanston, Ill.: Association of American Medical Colleges, 1958, pp. 25–33; *idem*, "Effect of Medical Education on Medical Students' Attitudes," *Journal of Medical Education*, 30, 1955, 559–566; *idem*, "Effect of Nursing Education on Attitudes," *Nursing Research*, 4, 1955, 24–27.

8. Kenneth R. Hammond and Fred

Kern, Jr., *Teaching Comprehensive Medical Care*, Cambridge: Harvard University Press, 1959.

9. George G. Reader, "The Cornell Comprehensive Care and Teaching Program," in Merton et al., *op. cit.*, pp. 81–104; *idem*, "Development of Professional Attitudes and Capacities," in Gee and Glaser, *op. cit.*, pp. 164–178: Mary E. W. Goss, "Change in the Cornell Comprehensive Care and Teaching Program" in Merton et al., *op. cit.*, pp. 249–270.

10. See Helen Hofer Gee and John T. Cowles, *The Appraisal of Applicants to Medical Schools*, Evanston, Ill.; Association of American Medical Colleges, 1957; Donald E. Super and Paul Brachrach, *Review of the Literature on Choice and Success in Scientific Careers*, Scientific Careers Project, Teachers College of Columbia University, Working Paper No. 1, November 16, 1956, hectographed, Chap. IV; Edward Gottheil and Carmen Miller Michael, "Predictor Variables Employed in Research on the Selection of Medical Students," *Journal of Medical Education*, **32**, 1957, 131–147.

11. Dael Wolfle, "Professional Students: Their Origins and Characteristics," in Gee and Cowles, *op. cit.*, pp. 10-16.

12. William Schofield, "Vocational Choice and Career Evolution," in Gee and Glaser, *op. cit.*, pp. 18-24.

13. Oswald Hall, "The Stages of a Medical Career," *American Journal of Sociology*, **53**, 1948, 327–336.

14. Natalie Rogoff, "The Decision to Study Medicine," in Merton et al., *op. cit.*, pp. 109–130.

15. Eli Ginzberg et al., *Occupational Choice: An Approach to a General Theory*, New York: Columbia University Press, 1951.

16. Dana Atchley, "The Orientation of an Undergraduate Medical Curriculum," *Science*, **104**, 1946, 67–70.

17. Quoted from materials of a continuing study of the sociology of medical education conducted by the Bureau of Applied Social Research of Columbia University under a grant from the Commonwealth Fund.

18. Edward O'Neill Harper, "An Experiment in Medical Education," *Medical Social Work*, **2**, 1953, 125–126.

19. Eron, *op. cit.*, 1958, p. 33; see also Richard Christie and Robert K. Merton, "Procedures for the Sociological Study of the Value Climate of Medical Schools," in Gee and Glaser, *op. cit.*, pp. 125–153.

20. Talcott Parsons, *The Social System*, Glencoe, Ill.: Free Press, 1951, Chap. 10.

21. Renee C. Fox, *Experiment Perilous*, Glencoe, Ill.: Free Press, 1959.

22. See Harold I. Lief and Renee Fox, "The Medical Student's Training for 'Detached Concern,'" in Harold I. Lief, Victor F. Lief, and Nina R. Lief (Eds.), *The Psychological Basis of Medical Practice*, New York: Hoeber, in press. This paper is separately published as Publication A-345, Bureau of Applied Social Research of Columbia University, New York.

23. Becker et al., *op. cit.*, 1961.

24. See Erving Goffman, "Some Characteristics of Total Institutions," in Goffman, *Asylums*, New York: Anchor Books, 1962.

25. The classic example is Fritz J. Roethlisberger and William Dickson, *Management and the Worker*, Cambridge, Mass.: Harvard University Press, 1939.

# 13. THE SYSTEM—BARRIERS TO QUALITY NURSING

## Luke M. Smith

### NURSING SCIENCE IN THE REALM OF KNOWLEDGE

A recently published sociological study of the young graduate registered nurse in her first position in the hospital came to the conclusion that it is not possible for a school of nursing to prepare its students to meet the demands of every hospital. Not only do hospitals differ from one another in their demands but also, within each hospital, there are conflicts between the nursing supervisor, the nursing instructor, and the senior nursing student as to what should be expected of her. It was suggested, therefore, that

nursing principles should be more clearly delineated and taught, practice in decision making initiated, and problem-solving approaches employed more extensively to prepare the neophyte nurse to adjust to the myriad situations which she may encounter.[1]

This study was made with a grant from a government agency; it was done with methodological sophistication—carefully constructed questionnaires distributed to a nationwide, randomized, stratified sample of hospitals and nursing schools, item analyses through and IBM Fortran Computer, and the construction of statistical tables accurately designed to test the hypotheses.

But how did the author define "social role," the thing which was being studied? Social role was defined in the beginning of the article in terms of demands, expectations, prohibitions, evaluative standards which were placed on the individual by the society, that is, by other individuals, so that the individual appears as acting simply in response to external forces. Yet in the conclusion of the article the researcher speaks of decision making and problem solving by the individual acting in a given role. Now if social role is defined in terms of external forces, where does individual choice enter? Clearly there is a discrepancy here. The researcher starts out to study one thing and ends up studying something else, apparently unaware that his conceptual tool, through which he organized his data, was changed during the process of the study.

How was such a mistake possible? The question of why people make intellectual errors is similar to that of why people have physical accidents. We know that accidents are not "accidental" but have a structure. Often there are discrepancies in the social and cultural situation which make accidents likely to occur when people find themselves in such a situation. Is there, then, a discrepancy in the cultural or intellectual situation which made it likely for the researcher to shift his definition

Reprinted by permission of the author and publisher, from *The Modern Dialogue: Nursing and the Community*, papers presented at the Biennial Convention, Albany, N.Y., 1964; Brochure No. 4, New York State League for Nursing, Inc., pp. 3–13.

of social role from one involving external forces to one involving decision making?

The discrepancy in the intellectual situation lies in the conflict between what C. P. Snow has called "the two cultures,"[2] the humanities and the natural sciences. The theologian, the philosopher, the artist on the one hand; the physicist, chemist, and biologist on the other — each has diametrically opposed views of man and society. For the humanists, man is morally responsible, a decision-making entity unique in the universe; for the natural scientists he is completely reducible to a set of laws external to himself which make both man and society indistiguishable from the natural universe.

In a world which is increasingly made by the natural sciences, the social sciences attempt to mediate between these irreconcilable intellectual positions and are, therefore, in the position of greatest tension, veering now in one direction and now in the other. Adequate guides for social living can no longer be derived entirely from theology, philosophy, or the insights of the artist; yet when the social sciences attempt to use the model of the natural sciences, they fail to grasp the essential quality of human conduct as one of decision making, of choice, of creativity, and also of self-destruction. There will be no solution to the dilemma; the antinomy is permanent; the social sciences will continue to veer now toward the humanistic pole and now toward the natural-science pole; but it is precisely from this tension that will come their perpetual creativity. Therefore the researcher's "mistake" in starting with a natural-science model of social role and ending with a humanistic model was no simple error but was one made likely by the structure of the intellectual situation in which he found himself.

Now the various applied social sciences, those professions which deal with human beings as social animals, inevitably suffer from these same tensions. The clergy is at the humanistic extreme, while law, social work, and the applied science of administration are less so. On the other hand, medicine and particularly surgery lie well toward the natural-science pole. Nursing, like sociology, is in the center, at the point of greatest tension.[3,4] This is because nursing deals with the ill person who, by social definition, is excused from making certain kinds of decisions for himself, is excused from performing the obligations of some of his social roles provided that he "acts like a sick person." A sick person is considered to be acting according to the external forces of the natural universe beyond his control. Yet nursing deals with the total individual. And since both the patient and the nurse are total individuals, products and producers of a society, nursing necessarily involves some identification of nurse with patient, with the patient's family, and some acceptance of the high moral value which is placed on health and the preservation of life. The task of the nurse is not made easier if the society places a high value on all individuals, irrespective of who they are, what they have done, or what they are likely to do when cured.[5,6,7]

Unless one understands that nursing as an applied social science is at this point of maximum tension between two irreconcilable sets of ideas in the realm of knowledge, the humanities, and the natural sciences, then one cannot understand or deal with practical problems of nursing. Basically it is, then, not peculiarities of this or that personality or idiosyncracies of this or that hospital or other system organization which produces the problems. The problems lie deep in the antinomies of human knowledge, and they can be approached rationally only in this grand context. Since sociology, among all the social sciences, lies at this point of maximum tension, it is not surprising that there should be so much affinity between it and nursing.

## "QUALITY NURSING"

"Quality nursing," it now becomes apparent, means the treatment of the individual not simply as an organism having certain physical, chemical, and biological properties which can be treated segmentally by a number of specialists, but also as an entity having a family, social-class, racial, ethnic, religious, and community background which affects his role behavior as a patient and an ill person. In addition, quality nursing in this sense must take into consideration that the patient's contacts with the health personnel, whether in the hospital or some other institutional setting, are for him general social relationships as well as specifically technological ones; so that his health or illness may be affected by the role he plays, or things he plays, in these social relationships.[8] It is for these reasons that nursing may be considered to be an applied *social* science.

## "THE SYSTEM": FUNCTIONS AND DYSFUNCTIONS

Like all social functions, nursing must take place within an institutional structure and may be performed within a variety of institutional structures — the general hospital by ward nurses, the community by public-health nurses, industry, the school,[9,10] the armed services, or frequently the home where the function is performed by a person acting in the diffuse role of wife or mother. The most intensive development of any function occurs in the closed institution, one which is more or less segregated from the outside world. The hospital, like the prison, is a type of closed institution. It defines the client or inmate as performing a specific role, that of an ill person rather than that of a total individual. But since the hospital is *closed,* so that the total life of the client is lived there during his illness, there is built into the hospital situation the maximum tensions between the humanities and the natural sciences. Insofar as the ill person must be dealt with as a total individual, then the hospital with its highly specialized technologies and its large and highly specialized staffs, and the consequent administrative necessity of dealing efficiently with large numbers of inmates in order to reduce unit costs, is the focal point of "the system" which may contain barriers to "quality nursing."[11-15]

The hospital in contemporary society is first of all not a therapeutic device but essentially an economic device. Conceivably it would be possible to bring all the hospital equipment and personnel to the home of the individual patient. Of course at the present stage in development in health technologies this would be exceedingly costly so that only very few patients would benefit from these services; while the economic drain on other institutional areas in the society, such as schools, civil government, and the like, might be so great as to render the running of the society impossible. The manifest therapeutic function of the hospital, that of curing people, may to some extent be performed in other institutional structures, technology and economic resources permitting. But it is possible that the hospital as an institutional structure may have latent therapeutic functions, functions which generally are not recognized by the clients, the staff, or the public, but which can be performed only by the social structure and the culture of a closed institution apart from the technological advantages. This matter will be returned to later.

Apart from the manifest dysfunctions which arise from the tensions between the humanities and the natural sciences, there is also in the hospital as a closed institution a source of tension which is not cultural but social in origin. This is the power struggle which focuses about three points — the medical staff, the nursing staff, and the administrative staff. The medical doctors, who are the high-status practitioners both in the hospital and in the community, generally are not employees of the organization; while the nurses, who have lower status as practitioners, remain in the hospital, usually being attached to a single ward, and hence have effective control of the therapeutic activities.[16-20]

Formal control by the medical staff, however, was not always the case in the Western world. In the European Middle Ages hospitals were owned and operated by religious orders, so that it was then the organized nursing staff which had both formal and effective control. However, both nursing and medical technologies were poorly developed, and it was not until the early nineteenth century that marked progress was made first in medicine and then, as a result of doctors realizing the need for trained nurses to help them administer the new techniques, in nursing as well. Thus doctors took the leadership both in reorganizing hospitals and in nursing training and so obtained formal control of hospitals although they were not necessarily members of the hospital organization. In the latter nineteenth century, particularly in England and above all in the United States, nurses increasingly took the lead in organizing themselves professionally rather than in religous orders; and at the same time nursing schools aided in the development of an increasingly autonomous nursing technology.[21, 22] It is likely that as nurses, the less mobile and the lower-status practitioners in the work organization, gain technological and professional autonomy from the more mobile and high-status practitioners, they will regain both formal and effective control. Increased control will likely further develop the nursing technology and decrease the conflict with the medical staff. Studies have shown that there is more cooperation between doctors and nurses in out-patient departments, where nurses have formal control of the work organization.[23]

The social and the cultural factors in the conflict are, however, independent variables. Studies have shown that in surgical and operating-room nursing there is the closest teamwork between the doctors and the nurses, and informal rapport, less so on the medical wards, and the greatest conflict on the psychiatric wards. Note that in surgery the patient is viewed most nearly as an organism and indeed in the operating room is generally unconscious, on the medical wards the patient is conscious and acts more as a human being with social activities, while on the psychiatric wards the patient's difficulties in-

volve to a high degree his total social relationships. Furthermore, in surgery
there is the greatest agreement among
all members of the team, doctors and
nurses alike, as to the nature of the patient; while in psychiatry there are a
number of schools of thought and practice ranging from lobotomy, shock treatment, and chemotherapy to psychoanalysis, to social psychiatry.[24,25,26] In
brief, as the intellectual basis of nursing
moves from the natural sciences to the
humanities, from surgery to psychiatry, tensions and conflicts increase because there is less and less agreement as
to the nature of the illness and the nature of the patient as a human being,
and hence less agreement as to the role
of the nurse.

These are some of the manifest therapeutic dysfunctions of the hospital as
these arise directly out of the high division of labor and depersonalization of
relationships with the patient. There are
also therapeutic dysfunctions which may
be termed *latent*, those which arise from
the cultural definitions of health and illness in the Western world. There is a
tendency for nurses to identify themselves with their patient, to feel guilt
over suffering and death, and to be subject to pressures, both imagined and actual, from colleagues, supervisors, members of the patient's family, not to
mention the pressures caused by legal responsibilities. Both formal and informal
structures are seized upon and developed
which serve to insulate the nurse from
contact with the patient as a total person
and to provide rituals which are rigidly
adhered to regardless of their appropriateness for particular cases. While such
latent dysfunctions would occur in any
institutional structure through which
nursing is performed, they are greater

in the intensiveness of the hospital as a
closed institution.[27,28]

## TWO DIRECTIONS OF SYSTEM REFORM

It is now time to consider how reforms
in an institutional system, in this case
the hospital, may occur in order to remove barriers to quality performance.
Such reforms may occur in two directions: first within the system itself, and
second through a softening of the boundaries which separate the system from
the outside world.

In the case of quality nursing, internal reforms in the hospital would seem
to be in the direction of technological
and administrative autonomy for the
nursing staff, thereby giving both formal and effective control to the group
which is "on the ground" and which is
also in a position where it must treat
the patient as a total human being. Such
a reform taken by itself could, however,
be only a transitional stage, for it would
result in the setting up of parallel and
competing authority structures whose
conflict would hardly be conducive to
quality performance of anything — certainly not restoring the patient to health
as a total human being. But increasingly
there is emerging in hospitals and in
other organizations the concept of "the
team," a work group composed of specialists in various fields, each an authority in his own field and therefore not an
authority in any other. In hospitals,
with a developing intellectual autonomy
in many fields, the team may be composed of specialists ranging along the
entire spectrum of knowledge, from the
surgeon on the one hand to the chaplain
on the other.[29,30] It may be suggested
that nursing, being at the point of great-

est intellectual tension, may for this reason be at the focus of coordination of the health team.

The second direction in which system reforms may occur lies in reducing the sharpness of the boundaries which separate the system from the rest of the society, that is, from other institutional systems. Changes from the custodial to the therapeutic function of the hospital, the shortening of the stay of patients (as in rapid ambulation after surgery or obstetrics), greater flexibility in visiting hours,[31,32] "living-in" privileges for the parents of the child patient, out-patient clinics, daytime and open wards in the mental hospital, the shifting of mentally ill patients from the specialized mental hospital to the psychiatric ward of the general hospital, public-health nursing, health education by nurse-teachers in the schools, endeavors to teach and motivate geriatric patients to live in relative independence outside of nursing homes — all of these activities have the effect of increasing the normality of the ill or disabled person, of keeping him as much as possible in the life of the community, in brief, of treating him as a total individual rather than a specialized role.

But it should be pointed out that such reductions in the sharpness of the boundaries separating the system from the outside world are not necessarily motivated by or result in improvement in quality nursing. Just as the hospital itself is an economizing device, so these other institutional changes may be devices to reduce financial cost per patient as health technologies become more expensive and as improved health care becomes along with education a civil right of the masses.[33] Before final decisions are made as to whether these changes in institutional structure result in quality

nursing, inquiries must be made as to whether the social deviant, now defined as an ill person, should have a vaguely or a sharply defined role, and also inquiries should be made as to the stage or stages in the therapeutic process in which his role definition should be changed from one direction to another. In brief, when should he "act like a sick person," and when should he "start to get well"?

## LATENT THERAPEUTIC FUNCTIONS OF HOSPITALS

An effective reform of "the system" cannot, in contemporary society, be simply that of putting the ill person in a less specialized system, such as leaving him in the home. Earlier it was pointed out that the hospital is essentially an economizing device at a given stage of technological development, and that as such it had a manifest therapeutic function. Now it remains to be seen whether the hospital has latent therapeutic functions as well. Quite apart from whether it would be economically possible to bring the hospital services to the patient rather than the patient into this closed institution, it must be remembered that the patient is a social deviant. As Talcott Parsons and Renee Fox point out in their essay, "Illness, Therapy, and the Modern Urban American Family," it may be necessary to define the patient as a special person and at some point in the therapy to isolate him from conforming individuals in order that he may become aware of the desirability of returning to conformity.[34]

Furthermore, as Parsons points out in another one of his essays, "Some Definitions of Health and Illness in the Light of American Values and Social Structure," illness is a culturally defined deviation, and some deviant behavior may be defined and treated as illness, as crime, as disloyalty, or as sin — each cultural definition carrying with it its specialized institutional structures for dealing appropriately with the deviation — medicine, penology, political police, the clergy. Thus the hospital not only specifies the ill person as a deviant but also specifies the kind of deviant he is supposed to be and how the rest of the society is supposed to act toward him.[35,36,37] Whatever may be the dysfunctions of the hospital system as presently organized, there may be serious consequences not only for therapy but also for the character of the society if one were simply to attack the system as such. The more remote as well as the more immediate consequences of the reform must be inquired into.

In addition, the very social structure of the hospital itself performs a latent therapeutic function — that of socialization. However desirable it may be for members of the hospital staff, particularly nurses, to be aware of the family, community, social class, racial-ethnic, and religious backgrounds of the patients,[38] the fact remains that an important latent therapeutic function of the hospital lies in that it does not reproduce the social atmosphere of the home but does require the patient to adjust himself to a situation involving wider, more specialized, and less personal social relationships — where neither his fellow patients, the staff, nor the organization itself represent his kinsmen or any of the personal groups of which he was a member in civilian life. Apart from the manifest therapy, he can be socialized into professional norms in the hospital experience, norms involving a more mature outlook on life.[39,40] Many institu-

tions in contemporary society perform this latent function.[41,42] For illness the problem is a delicate one, for the ill person is often withdrawing from the pressures of mature life and needs massive emotional support, yet he must ultimately be encouraged to enter normal and perhaps even greater life involvements.[43,44,45] It is just here that genuine nursing, not simply in the sense of taking care of the total individual as he is, but in the sense of further socialization as part of the therapeutic process, really begins.

The societal effect goes beyond the nurse-patient relationship, for presumably many people do not have enough hospital experience in their lifetime to profit from this resocialization. More important still is the symbolic function of the hospital and the health professions for the community and the society. To what extent are the hospital and the health professions able to represent themselves in people's minds as involving a standard of mature conduct? Quality nursing can effect the well no less than the ill.

## HISTORICAL CHANGES IN INSTITUTIONALIZATION

These observations regarding the two directions of reform of an institutional system, the one lying in decentralization and teamwork within the system, the other in the direction of reducing the sharpness of the boundaries which separate the system from the rest of the society, are not unique to nursing. Throughout a large part of the urbanized world one could almost hear it said today: "The System — barriers to quality — penology, soldiering, economic production, education, religiosity . . ." and so on.[46,47,48] And the solutions clinical research. Many of these installations would entail the employment of more nursing service administrators. The influence of these installations would be expected to extend among all the community hospitals and health agencies in the area served. The need for qualified nurses, therefore, would be extended to include these hospitals and health agencies. It is impossible to estimate the number of such nurses needed, but it would not be farfetched to conclude that a large proportion of nurses now employed would participate in some fashion in such programs, and many more nurses would be needed.

## LEVELS OF CARE

Let us speculate about levels of competence in care of patients with heart disease, cancer, and stroke. We can conclude that many would receive a portion of their care in intensive treatment units, myocardial infarction or coronary units, and the like. Nurses in these units would require specialized education at a level above that now given in our three types of basic educational programs—baccalaureate, associate degree, and diploma. So, also, would nurses to staff operating rooms. These nurses could be termed clinical specialists. Nurses to care for patients in other than intensive-care units of hospitals would need less specialized education than those in operating rooms and intensive care and other special units. They might, therefore, be expected to acquire needed new skills and continuous updating through in-service and short-term training.

It has been said that a nurse who was graduated five years ago and has not studied in this field since is seriously out of date. We have a double responsibility—to keep the teaching in basic programs up to date in this fast-moving area of practice and to provide continuing education for updating graduates in very large numbers. This involves close to 100 per cent of all nurses. Challenges to create new mass methods of continuing education exist: not the least of these would be the stimulation of self-directed study in well-designed programs.

We need careful thinking about what skills are general and what are special in order to guide planning of study programs for practical nurses and registered professional nurses, and in-service education programs, continuing education, and graduate education. The report of the Second National Conference on Cardiovascular Diseases (November 1964), soon to be published, will be useful in solving these problems. The portions of this report that pertain to nursing are also to be published separately and distributed widely.

Community nursing agencies will need nurses who know how to give expert, up-to-date service to these patients and their families at home and in clinics and community centers, and how to contribute to the organized continuum of care for each patient. These agencies will need consultation services, expert supervisors, and specialist in-service-training experts. Agencies could be expected to share with each other and with hospitals some of these expert services for their nursing personnel.

## CLINICAL SPECIALISTS

All this speculation about kinds of specialists raises questions about clinical specialization on the graduate level. Do we need medical-surgical nursing specialists for this purpose? Or medical nursing specialists and surgical nursing specialists? Or cardiovascular disease (including stroke) nursing specialists and cancer nursing specialists? Or medical-cardiovascular-disease and surgical-cardiovascular-disease specialists? Can the depth and breadth of knowledge and skill needed be achieved in a master's degree program? What portions of the needed learning will require post-master's study?

The challenges of programs like those recommended by the Commission on Heart Disease, Cancer, and Stroke catch us at a stage of making up our minds about answers to such questions. It can accelerate our "principle formulation" and decisions. We are already questioning the lack of depth of science instruction in basic programs. Clinical specialization in heart, cancer, and stroke only emphasizes the need for a better background in biological, physical, social, and behavioral sciences at both the basic and graduate levels. Perhaps we shall decide that the nurse clinical specialist who cares for patients can learn her specialty at the master's level. With required clinical practice and increased scientific content, such masters' programs might be two years in length. And for clinical specialists who are also teachers, consultants, in-service education instructors, administrators, and supervisors in the field of heart, cancer, and stroke nursing, post-master's education would be necessary. For some, including those who expect to do research, this should be doctoral or post-doctoral study.

Proceeding from our present stage of unreadiness, we shall be forced to depend on short-term training for more of this preparation than we would like. Even the job of finding short-term trainers seems staggering. But the development of facilities and programs

for patients with heart disease, stroke, and cancer will take time. Nursing can use that time, beginning now. Setting our goals for levels of education for various kinds of specialists will prevent the stage of stopgap, short-term training from becoming permanent. It will place present and future needs for short-term training in the perspective of total needs for education in this field.

## COORDINATION

This is a big order of great complexity. Where do we begin and who does what? How can we coordinate our actions, share responsibility, and avoid duplication of effort? Only a few of the independent and collaborative actions can be mentioned here.

The question of how many graduate programs we need to prepare nurse specialists and of what kinds of programs and where these programs should be located involves: (1) the universities; (2) those nurses and other professional people and public-minded citizens who are knowledgeable about community and regional needs; (3) and the nurse clientele of the programs. The leagues (National League for Nursing, state and local) with members representing all of these, the special interest organizations (medical, hospital, and public health, heart, and cancer, for example), the regional educational organizations (Southern Regional Education Board, Western Interstate Commission for Higher Education, and the New England Board of Higher Education), and the professional organizations for nurses (the American Nurses' Association and state and district associations) are all concerned with these decisions. We have an acute need for an organizational design for such cooperative planning for educational programs in nursing in which so many people have a stake.

Obviously the universities have ultimate responsibility for decisions as to whether they do or do not start new programs; but the mobilization of nurse thinking (the job of the ANA), and the consolidation of thinking of directors and faculties of graduate programs (the job of the National League for Nursing Councils of Member Agencies in the Department of Baccalaureate and Higher Degree Programs) are essential elements in university decisions and successes. Perhaps collaboration with all the other agencies comes only at the regional and state levels, though one can see values in national planning which involves some of these other interests. A good start on tackling this nationwide planning problem could be made by the ANA-NLN Coordinating Council acting on substantive staff papers on the subject, delegating responsibilities, and guiding actions of state coordinating councils.

The formulation and application of criteria of excellence to these graduate programs are the functions of the League's accreditation program, involving member agencies and departments and contacts with their accrediting agencies.

The task of helping public-health nursing agencies with improving and expanding community nursing services for heart, cancer, and stroke patients and their families can be undertaken fruitfully by the League's Council of Member Agencies in public-health nursing with collaborations similar to those discussed above as pertinent, emphasizing particularly those with the public health, heart, and cancer associations.

The task of including expanded functions in the definition of nursing is the task of ANA. Nursing and other researches in heart disease, cancer, and stroke are already showing the direction in which some of these expansions will go. Formulation of functions, standards, and qualifications of all types of nurse clinical specialists and of in-service education directors, both so important to expansion of services to patients with heart disease, cancer, and stroke, might be sparked by the planning done in this special area of nursing practice. Incidentally, it should be reported that the nursing section of the Second National Conference on Cardiovascular Diseases recommended to the ANA that these two positions be added to those for which ANA has already formulated functions, standards, and qualifications.

The task of providing improved in-service training in the nursing of patients with heart disease, cancer and stroke for nurses in hospitals, nursing homes, and public-health nursing agencies is a concern of the ANA and NLN and of employing agencies and related associations, among them the American Hospital Association, the nursing home, and practical nursing organizations. Cooperative planning might well be facilitated through action of the Coordinating Council and collaboration by the staffs of the two nursing organizations. Guides and manuals with content on this field of nursing should be produced for use of in-service education directors in all kinds of employing agencies. Short-term training programs for teachers in in-service education programs should be a part of this effort.

Almost every section of ANA will be involved in improving practices of their members in the area of heart disease, cancer, and stroke. The ANA clinical conferences should be stepped up, as should all efforts at the production of clinical papers, particularly in the field of heart disease, cancer, and stroke.

The responsibility for continuing education outside the employing institutions is shared by schools who are concerned with keeping their graduates up to date and with the quality of services in their communities, by employing agencies (who can work together through their League Councils of Member Agencies) and by "the profession" whose agent is the ANA. Here again, collaborative effort is desirable and the coordinating councils (national, state) can promote it.

Nursing research should be encouraged by all possible means. In addition, it should be included in studies supported by special funds for research in heart disease, cancer, and stroke—federal and other. The American Nurses' Foundation might attempt to give emphasis to research in these areas as a means of promoting the production of new knowledge supportive to the expanded effort on all fronts for improved care of these patients.

The Public Health Service and other constituents of the Department of Health, Education, and Welfare have expanding programs, personnel, and funds to promote improvement of services for patients with heart disease, cancer, and stroke, for community services, and for training and research grants. The professional nurse traineeship program can now be used for preparation for clinical specialization as well as for teaching, supervision, and administration, both long-term and short-term training. Fellowships for training for research are available.

New actions are needed. Central to all action for nursing in this field are the ANA and NLN. While taking a holistic view is important, all potential actions cannot be delayed until the whole plan is made and parts delegated. Wise direction from staff and boards of the two organizations is required, and they are set up for coordinated and collaborative planning and action. The coordinating councils (national and state) become strategic in unified planning and action. Working papers on the nature, scope, and interrelatedness of actions prepared by nurses and others, both specialists in the heart, cancer, and stroke field and specialists in program organization, should be presented to the coordinating council to promote clarity in thinking and choice of goals. Collaboration by staffs of the two organizations is essential. With these potentials of our organizations, our specialists, our education and service institutions under competent leadership, we have exciting prospects for contributing to the national program to conquer heart disease, cancer, and stroke.

The patterns for cooperative planning and effort designed for promotion of heart disease, cancer, and stroke services and education could serve as prototypes for other planning in which nurses will be engaged, either in relation to the development of nursing itself or as participants in the designing of general and other special health programs.

We can be grateful to the Commission on Heart Disease, Cancer, and Stroke for its thorough analysis of this area of human health needs and the challenge its report gives to the nursing profession for planning resources to meet these needs.

# Epilogue to Part Two

As we stated earlier, society has both normative and action systems. The former system consists of norms, values, mores, and law; the latter consists of human behavior. Society also has certain functions—familial, economic, political, religious, and educational—which are regarded as essential for the maintenance of its existence. Norms and values become centralized around these functions in a configuration called institution. Changes occurring in any one of the institutions bring about changes in the others. The various institutions are tied together by intermutual dependence. When the normative and action systems of the various institutions are coordinated, there is social organization. Whenever social norms become conflicting, ambiguous, or cease to exist, a temporary state of disequilibrium occurs which may give rise to a variety of social movements. The types of individual and group reactions to various societal changes vary considerably. The table on page 98 indicates the kinds of consequences that may occur as a result of profound societal changes.

Many of the changes indicated in the table are in part a reaction to cultural lag. Frequently societal changes such as war and economic fluctuations create behavioral changes long before changes in value systems occur. Adopting new programs and innovations may take a long time, since values must be changed before acceptance. Programs or innovations that do not require changes in values are accepted more readily.

The extent of the lag is based to some extent on the degree to which diffusion and adoption takes place. The rate of diffusion of cultural changes or innovations varies, but the process is, as Lazarsfeld indicates, fairly well known. Frequently the initial information is diffused through the mass media. The actual acceptance of change or innovation, however, takes place through personal contacts of the individual with influential opinion leaders in his reference groups. So it is that new drugs are adopted by physicians, new curricula implemented by schools, and new treatments and attitudes accepted by the larger community.

The government also is both affected by and a creator of change. Within broad legislative enactments are specific programs that affect health and welfare. As indicated earlier, the new experiential social movement is particularly conducive to creating concern within the government for creating and implementing such programs. Without this type of social movement, some of the current legislation would be neither practical nor possible. After legislation, however, there may still be a delay because resources are not yet available for implementing the change. For example, it may take years to educate or train individuals who will be able to carry out these innovations.

The health professionals who are constantly aware of societal changes can anticipate new ones and can prepare long-range plans to alleviate possible gaps. Again, medicare exemplifies a program in which gaps must be filled before it can be fully implemented. Posthospital extended care facilities exist in only a few

## Types and Consequences of Social Disequilibrium or Disorganization

| Types | Consequences | |
|---|---|---|
| | Personal | Social |
| 1. Anomie | ⋏ mental illness<br>⋏ suicide | ⋏ unrest |
| 2. Mass immigration or emigration | ⋏ confusion<br>⋏ physical illness<br>⋎ suicide | ⋏ ghost town<br>⋏ juvenile delinquency<br>⋎ marriage rates |
| 3. Alienation | ⋏ mental illness<br>⋏ suicide<br>⋏ physical illness | ⋏ adult crime<br>⋏ juvenile delinquency<br>⋏ divorce |
| 4. Catastrophe | | |
|   A. natural, i.e. tornado | ⋎ suicide<br>⋎ temporary disorganization and confusion followed by organization | personal—increase in anomie followed by immediate decrease in alienation and increase in cohesion |
|   B. war | ⋎ suicide<br>⋎ neurosis<br>⋎ alienation | ⋏ organization<br>⋎ divorce<br>⋏ marriage<br>⋏ delinquency<br>⋎ adult crime<br>⋏ anomie<br>⋏ birth rate (immediate postwar) |
| 5. Economic depression | ⋏ neurosis<br>⋏ suicide<br>⋏ alienation | ⋏ divorce<br>⋎ marriage<br>⋎ birth rate<br>⋏ disorganization<br>⋏ anomie<br>⋏ social movements<br>⋏ adult crime<br>⋎ delinquency |
| 6. Economic inflation | ⋏ neurosis<br>⋏ psychosis<br>⋏ alienation | ⋏ marriage<br>⋏ anomie<br>⋎ adult crime<br>⋏ delinquency<br>⋏ divorce |
| 7. Death (single) | ⋏ depression<br>⋎ alienation | ⋏ anomie |
|   Death (multiple) | ⋏ alienation, i.e. war camps, epidemics, etc.<br>⋎ suicide<br>⋏ depression | ⋏ anomie |

⋏=increase; ⋎=decrease.

places throughout the United States. Since passage of medicare, however, veterans' hospitals and private institutions have begun planning to build and maintain semidomiciliary hospital institutions.

Passage of medicare has far-reaching effects on the role of health workers and health. Convalescent hospitals will continue to increase in number. More care will be given in the home. The hospital will be viewed increasingly as only a "stopgap" in the care of the sick. With the increase in federal insurance and funds for care of the sick, county hospitals will be reorganized around other than indigent persons. New helping personnel will emerge. It is possible that legislation will be passed to care for other age groups. Hospital structure and policies will have to be changed further. Roles of staff will be reidentified with an increasing overlapping of the roles and functions of all the health workers.

Although the availability of monies for various types of care, research, and study in specific areas is inevitable and necessary, it has created many problems for educators within the professional groups as well as for practitioners. For the educator one of the major problems is the determination of specialization areas on which school support should focus. Should all schools attempt to prepare all specialists in all areas where money is allocated? This is one of the quandaries in which health educators find themselves today. Though the demand in health work is for a generalist who can function in many situations with varied types of patients, the money has been allocated for specialists (in areas as cardiac, tuberculosis, neurological care, and treatment).

This trend toward highly specialized professionals will probably continue as the vast amount of scientific knowledge makes it virtually impossible to encompass a total discipline such as medicine. For the patient and the practitioner, these highly specialized individuals create problems. For the patient to have a semblance of total patient care, he must come in contact with a variety of specialists frequently just for diagnostic purposes, but at the same time a large number of individuals viewing a patient tends to dehumanize him. Despite the fact that the value orientation is toward total patient care, the reality of the need for specialists may require a change in this value. One possible solution would be to have the generalist work closer to the patient, calling in the specialist only as needed.

The health worker has a responsibility and is in a unique position to initiate changes in health practices and in health education. Communitywide changes are usually best instigated and enacted through voluntary and professional organizations. An example of how voluntary and professional organizations can function together to improve health care was demonstrated in San Francisco in 1964. For many years the mental-health facilities were known to be inadequate for the needs of the community; however, small interest groups had very little influence on the political leaders toward appropriating funds to improve the situation. So the San Francisco Chapter of the Mental Health Association called together representatives from thirty professional and voluntary organizations to study the mental-health facilities and make recommendations for change. The press cooperated by printing the findings and recommendations. The combined pressure from these professionals, voluntary agencies, and press resulted in the passage of appropriations for a new mental-health center.

# PART THREE

## *The Routes to Becoming: The Professions*

The process of becoming a professional is a process of adult socialization. Thus the health professions, like others, are affected by culture, class, and communication processes. As in any other role position, social forces and trends influence each individual toward or away from particular life goals, as stated by Orzack. The decision to become a health professional is influenced by perceptions of positive and negative consequences which are weighed in one manner or another.

As the individual interacts within his family, peer, or work groups, he is socialized into a way of thinking, believing, and acting which becomes known as team effort if he engages in the process of becoming a professional. If effective, this effort results in a cooperative type of interacting and behaving. It requires the skills of role taking in that the team notion involves a cooperative venture of negotiation and renegotiation. That is, compromises of values and action must occur before the team can become a functioning whole.

If the team effort includes a very large group of people, it may become a profession. This implies the possession of a particular body of formal and informal knowledge and skills. A profession requires not only formal education, with emphasis on altruistic service to mankind, but also an informal, internalized system of ethics used in practicing the role of professional. Because the profession regulates the education of its practitioners, it requires a sense of loyalty, obligation, and cooperation with the group known as "we." The processes by which one becomes a professional are not totally dissimilar. McLemore and Hill state the case for nursing while Bloom elucidates the studies of the socialization of physicians. These studies show that the content of knowledge necessary for achieving professional status may vary, but the processes are not totally unlike each other. The process that one undergoes in becoming a health professional, however, may further the gap between practitioner and patient.

It is not always sufficient to say that differences between patients and health professionals are related to socioeconomic and educational backgrounds. There are other inter- as well as intrapersonal differences that operate. Individuals do not always act in the same manner, for each holds many different systems of logic that he uses simultaneously or intermittently. To some extent these competing or contradictory uses of logic are built into the systems and institutions in which individuals are socialized.

As can be seen in the following paradigm, there are five major belief orientations. The world of the patient may include one or more of these. The world of each professional group, however, has a system of primary beliefs, as we indicate. This paradigm is not meant to imply that these are the only beliefs and logical systems from which action emanates. But it does indicate the primary emphasis of each of these socialized groups. It also points out the areas in which

101

PARADIGM OF BELIEF ORIENTATIONS

| Field | Action | Goals | Primary time orientation | Participant orientation | Validity or truth |
|---|---|---|---|---|---|
| Magic | Ritual | Control | Present | Participant to supernatural | Ritual performance |
| Religion* | Prayer | Salvation | Future | Participant to clergy to supernatural | God |
| Philosophy | Thought | Utopia† | Future | Participant to universe | Ideal absolute |
| Science | Methodology through senses | Prediction and control | Present, future | Participant to sample | Relative |
| Problem solving | Pragmatic action through technology | Temporary relief | Present | Participant to recipient | What works |
| Medicine | Ritual, senses and methodology, pragmatic action, technology, symptomatic treatment | Prediction and control, temporary relief, care and prevention | Present, future | 1–1‡ | Ritual performance, relative, what works |
| Surgery | ritual, pragmatic action or technology | Control (may be temporary or permanent cure) | Present | 1–1 | Ritual performance, what works, absolute |
| Psycho-analysis | Ritual, thought, talk, and introspection | Control, utopia, resolution of conflict, and change of behavior | Past | 1–1 | Ritual performance, unconscious |
| Nursing | Ritual, thought, senses, pragmatic action, technology, symptomatic treatment | Control and temporary relief | Present | 1–1 or team–1 | Ritual performance, what works, relative |
| Public health | Thought, senses, methodology, pragmatic action, technology | Prediction and control (prevention), utopia | Future | Participant to universe | Relative |

*Religion: refers to organized religion in the United States.
†Utopia: ideal way of living.
‡1–1: participant to patient.

beliefs of one professional group are similar to and different from the major beliefs of other professional groups. The paradigm makes clear why problems do exist in patient-professional and professional-professional relationships.

As we suggest, man is constantly confronted with a series of individual, professional, and/or institutional conflicts, many of which stem from social movements and change, family structure, individual and group socialization, and health and illness. Such conflicts may lead to barriers in quality care, as developed by Smith. For not every professional can meet and adapt to the challenge of ambiguous or conflicting confrontations. For some, the confrontations become a challenge, for others an albatross. As Schatzman points out, we may internalize the notion of "I am an X professional," but never become a "pro" in the sense of living and acting within, but also beyond, the specific mandates of the profession in which we practice.

# 10. SOCIAL FORCES AND MANPOWER

## Louis H. Orzack

The purpose of this paper is to assess some of the relations between social forces and the recruiting of manpower and its training, use, and retention. In the area of mental retardation these are especially difficult problems, problems for which many solutions have been offered. And as one sees the current and prospective increases in the number and kinds of organizational and community programs for the retarded, one readily imagines that the many problems already associated with manpower will multiply. Thus it may be helpful to those in the field of mental retardation to look at the discussions and appraisals of economists and sociologists of current trends in the field and of what may be in store.

First, we shall briefly discuss manpower in the organizational settings in which services are provided to the residential retarded[1] and consider the manners in which behavior patterns of staff members are structured in these institutions. Second, we shall review the impact or probable impact of broader social forces and trends on manpower recruitment and utilization in the field of mental retardation.

Concerning organizational settings, two major points stand out as striking to a sociologist. The first is that in the residential institutions there is a good deal of role conflict. This means some-thing fairly simple, namely that the ways in which staff members organize and pattern their daily rounds of task performance bring them into conflict with each other. The physicians, psychologists, psychiatrists, social workers, nurses, teachers, counselors, rehabilitators, and physical and occupational therapists do not agree and probably cannot be expected to agree in their conceptions of the nature of mental retardation, in their views of the developmental prospects of the residents, or in their assessments of the worth of each others' work and capabilities. By virtue of their diverse educational backgrounds and the significant differences in the kinds of work experience that often precede their involvement in the field of retardation, staff members approach their work with widely varied notions of what they are supposed to do and how they are supposed to act.[2]

This conflict has historic roots and is often quite independent of the psychological make-up of the persons engaged in conflict. It goes back to the manner in which institutions for the retarded have developed in the United States and to the degree of priority that work with the retarded has had in the various professions and occupations. This may be put in the form of a general proposition that the residential centers for the retarded historically have not

Revised by Louis H. Orzack as a contribution to this book from the original presentation at the Mental Health Institute on Manpower and Expanding Retardation Programs, Edward R. Johnstone Training and Research Center, Bordentown, N.J., December 1965.

had a high social priority in the allocation of scarce economic and social resources. Both governmental and private support, although occasionally lavish for particular institutions or in selected regions, has been less than that which would provide professionally satisfactory care and treatment. A reflection of this may be seen in the (now disappearing) belief that the centers should be economically self-sufficient and should be located in out-of-the-way places that are both salubrious and invisible. This was based, of course, on the view that the colonies were necessary to prevent both the retardate and society from harming one another, coupled with the belief that retardates were a necessary burden.[3]

This meant having a low priority in the claim on society's resources, and these resources include manpower. Primarily the dedicated, who were perhaps by chance the competent, accepted assignments in these centers. In any event the systematic patterning and organization of the tasks for their assignments or roles was also largely neglected by the established organized professions. This was due in part to the then existing state of knowledge concerning retardation and of course the then existing body of attitudes, beliefs, and stereotypes concerning retardates. Whatever the orgin of this neglect, the effect was that the established, organized professions did not encourage their members to select retardation as a field, and did not provide those who did make that choice with ready-made and useful guidelines to behavior.[4]

This suggests that the role-defined patterns of behavior have had to be developed by local improvisation, and that these patterns have not been evaluated, codified, and extended systematically through the sanctioned channels that exist in the various professions. Three processes have contributed to this: (1) Insufficient scientific study and research has been supported in the field of retardation. (2) The men and women who have worked in retardation have not received adequate guidelines for their work from the organized health, welfare, and education professions or from the leaders of these professions. (3) An extensive, informed, and interested set of representatives of the professions has not been a characteristic feature of the field of retardation.

As a consequence of these factors, professionals and nonprofessionals who have worked in this field have largely been on their own. Within the residential centers we have seen the extensive development of what sociologists call work groups, and these seem to have been the dominant feature of the kind of social organization that has developed there.[5] In these kinds of settings, improvisation has dominated rather than innovation informed by a clear-cut set of professional imperatives. Programs have developed, but these have been adaptive to immediate problems, and have represented solutions very often worked out on a trial-and-error basis. We have not seen these overtaken by thoughtful, scientifically based, and professionally supported norms such as might be assumed to be associated with the conceptions of professionals who constitute any interested colleague group. This suggests that there has been a rather gigantic failure on the part of the professions which have neglected, ignored, and therefore not coped with the manifold problems of the mentally retarded.

The individual professionals and nonprofessional staff members have imported into the residential facilities conceptions of their work and views of the mentally retarded that largely seem to be vestiges and partial misapplications of ideas and perceptions acquired in other training and work contexts. Little general agreement seems to exist concerning the nature of retardation, the problems of the retardate, his family and community, and how best either to conceptualize or to handle the situation. The result often is a focused attention on factors of care which are common to most institutions: mere physical survival, maintenance of clean wards and play rooms, and reduction of per capita costs. In some cases these become the goals; in all cases they directly influence a sizable proportion of money spent and manpower used. (In Massachusetts these costs for the retarded average about 25 per cent of expenditures for the care of the emotionally disturbed children.)

The individual professionals and staff members vary widely in their views and activities. Very many occasions arise in the daily care, management, and treatment of the retarded in which conflicts occur. Such conflicts may range from such relatively minor matters, such as the appropriate timing for classes and training programs, to questions of large theoretical import, such as the extent to which learning reinforcement programs that stress social learning and development can either intrude on nursing-care time or can be incorporated into the roles of nurses and attendants. Such conflicts might occur over whether experimental and demonstration programs for a limited number of residents ought to be developed and continued perhaps temporarily by volunteers or students at the cost of bypassing and possibly offending the regular attend-

dant nursing personnel. Other examples of conflict may be found in the manner in which newly funded programs for rehabilitation, education, and research may seem to contravene the authority, competence, and worth of the regular staff, or in the introduction of nursery-school programs and teachers into a nursery area previously controlled without question or threat by physicians and nursing staff.[6]

Role conflicts of this sort can be found, I believe, in very many residential centers, although the specific illustrations I have provided undoubtedly can be altered to accommodate differing situations. The implications of such conflicts are important in assessing the structure of residential centers and they point to another important feature: the relative lack of well-supported guidelines as to the way in which authority should be exercised. Do we yet know if these centers are to be called hospitals, schools (in the academic sense), training centers, or rehabilitation facilities; should we employ primarily physicians and nurses, teachers and educators, child-development specialists and social workers, or sociologists and social workers? Do we know how and when to integrate these organizations with other existing community centers and facilities; do we place them close to centers of population and in proximity to university research centers and other schools? On what basis do we encourage staff members of the residential institution to be flexible, adaptive, and supportive in their relationships with the children, so that, for example, they *can* be willing and ready to spend much time in helping an individual child learn how to dress or eat, perhaps at the cost of slowing down the dressing or the eating of other children on the ward, and perhaps interfering with the daily routines of housekeepers and porters, of cooks and laundry personnel?

It strikes me that our state of knowledge about mental retardation and mental retardates, as well as the management techniques we employ, is relatively primitive, and that there is a great gap between the problems that residential staff members confront when they provide care and the theoretical principles of the various helping professions. The model that has been followed in the past in operating residential retardate centers is largely what might be called a physical care model; current theory and fashion stress a human developmental model. A general set of principles concerning how they are to be integrated seems to be missing, and ways in which their combination may be translated into the resources of staff abilities, staff assignments, and time, space, and equipment that are found within these settings are generally absent. This is my second point about organizations.

There are many ways, of course, in which guidelines are acquired by the staff when professional or institutional rules either are absent or in conflict. These are unofficial but known to anyone who has confronted daily problems at work. One may ask the old guard or the residents, apply one's former experiences to any new situation, or perhaps simply muddle through. Indeed, "do what you can" may be the reply to a question addressed to a supervisor by an attendant, and as long as the resident is not abused or maltreated in a public way, some kind of care will be provided. Solutions will somehow be found to workaday problems in this fashion, but clearly the role obligations into which solutions of this kind must be translated are likely to have limited usefulness.

The main reason for the wide variety of role obligations of manpower in the mental retardation field is found, it seems to me, in this very process. Roles have not been secured to a widely known and accepted body of professional principles from which they derive.

The roles of attendants, nurses, training-school teachers, physicians, and other care personnel have developed in helter-skelter fashion from principles, to be sure, but the principles often have been rather distorted and constricted. One principle for determining the responsibilities of aides and attendants may be "what worked in the last place I was at," and that place might have been a general hospital, a prison, a school, or a clinic, fields having many criteria different from those of retardation.

This format for establishing and justifying the roles and obligations of professional and subprofessional staff permits too many degrees of freedom to the staff members of particular residential centers, and encourages, I submit, the tendency toward looking only for common denominators in treatment mentioned earlier. New approaches to control, institutional renovation, innovations, and experimentation in care and treatment programs—any of these may be introduced to these centers only to confront staff resistance at any level of responsibility, often at all levels. But this is not a simple personally based antagonism to change of any kind. Change is tolerated in our society. The resistance and antagonism derive, it seems to me, from the simpler fact that in the residential centers for the retarded, the sources of control, authority, and change behavior that are considered legitimate by the staff have been largely internal to each institution. And efforts toward change that have been begun by qualified professionals and by interested nonprofessionals — by parents, volunteers, and others — have not been mounted on a broad enough scale over a long enough period of time on more than a demonstration basis to sustain the impact of momentary changes.

Whether the changes proposed have been sufficiently imaginative and creative, I cannot of course say with finality. But I would suggest that the necessity for imagination and creativity in both the formation of service orientations and goals and in the ways of implementing these goals is daily becoming more essential.

For we are slowly and somewhat awkwardly moving toward a society of increased abundance, toward a Great Society, to be sure, but one in which categorical handicaps and social stigma may still be associated.

New social, psychological, and medical techniques give promise of prevention of at least certain types of mental retardation and of the reduction of disabilities associated with them. Community facilities are being enhanced and these may provide greater opportunities for a fuller participation by the mentally retarded in society. Whether sufficient numbers of prepared personnel will be provided for the pattern of services that will be desirable is, however, problematical. Several factors account for putting this as a question. The first is the probable multiplication of the numbers of personnel in this field which an expansion of services may well require.[7] Second, we are seeing almost everywhere in the arena of social-welfare services predictions of great increases in manpower demand, and this means that competition for recruits to the fields in question will intensify.[8] Third, we may continue to see, although

possibly in different forms, continuance of the social ambivalence toward the retarded that exists now, and this may continue to discourage recruitment.[9]

The ambivalence toward the retarded that seems a part of our culture, and the hostility that may be part of that ambivalence, does not appear to rest on an economic base. The retarded may be excluded from all sorts of social and civic opportunities, but not as a result of a threat they pose to the achievement of others. The mentally retarded do not seem to prevent other people from getting ahead, from acquiring desired roles in our occupational, social, religious, educational, recreational, or familial institutions. It seems to me that the source of the culturally perceived threat comes from the other end of the continuum, from the very fact that the retarded either cannot or are prevented from, but in any case, are not, competing with others. They are dependent, some totally so, and their sustenance requires a commitment of resources and time that historically and culturally we may ordinarily be ready to give to anyone who competes effectively for these resources.

It may be true that we are becoming an affluent society, but ours is also a society with deprivation and a structured lack of opportunity; it is also a society in which achievement is the norm, one in which the possession of the right kind of educational certificates increasingly comes to mean almost guaranteed access to positions that carry prestige and other rewards; it can surprisingly be moving toward a tighter social structure, with categories of status set off by age, education, and sex; it may be a society where the residues of mistreatment of generations of human beings on the basis of mental retardation may continue for a very long time.

sought lie sometimes within the institutions through which the professional functions are performed, sometimes in softening the boundaries, sometimes in both directions. Is it simply accidental that this problem occurs in so many institutional areas in the contemporary world?

There seem to be periods of history in which institutional systems build up and segregate themselves and other periods in which they decentralize internally and often at the same time reduce the sharpness of their boundaries against the outside world. Hospitals, for centuries during the Western Middle Ages and early modern times existing as places for the custodial care of the sick poor (usually where these people could die), became in the latter nineteenth century places for the cure of the rich, and by the mid-twentieth century the location of a considerable part of medical practice.[49,50] Prisons, for centuries places where people were confined prior to being taken out for punishment or places where punishment occurred, became in the eighteenth century the chief instrument of punishment itself.[51] Both hospitals and prisons reached maximum development by the mid-twentieth century, by which time decentralization trends such as out-patient clinics, public-health nursing, probation, parole, and reduction in the size of the institution were beginning.[52,53,54] In the army, close-order combat developed in the seventeenth century, giving way in the nineteenth and twentieth centuries to more and more open-order combat[55,56] and finally even to tendencies toward guerilla warfare. Internally, military institutions are undergoing decentralization and the development of team rather than line-of-command authority, much to the genuine anguish of the older type professional soldier who finds it difficult or impossible to give up the moral commitments of a lifetime and of an ancient tradition of soldiering.[57] Similar trends and similar problems arise in the development of teamwork in industry at all levels of decision making all the way from production workers to top policy makers. In education there are trends away from formal classroom teaching to the use of group projects, conferences, and independent study; in some colleges there are work-study programs while in others students are in greater numbers leaving at the end of the sophomore year for a sojourn "in the world" before returning to continue their formal education. In religion there are both decentralizing trends within institutions, such as the recent move toward collegial authority for the Roman Catholic bishops in making Church policy, and boundary modifications. Clergymen are entering teaching instead of parish churches, are becoming chaplains or religious directors in colleges, are moving into various kinds of nonparish community activities, and are being trained in theological schools to serve as members of medical teams in hospitals. The case of the French priest-workers after World War II, a movement which was suppressed by the Vatican on grounds that the lack of institutional segregation left the priests as vulnerable to Marxian indoctrination by the workers as the workers were to Christian proselyting,[58] opens a question as to the functional limits of boundary softening. Finally, it should be pointed out that the conjugal family itself as an institution became in the Western world from the sixteenth century onward increasingly centralized in authority and at the same time segregated from the rest of society; and that today this very limited institution is showing clear signs of incapacity to bear the burdens of modern society and that its functions are being increasingly shared by the community and the larger society. This problem is ably discussed by the French historian, Philippe Aries, in his excellent book, *Centuries of Childhood.*[59]

## SOME APPLICATIONS TO QUALITY NURSING

Now what do these facts regarding the historical fluctuations in institutionalization have to do with the system problems of quality nursing? How can nursing best go about solving these problems?

It can do so not simply by looking exclusively within itself but by looking outward to other professions, by being willing and able to sit about the conference table with representatives from penology, the military, industry, education, religion, and so on, by exchanging professional experiences, and by being able *systematically* to compare the similarities and differences in problems and attempted solutions. Nursing, as the applied social science which stands at the point of greatest tension between the humanities and the natural sciences, can best solve its problems (at least those concerned with institutional systems) by contributing to a *simultaneous* solution of system problems along with other professions which, in their intellectual backgrounds, stand at various points along the spectrum of knowledge.

And it is through a movement of nursing into the community, not simply in bringing its therapy outside the hospital but especially in meeting with other professions in a joint consideration of the functions which each have in the community as a social system, that there is the greatest possibility of a simultaneous solution of system problems.

1. Dagmar Brodt, "The Neophyte Nurse: A Role Expectation Study," *Nursing Research*, 13, 1964, 255–258. Quote from p. 258.

2. C. P. Snow, *The Two Cultures*, New York: Cambridge University Press, 1963; and *A Second Look: An Expanded Version of the Two Cultures and the Scientific Revolution*, New York: New American Library (Mentor), 1964.

3. Esther Lucile Brown, *Newer Dimensions of Patient Care*, Part 1: *The Use of the Physical and the Social Environment of the General Hospital for Therapeutic Purposes*, New York: Russell Sage Foundation, 1961, pp. 140–142.

4. Temple Burling et al., *The Give and Take in Hospitals: A Study in Human Organization in Hospitals*, New York: Putnam, 1956, pp. 81–160.

5. Esther Lucile Brown, *Newer Dimensions of Patient Care*, Part 2: *Improving Staff Motivation and Competence in the*

*General Hospital*, New York: Russell Sage Foundation, 1962, pp. 183–187.

6. Everett C. Hughes et al., *Twenty Thousand Nurses Tell Their Story*, Philadelphia: Lippincott, 1958, pp. 182–183.

7. Sam Schulman, "Basic Functional Roles in Nursing: Mother Surrogate and Healer," in E. Gartley Jaco (Ed.), *Patients, Physicians, and Illness*, Glencoe, Ill.: Free Press, 1958, pp. 528–537.

8. Esther Lucile Brown, *Newer Dimensions of Patient Care*, Part 3: *Patients as People*, New York: Russell Sage Foundation, 1964.

9. Robert W. Habenstein and Edwin A. Christ, *Professionalizer, Traditionalizer, and Utilizer*, Columbia, Mo.: University of Missouri Press, 1955, pp. 16–23.

10. Hughes et al., *op. cit.*, pp. 62–122.

11. Burling et al., *op. cit.*

12. Erving Goffman, "On the Characteristics of Total Institutions," in his *Asylums: Essays in the Social Situation*

of *Mental Patients and Other Inmates*, Garden City, N.Y.: Doubleday (Anchor), 1961, pp. 1–124.

13. Habenstein and Christ, *op. cit.*

14. Hughes et al., *op. cit.*, pp. 72–79, 123–185.

15. E. Gartley Jaco, "Introduction: Medicine and Behavioral Science," in his *Patients, Physicians, and Illness, op. cit.*, pp. 3–8.

16. Burling et al., *op. cit.*, pp. 21–22, 43–124.

17. Hughes et al., *op. cit.*, pp. 184–185, 194–198.

18. Edith M. Lentz, "Morale in a Hospital Business Office," in Dorrian Apple (Ed.), *Sociological Studies in Health and Illness*, New York: McGraw-Hill, 1960, pp. 249–259.

19. Harvey L. Smith, "Two Lines of Authority: The Hospital's Dilemma," in Jaco (Ed.), *op. cit.*, pp. 468–477.

20. Albert F. Wessen, "Hospital Ideology and Communication between Ward Personnel," in Jaco (Ed.), *op. cit.*, pp. 448–468.

21. Burling et al., *op. cit.*, pp. 3–7.

22. Richard H. Shryock, *The History of Nursing: An Interpretation of the Social and Medical Factors Involved*, Philadelphia: Saunders, 1959, pp. 105–318.

23. Burling et al., *op. cit.*, pp. 273–283.

24. *Ibid.*, pp. 244–272.

25. Hughes et al., *op. cit.*, pp. 162–163.

26. Robert N. Wilson, "Teamwork in the Operating Room," in Jaco (Ed.), *op. cit.*, pp. 491–501.

27. Brown, *op. cit.*, Part 2, pp. 183–194.

28. Julius A. Roth, "Ritual and Magic in the Control of Contagion," in Apple (Ed.), *op. cit.*, pp. 332–339.

29. Brown, *op. cit.*, Part 2.

30. Habenstein and Christ, *op. cit.*, p. 4.

31. Brown, *op. cit.*, Part 1, pp. 64–84.

32. Hughes et al., *op. cit.*, pp. 76–77.

33. Burling et al., *op. cit.*, pp. 7–10, 22–24, 28–29.

34. Talcott Parsons and Renee Fox, "Illness, Therapy, and the Modern American Family," in Jaco (Ed.), *op. cit.*, pp. 234–245.

35. Talcott Parsons, "Some Definitions of Health and Illness in the Light of American Values and Social Structure," in his *Social Structure and Personality*, New York: Free Press of Glencoe, 1964, pp. 257–291.

36. Talcott Parsons, "Deviant Behavior and the Mechanisms of Social Control," in his *The Social System*, Glencoe, Ill.: Free Press, 1951, Chap. VII, pp. 249–325.

37. Edwin M. Lemert, *Social Pathology: A Systematic Approach to the Theory of Sociopathic Behavior*, New York: McGraw-Hill, 1951.

38. Brown, *op. cit.*, Part 3, pp. 56–163.

39. Apple (Ed.), *op. cit.*, pp. 1–221.

40. Brown, *op. cit.*, Part 1, pp. 85–98 et passim.

41. Talcott Parsons, "The School Class as a Social System: Some of Its Functions in an American Society," in his *Social Structure and Personality, op. cit.*, pp. 129–164.

42. Myles W. Rodenhaver, Vincent R. Mancusi, and Luke M. Smith, "The Socialization Function of Recreation Groups in a Maximum Security Prison," *American Journal of Correction*, **26**, 1964, 20–24.

43. Talcott Parsons, "Social Structure and the Development of Personality: Freud's Contribution to the Integration of Psychology and Sociology," in his *Social Structure and Personality, op. cit.*, pp. 78–111.

44. Talcott Parsons, "Propaganda and Social Control," in his *Essays in Sociological Theory*, rev. ed., Glencoe, Ill.: Free Press, 1954, pp. 142–176.

45. Talcott Parsons and Robert F. Bales, *Family, Socialization, and Interaction Process*, Glencoe, Ill.: Free Press, 1954, pp. 41 et passim.

46. Donald R. Cressey (Ed.), *The Prison: Studies in Institutional Organization and Change*, New York: Holt, Rinehart, and Winston, 1961.

47. Joseph H. Fichter, *Religion as an Occupation: A Study in the Sociology of Professions*, South Bend, Ind.: University of Notre Dame Press, 1961, pp. 185–233.

48. Nevitt Sanford (Ed.), *The American College: A Psychological and Social Interpretation of the Higher Learning*, New York: Wiley, 1962.

49. Burling et al., *op. cit.*, pp. 3–10.

50. Shryock, *op. cit.*, pp. 105ff.

51. Edwin M. Sutherland and Donald R. Cressey, *Principles of Criminology*, 5th ed., Philadelphia: Lippincott, 1955, pp. 445ff.

52. Burling et al., *op. cit.*, pp. 273–283.

53. Shryock, *op. cit.*, pp. 310–311.

54. Sutherland and Cressey, *op. cit.*, pp. 421–442, 556–588.

55. R. Ernest Dupuy and Traver N. Dupuy, *Military Heritage of America*, New York: McGraw-Hill, 1956.

56. Max Weber, "The Meaning of Discipline," in his *From Max Weber: Essays in Sociology*, New York: Oxford University Press, 1946, pp. 253–264.

57. Morris Janowitz, *The Professional Soldier: A Social and Political Portrait*, Glencoe, Ill.: Free Press, 1960, pp. 21–75.

58. Thomas F. Stransky, "The End of the Priest-Worker Experiment," *The Catholic World*, **190**, 1960, 240–245.

59. Philippe Aries, *Centuries of Childhood: A Social History of the Family*, New York: Knopf, 1962.

# 14. VOLUNTARISM AND PROFESSIONAL PRACTICE IN THE HEALTH PROFESSIONS

## Leonard Schatzman

This chapter deals with "voluntarism" or elective action in the context of professional work in the health fields. It offers a perspective rather than "findings" on certain observed phenomena in professional health practice. The aim is to outline broadly several logical models that might elucidate medical practice as performed according to personal choice rather than according to professional prescription or mandate.[1] But first we should place this topic in proper perspective and illustrate what we mean by elective medical practice.

The writer (a sociologist) recently participated in a conference of health professionals concerned with "problems" related to the care of long-term hospitalized patients, even though he could not, in advance, clearly visualize any special problems associated with such patients which health professionals themselves, with training and experience, might not know about and be able to handle adequately. Indeed, as it turned out, the conferees generally exhibited considerable acumen as to the needs of such patients, hence a lack of knowledge about what was needed did not become a central issue. What did come to concern the conferees was an apparent deficit (as they defined it) in motivation to perform the necessary work. Consequently much of the conference was taken up with self-admonition for "failure" to meet pa-tient needs and exhortation to do better. When a few of the participants attempted to blame bureaucratic demands and staffing problems for the failure, they were rhetorically over-powered by the majority who denied the validity of such an argument and insisted that if a professional really *wanted* to do the correct thing, he would find the way and the time to do so. As the discussion developed, it became increasingly apparent that most of the conferees were injecting into the idea of professionalism a strong dose of voluntarism, with the implication that a "real professional" (assuming requisite skills) was simply a highly motivated one. As if to underscore this inference, a nurse related how on one occasion she "decided" to converse at some length with a patient whose frequent complaints (according to her) had led to his being increasingly ignored by the staff. As she told the story it was clear that she was proud of her action and its favorable outcome, and others in the audience praised her for her "willingness," "dedication," and "initiative." But what was particularly clear and striking to this sociologist was that a professional had *elected* to perform a professional act, and that the act in this instance was a personal choice rather than a professional prescription.

This kind of story is by no means

This paper was prepared especially as an original contribution to this book.

unique; the writer has heard similar ones many times, not to mention the self-recriminations and admonitions about patient care. But there was something here that seemed to have made a difference. The topic concerned the care of long-term hospitalized patients. The image or model drawn was that of a patient whose major complaint was known and manageable, whose medical status or condition was stabilized, and whose treatment and care were relatively routinized. Also, the level of stabilization and the extent of patient incapacity were such as to require continued hospitalization. Although this class of patient is by no means representative of all types of long-term hospitalized patients, it offers what seems an especially fruitful model for examining medical practice that could be termed elective. For here we have a patient requiring little more than routine, medical service — no emergencies expected, no call for medical heroics. The point is, in a more narrow medical context, that any or all members of the hospital staff can elect to leave the patient alone — to his own pleasure or misery.

## PSYCHOSOCIAL CARE

The question is, then, under what circumstances does voluntarism occur? The hypothesis we offer is that it occurs most clearly and certainly when psychosocial care and involvement is the indicated action or "intervention." Anticipating the reader's protests about any medical distinction between the somatic and the psychosocial, we hasten to state that the distinction is not one that we hold to be valid. We do claim, however, that it is made frequently by health professionals in practice, if not in theory or in

expressed sentiment. In any event we shall make the distinction here, mainly to develop our hypothesis. It is not our intention to test the hypothesis; rather we intend to examine it, help explain it, and logically search out its implications. The reader can then judge for himself the plausibility of the entire discussion.

By psychosocial action we refer to the practice of dealing directly with a patient primarily or solely in terms of how *he* comprehends his own situation, including his current condition, his prognosis, and the consequences for him and others of these facts in his life. According to the hypothesis, the model patient will receive somatic treatments and care first and psychosocial attention second, if at all. When medications are called for and lab tests are ordered, these and a host of other somatically oriented decisions will be carried out, regardless of the attitudes of the staff toward the patient or toward each other and despite fatigue, ready staff availability, or almost any other limiting condition. Staff may exercise some latitude as to the exact time and manner in which these decisions are carried out, but they will not likely exercise a choice as to their performance. This would not be the case for psychosocial acts.

What will explain this distinction in professional performance? Psychologically oriented people might turn quickly for an answer to the concept of variability in motivation or to personality differences. Although sociologists do not ignore these variables, they do not characteristically address themselves directly to them. Their starting point in the examination of behavior — professional or otherwise — is usually the context within which the behavior occurs. This means examining action with reference to social organizations and institutions.

For without such reference, they may begin and end their examination of action solely in terms of personal attributes or traits, such as "dedication," "cheerfulness," "determination," "patience," and so on; even terms of "hostility," "guilt," "anxiety," or "latent" this or that. Sociologically, motivation is best handled in a context of developing skills, including learning when, where, and how to apply them; the context of work settings where these skills are practiced is also an important consideration. Thus motivation is seen as implicit in the training and conditioned by the setting in which skills are performed.

## PREPROFESSIONALS AND VOLUNTARISM

We have constructed a model patient and now need a model training or professional socialization that may help us in our search for an explanation of the somatic-psychosocial practice differential. Unfortunately the most notable current sociological model will not help us.[2] It tells how the preprofessional makes a career choice, enters a training program that teaches him the appropriate knowledge and skills, develops a sense of identity with his chosen profession, commits himself to its mission, accepts its values and controls, and finally seeks out a work situation that will allow him to exercise his skills and fully establish his professional identity. This model has its merits principally in that it helps us distinguish between professional and nonprofessional status, attitudes, training, and work, and generally enriches our understanding of certain processes that produce social configurations or structures. However, we want to look beyond (as well as

include) concepts of professional choice, identification, commitment, and social roles. We need to examine the nature of professional training that most directly impinges on the psychosocial sphere of health practice.

Students come to professional schools for various reasons: to achieve a certain status in society, to become specifically this or that kind of professional, to please their parents, and so on; indeed, some come to avoid other occupational alternatives. But motives and reasons always come in mixtures, so let us grant that pre-professionals in the health fields come into training also because they "like people" and want to "help" them. Initially they are equipped to do so in various "natural" (preprofessional) ways, but they lack the special knowledge and technical motions or procedures of professional action. The equipment they come with is "natural" and more or less suitable for meeting the requirements of social intercourse with widely different kinds of people in varying kinds of situations. They have had, as young adults, distinctive life experiences which, when thought of as patterned, constitute interpersonal behavioral styles. Whether we think of these patterns as attributes of personality or as interpersonal styles, they probably constitute a wide range of behavior patterns — even within a limited social stratum.

Our preprofessionals are variously shy or bold, quick or slow, casual or formal, direct and concrete or abstract and subtle in varying situations involving other people. In the same way, the people to whom they would be of help have varied styles and expectations of interpersonal behavior. Thus in the ordinary course of human interaction the parties engaged make adjustments that control the effects of differences in each other's speech patterns (including clarity, dialect, speed, vocabulary), in facial mobility, expressed affect, characteristic form of eye contact, body distance, and so on — all this, as part of or added to differences in age, sex, marital status, occupation, and education. It is not our purpose to write a book on social psychology; rather it is to focus the reader's attention on the properties of ordinary social skills operative in interpersonal approach and engagement — skills held in varying forms and amounts by almost everyone. These may be as simple as the approach: "How do you do; my name is . . . ," or as complex as an engagement with a dying person and his relatives.

## THE TRAINING INSTITUTION

Contrasted with this spectrum of behavior forms that are characterictic of its students, the institution offers a relatively standard training program with a limited number of objectives. The institution probably cannot concern itself more than roughly and nominally with the variety of preprofessional behavior patterns. Yet in some respects it must and does, if for no other reason than that certain of these patterns are apparently inimical to professional roles, and must be modified or eliminated. Doubtless many patterns are compatible with professional roles — may even enhance them — and these may be recognized and reinforced. We must accept the possibility, however, that experiences in training and in later professional work will modify all the patterns. We may refer to this process as education or growth, or simply as change; it can also be seen as a correction — even a distortion — of natural, interpersonal styles of conduct.

However well motivated the preprofessional, and whatever his repertoire of natural techniques for helping people, it is understood by both the student and the institution that new ways of helping people must be learned. This is the rationale of the institution's existence. Neither suspects, however, that these new ways supplant, rather than simply supplement and complement, the old ways. This process of supplanting is assured by the medical orientation of the training institution, the same orientation later in the work institution, and by the ways the student professional learns to survive and succeed in school and work. In medicine and nursing, "help" is organized by knowledge and technology into specific acts directed at specific disorders in human organisms. The specificity is a function of an orientation toward diseases and specialized procedures for dealing with them. The student becomes concerned mainly with organic structures and functions, with symptomology and appropriate treatment processes.

The "helping" model is medical, an interaction between a physician and a sick person — as powerful a model as any in Western tradition. The model of "help" is also medical: a search by the physician for the cause of the ailment and his dealing with "it." This too is a most powerful model, not only because it is rooted in tradition but also because it is backed by a vast and relatively effective medical science and technology. These models are so pervasive that the student comes to regard medical action as the equivalent of (all) "help," or at the very least, sufficient. The student convinces himself of this if only because he must organize for himself an economical expenditure of time, energy, and interest in order to complete his training. He is confronted with, and accepts, an apparently complete and logically tight system made up of the two medical models of helping and help, a content that is oriented toward somatic structure, functions, and disorders, and of a thought system rooted in cause and effect. When tied to a massive and effective technology, it is a most impressive and satisfying professional career.

In contrast to somatic empiricism, the psychosocial realm presents itself as abstract, complex, nonorganic, and lacking in causal specificity. As a help system, however humanistic it may appear, it is just barely rationalized into a science and even less a technology. Since the effect of psychosocial action is not immediately apparent, or ever ascertainable at all, such action often seems wasteful in the context of somatic medicine. In the face of all the subject matter and procedure which the student must master, the content and procedures of the psychosocial approach to "help" are least impressive to him.

Doubtless the training institution would not downgrade the importance of humanistic principles; it would never wish its students to forget that organism is inseparable from person. But natural psychosocial action gets little formal attention beyond some practice in interviewing patients to gather medically relevant data. This, however, is seen as functional in a medical context. It is assumed that the student is sufficiently socialized as an adult to help the patient as well as to treat him. The student is informally guided in this primarily by watching his clinical instructors and learning to emulate them.

## PSYCHIATRY AND MEDICINE

In view of the complexity and importance of the psychosocial realm, and notwithstanding its reliance on a fund of natural patterns, the institution includes in its program a curriculum that deals with the field of human psychology. The form and content of the psychology is mainly psychiatric, simply because the medical orientation dictates a focus on pathology, and psychiatry is a psychology (and a treatment) of pathology in behavior. Disturbances in behavior are viewed as medical problems and are seen as "illness"; hence helping the "mentally ill" parallels the somatic healing pattern and follows the medical model. The psychiatric training is presumed to take care of the personal element in the medical situation. Yet, in some ways, even more than training in medical or organic empiricism, this aspect of the educational process alters "natural" interpersonal styles. It does this because it is deceptively similar to natural styles of interpersonal engagement in content and form. Therefore the student is likely to accept psychiatric—principally psychodynamic—principles of behavior and interpersonal relations as real and adequate renderings of the human condition and human behavior. Since these principles of behavior are gained largely through the study of psychopathologies, the student may come to see his organically distressed patient as psychiatrically disturbed or as characteristically predisposed to certain responses, and deals with him accordingly.

The association of psychiatry and medicine has some advantages for each. Medicine gains an organized perspective on human behavior and on behavior disorders; additionally, it gains sets of diagnostic and treatment categories that flow logically from a structure-function orientation. Although psychiatric categories are more complicated and abstract than somatic categories, they are far better rationalized than lay or pre-professional categories and immediately more useful clinically than those of other psychologies; they are therefore amenable to integration into the medical curriculum. In its turn, psychiatry gains much from medicine: the medical model and the status of a prestigious profession.

Certain important consequences for professional thought and clinical procedure flow from this association. Principles of psychopathy are generalized to make them functionally equivalent to a psychology of human behavior. In this context and with this orientation, social relations are easily converted into treatment procedures and vice versa. This means, among other things, that forms of patient behavior (especially "feelings") are presented and later dealt with as "properties" or structures and therefore subject to analysis in the same manner that tissue is analyzable.

Thus far our discussion has been more relevant to training and practice in medicine and nursing than to other health professions. With the inclusion of psychiatry in our discussion, however, we can include other professions, such as social work, psychology, occupational therapy, rehabilitation counseling, and the like; for although we have shifted our attention from *soma* to *psyche*, we have retained all other attributes of medicine. The psychiartic perspective, particularly the psychodynamic variety, provides much of the content and forms of practice of these professions; it supplies them with both substance and status. Because of this, nonphysicians can act very much according to the model of the medical practitioner: that is, think and act in terms of "illness,"

causation, prognosis, treatment, and referral.

The importance of this orientation is that, regardless of which health profession or clinical function, preprofessional styles are significantly altered. For built inevitably into the training is an uncommon sensitivity to pathology in behavior, emotion, and tissue, and developing procedures for dealing with it. The sensitivity to it derives from categorical imperatives to evaluate, interpret, diagnose, and treat whatever falls within professional clinical jurisdiction. In a society prone to view any aspect of the human condition in evaluative terms and to "do something" about it if necessary, this attitude is entirely plausible. Moreover, knowing how to evaluate and what to do about it are the important, if not the sole, criteria for measuring professional performance.

## THE PROFESSIONAL IN INSTITUTIONAL PRACTICE

If we can accept this model of training — and we admit it is a bit severely drawn — we can now look at the professional in institutional practice. As before, we shall construct a model, this time of an institution, and thus find a home for our model patient. Much of what we have said about professional training has a distinct carryover into institutional practice, hence our institutional model will be more briefly drawn.[3]

A medical institution is a complex organization of people, equipment, procedures, and other human arrangements. It tends to be a rational order in the sense it is a contrived or designed arrangement suitable to the performance of certain tasks, and ordinarily is so complex that without a rational arrangement it could not do its work. When such institutions add research and teaching to clinical service, they are quite complex indeed. The arrangement or ordering is not to be seen as fixed because, insofar as the institution is contrived and responsive to social and technological changes, the order will probably change. Nor is consensus on how it should be ordered ever fully established or assured.[4]

Whatever the form of institutional order, the newly arrived professionals who begin their work there encounter compelling sets of conditions, of which immediate patient needs are only one set. Medical requirements do not always take precedence over those of the institution. The latter is concerned with personnel shifts around the clock, with patient-staff ratios, housekeeping and feeding routines, and so on. These suggest a relatively fine coordination between many professionals and the many tasks. The tasks ordinarily are handled in a context of a division of labor among several classes and levels of personnel. Although it might be argued that all tasks are essential in a rational system, it cannot be argued that all are of equal importance. Even specialists perform more than one task, and, under general or specific conditions, will perform them in the context of priorities — commonly understood or specifically ruled. In his training the preprofessional gets an idea of which events or tasks are more important than others. If the training is effective it will provide a model of priorities suitable for most settings. Later, in practice, the professional will find that each institutional setting has a unique priority configuration. The rewards and punishments of any given

institution will provide the necessary cues and inducements to learning its configuration.

By no means is the institution the sole arbiter of what takes priority. Staff are also professionals and respond to the requirements of profession which frequently enough conflict with institutional requirements and so have to be adjudicated. And certainly the professional as a person has his own requirements; like any other person who works, he is concerned with the conservation of his time and energy so that he may leave his place of work in time and in condition to take care of his other concerns and interests. Hence he organizes his work in terms of what is necessary and important to himself and builds a personal-professional economy of time and motion. In effect, he gears his own personal and professional requirements into those of his colleagues and the institution.

## PATIENT-PROFESSIONAL RELATIONS

The hospital, as well as the training program, emphasizes in many ways that the "treatment" of patients is very important as is their physical safety. Institutional order embodied in rules and routines is important, as are charting and other medicolegal communicative activities. In such an ordered context, what values are placed on the patient's psychosocial needs? According to professional and institutional priorities, in theory and sentiment at least, these needs are considered of major importance; in actual practice they are implicitly assumed to be taken care of because of their occurrence in a medical setting. Yet we do know that specific psychosocial attention is given. It is, indeed, under two relatively distinct circumstances: (1) when the patient's psychosocial problems affect treatment (which is important), and (2) when the patient's psychosocial problems affect ward or institutional order (which is important). Under these conditions, intervention is professional rather than elective. Earlier we indicated how the logic of medical empiricism dictates that psychosocial intervention is seen as wasteful, since it is abstract, time consuming, and offers little direct evidence or specific effect. Yet when treatment of ward order is threatened, that is, when profession and institution are threatened, actions are taken to protect what is valued, though under other circumstances these may seem "wasteful" in time and energy.

More than priority and value is involved in such a situation; a question of skill also arises. Acts that have priority exhibit their value in a medical context when they are rationalized and take on the appearance of exact procedures; then they do not seem wasteful or irrelevant. No one is likely to deny the value of the person in the patient, but few professionals have rational approaches (proven or simply convincing) to persons as demonstrably economical or as efficacious as somatically oriented procedures. In the model hospital, even psychiatric intervention is a "sometime" thing; when behavior is grossly pathological, the professional transfers the patient or calls in a psychiatric consultant; the simpler disturbances expressed through worry and anxiety are met with palliative words.

In the interpersonal area, we are not referring simply to intervention as "treatment" but to a dialogue with the patient as person to the end that he is

dealing comfortably and adequately with whatever is important to *him*. In addition to time, this sort of engagement requires skill in conversation and role taking and skill in dealing with the person in terms of *his* mode of understanding. Why should the nurse or doctor sit with the patient in this sort of dialogue? Perhaps just as importantly, who is prepared, in the sense of being skilled, to deal with the kinds of intelligence gained from the patient about his world? Few colleague or institutional rewards are to be gained for psychosocial action. A nurse, in fact, might be punished for having neglected such important matters as medical charting, securing the medical cabinet, or answering the phone.

The question of skill in interpersonal relations (in a medical context) becomes of paramount importance, since not knowing quite what one is supposed to do, why it should be done, or wondering whether one is doing the right thing mitigates against doing it. In interpersonal relations there is a social gap between the parties to the interaction. Health professionals supposedly are trained to bridge such gaps. In a sense there is only a physical gap between a health practitioner and a piece of tissue, and by analogy, between him or a "feeling"; theoretically and practically one can reach for these without reference to the owner. But if one is to bridge the gap via the owner as a person, it is necessary to engage with him in some way that takes into account his interpersonal styles. One discovers this and builds a bridge across.

This is only part of the act, however; one not only must be skilled in crossing over, but also must know why one has crossed and what to do when one is there. "Wanting" to get across for reasons of sentiment is voluntary; "having" to get across in order to establish a relationship or, indeed, to give treatment is professional and mandatory. Yet until and unless the bridging process and its consequences are rationalized and built into training and into institutional economics, its performance remains subject to personal sentiment and whim. When viewed from the perspective of current institutional values, priorities, and imperatives, this is not likely to happen.

## CONCEPT OF THE "PRO"

We admit to having drawn rather somber models of training, institution, and, by implication, profession. Surely there are professionals who are different. The concept "professional" itself neither provides nor suggests distinctions among good, bad, or indifferent performance. It merely denotes status or position in the social structure, and implies that roles are performed at an adequate level. As we have seen, training and practice institutions place a high value on helping and on prolonging healthy life. Then who is the professional who might meet the standards implicit in our models? Perhaps we require a concept that provides us with some manner of identifying and analyzing that professional who performs in a consistently superior manner. The reader is surely familiar with the vernacular term "pro." This is a folk term, a version of the concept "professional," which came into use with the rapid growth of professions in our society. As a status term it is a poor construct; as an ideal model of high professional performance, it will serve.

The term "pro" has various uses, depending on which tasks and situations are being examined. Thus it is often used to indicate a status passage from amateur to professional, as in sports. It may imply a transition from unremunerated to remunerated work. For our purposes these are irrelevant, as are formal training and even occupation. Our use of the term allows us to examine the performance of any complex and specialized set of tasks performed repeatedly and consistently at a high level. Thus the "pro" can be a musician, soldier, physician, sportsman, and even part-time gardener or mountain climber. It is its connotative meaning we wish to stress. For this purpose, lest we quibble over whether every "pro" is consistently excellent, we shall adopt its superlative form: "real pro." What is distinctive about the "real pro," as commonly recognized, is that his skill, though quite complex, is exceptionally well performed and economical (or rational) in the expenditure of time, motion, and energy. Purpose, time, and task are perfectly coordinated. The "real pro" works effortlessly, unemotionally, and confidently — or so it seems to the nonpro. It seems effortless because there is no apparent delay in searching for appropriate action; unemotional because affect is controlled through knowledge of consequences and contingencies, confident because there is no waste of motion except, perhaps, for that which indicates style or flourish.

Of course, this is a fiction, an ideal model of high craft performance. In this model we have left little or no room for voluntarism. As applied to any craft it signifies that the actor has built into his economy of action all of the essential attributes. As applied to craft in the field of health, it would require incorporating into professional economies the psychosocial actions — not merely as sentiment, for this is not equivalent to craft, but as fully rationalized procedure.

## CONCLUSION

In this paper we have focused on voluntaristic actions in professional work related to health. One might well point out that the same phenomenon exists in many other segments of contemporary life. This is probably true. Technologically advanced societies — particularly our own — are likely to stress the importance of instrumental and utilitarian thought and action. Very often rationality is measured precisely in these terms. Philosophers and scientists of earlier centuries probably did not anticipate that their pragmatism and humanism would be radically altered by developments in science and technology. Somehow we are willing to accept these shifts in orientation in the fields of business and industry, for these deal primarily with commodities, making it possible — even mandatory — to produce and distribute commodities rationally and economically. However, this was probably not meant to happen in the service trades and professions, yet advances in technology and social organization have brought us paradoxically to this point. The frequent reminders and exhortations to value the "whole person" which are heard throughout the service professions attest to the "struggle" between this sort of rational utilitarianism and the older humanism. The logic of our earlier discussion forces us to accept this as a real dichotomy, and we would indeed defend it as being a real condition. The medical empiricism we have referred to engenders a view of man more as a structure of parts than as a singular developing process. The parts come to appear as real and the whole as an abstraction. Indeed, the modern hospital distributes among its wards whole persons according to afflicted parts and professionals according to knowledge of these parts. It is, in fact, economical to do it this way, but places considerable strain on natural patterns of approach, engagement, and disengagement between professionals and patients. The increasing rapidity of patient turnover and an efficient ratio of patients to staff provide the conditions for rapid, variable, and parts-oriented encounters. The very timing of these visits and the particularity of their focus more often than not run counter to more casual and "uneconomical" forms of social relations.

The writer is more hopeful than his writing. The dichotomy between rational utilitarianism and humanism is not inevitable or irreversible; institutional order and consensus are never fully established, hence we can expect the emergence of new helping models. We know there are professionals who meet ideal standards of humanism as well as technical proficiency. These are "real pros" who have somehow built into their own working economies actions that involve persons per se as well as their pathologies. We might guess that these professionals have somehow escaped the harsher consequences of radical empiricism in training and the immediate and compelling priorities of institutional practice. Perhaps they answer to standards or audiences removed in time and place from immediate colleagues and work settings and thereby convert voluntaristic psychosocial action into professional prescription. In any event the "real pro" has fitted the psychosocial realm into his economy and has thereby coordinated purpose with time and motion, or task and energy. If he has, indeed, retained his "natural" interpersonal style or has developed a new and adequate one, it is not likely to be exercised whimsically or "voluntarily," but professionally. Finally, the logic of our discussion allows for training and practice institutions to find opportunities to develop this sort of professionalism.

---

1. In this paper several theoretical models are presented. All the models are hypothetical, ideal constructs and are designed solely to stimulate thinking about voluntary professional behavior. They are not derived from the systematic study of phenomena they appear to represent. Nevertheless we expect the reader will recognize the kinds of institutions from which these models are developed.

2. For a good discussion of the literature on aspects of this model, see Edward Cross, *Work and Society*, New York: Crowell, 1958. More pointedly, the reader may refer to Robert Merton, George G. Reader, and Patricia Kendall (Eds.), *The Student Physician*, Cambridge, Mass.: Harvard University Press, 1957. Also William J. Goode, "Community within a Community: The Professions," *American Sociological Review*, XX, 1957, 194–200.

3. For a brief discussion of the rational model of organization, see Alvin W. Gouldner, "Organizational Analysis," in Robert K. Merton, Leonard Broom, Leonard S. Cottrell, Jr. (Eds.), *Sociology Today*, New York: Basic Books, 1959, pp. 400–428. This is a view of organization development by Max Weber. The writer is not an organizational rationalist in perspective. The position taken in this paper is one that regards utilitarian and instrumental features of contemporary medical practice as important and limiting conditions to professional action.

4. The changing character of medical institutions and the negotiative processes that express and give form to change are discussed in Anselm Strauss, Leonard Schatzman, Rue Bucher, Denuta Ehrlich, and Melvin Sabshin, *Psychiatric Ideologies and Institutions*, New York: Free Press of Glencoe, 1964.

# Epilogue to Part Three

As the foregoing articles demonstrated, adult socialization is most intensive during the periods when individuals either are forced or choose to adjust to new situations. When a person makes a career choice or becomes ill, a state of crisis develops. To take on a particular role requires a learning process involving changes in beliefs, values, and self-conception. It is during the movement from health to illness or from nonprofessional to professional status that the individual is most vulnerable to significant revisions of old attitudes and styles of life.

The person who aspires to be, or even accidentally becomes, a member of a new social category must learn the specific behavior appropriate to that role. The interplay of roles and personality, however, may create untoward or unexpected problems. If, for example, the individual has been or at least has perceived himself as being independent and aggressive, it may be difficult for him to take the role of patient; such new role taking requires a change in self-concept.

In any event, if a person becomes a health professional or a patient, he goes through a process known as anticipatory socialization. That is, to take up the role he has to develop some notion of the values and self-conception that he must hold for himself, that others expect of him, and that he can expect from others.

As an individual is socialized into a role, changes occur in him very slowly and almost unnoticeably. But gradually this new life becomes all-encompassing and requires a thorough break with the old ways of living; the patient must devote himself to being a patient, rather than a member of X labor force; the health professional, while in the process of being socialized into his profession, must make a break with many of his earlier social and occupational identities.

In order for the all-encompassing break with the past to be achieved and the new role created, the socializing agents must somehow gain control of the individual, "bleach out" or force him to deny his old self and "dye in" new values, beliefs, and status aspirations. In the preparation of the professional, attributes deemed positive by the profession — desires for achievement, mobility, decisiveness, aggressiveness, organization, and a strong sense of identity — must be instilled in the individual if they do not already exist. Negative attributes such as fear of failure, uncertainty and inability to control the situation, are "bleached out" of the self-concept. Positive sanctions from both public and private sources support the aspirations leading to the successful realization of the new role.

Much behavior of the individual in his newly acquired role occurs within a private domain; for example, the patient's relationship to his family or nurse and the health worker's relationship to his patients are not always perceptible. What occurs in the one-to-one situation of psychoanalysis, for example, is in reality known only to the two individuals involved. Any information regarding the content or process of that relationship which is related to others is subject to the perceptions of the "teller" and the "listener"; therefore what *actually*

156

happens between the patient and analyst is not communicated. The psychosocial aspects of care and treatment, for this reason, are more imperceptible to the observer than is physical care. The reward system, however, is predominantly in terms of visible behavior; that is, a good patient may have several psychosocial problems, but if he appears to play the role of a "good patient" by creating no special perceptible problems for the professionals, he is then rewarded by particular kinds of attention. Also the professional may be rewarded for behavior that is invisible to the public but strongly sensed by his professional colleagues. It is important for health workers to look beyond a patient's "good" behavior and become aware of any psychosocial problems not apparent on the surface.

As was stated earlier, all individuals play many roles. These roles are not played simultaneously. Rather, a hierarchy of role sectors is established by the individual. For example, the role of father is not enacted in the same fashion when the son breaks a window as it is when the son performs a heroic deed. The self-concept of the individual who is accustomed to and esteems the role of manager may undergo severe changes when he is forced to play the subordinate role of patient. Professional and nonprofessional roles are abstract concepts, and the roles become real only when there is a referent — that is, a physician becomes a physician only when he has a referent called "patient." Patients are not passive objects, and the doctor or other health worker must in some way learn to interact with the ever-changing patient. Each, because of his socialization, brings with him certain expectations about how he and others should function within that relationship. In addition, the ethnic group and the social class to which each belongs influences how each functions and perceives the other.

All roles within the health professions are constantly in a state of transition, thus creating problems in role fulfillment. To a certain extent the type and state of transition are influenced by social movements. The ideology of total patient care, or seeing every individual as a whole person, is a concept that the professional should aim at, but cannot always reach. Although this ideology has caused the health professional to become aware of many previously neglected aspects of the patient's life, the necessity and practice of specialization has made the ideology of total patient care an almost unattainable goal. Such conflicts between ideology and practice are not uncommon. Many times they are resolved by negotiation, avoidance, or denial. In other cases, direct confrontation of the problem or a change of job or career may be necessary. The transitional aspect of roles in the health professions is not only the result of social movements; it is, indeed, intrinsic in the career of health worker or patient. For, whether professional or patient, one is engaged in a career which consists of a series of status passages tending to become "turning points." At each of these points the self-concept alters. The decision that one is ill, that one ought to seek help, that one participate in treatment, that one is now "well"— these are all turning points in the career of patienthood. The movement from the status of initiate, to that of novice, to graduation from professional school, to specialization, to practice choice — these are turning points for the health professional. At any one of these junctions the self-concept is modified and the perception of conflict and techniques for resolving it are changed. The professional must be aware of these turning points.

## PART FOUR

# Influences on the Road: The Family

Culture and society are integrated systems that continue to exist only when there is replacement of individuals by others and when there is provision for the means of life. Elemental biological facts of mating and the helplessness of infants become translated into a set of socially defined relationships called family. The concept of family implies wedlock, which in turn consists of formal prescriptions defining the mutual responsibilities and rights of the couple, their offspring, and society as a whole. One of these responsibilities is the establishment of a household in accordance with custom and law.

The structure and activities of the family vary with the culture, social class, region, country, and period of the family cycle. The three main aspects of culture that influence the family are norms, values, and sentiments. Norms define and regulate many aspects of family life, such as sexual behavior, creation and size of the family, and the role responsibilities and privileges of each position within the family structure. Thus the family is responsible for population maintenance and control as well as the care, training, and socialization of children. Values define the kinds of gratification expected from the family and provide the individual with criteria by which to select his mate. Sentiments, on the other hand, involve the subjective feelings and desires for action within culturally defined categories, such as mother love and romantic love.

To the health worker, the concept of family is of crucial importance, but there are pitfalls in assuming that it means the same thing to everyone in a given society. As we indicated in Part Two, two main systems of ethics permeate Western civilization and influence all aspects of family: the Protestant and the Freudian.

To establish a family, one must select a mate. Kernodle[1] provides theories of individual mate selection. That is, an individual may select a mate because (1) he or she is in geographic or social proximity; (2) they have opposite psychological needs (to dominate and to submit); (3) the partner is like one's parent of the opposite sex; or (4) the partner is an "ideal image" mate. Although these theories may give clues to why one partner chooses another, the cultural ethics (Protestant and Freudian) indicate the "field" from which such a choice is made. That is, if a group, class, or society uses the sanctions and taboos of the Protestant Ethic, the choice of mate, as well as subsequent family structure, and modes of communication will be quite different from that in which the Freudian Ethic predominates. Within a predominantly Protestant Ethic subculture, males will be selected on the basis of being industrious, good providers, successful in an occupation, and a potential disciplinarian for his children. The father will be expected to continue in these roles and also serve as the family's chief spokesman to the outside world. The female will be chosen for being a good housekeeper, cook, and potential mother, with no aspirations for a career outside the domain of the home.

The Freudian Ethic, on the other hand, dictates that mates be selected as fitting the romantic ideal of good companionship, mutual sharing and enjoying of outside interests, sexual attraction and compatibility, and the potentiality for being a friend to subsequent children.

Although these ethics are models and rarely exist in their pure form, the emphasis on one as opposed to the other structures the kind of relationship that will exist between husband and wife, parents and children, family and the outside world. As Hill indicates, sex roles within the family, parental responsibility, and the rights and privileges of parents and children also will be structured within this context. Contemporary society has seen a blurring of marital sex roles and the formation of a system of joint responsibility for instrumental (household and breadwinning) and expressive (emotional feeling) roles between male and female.

The parental roles assumed in mass society are, as Barth and Watson state, directly related to tensions in parent-child relationships. Such tensions create potential health and social problems. The norms governing the social relations between parents and children are, in fact, significantly important in the area of health and illness and patient care.

As Glick[2] states, various kinds of illness create greater or lesser degrees of problem and crisis for families, depending on the stage of the family cycle and the ethic that dominates its structure. The addition of a child, for example, does not mean that the family becomes husband and wife plus a child. It has many far-reaching implications. The birth of a child demands a complete restructuring of the family relationships and responsibilities. There are now three who are involved in intimate interpersonal relationships. The relationship of father and mother is altered through the positive and negative consequences of the new role of parent, requiring a period of adjustment to each other, to the child, and to the surrounding society.

The same illness may have different meaning and implication to different families as well as to different patients. Disfiguring disease, injury, or surgery do not mean the same thing to the spouse who prides physical attraction and sexual compatibility as it does to the spouse who values the hard-working, dependable provider over a mate with the former characteristics. For instance, the wife of a patient who had cancer of the genitals told a staff nurse that she could no longer bear to be near her husband or to think of his return home. The value of their marriage — physical compatibility — was destroyed. "Nothing is left — that's all we had." This patient, who will be capable of working for a time at least, would have received quite a different reaction to his illness had his wife been a Protestant Ethic type. On the other hand, a patient who could no longer work, but could still participate in a sexual life, might have had the same horrified reaction from a Protestant Ethic wife.

Not only do the same illnesses create different problems for the family while the patient is hospitalized, but if the illness requires a lengthy absence from home, new relationships between him and his family have to be forged upon his return. The wife who had to go to work develops new friends, new interests, and a new style of life. The patient's return may be as difficult for her as it is for him. She may have to give up her outside job and return to the role of housewife, a role she may no longer desire. Lengthy illnesses, such as tuberculosis or mental disease, which require prolonged hospitalization, may also force a complete restructuring of the family. In many cases the marital partners have grown so far apart that this is an extremely difficult if not impossible task. Under such conditions it may be better to send the patient to a home other than his own.

Family values, norms, and resources help the individual members to interpret problems, recognize illness, and participate in treatment, as well as to adjust their routines to the patient's needs. Adjustments must be made within the collective family structure, as well as by individual members. Long-term or serious illness of any family member creates many kinds of strain in family relations. In every family there are individuals responsible for exercising the instrumental role — that is, the breadwinners — and others responsible for fulfilling the expressive role — that is, those who satisfy emotional needs. In situations where one or the other role performer is absent or unable to function, others must perform these roles. If the father, who usually finances the household, becomes ill, the mother may have to find a job to support the family, thereby fulfilling both roles. If there are young children in the family, their needs may have to be subordinated to the dependency needs of the father which are created by his illness.

Family resources are regulated to some extent by the kinship patterns of the group, as well as by socioeconomic factors. In the contemporary twentieth century, the structure of the family is predominantly nuclear rather than extended. Contacts with members of the extended family tend to be minimally significant and largely confined to special occasions such as weddings and funerals. Further, families may be geographically isolated from each other. The reduced size of the family also tends to make fewer kin available in time of need. If the illness is chronic or socially unacceptable, few family members may be willing or able to assist in the care of the patient. Resentment on the part of some family members may isolate the patient even further. In many instances it is not that the extended family members are not concerned with the patient, but rather that their concern is greater for their own nuclear family.

As Bell and Stub point out, the impact of illness or death upon the family and the family's ability to adjust depends to some extent on the stage of the life cycle at which it occurs and the roles played by individual members. The birth of the youngest child, when it occurs early in the family cycle, requires a different kind of adjustment than when it occurs at a later date. The stages of the family cycle also determine in part the availability and numbers of members who are able to contribute effectively to the solution of the problem. If the diseased condition creates excessive demands on the family, or if relatives are unavailable or unable to assist, the consequent need for outside agency help and support is greatly increased.

1. Wayne Kernodle, "Some Implications of the Homogamy-Complementary Needs Theories of Mate Selection for Sociological Research," *Social Forces*, **38**, 1959, 145–152.

2. Paul C. Glick, "The Life Cycle of the Family," *Marriage and Family Living*, **17**, 1955, 3–9.

# 15. CHANGES IN SEX ROLES IN THE FAMILY

## Reuben Hill

As a consequence of many changes — younger age at marriage, changes in child spacing, as well as changed ways of making a living and the changed emphasis on services performed in the family — the relationships between husband and wife and between children and parents have changed sharply with respect to the locus of power and in the division of duties and responsibilities in the family. Wives and children are becoming economic partners with the husband-father in spending as well as in earning the family income. The family is becoming democratized in the process.

Participation by wives in family decision making extends beyond financial matters, and is concurrently being strengthened by their higher education, wider contact outside the home, exercise of responsibility in civic associations, activities in professional organizations, and by explicit encouragement by experts. Male pretensions to superior authority are widely ridiculed in contemporary comedy, cartoons, children's literature, and other forms of popular art. Moreover, when family decision making is viewed as a symbol of power, the superiority of shared power in creating and maintaining warmth and affection becomes evident. It is easier to love a reasonable, companionable man and harder to love an authoritarian husband and father today.

Equally striking in the blurring of sex lines are the changes in the division of tasks and responsibilities in the home. Here the middle classes lead the way, according to a recent study covering hundreds of Omaha families at various educational and occupational status levels. The investigator asked who was primarily responsible for the performance of each of a hundred homely tasks that must be performed to keep a family going. His findings may be stated briefly:

1. The middle classes have gone farthest in bringing the husband into taking responsibility for family tasks, and also designate more tasks as the *joint responsibility* of husband and wife.

2. The lower classes placed more of the burdens on the mother and the children, while the upper classes were the only group to turn to outside help for any substantial proportion of family jobs.

3. For all classes, to be sure, the majority pattern is for the wife to assume responsibility for the greatest number of tasks (40–50 per cent). Second most popular pattern is that of *joint responsibility* (25–28 per cent); third in line is the husband assuming chief responsibility for 20–23 per cent of tasks, followed by children with 6–10 per cent, and outside help 1–14 per cent of tasks.

4. Joint responsibility was the majority pattern for certain types of tasks involving especially control and decision

Excerpted by permission of the publisher, from "The American Family Today," in Eli Ginzberg, *The Nation's Children*, New York: Columbia University Press, 1960, pp. 90–101. Copyright by the Columbia University Press.

making, such as disciplining children, training in manners, supervising school work, deciding when to buy a new car, planning the budget, and so on.

There remain today only two or three tasks securely monopolized by one sex: childbearing and sewing by the wife, and the most arduous physical maintenance chores by the husband. Painting, repairing, fueling, and car washing are increasingly taken on by the wife, sometimes alone, often with the husband. Her dress on these occasions will be male work clothes, and her language will also often be appropriate to the task!

The same crossing of ancient boundaries by the husband is also fast becoming commonplace — diaper changing, dishwashing, cooking, house cleaning, laundering, and shopping are duties shared with the wife, especially if she is gainfully employed — and he has learned to wear an apron, a butcher's apron, to be sure, but an apron! Such sharing of tasks fluctuates, rotates, and changes unevenly, frequently provoking conflict, but the net effect is greater companionship between husband and wife, and more freedom for later leisure time pursuits together. Some women and men resent this as a usurpation of their prerogatives, indeed some feel bereaved of function, but most welcome it.

Still another source of marital integration is the trend in America to undertake leisure-time pursuits together. Except in family enterprises like farming, or small family retail enterprises, few couples have been able to coordinate their work lives at the same vocations, but the decline of segregated amusements, "for men only" and "for women only," in favor of recreation for couples, more than offsets this handicap. It has become impolite to invite husbands only, or wives only, to most social

functions; today, as a consequence, agreement upon friends and outside interests now appears as important in predicting marital adjustment as approval by the parental families once did. It appears probable that the urban husband spends more hours per week in the company of his wife than in any decade since factories removed manufacturing of goods from the home. Recreation and social activities now integrate the sexes.

But companionship in marriage is more than sharing common tasks in the home and participating in common leisure-time activities. Nelson Foote has advanced the concept of "matching careers" to describe the phenomenon of mutual stimulation to development which occurs in a highly companionable marriage.

To expect a marriage to last indefinitely under modern conditions is to expect a lot. The conception of marriage as continually requiring the incitement of new episodes of shared activity will have more consequences than can be foreseen, but a few implications can perhaps be inferred. Happiness as a criterion of success, for instance, is inherently unstable over time. And even at a given time, the prospect of future achievement of aims may have more effect on the judgment of a marriage by its partners than their current state of gratification. Certainly marriage counselors report many cases of mates who disclose no specific cause of dissatisfaction yet complain that they have lost interest in their marriage. Successful marriage may thus come to be defined, both by married people and by students of marriage, in terms of its potential for continued development, rather than in terms of momentary assessments of adjustment. . . .

In particular the notion of matching careers need not imply that husband and wife pursue identical professional careers outside the home. . . . Though their careers be differentiated both in and out of the home, the point that seems decisive in understanding the quality of their marriages appears to remain in the degree of matching in their phases of distinct but comparable development. A simple test may be this, how much do they have to communicate when they are together?[1]

How is this self-conscious appetite for a marriage that will lead to further development of the partners distributed within the occupational classes? Our information on this question is inadequate, but it would appear that it is primarily in the professional classes that companionship and mutual development are sought. In rural and working classes, the relative prominence of functional economic interdependence as the basis for family stability seems much greater than in the more leisured white-collar, business, and professional levels. Moreover the trend is for more and more of the working force to move from agriculture and manufacturing into the services. If in turn they shift their interests in marriage to the focus of the professional classes, the implications for family stability are provocative, for repeated studies show that the professional classes are the least vulnerable to divorce of all occupational strata.[2]

The standard view that industrialization and urbanization are inexorably destructive of family stability and solidarity is thus contradicted by the fact that the professional group, which has a low divorce rate, is also the fullest beneficiary of such aspects of industrialism and urbanism as the reliance of science, spatial and social mobility, and emphasis on the welfare and freedom of the individual. The professional group is most liberal in its views about divorce, and is most egalitarian in its views on the propriety of employment of married women, and in espousing the notion of

equal authority for husband and wife within the family. It appears to be the most cosmopolitan in the range of its choice of marriage mates; most heterogamous in crossing ethnic, class, and religious lines; least affected by propinquity and closest in ages at marriage. It would seem that voluntary commitments emphasized by the professional groups may be stronger bonds for marriage than the economic and legal sanctions which held together traditional families. To adapt an old saying, what is poison to the rural, traditional family may be meat to the urban, professional family.[3]

## PROFESSIONALIZATION OF FAMILY ROLES

What do these trends I have cited add up to? Increasing specialization by the family in services performed for its members, increased emphasis on quality of performance, shift in focus from production of goods to interest in personality development of children, and high affirmation of companionship in marriage and parent-child relations. Possibly Nelson Foote's term, "The Professionalization of Marital and Family Roles," describes best what is taking place in America today.

Marriage is increasingly viewed as a kind of joint career for which preparation can provide the skills and insights to achieve success. Miller and Swanson have been tempted to call the emerging family the "colleague" family.

As specialists at work may find in each other skills they lack, but skills they equally need, and as they defer to one another's judgment on the grounds of different competence without feeling that they have personally lost in prestige, so husband and wife may now relate in this way.[4]

They see this trend toward specialization leading to the professionalization of the wife's functions. She can no longer learn them satisfactorily from her mother's tutelage and example; they must be rationalized. Intuitive processes give way to formal rules and special technical knowledge. Moreover the skills employed are subject to improvement as they are submitted to critical appraisal and functional selection. In career terms the women's magazines provide a kind of in-service training, supplemented with the postgraduate work of the mother study clubs, the meetings with the specialists at the nursery school, the cooking classes, and the growing number of handbooks for preparing unfamiliar or exotic foods.[5] The rise of college and high-school courses in preparation for marriage and parenthood attended by men as well as women, and the development of counseling services further affirm this desire on the part of young people to get professional training for marital and parental roles.

Planning for parenthood today actually goes beyond planning for the control of conception, although a recent nationwide study reveals that children born today are more likely than ever to be wanted, planned children. They are more likely to be seen as a fulfillment rather than a frustration of marriage goals today than in the depression and postdepression period. Planning for parenthood today includes programs of education for parenthood to facilitate the understanding of children in general and one's own children in particular, and thereby to help parents contribute to the maximum development of their personalities. This is a trend of vast significance for personal growth and mental health.

Not only are parents professionalizing their marital and parental roles, they are undertaking once again training of the child for the job world, not by providing technical skills, but by helping him in human relations. The child must learn the nuances of interpersonal relations to function in the large and complex organizations of industry, business, and government. The child must study his own relations to others and gain better control over himself and his associates. Parents in the professions today do have relevant, hard-bought skills to make the critical judgments of social situations that their children will need. Miller and Swanson expect, moreover, a reappearance of the parent as the counselor and aid of his children after they have become adults and parents in their own right, thus enabling children to serve as a means of self-continuity and companionship as well as fulfillment.[6] In sum, parents have learned that in the contemporary world, a parent is far better advised to endow his child with competence in interpersonal relations than to leave him with "a competence" in the old sense of the word.

---

1. Nelson N. Foote, "Matching of Husband and Wife Phases of Development," in *Transactions of the Third World Congress of Sociology*, London: International Sociological Association, 1956, Part IV, p. 29 (2nd reprinting by permission).

2. W. J. Goode, *After Divorce*, Glencoe, Ill.: Free Press, 1956, see especially Chaps. IV and V, pp. 43–67, which summarize these studies.

3. Foote, *op. cit.*, p. 30.

4. Daniel R. Miller and Guy E. Swanson, *The Changing American Parent*, New York: Wiley, 1958, pp. 200–201.

5. *Ibid.*, p. 201.

6. *Ibid.*, p. 204.

# 16. PARENT-CHILD RELATIONS IN MASS SOCIETY

*Ernest A. T. Barth, Walter B. Watson, and Wayne Blanchard*

## INTRODUCTION

Numerous popular writers commenting on the present character of American youth have concluded that the nation is "going to the dogs." Respect for authority seems to have declined while the rates of juvenile deviance have increased. Acts ranging from the ritual burning of draft cards, through officially recognized delinquency, to high rates of mental illness are used to support this conclusion. Although we will not attempt a technical evaluation of the evidence on which these charges are based, it can be observed that whether or not the "true" rates of deviance have increased, our sensitivity to the existing deviance has become more pronounced. Many more adults are concerned about the condition of our nation's youth, including more and more parents whose relationships with their children are marked by tension and stress.

This paper seeks to identify and analyze one important source of tensions between young Americans and their parents. Our particular concern is with the effects of a norm; the norm of nonintervention which, when combined with the particular characteristics of social relations in the urban neighborhood community, limits the ability of parents to maintain effective social controls over the behavior of their children. When combined with the almost universal sense of personal responsibility for the behavior of these children (i.e., the norms of parental responsibility), these conditions produce tensions in the relationships between teen-aged children and their parents.

Evidence obtained from a study of one urban residential community will be presented in support of this argument and a question will be raised as to whether the conditions and consequences discussed in this paper are causally related to the nature of "mass society."

## URBAN MASS SOCIETY

Urban mass society is residentially mobile. Approximately one out of five Americans changes his place of residence every year.[1] Viewed from the perspective of the average neighborhood resident, this means that new neighbors are constantly moving in as old neighbors, friends, and acquaintances move out. Such a process is continually at work undermining the primary-group nature of neighborhood relationships. If the members of one's community are to be one's friends, or even if they are to be acquaintances, one must get to know something about them. Their values, interests, and beliefs are important, particularly as these are relevant to neighborhood social relations. This task is virtually impossible for many persons who spend a major part

---

This paper was prepared especially as an original contribution to this book.

of their time in activities located outside the neighborhood. Even the increase in leisure time, insofar as it is manifested in gardening, for example, tends to relate only to immediately adjacent neighbors rather than residents in a broader area. Thus the scale of the primary neighborhood has declined and most residents living even within a few blocks of each other are not acquainted.[2]

The point is not that intimate relationships have necessarily diminished either in frequency or in intensity for most urban dwellers, rather that the ecology of such relationships has changed. In response to modern developments in transportation and communication, such relations have become more diffuse. Their primary locus is not in the residential neighborhood, but on the job, at a club meeting, or over the phone. Although it is true that kinship relations appear to play a significant part in the social life of urban people, the ecology of these relationships also has changed; in a sense, one truly "visits" one's relatives and friends rather than "dropping in" on them. These visits become less spontaneous as distance between residences increases.

A second feature of the urban mass-society type of social organization is a high degree of role differentiation and role insulation. Urban dwellers play a wide variety of different roles. They are parents, neighbors, church members, and employees, and they are active in a variety of recreational associations and social clubs. As the degree of urbanization increases (i.e., as the scale of social organization increases), the tendency to relate to other people specifically on the basis of one particular role increases. People relate to others on the basis of the particular role they are playing at any given time and not in terms of their "total self," as displayed in the total set of roles they play. Few know one another as individuals. This role insulation and differentiation is a primary characteristic of the urban mass society.[3]

Although not at all unique to the urban mass society, the phenomenon of age grading of activities is another feature of this type of society. The bulk of associations people have are with others of roughly their own age group.

Finally, and particularly important for this paper, is the nature of social controls in this type of social setting. A considerably oversimplified typology would specify two primary types of social controls. The first would include those resulting from the internalization of values, role norms, and role expectations combined with a self-image consistent with action in conformity with such culturally stylized prescriptions. The second would be external controls, the effectiveness of which rests on the manipulation of sanctions by others. It appears that, wheras over the total range of societal types internal social controls take precedence, external controls become increasingly important as a society moves toward the urban-mass type.[4]

## CONDITIONS RELEVANT TO EFFECTIVE SOCIAL CONTROL

If the argument set forth in this paper is to be seen in full context it will be necessary to specify conditions that are generally relevant for the control of any individual (or group) by any other. Such conditions include: (1) access on the part of the agent of control to adequate knowledge of the behavior of those being controlled, and (2) access to effective sanctions, either direct or indirect. Knowledge of deviant behavior cannot be implemented in the absence of effective sanctions; effective sanctions are useless in the absence of such knowledge. Any conditions that effectively reduce the capacity to sanction or the availability of knowledge restrict the power of control.

In a number of ways the effectiveness of parental sanctions has been reduced in the urban-mass context. Faris has pointed out that the reduction in the patterns of intergenerational associations has undermined the traditional authority of parental norms.[5] Numerous researchers have documented the increasing significance of peer-group norms in the socialization of children. Thus the sanctions available to parents have diminished in their effectiveness.

Our present concern is primarily with the knowledge dimension, however. The compartmentalization of behavior systems has rendered the behavior of youth "less visible" to their parents. Most of the activities of young adolescents occur in situations where the parents are absent. The bureaucratization of an ever-widening range of areas of social life also has increased the barriers to adult communication about children.

In one sense the problem with which this paper is concerned represents an example of institutional malintegration, where norms relating to the roles of parents are inconsistent with norms relating to the organization of the informal communication system of a neighborhood. Following the lead of most functional theorists, Wilensky asserts that there is a "strain toward consistency" in the interrelationship of diverse institutional norms.[6] But he leaves unspecified the problem of identifying the mechanisms producing this "strain" and the barriers to the achievement of interinstitutional integration. It is just as reasonable to assume that the *barriers* to integration are equally as strong as (if not stronger than) the forces to produce it.

In studying interinstitutional integrative structures that have failed to produce integration, a clue to some of the structural barriers to such integration may be discerned. An example of one such structure is the Parent-Teachers' Association in the United States. Initially developed, at least in part, as a device to facilitate coordination between teachers and other school representatives on the one hand and parents and other community residents on the other in the socialization and social control of young people, this movement increasingly has been "subverted." In fact, typically it has come to be used as an adjunct to the administration of the public school system. Its most exciting activities include student "talent shows," fund-raising activities, and sometimes, political support in school bond elections. If we ask "why is this so," the answer is revealing. It is to some extent the consequence of the basic structural features of the urban-mass type of society. As the scale of public-school education increases, the bureaucratization of school systems increases. Specialists emerge in almost all areas of school administration from curriculum planning to student discipline. Active intervention of any significant segment of the public in the administration of the schools challenges the "expertise" of these administrators. Barriers to such intervention tend to be erected so that the initiation of change remains in the hands of representatives of the schools. Thus, in providing an opportunity for the recognition of parents' interests and for their collective expression in the form of demands for change, the P.T.A. constitutes a potential threat to the autonomy of the schools. Strong strains toward coopting representatives of the organization and toward "managing" its activities on the part of the school representatives follow, so that even the most resolute of parents find it difficult to effectively represent their values and interests in the school experiences of their children.

It seems entirely possible that the "strain" toward integration in this area is more than counteracted by counter strains. In the following paragraphs we will return to the central thesis of this paper. The norm of parental responsibility and the norm of nonintervention will be defined, and their implications for parental social control discussed. Then the findings from a study of these norms will be presented.

## THE NORM OF NONINTERVENTION

It is an old adage that people should "mind their own business." This bit of folk wisdom, however, fails to specify the conditions under which "someone else's business" becomes the legitimate concern of ego. There seem to be at least two types of such conditions. The first of these involves the closeness of the relationship between ego and the "someone else." In general it is probably true that as the degree of social intimacy increases in social relationships, the perceived legitimacy of intervention in another's affairs increases. Consider, for example, the recent incident in New York in which a girl was attacked on the street by a knife-wielding man. The attack was witnessed by a number of onlookers none of whom offered to intervene. Now suppose that

this girl had been the sister of one of the onlookers, or even the wife of a friend. The reaction would probably have been different. Further, it is likely that had one of the onlookers even been acquainted with the victim some sort of aid would have been offered.

In addition to this "intimacy" factor, it is likely that the degree of seriousness of the problem facing another is related to the perceived legitimacy of intervention by ego. It is one matter to refrain from reporting a neighbor's child for smoking, but another to fail to report him for auto theft.[7]

As urban society has witnessed the growth of bureaucratic organizations charged with the formal responsibility for the social control of deviance, the willingness of the average citizen to intervene in this process seems to have declined. As residential mobility has increased, and given the regional, racial, ethnic, and religious heterogeneity of the population, neighbors have become increasingly unsure about how "others" (i.e., other parents) would react to any proffered information. One cannot be sure that one shares with others the values that might define such communications as legitimate.

Over the years the attitude that appears to have characterized the situation of the stabbing in New York (i.e., "it isn't my business to interfere") seems to have spread to a wider and wider range of human social behavior. This paper is specifically concerned with this norm as it relates to the process of parent-child relations.

## THE NORM OF PARENTAL RESPONSIBILITY

The traditions of Western societies, indeed, the traditions of the majority of the world's societies, hold that parents, or parental substitutes as primary agents in the socialization of children, are "responsible" for any deviant social behavior in which their children engage. As an intense sense of "shame" is expected from parents whose children are deviants, so too does the "successful" parent manifest pride in the child who successfully conforms to the demands of his society. Perhaps this is a necessary feature of successful social organization.

In an extensive series of case studies, only two cases were uncovered in which parents denied their responsibility for the social control of their children. Both of these were lower-class families in which the parents simply said that it was impossible for them to either know about the behavior of their children or to control it if they did know. In each case both parents worked and were absent from the home during long periods of time. Even in these cases the parents evidenced a sense of frustration at not being able to "do their parental job well."[8]

This norm is integrated into the law regarding responsibility for minors as well as into the religious beliefs of most Westerners. It may be asserted, therefore, that the vast majority of Westerners grow up to hold themselves responsible for the behavior of their children.

## THE STUDY

As a part of a larger project designed to measure social costs and benefits associated with major highway changes in a well-established residential community, a household census was conducted.[9] Background demographic information and data on organizational participation, attitudes toward the community, and residential mobility intentions were collected. Several months later a mail-back questionnaire was sent to each household. The original plus two follow-up questionnaires produced a total of 575 (70 per cent) completed and usable responses. A detailed examination of the social and demographic characteristics of the households in the original census and those in the final panel of respondents to the mail-back questionnaire indicated virtually no bias in the final sample traceable to nonrespondents.

In the questionnaire respondents were given the following hypothetical situation:

Suppose that a young girl, about fourteen, was seen by some neighbors climbing out of her first floor bedroom window late at night, after her parents were in bed, to keep a date with a boy who picked her up in a car.

The respondents were then asked:

In this situation, what do you think these neighbors *should* do? What do you think most of the people *actually would* do? What would *you*, yourself, do in this situation?

They were asked to respond to these questions on the assumptions that the neighbors were "friends," "acquaintances," and "strangers" to the girl's parents.

## THE FINDINGS

As just indicated the normative prescriptions for the neighbors' behavior were measured by the question, "What *should* the neighbors do?" Actual predictions of behavior in the situation were elicited in response to the question, "What do you think the neighbors *actually would* do?" Our respondents agreed on the norm under conditions in which the neighbors were personal friends of the deviant child's parents.

TABLE 16-1

ROLE NORMS, ROLE EXPECTATIONS, AND PREDICTED ROLE
BEHAVIOR IN REPORTING A CHILD'S DEVIANT ACT

|  | Per cent responding | | | |
|---|---|---|---|---|
|  | Tell parents | Tell neighbors | Tell no one | N |
| Role norms: What *should* the neighbors do if they were — | | | | |
| Friends ...................... | 95 | 0 | 5 | 539 |
| Acquaintances ................ | 74 | 3 | 23 | 516 |
| Strangers ................... | 48 | 8 | 44 | 508 |
| Role expectations: What would the neighbors do if they were — | | | | |
| Friends ...................... | 85 | 7 | 8 | 522 |
| Acquaintances ................ | 40 | 38 | 22 | 506 |
| Strangers ................... | 11 | 47 | 42 | 501 |
| Prediction of own behavior if parents were — | | | | |
| Friends ...................... | 94 | 0 | 6 | 538 |
| Acquaintances ................ | 68 | 4 | 28 | 515 |
| Strangers ................... | 34 | 13 | 53 | 503 |

Ninety-five per cent said that they should "tell her parents," none felt that they should "tell other neighbors," and only 5 per cent felt that they should "tell no one." (See Table 16-1.) It is clear, however, that as the degree of personal intimacy decreases, the respondents become less and less convinced of the correctness of this course of action. If the parents were *acquaintances,* 74 per cent of the respondents felt that they should tell the girl's parents, 3 per cent felt that they should tell neighbors, and 23 per cent felt that they should tell no one. When the neighbors observing the deviant act were *strangers* to the girl's parents, only 48 per cent of the respondents felt that the parents should be told; 8 per cent felt that neighbors should be told, and 44 per cent felt that no one should be told. Thus the conditions of close friendship elicited almost perfect consensus on the proper course of action, but under conditions in which the neighbors are strangers, there was little agreement on the proper course of action.

The findings also indicate a systematic discrepancy between the statements of norms relevant to behavior in this situation, and the patterns of expectations for the behavior of the neighbors. In general a sizable proportion of the respondents did not expect the neighbors to live up to the norm. As with the reactions to the question on the norms, the degree of personal intimacy was deemed very important in assessing how the neighbors would react. Although 85 per cent of the respondents felt that the neighbors would tell the girl's parents if they were friends, only 11 per cent felt that they would tell the parents if they were strangers. As the degree of intimacy declined, our respondents were increasingly likely to expect gossip or complete silence.[10] Thus our respondents report expecting very real barriers to the flow of this important information from people in the neighborhood under conditions in which the neighborhood includes relatively few close personal friends of the parents. As suggested earlier, this is the situation in most mass societal residential areas, and it was precisely the state of affairs in this community. Most people (81 per cent) reported that relatively few of their close personal friends lived in the neighborhood.

It is interesting to note that there was a strong tendency for the respondents to claim for themselves greater conformity to the norms than they expected from others. In general, few were willing to admit that they gossip (i.e., tell neighbors). A majority (53 per cent) indicated that if they did not know the neighbors they would tell no one. This may reflect projection or social desirability distortion in responding to the questions, or more interestingly it may reflect neighborhood pluralistic ignorance.[11] One would expect such pluralistic ignorance given an inefficient neighborhood communication system.

## SUMMARY

In the previous sections changes in urban social organization affecting the ecology of intimate relationships have been identified and discussed. The increasing dominance of large-scale bureaucratic organizations over the social life of man, increasing rates of residential mobility, improvements in transportation and communication, and the elaboration of role differentiation and role insulation have all combined to fundamentally alter the functions of the residential neighborhood and community. Increasingly the activities of young children and those in their teens are not directly visible to parents. Within this context effective parental control rests in part on the willingness of other adults to provide parents with information about their childrens' (deviant) behavior. As the character of the relational system has changed, the norm of nonintervention has extended to an increasing proportion of the population, thus effectively reducing the likelihood that any deviant acts will come to the attention of parents.

In this setting the norm of parental responsibility has persisted and most parents judge themselves in part on the basis of the degree to which their children are seen as conforming to American success norms. With increased opportunity for deviance among children, an increased strain has been introduced into parent-child relationships. Thus parents hold themselves accountable for something over which they exercise decreasing control. This condition is seen as a correlate of mass society.

## DISCUSSION

Given the conditions described in this paper, it is important that the modes of adaptation to this type of strain be identified. Some types of adaptation could lead to a new, and more highly integrated, type of interinstitutional relationships; others may simply mask the effects of existing disjunctures.

Adaptation can occur at the level of the specific family experiencing strain or at the community level. At the family level some parents probably develop the myth of high rapport with their children, telling themselves that if and when their children misbehave, the children trust them enough to tell the parents what they have done. This pattern often is combined with parental unwillingness to interpret anything their child does as indicative of misbehavior. Low grades in school or reports of misconduct often are interpreted as prejudice on the part of school officials and teachers. The parents tend to adopt their children's perspective and interpretation of what has happened.

In other cases parents suspecting that their children have been misbehaving but sensing that they can exert little effective control may "give up." They often come to depend on external agents of control (i.e., the police, the courts, the school officials, or social workers) to resolve their problems with the child. Frequently this mode of adaptation is coupled with extreme hostility directed toward the child (partly, perhaps, because the norm of parental responsibility implies that they, the parents, are failures).

Finally, many parents give over a good portion of their time to chaperoning their children or to "checking up" on their activities. Interviews with young teen-age children in Seattle suggest that they develop a facility for evading this surveillance. They quickly learn who will and who won't "rat" on them, and they simply avoid the homes of adults who "rat," and frequent the homes of those who don't.

At the community level at least three modes of adaptation are possible. One of these involves the extension of responsibility and authority over children to other parental agents of social control. These include the school, the police and juvenile authorities, social workers, and perhaps even other adults in the community. This shift toward a norm of more communal responsibility for children would lessen, of course, the moral burden on parents and thus reduce parent-child tensions. There are some indications of a movement in this direction with the development of youth commissions and other official agencies charged with a responsibility for administering programs for pre-delinquent youth.

A second possible general mode of accommodation to the present situation would be a modification of the norm of parental responsibility itself. It is entirely possible that allied with the previously discussed trend (the extension of authority and responsibility for children to agents outside the nuclear family), it may be generally recognized (and normative) that parents alone cannot "be responsible" for the behavior of their children. As a result, the responsibility could come to be shared with other agencies of socialization and social control.

Finally, it is possible that as a result of changes in socialization practices, American young people can be induced to develop more effective internal controls. This alternative seems unlikely unless the various agents of social control come to be organized such that the behavioral norms and expectations that impinge on youth are relatively consistent and supported by an effective system of sanctions.

Whatever the modes of adaptation

to stress in parent-child relationships, this paper has sought to demonstrate that at least some of the causes of these stresses are "structural." They are traceable to disjunctures between elements in the normative (cultural) system and those in the system of social organization. It is problematic as to whether any mechanisms of interinstitutional integration can eliminate these sources of stress in the urban-mass social context.

Several of the more "traditional" "theories of deviance" concentrate on the structural disjuncture between relatively universal middle-class success goals and the lack of access of lower-class youth to the means of achieving these goals.[12] Such theories go a long way toward explaining the higher rates of delinquency among lower-class than among middle-class youth, provided, of course, that the evidence that lower-class rates are higher is valid; a point which itself has been subject to considerable questioning. In any event these theories do not contribute much to the understanding of a relatively high rate of deviance for all classes or among the middle class. This failure may become more critical as increasing affluence and diminishing racial segregation barriers further erode the ranks of the severely disadvantaged.

The interference with the administration of effective social controls over their children by parents, imposed by the social ecology of the modern residential neighborhood, is a major variable in constructing an adequate structural theory of middle-class juvenile deviance in mass society.

---

1. "Mobility of the Population of the United States, March 1963 to March 1964," *Current Population Reports, Population Characteristics*, Series P-20, No. 141, Sept. 7, 1965, 15–16. A part of the high rate of mobility is contributed by a relatively small portion of the population making relatively many moves. See Sidney Goldstein, "Repeated Migration as a Factor in High Mobility Rates," *American Sociological Review*, 19, 1954, 536–541.

2. L. K. Northwood and Ernest A. T. Barth, *Urban Desegregation*, Seattle: University of Washington Press, 1965, pp. 36-37.

3. Walter B. Watson and Ernest A. T. Barth, "Questionable Assumptions in the Theory of Social Stratification," *Pacific Sociological Review*, 7, Spring 1964, 16.

4. The authors are aware that this sweeping generalization may greatly overemphasize the specific case of the United States and that it may therefore be of limited value. However, it seems to be a fruitful point of departure for this investigation.

5. Robert E. L. Faris, "Interaction of Generations and Family Stability," *American Sociological Review*, 12, 1947, 159–164.

6. Harold L. Wilensky, "Mass Society and Mass Culture: Interdependence or Independence?," *American Sociological Review*, 29, 1964, 179.

7. One other type of circumstance that is relevant here is the degree to which the act observed by ego or the consequences of intervention threaten ego personally. One is more likely to report a child for breaking one's own window than for breaking someone else's. Likewise the risk of being stabbed has implications for the likelihood of intervening to prevent another's being stabbed.

8. Class projects at the University of Washington involving 180 interviews for Sociology 352, "The Family," under the supervision of Dr. Ernest A. T. Barth.

9. Ernest A. T. Barth, Walter B. Watson, and Wayne A. Blanchard, "Measuring Secondary Consequences of Urban Corridors on Social Values," Chap. 6 in

Robert G. Hennes et al., *Criteria for Highway Benefit Analysis*, Seattle: University of Washington, Aug. 31, 1965.

10. Controls were introduced in the analysis of these tables for the influence of the "stage of the family life cycle" in which the respondent was located. The only significant variation from the general patterns reported here was for the "older, childless" stage. People in this stage tended to be less willing to agree that it was right to tell the parents, and they also were less likely to expect the neighbors to do so. In addition, fewer of them reported that they, themselves, would inform the parents.

11. Northwood and Barth, *op. cit.*, pp. 84–86.

12. Many of these theories stem from Robert K. Merton, "Social Structure and Anomie," Chap. 4 in Merton, *Social Theory and Social Structure*, Glencoe, Ill.: Free Press, 1957. See also Albert K. Cohen, *Delinquent Boys*, Glencoe, Ill.: Free Press, 1955; and Richard A. Cloward and Lloyd E. Ohlin, *Delinquency and Opportunity*, Glencoe, Ill.: Free Press, 1960.

# 17. THE IMPACT OF ILLNESS ON FAMILY ROLES

## Robert R. Bell

The twentieth-century American family has been influenced by numerous changes which are complexly interrelated with the broad social changes characteristic of modern American society. This paper focuses on some social changes related to family patterns for dealing with the illness of a family member. Since one of the major changes in the American family has been a shift from a large extended family to a small conjugal one, illness to one family member leaves fewer immediate family members to care for him. If the husband or wife becomes ill the other spouse usually must take on many new role obligations.

The concept of role is used here to refer to the range of expected behavior attached to a social-group position. It is assumed that every role has certain counterroles; thus any significant influence on one role within a complex of interrelated roles implies alterations or adaptions in related roles. Furthermore roles do not remain static; they may change over time, both in role prescriptions and as these prescriptions are actually filled by individuals. For example, the role prescriptions of mother today are different from the past, and individuals filling the mother role find that their rights and obligations change over time.[1]

In the following discussion we shall examine: (1) some changes in the family, with particular relevance for family adaptations to illness; (2) the changing nature of the patient role; and (3) how certain family and patient roles are interrelated.

## FAMILY ROLE CHANGES

Rather than attempt to discuss the many changes in the American family, we shall direct our comments primarily to some changes in the family roles of women. This stress appears justified because many of the most significant changes in the modern American family have been related to the changing roles of women. Also, since our interest is in the impact of illness on the family, our female stress seems further justified because women's roles generally are more affected by illness (both as patient and nurse) than are other family roles.

In the past the role of the woman was clear and relatively simple — her primary adult role was that of wife-mother. She met certain needs of the husband, had the main responsibility for the care and the rearing of children, and maintained the home. Although she might have had some fustrations and dissatisfactions in filling the traditional wife-mother role, the role was generally accepted as the "natural" behavior pattern for women. "It was 'natural' because it was what women had been doing for centuries, and few other significant adult roles were being filled by women to indicate any alternatives."[2]

---

This paper was prepared especially as an original contribution to this book.

Today the vast majority of women undoubtedly enter marriage with a strong desire to fill most of the role demands of the traditional wife-mother. As in the past most women want children and want to maintain a home of their own, and in many cases the marriage will seem to be lacking if these traditional role expectations are not achieved.

Compared to the past, the difference today is that the woman often wants something more. This does not necessarily mean that she loves her husband, children, and home any less; but because of greater time and more greatly developed capacities for other interests, she often has other strong desires that seek fulfillment.[3]

The changing nature of family role demands by the modern woman is reflected in a number of social changes. Yet the new role interests of the woman are not at the expense of less interest in marriage — a greater proportion of women today are married than in the past.

In 1900, 2 out of 3 women in the total population had been married at some time in their lives; now this is true for 4 out of 5 women.[4] Furthermore women are entering marriage at younger ages; between 1890 and 1962 the median age of marriage dropped from 22.0 to 20.3 years for women.[5]

Another important change is that the modern woman lives in a world where increasingly the pattern is for her to live her older years without a husband. For example, "at ages 65 and over there now are 1276 women per 1000 men; by 1980 this ratio will be 1403 per 1000."[6]

The relative improvement in longevity of females is particularly striking because it has increased the disparity in expectation of life between the sexes. The average duration of life has increased by 19.32 years for white males and 23.11 years for white females.[7]

The greater life expectancy of women also is reflected in the increasing responsibility of women as family breadwinners. For example, the proportion of women who head households increases from 11 per cent at ages 40–44 to 36 per cent at ages 65 and over.[8]

Other important alterations of the woman's role are related to changes in education and occupational opportunities. In the United States today 66 per cent of the women now under age 30 are at least high-school graduates. By contrast, of women now age 65 and over only 24 per cent completed high school.[9] Furthermore the number of women pursuing higher education is increasing rapidly. The number of women earning B.A.'s was 5237 in 1900, 76,954 in 1940, and 145,514 in 1961.[10]

One of the most important changes in the woman's role has been entrance of a large number into the work force. In 1962 there were 23 million women in the work force and the forecast is for 30 million in 1970.[11] About 60 per cent of all women workers are married, or, to put it a different way, among married white women about one-third are working.[12] The kinds of occupations that women enter are partially related to their age; for example, in the "clerical and kindred worker" category are 48 per cent of the employed women in the 25–29 age grouping, but only 15 per cent of the employed women of age 65 and over.[13]

A common statistical picture of the modern American woman indicates that she enters marriage at a young age, has a long period of married life, and often finds herself in the role of widow in her later years. Her increased educational background and occupational involvement is reflected in her participation in adult roles beyond the traditional wife-mother role. A greater importance is given to the family roles of the young woman in the maintenance and direction she provides for her family whether she works or not. This results in part from her husband working away from home and because his occupation is often his major adult role commitment. Also because of geographical mobility the modern wife-mother has fewer relatives to turn to and must herself make the major adjustments to new communities. For many modern women this means participation in the traditional wife-mother roles plus other roles. In the recent Report of the President's Commission on Women it was stated that "women's ancient function of providing love and nurture stands. But for entry into modern life, today's children need a preparation far more diversified than that of their predecessors."[14]

A great deal of controversy has arisen over the personal significance of the traditional roles performed by women in the modern family. Part of the trend for giving these roles greater significance has been the attempt to "professionalize" the wife-mother role.

By professionalization is meant the development of a set of rationales for an intellectual and emotional commitment to the functions of being a modern wife and mother. The new belief is that being a "good wife" and mother today calls for dedication, knowledge, and a sense of creativity similar to that found in professions.[15]

For example, although the health of the child has always been of vital concern to the mother, she was usually anxious about the child's physical health; today she is more likely to be anxious about psychic dangers.

Concerning oneself with the psychological health of a child revolves a greater intellectual commitment than simply worrying about his physical health. Child rearing takes on certain professional overtones with the woman who has been educated, and she keeps herself informed about various writings in regard to personality development.[16]

A part of the "professionalization" of the wife-mother role has been changes in her functions as family "nurse." In the past the wife-mother cared for the ill members in her family, but she did it primarily through "folk" wisdom. Medical remedies and suggestions were often acquired from older women who also frequently were available to help out when family illness occurred. Often the woman could put goose grease on the patient's chest, feed him chicken broth, and thus fill the role of family nurse. Today, however, the modern woman does not rely on "folk" knowledge but turns to medical experts. This means that the wife-mother is often the intermediary between the patient and the medical expert. Because medical knowledge is so complex and technical the wife-mother must be greatly concerned with correctly following the prescribed medical course. This is often true even when the diagnosis of the illness is not particularly serious because of the constant threat that it will develop into something more dangerous. It is ironical that as medical knowledge has alleviated many problems those problems that remain have often become even more frightening. That is, for the wife-mother the fear of not doing the right thing because of potential medical dangers is often greater than the actual medical problem involved. Thus new problems may be created.

Another related social trend that places increasing demands on the nursing role function in the home is the growing medical pattern of sending patients home from the hospital during the recovery period (and sometimes when there is little or no possibility of recovery). This often means that the woman must have knowledge and even some medical skills in taking care of the family member. The development of home-care programs appears to be on the increase. "The advantages of care in the individual's own home, provided adequate medical nursing and other needed services are available, is generally accepted in theory today."[17] That the home-nursing function is believed to be a part of the female role is also indicated in the Report of the President's Commission:

Modern family life is demanding, and most of the time and attention given to it comes from women. At various stages, girls and women of all economic backgrounds should receive education in respect to physical and mental health, child care and development, human relations within the family.[18]

Although the increasing care of some ill members may be argued as a function of the family, there is evidence that some general social values may not support the argument. For example, Farber found that

the community of "normal" families is not supportive of the revised norms of child care that must be established by families with a severely handicapped child. In effect, the norms and values regulating participation in the community of "normal" families are hostile to the demands made upon the parents of severely handicapped children.[19]

In general it is our contention that in the middle-class family a part of the "professionalization" of the modern woman's role includes her caring for

ill members, but in her role of caring for the ill she is not the decision maker but rather has her "nursing" role defined by the medical community. Furthermore, with the home-care movement she will be called upon increasingly to fill a nurse function within the family, but defined for her from *outside* the family. This means that she will function in a mediating role between the impersonal, rational role decisions of the medical expert and the application of those decisions within the highly emotional context of her relationships to her husband or children. The psychological implications of this mediating role are great for both the woman and the ill member in the family. It might also be added that the shouldering of this mediating role function by women will contribute to a further extension of the impersonal relationship between the medical authority and the patient.

## CHANGING PATIENT ROLES

The general observation that roles in American society have been undergoing significant change is also true with regard to the various roles related to illness. Within the limits of this paper we can focus only briefly on some of the changes in patient roles with particular reference to family members in the patient role and other family roles as related to the family member patient. That is although the changing role of the patient has many implications, we are primarily interested in how this role change is related to the family.

Becoming ill means that the individual is assigned a new and special role, that of the patient. "In this role he exchanges freedom, autonomy, and self-direction for control, but at the same time he gains protection, freedom from responsibility, and care."[20] One of the most important changes with reference to the patient role has been its expansion to include more persons with more different types of medical problems. The most obvious illustration has been the twentieth-century acceptance of the mentally ill patient. Jessie Bernard suggests that the inclusion under the patient role of "many persons formerly viewed as wicked or as criminal is one of the major results of an age of abundance. We can afford to treat them as medical rather than moral or legal problems."[21]

We must place a further restriction on our discussion because we cannot comprehensively discuss the range of physical and mental illnesses as related to the patient role. It is clear that there are differences in having a mental patient versus a physically ill patient in the family. There are differences in both the development of mental illness in the patient and the perception and understanding of that illness by others. On this point Rusk and Novey write:

Despite the progress in public understanding of the amoral nature of emotional and mental illness, there is still likely to be a greater feeling of failure and shame in such cases than when physical and organic illness occurs.[22]

In the family, which depends for efficient operation on the congruency of role relationships, any significant changes in roles may be difficult for other family members to accept and adapt to. But entering a patient role is generally one that other family members can accept as a condition of life because it is not a role change seen as deliberately entered, but rather as beyond the control of the individual. Although family members may sometimes find the means of adaptation to the patient role difficult, they generally see it as something they

must attempt to adapt to. This is also true because a state of illness is partially and conditionally legitimized. "That is, if a person is defined as sick, his failure to perform his normal functions is 'not his fault,' and he is accorded the right to exemption and care."[23]

The process of family adaptation to illness is closely linked to the family's definition of the event as a family crisis and what they see as their alternatives for future action. In general, a family crisis calls for new family role procedures because it

is an event which strains the resources which families possess, cannot be solved by the repertory of ready-made answers provided by the mores or built up out of the family's previous experience with trouble, and requires the family to find new (and usually expedient) ways of carrying on family aspirations.[24]

The definition of and adaptation to the crisis of illness of a family member is influenced by the patient's and other family members' perception of the illness for the future. Farber suggests that "the existence of a family crisis depends upon the extent to which the family members regard an event as changing present or future family life in an undesirable way."[25] An important part of a crisis definition may be the extent of significant alterations that the family members see for their family roles. For example, if the man is chronically ill it may mean his leaving his occupational role, requiring his wife to enter that role. This implies for the man the loss of a highly significant role and for the woman the addition of another highly significant role to those she already fills. As Farber has pointed out, this crisis adaptation does not necessarily mean family disorganization, but rather an alteration of family roles and patterns of behavior.[26] Waller and Hill have suggested that

at least three variables help to determine whether a given event becomes a crisis for any given family: (1) the hardships of the situation or event itself; (2) the resources of the family: its role structure, flexibility, and previous history with crisis; and (3) the definition the family makes of the event; that is, whether family members treat the event *as if it were* or *as if it were not* a threat to their status, goals, and objectives.[27]

The role adaptations of the family to illness are often of a temporary nature with a return to "normal" family roles when the illness is corrected. In this kind of situation, role adaptations generally are easier because they are seen as temporary with a foreseeable return to the usual family roles. Of course, what may initially appear to be temporary role adaptations may last far longer than anticipated. There may also be an unwillingness to return to the pre-illness family roles. For example, a woman who temporarily becomes the breadwinner because of her husband's illness may want to stay in her occupational role even when her husband has recovered and returned to his job. Or it may be that the ill family member may desire or be induced to stay in the patient role. It has been pointed out, for example, that sometimes patients released from mental hospitals may be so "protected" by their families that they feel no need to improve and thereby leave the patient role.[28]

In the following discussion we shall look at some implications of illness for both marital and parental role relationships. Before doing so, however, it should be made explicit that our discussion and its impact on family roles is restricted almost entirely to the middle class. The values and patterns of be-

havior often found in the lower class lead to different family adaptations to health problems. This means that the attitudes toward health presented by the middle-class medical profession often have limited impact on the lower class. Rainwater has pointed out that in the lower class

people will be inclined to slight physical difficulties in the interest of attending to more pressing ones such as seeing that there is food in the house, or seeking some kind of expressive experience which will reassure them that they are alive and in some way valid persons. The same kind of medical problem will stand out much more sharply in the middle-class person because he tends to conceive of his life as having a relatively even and gratifying tenor; his energies are quickly mobilized by anything which threatens to upset that tenor.[29]

Many lower-class homes are one-parent, mother-head families and therefore the mother has many family responsibilities with often little time to devote to illness — whether it be her own or that of a child. When the illness is her own she may have little time or inclination to seek medical help.

The attitude toward illness (even when it becomes chronic) in this kind of a situation is apt to be a fairly tolerant one. People learn to live with illness, rather than using their small stock of interpersonal and psychic resources to do something about the problem.[30]

Because of the limited family resources, Rainwater goes on to point out, "we observe lower-class parents seemingly relatively indifferent to all kinds of obvious physical illnesses that their children may have — particularly infections, sores, colds, and the like."[31] Therefore most of the following discussion of illness in middle-class families can have only limited application for lower-class families and their role adaptations to illness.

## ILLNESS AND MARRIAGE ROLES

In this section the focus is on some of the consequences of illness for the husband-father and the wife-mother. As previously suggested there are differences in consequences for the patient role and the other family members roles as related to whether the illness is physical or mental. We cannot take the space to explore many of the differences but we shall try to indicate from available research some of the implications related to physical versus mental illness for the family members. In general we suggest that there is often some personal and social stigma attached to mental illness, both for the patient and for other family members; whereas with physical illness both the patient and other family members are almost always absolved of any personal responsibility because they are seen as victims of circumstances beyond their control.

The stigmatic nature of mental illness for a family member is reflected in the common resistance to defining the member as having a mental-health problem. In many marriages the observable level of mental illness in a spouse necessary for overt recognition by the partner may vary greatly. In a study of mentally ill husbands, Yarrow suggests that the wife's recognition of illness may come when she

can no longer manage her husband; in others when his behavior destroys the status quo; and, in still others, when she cannot explain his behavior. One can speculate that her level of tolerance for his behavior is a function of her specific personality needs and vulnerabilities, her personal and family value systems, and the social supports and prohibitions re-

garding the husband's symptomatic behavior.[32]

There are several implications of recognizing that a spouse has a severe mental-health problem. First, there is the emotional drain of identification with the person and his problem; that is, the many consequences for the emotional interaction between two closely linked persons. Second, there are implications of altered roles for the future. Yarrow points out that for a wife of a mentally ill husband it is not only threatening to recognize his mental illness and her own possible relationship to its development but also that she may have "to give up modes of relating to her husband that may have had satisfaction for her and to see a future as the wife of a mental patient."[33]

In severe illness, whether physical or mental, the major implication for the family is that basic roles can no longer be adequately filled by assigned family members. Therefore one basic adaptation by the family to illness must be the redefinition of role responsibilities, which usually means an expansion of role by the unafflicted adult. Yet the role problems and attempts at solutions are bound to have important differences depending on whether the wife or husband is ill and the nature of the illness.

When the husband is seriously ill this generally means that he is no longer able to function in his major role as breadwinner. For him this results in his being removed from the interactional setting of his occupation and being placed in the very different physical and social setting of the hospital or the home. When he is in the home as a patient he is not functioning in the same past role setting where he was usually in the home during the evenings and over the weekend. That is, in the past his role involvement in the home was limited in time and involved activity in his husband-father roles. With illness he may be spending almost all his time in the home in the new role of being a patient. Therefore for many male patients the home may appear to be a prison in the sense that they must stay there and be passively cared for rather than be away from home in the different and active role performance of their occupations.

Although the husband must make adjustments to his new patient role and the loss of his occupation role, his wife must adapt to him in his husband-patient role and she must often take on his previous breadwinner role. One common consequence is that the wife takes on the added roles but must do so within a restricted economic setting. She must often adapt to a lower income and greater medical expenses because of her husband's illness. If the husband is hospitalized she often has the added time problem of getting to and from and visiting with him in the hospital. Most of the time the wife has few guides to turn to for her new roles and must usually "play it by ear." Deasy and Quinn suggest that

the wife of a man who has been hospitalized as a mental patient for the first time finds herself in an anomalous position — she has not been prepared by personal experience to play this role, she probably has few role models within her immediate purview, and in most instances she feels constrained not to talk about the situation.[34]

It would also appear that when her husband is physically ill the wife may more easily turn to others for moral support and physical help than when her husband is suffering from mental illness.

If this is true then the role responsibilities of the wife with a mentally ill husband are carried on with more isolation than a wife with a physically ill husband. The isolated world of the wife with an institutionalized mentally ill husband is clearly suggested in one study.

According to the wives' report, 50 per cent of the patients in this study had no visitors outside the family during all the months of hospitalization, 41 per cent had only a single or a very occasional visitor, 9 per cent had frequent visitors. Friends telephone the wife to inquire about her husband, with vague promises of "wanting to see him" which never materialize.[35]

It would appear that mental illness often leads to loneliness for both the patient and the family. The patient and his family cannot escape the illness but others can and very often do. Because illness is something to be avoided in American society, the patient often finds that he suffers from a stigma which results in the loss of many persons with whom he had previously interacted. The stigma of the husband's illness also may alter the wife's interpersonal relationships with relatives and friends. Farber points out that "not only is she a 'single' person but she also becomes 'special' because of her problem."[36]

When the wife rather than the husband is the ill partner there are different implications for family roles. If the wife is hospitalized she, like the ill husband, is removed from the environment in which she performs her major roles — the home. This generally means the removal of the most significant family role member. Yet she is generally in contact with her husband who tells her about their home and family events, whereas the male who is ill often has little knowledge about what is going on in his occupational role setting. When the wife is ill and in her home, however, her role frustration may be even greater than when hospitalized because she is physically a part of her family setting yet unable to fill her usual family roles.

The husband may have to broaden his role participation when his wife is ill, but probably to less extent than the wife with an ill husband. This is suggested because the husband may often hire someone to do the chores normally done by his wife. Also the economic problems are relatively less when the wife is ill because even though the medical expenses are added the income level of the husband is not usually affected. And often the husband can acquire volunteer help from relatives and friends to help take care of the home. The wife with an ill husband is less likely to receive the kind of voluntary help she needs. This may be a reflection of the belief that men are often incapable (or unwilling) of taking care of many of the tasks necessary for running a household. Also the role of caring for a home is common to women and one may take over the chores of another in essentially the same way she performs those roles for herself. Yet the reverse of this, a man willing and able to substitute for the ill husband by taking over his breadwinner role, is far less common.

The hospitalized wife-mother may be greatly agitated by her withdrawal from domestic roles, especially from her mother role. If she is hospitalized, and has young children, it may be very difficult, because of hospital rules, for her to see her children. One study of wives hospitalized because of mental illness found they were "uniformly concerned with their abilities as mothers and with the possible effects of separation from

their children." The medical solution "was handled by emphasis on the necessity of hospitalization and its function in preparing them to be 'better' mothers (and wives)."[37]

Because the role of being mother to her children is held to be so important, the conditions for her removal from the home must be justified. In the case of both mental and physical illness the hospitalization of the mother is legitimized by the medical decision. In the case of mental illness the medical decision to hospitalize removes the burden of decision making from the husband. One study of hospitalized wives with young children found that "for most husbands, the hospital's acceptance of their wives as patients was enough to confirm the legitimacy of separation and to suppress overt reproaches of abandonment."[38]

The hospitalization of a spouse for reasons of mental illness may also provide a rationale for redefining the marriage relationship. That is, the hospitalization of the spouse tends to put marriage and family roles in a state of suspension, rather than dissolving past family roles. This is particularly important with regard to the impact of mental illness on marriage roles. In many marriages the history of the mental illness prior to diagnosis and hospitalization may have been one of conflict between the marriage partners. Yet the hospitalization of a spouse for reasons of mental illness redefines the situation. For example, in the study quoted above it was found that "husbands who had been planning to separate from or divorce their wives met legal obstacles. Besides these, they experienced moral constraints, from within and without, which often moved them to reconsider their decision."[39]

In a study of husbands hospitalized

for mental illness it was found that some of the wives had considered ending their marriage but that none actually did so. This study

hypothesized that a recurrence of the husband's illness, especially if it produces the same traumatic developments as were involved the first time, is likely to represent the "last straw" for some of these wives. It appears, however, that complete rejection of the patient is not very frequent after a single relatively brief period of hospitalization.[40]

One important consequence of serious illness for the marriage relationships may be the altering or ending of the sexual relationship. In American society, which gives approval only for sexual relations between marital partners, the inability of one spouse to sexually participate means that both partners are expected to end their active sexual life. For one physically incapable of engaging in coitus there is the added burden of guilt about his inability to meet the sexual needs of the spouse. Even if the well partner thinks about seeking out other sexual partners he would often be restrained by feelings of guilt toward the physically incapable partner.

Our main stress has been on the impact of illness on marriage roles. Of course marriage roles often overlap with parental roles. When one of the parents is ill the well partner must translate and mitigate adjustment as much as possible for the children. The well partner must often try to translate the altered role of the ill parent to the children. In the case of a parent suffering from mental illness the other parent may try to protect the children from the stigma of the parent's illness. One study found that in interpreting the father's mental illness to young children:

almost all the mothers attempt to follow a course of concealment. The child is told either that his father is in a hospital (without further explanation) or that he is in the hospital suffering from a physical ailment (he has a toothache, or trouble with his leg, or a tummy ache, or a headache).[41]

The same study found that adolescent and adult children share with the mother the problems of the father's illness more than any other group of persons. Many times, however, the mother is left on her own because the reactions of adolescent and young adult children are about equally divided into two patterns:

(a) Either the children visit their father regularly and assume much the same role and attitude toward the illness as their mother or (b) they refuse to visit, expressing openly a great deal of hostility toward their father.[42]

There is little research with regard to the possible effects of a parent's illness on the family roles played by children. When one parent is physically or mentally incapacitated and the well parent has to fill the combined roles, the children may respond in several different ways. Some children may see the care directed at the patient, especially if the well parent is the mother, as threatening to their relationships with their mothers. One consequence might be the regression of the child resulting in another added burden for the mother. On the other hand some children may react to illness of a parent by maturing rapidly insofar as taking on added responsibilities in helping the well parent. This may be particularly true for daughters because of the high identification with their mother and her roles. There is some evidence in studies of working mothers that daughters take up some of the responsibilities of their mothers when they have other role demands. Douvan found that the proportion of girls who carry major responsibilities is larger where the mother works either full time or part time than in homes where the mother is not employed.[43]

One other factor of marriage as related to illness impact occurs as the married couple grows older. Many times when serious illness of one of the spouses (most often the husband) first occurs is when the conjugal family unit has been reduced to only the husband and wife. This is the period of the postparental years when the last of the children have left home. Fifty years ago marriages ended through the death of one of the parents about the time the last child was leaving the parental home. But today's married couples have an average of about 15 years to share together after their youngest child has left home.[44] That the woman is most often the marriage partner who survives and who has filled a nurse role for her husband's terminal illness is reflected in the statistics of life expectancy. Slightly more than one-fifth of all the American women at age 55 to 64 and more than half of those at 65 and over are widows. "There are currently about 8½ million widows in the U.S., two-fifths of them under 65 years of age."[45] That increasing rates of illness are related to increasing age is obvious. For example, "while persons over 65 accounted for only one in twelve of the total population in 1955, one-fifth of the patients occupying hospital beds were in this age group."[46] Therefore women can increasingly expect to perform some nursing roles to their husbands with increasing age, and

when the husband is not hospitalized the care often will take place in the home with no members other than the husband-patient and the wife-nurse.

## PARENTS AND CHILDREN

In this last section we shall look briefly at the impact of illness on the parent-child relationship. When both parents are present the illness of a child usually places the greatest role demands on the mother. In general this is a part of a greater commitment to the parental role by the mother than by the father. One study found that where there were retarded children they tended to highlight parental role differences. "The findings tended to support predictions that fathers would be more vulnerable to social stigma and extramarital influences such as children's physical appearance and sex."[47]

An important difference with implications for role relationships occurs when an adult in contrast with a child is ill. Although in both cases we assume strong emotional involvement, when the child is ill there is added his dependency and immaturity. There is a dimension of "unfairness" in seeing a child ill because he appears so vulnerable and helpless. Therefore the parent responding to a sick child is responding to both the sickness and the helpless dependency of the child. Even though many of the serious illnesses of childhood have been alleviated, middle-class parents generally take a preventive medical approach to children. This approach not only protects the child from possible illnesses but it also helps protect the parents from the emotional drain of coping with sick children.

Yet even with the great medical advances with regard to children, the parents (especially the mother) have a new nursing role with regard to their children. As pointed out earlier the mother today finds herself constantly turning to medical experts for instructions in dealing with an ill child, and she is kept constantly aware of the potential dangers of mental illness for children. Because of the dependent and vulnerable nature of the child she is particularly sensitive of doing the "right" thing in treating her child, both for his health improvement and for her own reassurance that she is being a good mother.

There is some evidence that certain types of illness, particularly those that indicate long-term physical disability, have a variety of implications for parental roles. There is often a resistance to the fact that a problem really exists. For example, in a study of families with physically disabled children it was found that parents showed "an active resistance to the medical reality, which delayed the initiation of necessary treatment and the beginning of realistic adjustment."[48] The illness of the child may lead not only to new definitions within the family setting but also be altered role patterns for the parents outside the family. Farber points out that

investigations consistently indicate a tendency for parents of handicapped children to be less sociable and more withdrawn, and for these mothers to be less likely than other mothers to take employment outside the home.[49]

## CONCLUSION

In this paper the main purpose has been to look at some changing roles in the family, especially the role of wife-mother as related to illness. It appears

that increasingly the family is expected to handle a greater amount of illness and that increasingly this is becoming a part of the "professional" role of the wife-mother. For the most part the family's involvement in the care of its sick members is seen as meeting medical needs with little concern with how this affects the overall needs of the family.

The home-care movement is supported by funds and agencies for increasing facilitation of their beliefs about the care of the ill. The assumptions and aims of this are well illustrated by programs to return the mentally ill to their families. Vincent writes,

the family is expected to adapt to the return of its mentally ill or emotionally disturbed members, just as it was expected to adapt to the return of the parolee member of the family several decades ago. The family will also be expected to adapt to the intrusion of the mental-health personnel concerned with the rehabilitation of the patient, just as it has adapted to the intrusion of the parole and probation officers, the judge of the juvenile court, and the social worker.[50]

Given the emotional involvement of family members with one and another it is not difficult to persuade them as to their "responsibility." As Vincent puts it:

Given the mores of our society how could the family maintain its ideological image if it refused to accept one of its members convalescing from mental illness or rehabilitating from crime or delinquency?[51]

It appears that the primary concern in research has been with how the family may be used in the care of its ill members. That is, the family is seen as a means for facilitating medical decisions. But rarely is the question asked: what does the involvement of the ill do to other family roles? A second related question rarely asked is: does the family really provide a more effective setting for the handling of illness, or is this often primarily a means of resolving some of the problems of the medical authorities? Although we have suggested some possibilities for answering these questions, further exploration is needed. From the perspective of the sociology of the family we need to know far more about the implications of what the family is being asked to do medically for the family itself and its impact on society in general.

---

1. See Robert R. Bell, *Marriage and Family Interaction*, Homewood, Ill.: Dorsey, 1963, pp. 16–23.

2. *Ibid.*, p. 255.

3. *Ibid.*, pp. 259–260.

4. Margaret Mead and Frances B. Kaplan (Eds.), *American Woman*, New York: Scribner, 1965, p. 80.

5. *Ibid.*

6. "The American Woman," *Statistical Bulletin*, New York: Metropolitan Life Insurance Co., February 1965, p. 1.

7. "United States Life Tables: 1959–61," Washington, D.C.: U.S. Department of Health, Education, and Welfare, 1964, p. 5.

8. "The American Woman," *op. cit.*, p. 3.

9. *Ibid.*, pp. 3-4.

10. Mead, *op. cit.*, p. 91.

11. *Ibid.*, p. 45.

12. *Ibid.*

13. "The American Woman," *op. cit.*, p. 2.

14. Mead, *op. cit.*, p. 19.

15. Bell, *op. cit.*, p. 261.

16. *Ibid.*, p. 262.

17. George Rosen, "Health Programs for an Aging Population," in Clark Tibbetts, *Handbook of Social Gerontology*, Chicago: University of Chicago Press, 1960, p. 536.

18. Mead, *op. cit.*, pp. 32-33.

19. Bernard Farber, *Family: Organization and Interaction*, San Francisco: Chandler, 1964, p. 314.

20. Jessie Bernard, *Social Problems at Mid-Century*, New York: Dryden, 1957, p. 191.

21. *Ibid.*, p. 192.

22. Howard A. Rusk and Joseph Novey, "The Impact of Chronic Illness on Families," *Marriage and Family Living*, May 1957, 195.

23. Talcott Parsons and Renee Fox, "Illness, Therapy, and the Modern Urban American Family," *Journal of Social Issues*, 1958, 32–33.

24. Willard Waller and Reuben Hill, *The Family*, New York: Dryden, 1951, p. 456.

25. Farber, *op. cit.*, p. 409.

26. *Ibid.*, p. 392.

27. Waller, *op. cit.*, p. 459.

28. Donald A. Hansen and Reuben Hill, "Families under Stress," in Harold T. Christensen (Ed.), *Handbook of Marriage and The Family*, Chicago: Rand McNally, 1964, p. 809.

29. Lee Rainwater, "The Lower Class: Health, Illness, and Medical Institutions," mimeo, March 1965, pp. 2–3.

30. *Ibid.*, p. 5.

31. *Ibid.*, p. 9.

32. Marian R. Yarrow et al., "The Psychological Meaning of Mental Illness in the Family," *Journal of Social Issues*, **XI**, 1955, p. 18.

33. *Ibid.*, p. 22.

34. Leila C. Deasy and Olive W. Quinn, "The Wife of the Mental Patient and the Hospital Psychiatrist," *Journal of Social Issues*, **XI**, 1955, 49.

35. Marian R. Yarrow et al., "The Social Meaning of Mental Illness," *Journal of Social Issues*, **XI**, 1955, 44.

36. Farber, *op. cit.*, p. 397.

37. Harold Sampson et al., "The Mental Hospital and Marital Family Ties," in Howard Becker (Ed.), *The Other Side*, New York: Free Press of Glencoe, 1964, p. 145.

38. *Ibid.*, p. 144.

39. *Ibid.*, p. 146.

40. John A. Clausen and Marian R. Yarrow, "Further Observations and Some

Implications," *Journal of Social Issues*, **XI**, 1955, 62.

41. Yarrow, "The Meaning of Mental Illness," *op. cit.*, pp. 40–41.

42. *Ibid.*, p. 40.

43. Elizabeth Douvan, "Employment and the Adolescent," in E. Ivan Nye and Lois W. Hoffman, *The Employed Mother in America*, Chicago: Rand McNally, 1963, p. 146.

44. Mead, *op. cit.*, p. 89.

45. "The American Woman," *op. cit.*, p. 1.

46. Rosen, *op. cit.*, p. 527.

47. Irving Tallman, "Spousal Role Differentiation and the Socialization of Severely Retarded Children," *Journal of Marriage and Family*, February 1965, 42.

48. Thomas E. Dow, Jr., "Family Reaction to Crisis," *Journal of Marriage and Family*, August 1965, 363.

49. Farber, *op. cit.*, p. 313.

50. Clark E. Vincent, "Familia Spongia: The Adaptive Function," *National Council on Family Relations*, Toronto: October 1965, p. 13.

51. *Ibid.*

# 18. FAMILY STRUCTURE AND THE SOCIAL CONSEQUENCES OF DEATH

*Holger R. Stub*

Though death is ever present and provides life with an inevitable conclusion, it makes a considerable difference to the living as to who dies and when. This fact gives the recent dramatic changes in the death rate the character of a demographic revolution. The sharp decrease in infant and maternal mortality as well as the saving of lives in the youthful, middle-aged, and later years of life have had profound effects on the sociological consequences of death.

It is striking that a phenomenon as important as death is dealt with so rarely in the literature of the social sciences. Death seems to have been tabooed as a topic of sociological discussion.[1] There are, however, numerous religious and mystical discussions of death, and studies using mortality statistics in dealing with age structure, life expectancy, and so on are also an important part of the literature on population. As the end point of individual existence, death has stimulated considerable speculation about the nature of death itself, but systematic research on the consequences of death for the living is extremely limited.[2]

The various supportive institutions and social practices which have developed to make death easier have evolved in such a way as to shield most people from the awareness of death. This seems to have included social scientists. The artistry of the funeral director, the chapel-like mortuaries, and all the attendant services have removed the factual presence of death from the home and neighborhood. Gone is the vigil or wake in the home of the deceased. Death occurs in a hospital and the remains go directly to a well-managed, softly lit, and ingeniously circumlocutory "funeral home."

Death, like poverty and hunger, has ceased to be socially visible.[3] This may be largely responsible for the social vacuum in which some of the nation's undertakers or "grief therapists" conduct their seemingly ridiculous and almost-fraudulent practices.[4] Along with the decrease in the visibility of poverty, hunger, and death, there has been a decrease in the visibility of some of the human conditions that often precede and sometimes cause death. Needless to say, poverty and hunger have long historical affiliations with death. No longer are men confronted with their fellow humans exhibiting the afflictions and stigmata of disease and disaster, such as can be seen in Pieter Brueghel's painting, "Carnival Fighting with Lent," in which numerous people are depicted with physical deformities, lost limbs, leprosy, scurvy, apparent mental retardation, and starvation. Though the afflicted, infirm, and the near-dead are still with us, they are shielded from public view. This may partially explain why death and its social consequences have

This paper was prepared especially as an original contribution to this book.

191

TABLE 18-1
DEATH RATES BY AGE IN THE UNITED STATES, 1900 TO 1960*

| Year | All ages | Under 1 year | 1–4 years | 5–14 years | 15–24 years | 25–34 years |
|------|----------|--------------|-----------|------------|-------------|-------------|
| 1960 | 9.5  | 27.0  | 1.1  | 0.5 | 1.1 | 1.5 |
| 1955 | 9.3  | 29.6  | 1.1  | 0.5 | 1.1 | 1.5 |
| 1950 | 9.6  | 33.0  | 1.4  | 0.6 | 1.3 | 1.8 |
| 1945 | 10.6 | 41.4  | 2.0  | 0.9 | 2.0 | 2.7 |
| 1935 | 10.9 | 60.9  | 4.4  | 1.5 | 2.7 | 4.0 |
| 1925 | 11.7 | 75.4  | 6.4  | 2.0 | 3.8 | 4.8 |
| 1915 | 13.2 | 102.4 | 9.2  | 2.3 | 4.1 | 5.8 |
| 1905 | 15.9 | 141.2 | 15.0 | 3.4 | 5.2 | 2.4 |
| 1900 | 17.2 | 162.4 | 19.8 | 3.9 | 5.9 | 8.2 |

* Deaths for both sexes per 1000 population based on mid-year estimates, exclusive of stillbirths.

not been more thoroughly explored by social scientists. This seems to be another instance of the cultural values of a given time period influencing the choices of scientific investigation.

The most salient social aspects of the change in the frequency and timing of death are: (1) that the presence of death as a *frequent* occurrence in the family has greatly diminished, and (2) that the death rates of the most productive members of society have also been decreased, namely those of youth and middle age. For this important segment of society, many deaths have been prevented or postponed. In former times death was literally "in the midst of life," as the cemetery was in the middle of the village. Since then, poverty, suffering, and death have retreated from public view.[5] The development of antibiotics and new advances in surgery and medical technology have increased the length of life. "It can be strongly argued that greater progress has been made in medical science in the past fifty years than in the previous five thousand."[6] The present situation gives Americans an average life expectancy of 70 years.

Table 18-1 provides dramatic testi-mony to the decrease in death rates during the first 45 years of the twentieth century. The importance of this decline is reinforced by the estimate that in 1800 the expected length of life was only 30 years. Substantial social changes have been experienced at almost all points in the life cycle, brought about in part by the increase in length of life. A number of these social changes have a rather definite connection with the frequency and timing of death (i.e., the age-specific death rates) of various segments of the population.

Our major interest in this paper is in speculating about the social and psychological consequences of the timing and frequency changes of the death experience. Although the general increase in life expectancy is attributable primarily to lowered infant mortality rates, our concern here is with the decline of maternal mortality rates and those of persons in the productive years.

Another, and almost equally important, factor affecting one's contact with death in this society is that the drastic reduction in the death of infants and small children decreases the possibility of any given individual having any di-

TABLE 18-1

(CONTINUED)

| 35–44 years | 45–54 years | 55–64 years | 65–74 years | 75–84 years | 85 years and over |
|---|---|---|---|---|---|
| 3.0 | 7.6 | 17.4 | 38.2 | 87.5 | 198.6 |
| 3.1 | 7.5 | 17.3 | 39.6 | 89.4 | 186.2 |
| 3.6 | 8.5 | 19.0 | 41.0 | 93.3 | 202.0 |
| 4.6 | 9.7 | 20.3 | 44.6 | 99.5 | 222.5 |
| 6.2 | 11.6 | 23.2 | 48.7 | 113.1 | 224.6 |
| 7.2 | 12.2 | 23.3 | 51.7 | 119.3 | 272.3 |
| 8.3 | 13.1 | 25.5 | 55.6 | 120.1 | 240.3 |
| 9.8 | 14.7 | 27.7 | 66.2 | 122.4 | 261.5 |
| 10.2 | 15.0 | 27.2 | 56.4 | 123.3 | 260.9 |

*Source:* U.S. Bureau of Census, *Historical Statistics of the United States, Colonial Times to 1957*, 1960, p. 28; and *Statistical Abstract of the United States*, 1963, p. 62.

rect experience with death until relatively late in life. Many persons now become middle-aged before they personally experience death in a way that has any real social and psychological consequences. This was not the case 50 to 100 years ago. On the basis of European data, Fourastie found that the "average age of an average child at the death of the first deceased of his two parents" was 14 years in 1750, is 40 today, and will rise to 55 in the year 2000.[7]

## MARRIAGE AND DEATH

"Until death do us part" has a very different meaning now than it did when the death rate for mature adults was higher. A century ago the high rates of maternal mortality made the average marriage relatively short-lived when compared to present-day life expectancies. In 1900 married women of 20–24 years of age had a death rate 44 per cent greater than that experienced by the unmarried of the same age.[8] The death rates in the United States at the turn of the century meant that the average family was broken by death before the end of the parental stage.[9] To-

day a married couple can expect to spend an average of twenty years together *after* the *last* child has left home.[10]

The impact of a change on family members in the frequency and timing of death can best be seen by focusing on the roles of family members. Seen from the viewpoint of social psychology, roles represent patterns of attitudes, values, and expectations, and any changes in the death rate have social consequences for family roles. The consequences of death in the family generally have been studied with the aim of of assessing the effects on the children of the loss of one or the other of the parents.[11] The parental roles, however, also are influenced by the death of children. Before the development of immunization techniques, childhood diseases took a heavy toll of the younger family members. The death of one or more children was an almost inevitable aspect of parenthood for a large proportion of all families. The fact that death was always near at hand must have influenced family relationships. An awareness of the high frequency of infant death undoubtedly has provided some of the motivation for large families. It took numerous births to ensure that a family would have offspring that reached adulthood. Moreover, the attitudes held toward young children would be conditioned by the very real possibility that the child would not reach maturity.

Evidence indicates that man arranges his attitudes and emotional attachments so that he is protected from too many psychological jolts. The mind seems to develop a "protective crust" against frequent strong stimuli that evoke pain, pity, grief, and horror.[12] Impressionistic evidence indicates that the role requirements of marriage and parenthood 100 to 175 years ago did not include a high proportion of intimate, gentle, and strong emotional relationships.[13] This kind of speculation raises the question of the ways in which parents a century ago actually behaved in order to protect themselves from the psychic consequences of the strong possibility of death of child or spouse.

Ways in which the frequent occurrence of death affects the family are related to the consequences of death throughout the whole of society. In the past, the use of myth, ritual, religion, and private discussion were all devices for dealing with the highly visible and ever-present fact of death. Today, with the relative invisibility of death, conversation may turn to the weather, minor sicknesses, or vacations, where formerly a similar situation might have centered on the suddent death of a friend's or neighbor's child. The socialization process of childhood and youth which formerly included the acceptance of ever-present death is no longer as important. The change in the timing of death has created a situation in which the psychological, social, and economic prepara-

tions for death are integral aspects of the role associated with advanced age. Essentially it is *only* in the socialization for the role of being aged that the social and psychic preparations for death occur.

To what extent has the remoteness of death in everyday life had an influence on the types of social relations characterized as "brutal," "violent," "inhuman," and so forth? Has it meant an increase in the frequency of the occurrence of "tender," "humane," "affectionate," and "loving" relationships? Such questions cannot be answered in an unequivocal manner. No social research provides evidence for asserting one or the other position, but the frequency and timing of death in a society might well have a bearing on future answers.

That modern society is the scene of a considerable amount of interpersonal conflict resulting in the destruction and disorganization of human relations does not necessarily mean that the relative absence of death is of no consequence. The extension of the average length of life is a recent occurrence in human history. Consequently it is conceivable that we are only beginning to learn to cope with all of the added years of life. Our major institutions of family, school, and religion are in the throes of rapid change, part of which may be directly related to the problems emerging from the age revolution. Presumably the "problem of retirement" for the aged, so prominent a few years ago, will disappear as an important social problem. Modern man may have an overabundance of time—a condition that has not yet fully reached his consciousness.

The possibility of marriages spanning longer periods of time because of the far smaller "premature death" rate has been a factor in the development of high rates of divorce and separation. With a current time potential of about 40 years for the average marriage, the status of that institution now depends on considerable versatility in adopting new roles and adapting to a spouse's role changes. This must be done within a relatively limited social structure—the family. Adding years to a marriage exposes the relationship to an increase in the possible disruptive influences.

Closely related to the wealth of time possessed by the modern married couple is the change in the dynamics of the marriage market. A few decades ago the high maternal death rate gave the marriage market the dynamic quality that now results from a high divorce rate. A woman's marriageability used to be related to the death rate; it now has a closer relationship to the divorce rate. Some of the women who failed to get married in the "first round" attained the matrimonial state in the "second round" due to the higher death rate of spouses. Now it is divorce that provides the possibility of a second round.

The early age at marriage, the closer spacing of children, and the decline in families with many children has resulted in median ages for family completion of about 26 years of age for the mother and 29 years for the father.[14] With life expectancies of 70 years and over, the mother role, which the female parent formerly never completed, has ceased to constitute even a majority of the years a woman spends in marriage.[15] A significant characteristic of the maternal role is that it tends to involve a high degree of dependency on the husband. This has meant that in a former day the average woman spent her entire life in a role that made her personally dependent on others. Now the average

woman may shed much of the dependent aspects of her feminine role at a relatively young age. At the age of 45 a great many women have completed their parental roles. Statistically they can expect to live another 29 years. Such a length of time demands the adoption of new roles and in general provides an opportunity for the exercise of considerable choice. The possibilities for higher education and subsequent semi- or full professional careers are considerable. Although the time for a productive career is available, its opposites, boredom and loss of direction, also loom as possibilities.

The type of marriage that is characterized by companionship may eventually be considered as the norm if marriages are to last until broken by death. The added length of life not only gives the woman a second career, but also reinforces the status of equality gained by companionship with her mate. Such a companionship seems to be based on leisure-time activities, since the likelihood of similar work careers is not great. The companionate marriage may be indirectly connected with the further development of leisure-time pursuits involving both husband and wife.

## THE TIMING OF DEATH AND FAMILY ORGANIZATION

The changes in mortality appear to have enhanced the status of the now nearly defunct extended family. The increased life expectancy, along with the decrease in the age at marriage and the younger ages of child bearing, has meant that the average child has at least some grandparents living for a large portion of his youth and early adult life. If nothing else, this means that the structure of the family has broadened in scope. As a result the socialization of children is more likely to include interaction with "old," or at least older, people in the family. Thus new generations of children will have learned how to behave toward persons who are two and even three generations older than themselves.

Not only will more families contain grandparents, but parents and grandparents will be relatively closer in age than in the past.[16] In addition, many families will also have one or more great grandparents living, and often in good health during, at least, the younger years of the children. This will probably mean a redefinition of the role of grandparent. It is conceivable that a considerable number of persons will become grandparents in their middle forties. This will obviously generate a different set of grandparent roles from the kind that are appropriate for 60- to 70-year-old grandparents. Another consequence of the lengthened life may be that the *great* grandparent roles may become more like the traditional grandparent roles with the result that present-day grandparent roles will lack clear definition in the near future. It is conceivable that youthful grandparents may become increasingly competitive with, rather than complementary to, the parents in child rearing.

The extension of family influences generated by the presence of grandparents and great grandparents may have important consequences for the adult members of the nuclear family. Variations in age at marriage, of course, affect the relations between generations. With the adding of years of life to the adult members of families, the question can be raised: Under what circumstances is the last generation most influential in its effect on the life of the generation immediately ahead of it? Is it when a person marries young and has two sets of parents (potential grandparents) to "contend with"? Or is it when he or she remains single longer and thus may spend a larger proportion of life with the family of orientation (differences between the sex roles imply further variations)? One might hazard a guess that the former situation promotes the greatest amount of family influence. Young parents, who are also most likely to have children earlier, are very likely to fall back on family aid and comfort in the first brush with the problems of child rearing.[17] This means increased interaction with parents (grandparents of the new child) and a greater likelihood that parents will exercise direct influence in an important phase of early family life. By contrast, couples who marry later are less likely to feel the full weight of parental demands in the choice of a mate, and since they are older when their first child is born and their parents (the grandparents of the child) are also older, the grandparents thus will probably not play as prominent a role in the initial phase of the child-rearing period. The increased age of the couple having the infant means that they have managed for themselves for a longer period of time before the beginning of parenthood and therefore may act to retain their independence even though the extra demands of child bearing and rearing are quite considerable.

The social consequences of the extension of the family through the alteration of the life cycle is difficult if not impossible to predict, but it is apparent that it will result in a change in parental roles, family interaction, childhood socialization practices, and perspectives and attitudes relative to family life. "A favorite remark of contemporary students of the family is to the effect that all that can be predicted about the future of the American family is that it will be different." In this vein, Margaret Mead has suggested that "the new function of the grandparental generation may be to serve as exemplars of successful adjustment to continuing change."[18] If this proves to be true, the socializing function of grandparents might be of substantial importance.

Women, especially those in the middle and upper classes, have probably experienced the greatest role changes as a result of the prolongation of life. In addition to the changes already discussed, the added years of life have made possible, to some degree, the expansion of the importance of voluntary associations in modern life. A large proportion of the time and energy expended in voluntary associations of all types is provided by women who are not "gainfully employed." Despite the charges of "do-goodism" often leveled at some of these voluntary efforts, it is evident that a great deal of important work is performed by this part of the population. The added years of life, the decrease in family size, the technological advances in home appliances, plus the traditions and values regarding voluntary associations have added a series of new dimensions to woman's role.

## THE TIMING OF DEATH AND SOCIAL STRATIFICATION

The age revolution has implications for both the stratification of society as well as the social mobility that occurs between strata. There has probably been a differential death rate between social classes for as long as there have been status differences. Expected length of life varies by class, but the overall limits on the duration of life are imposed by cultural conditions.

The increase in longevity introduces new elements into the nature of social mobility in a society such as ours. Those aspects of family life that either improve or inhibit a potentiality for upward mobility are connected to a degree with the length of life of each generation. A longer-lived generation makes possible the maintenance of stronger kin-group ties, especially where the cultural or subcultural norms tend toward endogamy. The increase in the duration of life in the earlier generation of a family means not only that there are more adults alive, but also that the total man-years of life being lived out, or available for enhancing *or* inhibiting the mobility chances of the on-coming younger generation, is considerably greater than it was 150 years ago. That is, families are now much more potentially powerful in helping *or* hindering their newest members.

This is not meant to overlook or deny the importance of family background in the well-ordered and more rigid stratification systems of earlier times. In modern times family background, as a crucial status variable, probably has decreased in importance. This is particularly true for that large mass of society that has gained so much in life expectancy. Naturally, where the norms and values of the nuclear family are very strong, these factors have less consequence. In some instances of lingering ethnic identification, the increase in sheer size of kin groups would seem to have an influence on social mobility. It is possible that ethnic norms of endogamy and kin-group solidarity may be coupled with norms that support certain prerequisites for mobility, such as professional or technical education and an emphasis on business and money making. Such is apparently the case with the American Jewish family structure, an extended family system that effectively meets the demands of contemporary urban life. In contrast, the Italian family structure, which is still defined to a degree in terms of geographical and occupational proximity, seems to impede upward mobility.[19] Thus it depends on the norms, values, and expectations of the particular extended family structure being considered as to whether or not it will impede or promote social mobility. In either case the age revolution has changed the size and age composition of modern extended families.

The high probability of long life for all members of a moderately sized family and the recent demands for increased education lend weight to the necessity of making financial plans for education. Though this has been a part of the parental role of upper- and upper-middle-class parents for over a century and a half, it is a new feature of the parental role for the mass of the population in modern society. Those parents who are willing and able to effectively make and carry out long-range family plans probably will be the ones who contribute a disproportionate share of the socially mobile members of society.[20] Moreover, the failure of parents to make long-range plans may have greater negative consequences than in previous times.

## THE AGE REVOLUTION AND LIFE INSURANCE

Life insurance became a practical consideration for the average man when the expected length of life rose to a point where the premiums became so small as to be economically possible. Imagine the size of premiums on a life-insurance policy that would give an average family a livelihood if the breadwinner had a life expectancy of 30 years. It is obvious that the advance beyond the practice of "burial insurance" was based on a greater life expectancy.[21] Although there had been religious prejudices against life insurance, they declined after 1840. Concurrently, the expected length of life continued to rise and the subsequent boom in the writing of life-insurance policies logically seems to be related to the resulting lower premium costs.

In the same vein, it has been pointed out that the life-insurance business ultimately rests on the norms and values involved in the balancing of *risk* and *security* by individual families.[22] Strong and extensive kinship systems decrease the importance of insurance, whereas the nuclear family system of industrial society increases the risk in the loss of a family member.[23] Basic family structure as well as a long life expectancy may support the large-scale adoption of life insurance.

In terms of social consequences, the widespread use of life insurance may be important in shaping and fostering certain kinds of family attitudes and values. The act of buying insurance forces the adult members of a family to think about death and its financial consequences. The nucleated family and marriage based on companionship makes the reduction of risk through insurance important. The minimizing of kin-group ties, the ideal of intimacy, and the close emotional ties of the nuclear family combine to promote the use of insurance. The allocating of some financial resources to insurance serves to keep the nuclear family together, even with the loss of the breadwinner. The prevention of financial dependency on the larger kin group in the event of death of an adult family member maintains the conception of freedom of choice and action which is part of the ideology associated with choosing a mate and establishing an independent nuclear family. This is most applicable to the middle classes, the stratum that has gained most in length of life and buys most of the life insurance.

Paradoxically, the age revolution may have the long-term effect of increasing the importance of kin groups. The longer life expectancy has favored the enlargement of present-day kin groups.[24] Thus, potentially, the larger family network may mean that an increased number of kin-group members may come to share similar styles of life and hence find intimate social relations more attractive than was the case during the acculturation period of American immigrant groups.

## CONCLUSIONS

All of the foregoing speculation about the influence of a change in the frequency and timing of death in modern society is not meant to imply that the changes in the phenomena of death are the *causes* of the social changes referred to, or even necessarily a salient factor in their occurrences. The major aim of this discussion is to point out that the seemingly "simple" fact of change in the frequency of death may be an important variable to consider. Its importance would be expected to vary from one area of life to another. It is conceivable that the focusing of renewed attention on some of the problems discussed could lead to fruitful research.

Some of the more obvious areas of study are: (1) importance of life cycle in family structure; (2) psychosocial processes (particularly socialization and role changes) and the life cycle; (3) increased length of life and its effect on social mobility and stratification; (4) residential mobility and housing as related to the life cycle; (5) affluence and the views of life accompanying it relative to education, leisure and travel, careers, sex and marriage, history and tradition; (6) continuity in public and private bureaucracies; (7) the consequences of lengthy life coupled with the rapid economic and political development of underdeveloped countries; and (8) increased life expectancy and mental disorder, crime, and other forms of deviance.

1. In the *Geography of Hunger*, De Castro pointed out that hunger has not been discussed in a way commensurate with its importance in the lives of the people of the world; see Josue De Castro, *Geography of Hunger*, Boston: Little, Brown, 1952.

2. Robert L. Fulton and William A. Faunce, "The Sociology of Death: A Neglected Area of Research," *Social Forces*, 36, 1958, 205–209; Herman Feifel, "Death — Relevant Variable in Psychology," in Rollo May (Ed.), *Existential Psychology*, New York: Random House, 1961, pp. 61–74.

3. Michael Harrington, *The Other America*, New York: Macmillan, 1963. The author very aptly pointed to the invisibility of poverty and its social consequences.

4. Jessica Mitford, *The American Way of Death*, New York: Fawcett World Library, Crest Books, 1963.

5. Jean Fourastie, "Three Comments on the Near Future of Mankind," *Diogenes*, **32**, Winter 1960, 5.

6. Raymond B. Allen, "Professional Education in the Service of Health," *Annals of the American Academy of Political and Social Science*, **273**, 1951, 209–210.

7. Fourastie, *op. cit.*, p. 4.

8. Paul H. Jacobson, *American Marriage and Divorce*, New York: Rinehart, 1959, p. 139.

9. Paul C. Glick, *American Families*, New York: Wiley, 1957, pp. 67–69.

10. Marguerite F. Levy, "The Joint Survival Years: A Changing Phase in the Family Cycle," *The American Behavioral Scientist*, **6**, May 1963, 3.

11. James H. S. Bossard and Eleanor S. Boll, *The Large Family System*, Philadelphia: University of Pennsylvania Press, 1956.

12. Eugene Kogan, *The Theory and Practice of Hell*, translated by Heinz Norden, New York: Farrar, Straus, 1951, p. 271.

13. Although the frequency of death in the family seems relevant in the development of intimacy in the family, it also has been pointed out that the evolution of the family from the medieval to the modern family is related to a great many cultural and social factors independent of the death rate. See Philippe Aries, *Centuries of Childhood*, translated by Robert Baldick, New York: Knopf, 1962, pp. 398–404.

14. Levy, *op. cit.*, p. 38.

15. In 1955 newly wed couples could look forward to 31.5 years, on the average, before their marriage would end in divorce or death; Jacobson, *op. cit.*, p. 149.

16. Robert R. Bell, *Marriage and Family Interaction*, Homewood, Ill.: Dorsey, 1963, p. 294.

17. For a discussion of parental aid, see Marvin Sussman and Lee Burchinal, "Parental Aid to Married Children: Implications for Family Functioning," *Marriage and Family Living*, **24**, 1962, 320–332.

18. Margaret Mead was quoted from an address she gave to the Child Study Association of America, New York City, March 4, 1963, quoted in Levy, *op. cit.*, p. 39.

19. Fred L. Strodtbeck, "Family Interaction, Values, and Achievements," in David C. McClelland et al., *Talent and Society*, Princeton, N.J.: Van Nostrand, 1958, pp. 135–195; cited in Eugene Litwak, "Occupational Mobility and Extended Family Cohesion," *American Sociological Review*, **25**, 1950, 20.

20. David Granick found that, despite the nominal cost of education in the Soviet Union, the children of white-collar parents had an advantage in social mobility. In American society, family planning for advanced education is generally a necessary, but not sufficient, factor in promoting upward mobility. See *The Red Executive*, Garden City, N.Y.: Doubleday Anchor Book, 1960, pp.35–45.

21. The first life-insurance policy seems to have been issued in England in 1583. In 1693 Edmund Halley constructed the first mortality table, thus making estimations of risk much more rigorous.

22. William J. Goode, "Perspectives on Family Research and Life Insurance," *The American Behavioral Scientist*, **6**, May 1963, 58.

23. A strong kin-group structure would only minimize the importance of insurance if there were no norms supporting a different approach. It is conceivable that a strong kin-group system could develop norms demanding a relatively high level of insurance protection for its members.

24. William J. Goode asserts that: "In the most industrialized nations, England and the United States, the few relevant small studies show that in fact most people maintain large kin networks, upwards of eighty to ninety members, with whom they maintain contact." *Op. cit.*, p. 57.

# Epilogue to Part Four

Since the family is the basic social unit, health workers must focus on it in order to understand the total impact of illness or wellness on the societal system. Whether health care is to take place in a hospital or in the home, the impact of illness on the family and the impact of the family on the patient and his illness must be considered.

The stages of the family life cycle indicate potential crisis areas for the individual or the family. One of the areas in which health workers may become involved is premarital counseling about sex, potential success or failure of the family, the realism of the perceptions and expectations that each person has of the other, and the potential problem areas of marriage. Either during this period or immediately after, the couple may seek help about planned parenthood. This information may be sought from one or more health professionals, clergymen, family members, or planned parenthood associations. Thus far, data indicate that the middle class, with its value orientation toward material, educational, occupational, and economic success, appears to be the most likely client for family-planning help. Specific information regarding techniques of birth control should be tailored to the physical and religious demands of the individuals involved.

During the early life cycle of the family, the couple's decision to have children may require the services of many health professionals. The young embryonic family needs information, not only about sex and the physiology of childbirth, but psychological help in preparing for the anticipated parental roles. Assistance from the families, clergy, social counselors, or health professionals should be given as preparation for the anticipated event. Long before the child is born, the health worker has a responsibility to disseminate information, either directly or indirectly, about child-rearing practices. Parents can be spared many hours of anguish and children many psychological upsets if the parents are prepared to anticipate a variety of potentially problematic situations.

The role of parent is neither biological nor instinctual; parents must be socialized into the sociopsychological roles of mother and father. The more assistance health workers can provide in developing sociopsychological insights, the less difficulties the couple will have assuming the new roles as parents.

Before the birth of the child, family, friends, and health workers all have certain expectations about the child's physique and potential. If for any reason the child is born physically or mentally abnormal, a crisis situation is created. In such a case it is imperative that the professional health worker intervene and help the family in the initial phase of the shock. Genuine reassurance and aid in accepting the situation are necessary to alleviate the potential horror, fear, and guilt. Not only is the psychosocial life of the child at stake, but also that of the family. Professional assistance has to be continued throughout the child's life and, if it should die, for a time after that.

The next crucial period in the family life cycle is when children enter school. It is often during this time that parents, especially the mother, experience a feeling of loss as children develop new friends and interests. While the child's world is enlarging, the mother's is narrowing. Whether she is from a Freudian or Protestant ethic, various aspects of her life revolve around her children. At this time the mother also is confronted with a number of childhood diseases and psychosocial difficulties. If the child is over- or undersocialized to the sick or well role, later problems in handling these roles may become evident.

As children approach adolescence, sex education is a must. Although it should be started earlier, in American culture it frequently is not. The health worker and particularly the school nurse need to be acutely aware of the potential problems involved. At the present time, both venereal disease and illegitimacy are prevalent in adolescent groups. The health worker may have to spend several sessions with the child, the family, or preferably both, to determine the value system, the kind and amount of sex education already received, and to explore the healthiest ways in which the entire family can handle the situation.

Another period in the life cycle which creates problems for the family is when the children leave home. At this point, if the mother does not have routine outside activities, the sense of loss may be great. This is particularly true if the children have moved away from the family, either geographically or socially. It is not uncommon for the mother faced with this "emptiness" to develop a series of psychosomatic illnesses or depressions. There are two modes of approaching this problem: preventive and restorative. The health worker may prepare the mother for her changing role from a "doer for others" to a "doer for self" during the children's adolescent years. New interests may be introduced such as community or private endeavors, adult education, hobbies, and so forth. Frequently, for each woman there has been a special interest or desire, never fulfilled, which at this time may be encouraged and developed. A restorative mode of intervention with the patient's loneliness often requires more time and frequently is not performed in the home but in the hospital. The specific needs of the patient and the source of help contacted have a direct bearing on the kind of service performed and which type of personnel will perform them. For example, if the patient has become acutely depressed, then she will need, and often seeks, therapy from a psychiatrist.

It is also during this period that the father, if he has not already retired, begins to think of doing so. If he is a member of the lower class and has frequently changed jobs during his life, he will find that as he ages, fewer and fewer places will hire him. If he is a member of the middle class, he will find his talents and skills are in less demand; if he is a member of the upper class, he may have already retired to other activities—cultural pursuits, travel, philanthropy, and so on. If he has maintained a sense of personal worth and self-adequacy throughout his life, he may not view retirement as a loss. But if his life style has revolved around his work, then retirement may be as traumatic as the loss of a loved one; consequently he may undergo a serious grieving process requiring the establishment of a new self identity.

As old age approaches, new and old problems confront the nuclear family.

The offspring by now have probably migrated toward new interests and a style of life apart from the family of orientation. Because of the health problem and increased potential of death associated with the aging process, the children may be called on for assistance, but frequently they have made no provision for economic and social assistance for the ill or widowed parent.

This does not mean that the offspring do not care for their parents. Social movements have created new values and concerns, and subsequently new ways of dealing with the aged. The primary focus of our culture is on youth, and, although we do not practice biological patricide, social patricide in the sense of isolating the aged is not uncommon. Mental hospitals and nursing homes serve to perform such a service in a socially acceptable fashion.

If illness is prolonged at any time during the life cycle, incapacitation or disfigurement may create financial burdens and eventually physical, psychological, and social isolation of both patient and family. If the sickness is associated with a negative prognosis, the problem of deciding whether or not to tell the patient, and who should and will be responsible for this action, enters the realm of the "twilight zone." It is not uncommon for the professionals, family members, and friends involved to believe individually that this responsibility will somehow be met by others. The ambiguity of the situation and/or the lack of norms places a strain on all involved.

The adjustment by friends, and particularly the immediate family, to situations involving potential death, as Stub indicated, is by no means a simplistic notion of the acceptance of the inevitable. The possibility of impending permanent separation requires not only a process of grieving, but also a restructuring of the interpersonal relationships between the dying and the living. It is not uncommon for the living to accustom themselves in such a way to the expected death of an individual that the death not only becomes conceptually inevitable, but actually must occur in order for the living to continue to "live" fully. Frequently, long before physical death occurs, the family members, because of their own beliefs and value orientations, have so restructured their relationships with the dying and themselves that the impending separation assumes the status of a completed event; the separation takes place before death does. A spontaneous unexpected cure in fact, may create intense problems for the living and the patient. Feelings of guilt may arise in members of the family as a result of their perception of either accepting the inevitable, desiring it, or being unable to do anything about it. If this guilt is at all extensive, the family may require professional assistance for its alleviation. The living are caught in a web of sociopsychological feelings, beliefs, and perceptions that demand recognition and acceptance in order for them to preserve their own functioning capabilities.

# PART FIVE

## *On the Path: Health and Illness*

As indicated in Part One, man's perceptions depend on the ways in which he is socialized. The process of socialization includes both cognitive and value orientations toward a variety of phenomena including health and illness, and makes it possible for man to categorize, count, and record the data in his environment. The federal government annually publishes a pamphlet, *Major Trends*, which categorizes data on the incidence and prevalence of disease among various age groups and social classes. It reports the rates of birth and death, diagnosed and reported illnesses, present and potential health problems, and expenditures for care and treatment. Only the known cases are reported, however, and they constitute but a portion of the total number in any given population.

It must also be remembered that there are many ways of collecting this kind of information and many problems in its interpretation. Such data may be gathered through research studies in epidemiology which provide a mode of identifying disease, its patterns, distribution, and recurrence as well as the factors that may eliminate or reduce the prevalence of a given disease in a particular population.[1] Another method of locating and identifying health problems comes through survey and field studies of entire communities.

Many health problems are more observable in certain social-class structures. The lower-class concern about health care, especially preventive, is minimal. Conditions of overcrowding, poor housing, sanitation, and nutrition, as well as differing values, in part contribute to the higher rate of infant mortality, infectious diseases, rheumatic heart disease, and psychoses among the lower class. On the other hand, the middle-class emphasis on sanitation ("Cleanliness is next to Godliness") may account for its lower rate of some communicable diseases. But its focus on getting ahead creates stress and tension which are now believed to contribute to the high rates of coronary conditions, ulcers, psychoneurosis, and psychosomatic disorders.

In addition to differences between classes, every period in history reflects greater or lesser emphasis on particular disease entities. Therefore in certain periods a greater number of incidents may be reported than in others. Until World War II, some states required both the reporting of childhood diseases (measles, chicken pox, whooping cough, and so on) and isolation of entire families who had a child with one of these afflictions. As a result, such diseases were more visible.

With the increase in knowledge and diagnostic techniques, other illnesses became well known. During World War II new diagnostic techniques for mental illness and retardation helped identify more cases, and potential inductees were rejected for these reasons. Techniques for diagnosing cancer and heart disease led to the discovery and eventual reporting of these illnesses. Multiple diagnoses, however, led to difficulties in reporting the exact cause of death. This reported rate for each disease depended in part on the interpretation of the physician, who often was forced to choose one among many potential causes of death. For example, a patient with terminal cancer who died of pneumonia might be listed as dying either from cancer or pneumonia.

Aside from the problems of diagnostic knowledge is, of course, the whole question of what criteria constitute health as opposed to illness. This has remained one of the ticklish problems of reporting and even of treating certain phenomena. Health and illness are relative concepts, determined in part by culture and historical periods, and in part by the health professionals. Certain kinds of phenomena may be considered as illness in one culture and health in another. As Miner illustrates, each culture also has customs and rituals that are related to the individual's perceptions and values regarding health and illness and the maintenance of a "healthy body" image. In some cultures, for example in Siberia, the hysteric individual is highly esteemed and even assigned the role of priesthood, denoting authority and prestige. In contemporary American society, coronaries and peptic ulcers are often considered signs of success in businessmen.

Suicide, too, may be viewed from different perspectives. It has a social as well as psychological connotation and does not always represent individual disorganization. For the Japanese Kamikaze it denotes a high degree of social integration, loyalty, altruism, and heroism, and is rewarded by national prestige. In certain other situations, the value orientation of individuals may make suicide imperative, and to avoid it would be viewed as deviant.

Historically, in this country, health has been viewed as an absence of disease—a static perfected state of being. In the past decade, however, both illness and health have been viewed as dynamic, changing states of becoming. They are now seen by many professionals as phases of life, styles of life, and means of livelihood. As Dunn points out,[2] "the health worker can no longer conceptualize good health as freedom from illness," but must assume the leadership and the responsibility for assisting individuals, families, and communities toward the development of their unique potential within a given society.

Whether an individual is seen as healthy or ill depends on the perceiver. As Sweetser's study shows, laymen define a sick person as "sick" when his symptoms are observable, acute, definitive, and impair his activity. As health workers know, however, most chronic and/or recurrent conditions frequently are more destructive and damaging to the individual than a state characterized by acute symptomatology. Perception (including an implicit definition) of illness and health, whether on the part of a health worker or a lay person, influences the type of care sought, the type of diagnosis and treatment given, and the person(s) and organizations providing this care.

Everyone has a variety of experiences that influence his perception of his own illness. Personal contact with family, friends, and neighbors who have been or are patients or with lay personnel who work in and around health agencies often leads to a perception that they are the best sources of information. Beliefs and attitudes developed from such sources are difficult to change. Lay attitudes, even among hospital auxiliary personnel, are not always in keeping with sound medical knowledge. Many, for example, still believe that mental illness is caused by heredity, masturbation, or some sort of deliberate immorality.

In addition, perception of health and illness is influenced to some extent by dissemination of health information. Women are often more knowledgeable about the variety and kinds of illnesses than men, partly because women's magazines include a considerable number of articles regarding health and illness. The range of articles includes ways of bringing up children, how to have a psychologically healthy child, and the symptoms of common diseases and their treatment.

Other media may deliberately or unwittingly transmit values, attitudes, and beliefs about specific kinds of illnesses, hospitalization, disease prevention, hospital life, and the health professions. Many television viewers, for example, may feel that they are capable of handling certain situations and therefore do not need the services of a trained professional, but unfortunately the information and attitudes to which they are reacting are not always accurate.

In any event the perception of health and illness influences the decision of when to seek help and from whom. As Haese and Meile point out, many do not perceive psychological problems as requiring any assistance; others would seek clergy, nonpsychiatric physicians, and others for such help; and those who do seek professional psychiatric care see no other solution for their problem.

There are approximately fifty kinds of persons to whom one may turn in time of health need. They range from palmists, relatives, druggists, herbalists, chiropractors, and faith healers to licensed physicians. But an individual who perceives himself as ill and seeks help often must be hospitalized. As Titmuss points out, this process may create new problems for the patient, because those who practice in hospital settings also have perceptions of their roles and the role of patient, as well as their concept of health and illness. Part Five will elucidate some of these problems.

---

1. Ernest M. Gruenberg, "The Epidemiology of Mental Disorders," *Scientific American*, March 1954.

2. Halbert L. Dunn, "High-Level Wellness in the World of Today," *Journal of the American Osteopathic Association*, **61**, 1962, 978–987.

# 19. BODY RITUAL AMONG THE NACIREMA

### Horace M. Miner

The anthropologist has become so familiar with the diversity of ways in which different peoples behave in similiar situations that he is not apt to be surprised by even the most exotic customs. In fact, if all of the logically possible combinations of behavior have not been found somewhere in the world, he is apt to suspect that they must be present in some yet undescribed tribe. This point has, in fact, been expressed with respect to clan organization by Murdock.[1] In this light the magical beliefs and practices of the Nacirema present such unusual aspects that it seems desirable to describe them as an example of the extremes to which human behavior can go.

Professor Linton first brought the ritual of the Nacirema to the attention of anthropologists twenty years ago,[2] but the culture of this people is still very poorly understood. They are a North American group living in the territory between the Canadian Cree, the Yaqui and Tarahumare of Mexico, and the Carib and Arawak of the Antilles. Little is known of their origin, although tradition states that they came from the east. According to Nacirema mythology, their nation was originated by a culture hero, Notgnihsaw, who is otherwise known for two great feats of strength—the throwing of a piece of wampum across the river PaTo-Mac and the chopping down of a cherry tree in which the Spirit of Truth resided.

Nacirema culture is characterized by a highly developed market economy which has evolved in a rich natural habitat. While much of the people's time is devoted to economic pursuits, a large part of the fruits of these labors and a considerable portion of the day are spent in ritual activity. The focus of this activity is the human body, the appearance and health of which loom as a dominant concern in the ethos of the people. While such a concern is certainly not unusual, its ceremoniäl aspects and associated philosophy are unique.

The fundamental belief underlying the whole system appears to be that the human body is ugly and that its natural tendency is to debility and disease. Incarcerated in such a body, man's only hope is to avert these characteristics through the use of the powerful influences of ritual and ceremony. Every household has one or more shrines devoted to this purpose. The more powerful individuals in the society have several shrines in their houses and, in fact, the opulence of a house is often referred to in terms of the number of such ritual centers it possesses. Most houses are of wattle and daub construction, but the shrine rooms of the more wealthy are walled with stone. Poorer families imitate the rich by applying pottery plaques to their shrine walls.

While each family has at least one such shrine, the rituals associated with it are not family ceremonies but are private and secret. The rites are nor-

Reprinted by permission of the author and the American Anthropological Association, from the *American Anthropologist*, Vol. 58, 1956, pp. 503–507.

mally discussed only with children, and then only during the period when they are being initiated into these mysteries. I was able, however, to establish sufficient rapport with the natives to examine these shrines and to have the rituals described to me.

The focal point of the shrine is a box or chest which is built into the wall. In this chest are kept the many charms and magical potions without which no native believes he could live. These preparations are secured from a variety of specialized practitioners. The most powerful of these are the medicine men, whose assistance must be rewarded with substantial gifts. However, the medicine men do not provide the curative potions for their clients, but decide what the ingredients should be and then write them down in an ancient and secret language. This writing is understood only by the medicine men and by the herbalists who, for another gift, provide the required charm.

The charm is not disposed of after it has served its purpose, but is placed in the charm box of the household shrine. As these magical materials are specific for certain ills, and the real or imagined maladies of the people are many, the charm box is usually full to overflowing. The magical packets are so numerous that people forget what their purposes were and fear to use them again. While the natives are very vague on this point, we can only assume that the idea in retaining all the old magical materials is that their presence in the charm box, before which the body rituals are conducted, will in some way protect the worshipper.

Beneath the charm box is a small font. Each day every member of the family, in succession, enters the shrine room, bows his head before the charm box, mingles different sorts of holy water in the font, and proceeds with a brief rite of ablution. The holy waters are secured from the Water Temple of the community, where the priests conduct elaborate ceremonies to make the liquid ritually pure.

In the hierarchy of the magical practitioners, and below the medicine men in prestige, are the specialists whose designation is best translated "holy-mouth-man." The Nacirema have an almost pathological horror and fascination with the mouth, the condition of which is believed to have a supernatural influence on all social relationships. Were it not for the rituals of the mouth, they believe that their teeth would fall out, their gums bleed, their jaws shrink, their friends desert them, and their lovers reject them. They also believe that a strong relationship exists between oral and moral characteristics. For example, there is a ritual ablution of the mouth for children which is supposed to improve their moral fiber.

The daily body ritual performed by everyone includes a mouth rite. Despite the fact that these people are so punctilious about care of the mouth, this rite involves a practice which strikes the uninitiated stranger as revolting. It was reported to me that the ritual consists of inserting a small bundle of hog hairs into the mouth, along with certain magical powders, and then moving the bundle in a highly formalized series of gestures.

In addition to the private mouth rite, the people seek out a holy-mouth-man once or twice a year. These practitioners have an impressive set of paraphernalia, consisting of a variety of augers, awls, probes, and prods. The use of these objects in the exorcism of the evils of the mouth involves almost unbelievable ritual torture of the client. The holy-mouth-man opens the client's mouth, and using the above-mentioned tools, enlarges any holes which decay may have created in the teeth. Magical materials are put into these holes. If there are no naturally occurring holes in the teeth, large sections of one or more teeth are gouged out so that the supernatural substance can be applied. In the client's view, the purpose of these ministrations is to arrest decay and to draw friends. The extremely sacred and traditional character of the rite is evident in the fact that the natives return to the holy-mouth-man year after year, despite the fact that their teeth continue to decay.

It is to be hoped that, when a thorough study of the Nacirema is made, there will be careful inquiry into the personality structure of these people. One has but to watch the gleam in the eye of a holy-mouth-man, as he jabs an awl into an exposed nerve, to suspect that a certain amount of sadism is involved. If this can be established, a very interesting pattern emerges, for most of the population shows definite masochistic tendencies. It was to these that Professor Linton referred in discussing a distinctive part of the daily body ritual which is performed only by men. This part of the rite involves scraping and lacerating the surface of the face with a sharp instrument. Special women's rites are performed only four times during each lunar month, but what they lack in frequency is made up in barbarity. As part of this ceremony women bake their heads in small ovens for about an hour. The theoretically interesting point is that what seems to be a preponderantly masochis-

tic people have developed sadistic specialists.

The medicine men have an imposing temple, or latipso, in every community of any size. The more elaborate ceremonies required to treat very sick patients can only be performed at this temple. These ceremonies involve not only the thaumaturge but a permanent group of vestal maidens who move sedately about the temple chambers in distinctive costume and headdress.

The latipso ceremonies are so harsh that it is phenomenal that a fair proportion of the really sick natives who enter the temple ever recover. Small children whose indoctrination is still incomplete have been known to resist attempts to take them to the temple because "that is where you go to die." Despite this fact, sick adults are not only willing but eager to undergo the protracted ritual purification, if they can afford to do so. No matter how ill the supplicant or how grave the emergency, the guardians of many temples will not admit a client if he cannot give a rich gift to the custodian. Even after one has gained admission and survived the ceremonies, the guardians will not permit the neophyte to leave until he makes still another gift.

The supplicant entering the temple is first stripped of all his or her clothes. In everyday life the Nacirema avoids exposure of his body and its natural functions. Bathing and excretory acts are performed only in the secrecy of the household shrine, where they are ritualized as part of the body rites. Psychological shock results from the fact that body secrecy is suddenly lost upon entry into the latipso. A man, whose own wife has never seen him in an excretory act, suddenly finds himself naked and assisted by a vestal maiden while he performs his natural functions into a sacred vessel. This sort of ceremonial treatment is necessitated by the fact that the excreta are used by a diviner to ascertain the course and nature of the client's sickness. Female clients, on the other hand, find their naked bodies are subjected to the scrutiny, manipulation, and prodding of the medicine man.

Few supplicants in the temple are well enough to do anything but lie on their hard beds. The daily ceremonies, like the rites of the holy-mouth-men, involve discomfort and torture. With ritual precision the vestals awaken their miserable charges each dawn and roll them about on their beds of pain while performing ablutions, in the formal movements of which the maidens are highly trained. At other times they insert magic wands in the supplicant's mouth or force him to eat substances which are supposed to be healing. From time to time the medicine men come to their clients and jab magically treated needles into their flesh. The fact that these temple ceremonies may not cure, and may even kill the neophyte, in no way decreases the people's faith in the medicine men.

There remains one other kind of practitioner, known as a "listener." This witch doctor has the power to exorcise the devils that lodge in the heads of people who have been bewitched. The Nacirema believe that parents bewitch their own children. Mothers are particularly suspected of putting a curse on children while teaching them the secret body rituals. The counter-magic of the witch doctor is unusual in its lack of ritual. The patient simply tells the "listener" all his troubles and fears, beginning with the earliest difficulties he can remember. The memory displayed by the Nacirema in these exorcism sessions is truly remarkable. It is not uncommon for the patient to bemoan the rejection he felt upon being weaned as a babe, and a few individuals even see their troubles going back to the traumatic effects of their own birth.

In conclusion, mention must be made of certain practices which have their base in native esthetics but which depend upon the pervasive aversion to the natural body and its functions. There are ritual fasts to make fat people thin and ceremonial feasts to make thin people fat. Still other rites are used to make women's breasts larger if they are small, and smaller if they are large. General dissatisfaction with breast shape is symbolized in the fact that the ideal form is virtually outside the range of human variation. A few woman afflicted with almost inhuman hyper-mammary development are so idolized that they make a handsome living by simply going from village to village and permitting the natives to stare at them for a fee.

Reference has already been made to the fact that excretory functions are ritualized, routinized, and relegated to secrecy. Natural reproductive functions are similarly distorted. Intercourse is taboo as a topic and scheduled as an act. Efforts are made to avoid pregnancy by the use of magical materials or by limiting intercourse to certain phases of the moon. Conception is actually very infrequent. When pregnant, women dress so as to hide their condition.

Parturition takes place in secret, without friends or relatives to assist, and the majority of women do not nurse their infants.

Our review of the ritual life of the Nacirema has certainly shown them to be a magic-ridden people. It is hard to understand how they have managed to exist so long under the burdens which they have imposed upon themselves.

---

1. George P. Murdock, *Social Structure*, New York: Macmillan, 1949, p. 74.

2. Ralph Linton, *The Study of Man*, New York: Appleton-Century, 1936, p. 326.

# 20. HIGH-LEVEL WELLNESS FOR MAN AND SOCIETY

## Halbert L. Dunn

The awakened interest of public-health circles in full-time local health departments and in the family and community programs of health maintenance is an indication that health workers are becoming more "health oriented." This shift in emphasis is in accord with the frequently quoted fundamental objective expressed in the Constitution of the World Health Organization, "Health is a state of complete physical, mental, and social well-being and not merely the absence of disease and infirmity."

To most of us, this concept of positive health is "seen through a glass darkly," because our eyes have been so long turned in a different direction, concentrating fixedly on disease and death. When we take time to turn our gaze in the opposite direction, focusing it intently on the condition termed good health, we see that wellness is not just a single amorphous condition, but rather that it is a complex state made up of overlapping levels of wellness. As we come to know how to recognize these levels objectively, more or less as we now diagnose one disease from another, we will realize that the state of being well is not a relatively flat, uninteresting area of "unsickness" but rather is a fascinating and ever-changing pano-

rama of life itself, inviting exploration of its every dimension.

It is my thesis, therefore, that both medicine and public health must undertake a multiple and thoroughgoing exploration of the factors responsible for good health. Without prejudice to the importance or the continuation and support of existing medical and health programs involving preventive, curative, or rehabilitative research and activities, it seems clear that many of today's and tomorrow's problems call for the stimulation and development of a new major axis of interest directed toward positive health—one strong enough to activate physicians, health workers, and others in devoting a substantial segment of their time, resources, and creative energies toward understanding and culturing good health in a positive sense.

## WHY A NEW HEALTH AXIS IS NEEDED

The need for this new axis of interest is rooted in the changing demographic, social, economic, and political character of civilization. These changes are well known, although their significance is usually not fully appreciated. They might be summarized thus:

Reprinted by permission of the author and publisher, from *The American Journal of Public Health and Nation's Health*, Vol. 49, 1959, pp. 786–792. Copyright 1959 by the American Public Health Association, Inc. (This paper was presented before the Second General Session of the Ninth Annual Meeting of the Middle States Public Health Association in Milwaukee, Wis., April 29, 1958; and in part before the Statistics Section of the American Public Health Association at the Eighty-Sixth Annual Meeting in St. Louis, Mo., October 30, 1958.)

1. *It is a shrinking world*. Communication time has shrunk to the vanishing point. Knowledge of events can span the world in seconds and can be known to the masses in a matter of hours. Travel time from the farthermost reaches of the earth has diminished from years and months to a matter of days and hours.

2. *It is a crowded world*. Turned loose in an all-out assault upon disease and death, the medical and health sciences have brought about generally falling death rates without a corresponding reduction in birth rates. The consequent "epidemic" of population growth has reached towering proportions in many parts of the world and brings with it new health problems arising from population pressures and the scarcities of materials and living space.

3. *It is an older world*, in terms of its people, productivity, and resources. A consequence of the revolution brought about by the health sciences is that relatively more people live to an older age. The per capita demand for the output of the economic and productive machinery is steadily advancing. Consequently it is probably a fallacy for us to assume, as so many of us have done, that an expansion in scientific knowledge can indefinitely counterbalance the rapidly dwindling natural resources of the globe.

4. *It is a world of mounting tensions*. The tempo of modern life and its demands on the human being and his society are steadily increasing with no corresponding readjustment and strengthening of the inner man and the fabric of his social organizations.

Because of these four factors among others, the problems that face the medical and public-health professions have changed character drastically in the last few decades. Chronic illness and mental disease are far more prevalent. A great range of neurotic and functional illnesses, which seldom destroy life but which interfere with living a productive and full life, are on the increase.

The preventive path of the future, both for medicine and public health, inevitably lies largely in reorienting a substantial amount of interest and energy toward raising the general levels of wellness among all peoples. This calls for spelling out in objective terms what high-level wellness actually means for the individual, the family, and the social structure.

## THE HEALTH GRID

In order to concretize the goal of high-level wellness, it is essential to shift from considering sickness and wellness as a dichotomy toward thinking of disease and health as a graduated scale. For the purposes of this paper, this scale is conceptualized as one axis of a "health grid" (Figure 20-1). The health grid is made up of (1) the health axis, (2) the environmental axis, and (3) the resulting health and wellness quadrants; that is (*a*) poor health in an unfavorable environment, (*b*) protected poor health in a favorable environment, (*c*) emergent high-level wellness in an unfavorable environment, and (*d*) high-level wellness in a favorable environment. The environmental axis includes not only the physical and biological factors of the environment but also socioeconomic components affecting the health of the individual. The health axis ranges from death at the left extremity to "peak wellness" at the right. The area between the extremes proceeds through serious and minor illnesses into the the area of positive health or freedom from illness. Thereafter it moves into an area of good health at present largely unchartered and undifferentiated, toward a goal as yet but dimly perceived which is indicated as peak wellness. This goal represents the extreme opposite of death, that is, performance at full potential in accordance with the individual's age and makeup. To make effective headway toward this goal, we need to crystallize our concept of what the goal is, not only for the individual but also for the family, the community, and society generally.

Since the nature of this goal is ever changing and ever expanding, we probably will never reach it in absolute terms; but we can come to know and appreciate its essential characteristics in relative terms. As the goal, at first seen far above us, becomes clearer and stirs response from deep within us, we will reach out toward it and fight for high-level wellness even as we have fought so valiantly and so long against sickness and death.

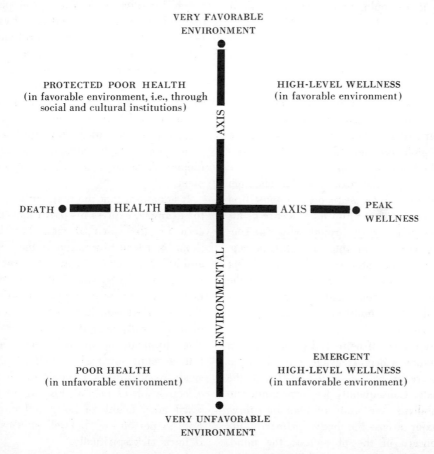

VERY FAVORABLE
ENVIRONMENT

PROTECTED POOR HEALTH
(in favorable environment, i.e., through
social and cultural institutions)

HIGH-LEVEL WELLNESS
(in favorable environment)

AXIS

DEATH ● HEALTH AXIS ● PEAK
WELLNESS

ENVIRONMENTAL

POOR HEALTH
(in unfavorable environment)

EMERGENT
HIGH-LEVEL WELLNESS
(in unfavorable environment)

VERY UNFAVORABLE
ENVIRONMENT

FIGURE 20-1. The health grid, its axes and quadrants. (Source: U.S. Department of Health, Education, and Welfare, Public Health Service, National Office of Vital Statistics.)

## THE SPIRIT OF MAN

Although this goal can be seen but dimly from our present level of knowledge, one element of certainty which emerges in clear relief is that we can no longer ignore the spirit of man as a factor in our medical and health disciplines. Many of us, as physicians and health workers, have become increasingly dissatisfied with our disciplines, which are designed as though the sum total of our concern is for the body and the mind of man, leaving to metaphysics and religion the affairs of the spirit. As if we could divide the sum total of man thus! If we are to move in the direction of high-level wellness for man and society, we cannot ignore the spirit of man in any discipline. In fact, the essence of the task ahead might well be to fashion a rational bridge between the biological nature of man and the spirit of man—the spirit being that intangible something that transcends physiology and psychology.

The spirit of man stems largely from within him. Consequently we must find ways of making him more aware of his own inner world through which he conceptualizes and interprets his perceptions of the outer world. This will bring us inevitably, sooner or later, into the arenas of social and religious affairs and into a multitude of controversial issues.

For most of us reared in the Western culture, a deep cleavage exists between the realm of the spirit and that of the body. Consequently we have tended to subdivide the study of man into three major areas—the body, primarily the concern of the physician; the mind, largely the concern of the educator, psychologists, and psychiatrist; and the spirit, entrusted to the custody of the religious preceptors. Similarly we have been inclined to consign the development and maintenance of man's physical, social, and economic environment largely to economic and political leaders.

This fragmentation of man into areas over which various groups struggle to maintain their jurisdiction appears to be nonsensical, since it tends to defeat the purposes of each group, which strives for the enrichment and fulfillment of that particular segment of man's nature over which it undertakes to maintain jurisdiction. Harmony between jurisdictions can come to pass only when each special interest group realizes that it does not and cannot have a monopoly over a particular area of the nature of man. Harmony will result when the fact is faced that man is a physical, mental, and spiritual unity —a unity which is constantly undergoing a process of growth and adjustment within a continually changing physical, biological, social, and cultural environment.

It is natural that the religious leader, for example, express his particular concern for the spirit of man, but this should not lead him to ignore the body and mind of man or the environment in which man lives, since all these elements affect the well-being of the spirit. Nor should it lead him to the exercise of a monopoly over the spirit of man. The physician, on his part, must take into account spiritual as well as physical considerations if he is to do an effective job of helping his patient toward good health of body and mind. For no person can be well physically if he is sick spiritually.

It is natural for each group competent in a special field of knowledge to approach the study and care of the well-being of man from its own particular point of vantage, but this must not preclude considerations of the unity of man as a whole living within a constantly changing total environment. High-level wellness can never be achieved in fragments, ignoring the unity of the whole.

To the study of man as a unity living within a total environment, the fields of medicine and health have much to offer. To adventure along this pathway of study and responsibility calls for the creation of methods by means of which various levels of wellness can be recognized objectively. Since this proposal has been developed more fully elsewhere,[1] it suffices here to say that, from the standpoints of medicine and health, the principal disciplines contributing to such a science will probably be biochemistry, physiology, and psychology.

The types of questions needing answer are: How do we distinguish and classify degrees or levels of wellness? What are the effects of age, sex, and race on these levels? In what ways can we recognize a particular level in and of itself so as to be reasonably sure we are dealing with a homogeneous group?

If an objective yardstick of wellness can be calibrated in biochemical, physiological, and psychological terms, it would soon become a powerful new tool for the physician, enabling him to recognize low-level wellness and to develop therapies to raise lower levels to higher ones.

If and when it becomes possible to differentiate between levels of wellness, all the indexes now available to us in the measurement of disease and death will become available to us in the area of positive health.

Wellness levels would then become susceptible to measurement in terms of prevalence rates much in the same way we now measure morbidity. Furthermore, we should be able ultimately to calculate the frequency constants of such measurements, correlating them with related social and economic phenomena.

## STEPS THAT CAN BE TAKEN TO QUANTIFY POSITIVE HEALTH

Even though such diagnoses of levels of wellness are not now available, much can be done to qualify positive health. For example:

1. Effect refinements in incidence and prevalence rates to demarcate more clearly the area of positive health from that of illness and disability.

2. Develop susceptibility indexes through the use of biochemical and functional tests to differentiate groups of persons most susceptible to specific diseases and conditions.

3. Establish precursors-of-disease indexes, closely related to the foregoing and designed to show variations from the normal.

4. Select groups of people who are disease-free and who are making full use of their talents, capacities, and potentialities; then measure them by biochemical, functional, and psychological tests to establish the characteristics of those enjoying a high level of wellness. Such groups would need to be selected so as to be representative of the various ages, sexes, and racial combinations.

Possibilities of measuring levels of wellness in the family have been set forth elsewhere.[2] They involve special studies aimed at obtaining answers to four major areas of assessment: (1) What are the day-to-day functional and emotional interrelationships of the family members? (2) What activities occupy the family and its members? (3) What values are important to the family and its members? (4) To what degree does the illness or wellness of a family member reflect the health status of the family as a unit?

It is worth pointing out that, if and when it becomes possible to diagnose levels of wellness in the individual, a very great advantage will accrue to social-science technics. For instance, the researcher trying to evaluate the effect of different types of community life on the family or on the individual could select a sample of individuals and measure the effect on their levels of wellness of varying community conditions.

Once the concept of high-level wellness as a health goal has been crystallized and enriched by many minds contributing to it from their own points of reference, the battle for wellness in man and society will be joined. There must be many points of engagement if the battle is to be won.

### KNOW THYSELF

It is the author's view that the central bastion to be conquered involves teaching people how to "know themselves." Psychology tells us through laboratory demonstrations that our perceptions of the outer world are indissolubly linked with the concepts and emotions fixed in our minds and body tissues. Without a knowledge of one's inner self, understanding of the outer world cannot have breadth and depth. A mind tortured with prejudice, hate, and fear projects itself in distorted human relationships.

Although psychiatrists have done much to relieve the twisted minds of the mentally ill, little has been under-

taken to help ordinary people, classified as "well," to know themselves and thus become better balanced and able to meet their daily problems more adequately. How much of the demand for sleeping pills, alcohol, and tranquilizers is due to this deep-felt need?

It will not be easy to help some adults achieve a better understanding of self. In fact, it is quite likely that the majority of people are fleeing from a deeper knowledge of themselves. With the very young, the task will be less difficult.

Since the personality of the child is formed largely in the preschool years, we must find ways to teach parents the importance of this inner world and how best to guide and nurture the child in his plastic early years, so that he may later be capable of high-level wellness and reach a mature and secure adulthood.

This process calls for the exercise of maturity and wisdom in addition to all the guidance that science can bring to bear. Growing children need broad and diverse opportunities for self-realization. Contact of the child with a wise and mature mind during this period offers one of the best means by which insight may be gained into family and social values and objectives. Maturity and wisdom must be made available to the growing infant and child in order to encourage, temper, and season his explorings and adventurings of self.

### RESOURCES OF WISDOM
### AND MATURITY

Untapped resources of wisdom and maturity are available to the nation among its retired people. Persons no longer active in their careers, but who have lived rich, full lives, acquiring wisdom and maturity in the process, might become part-time companions and counselors to our children, particularly in the case of the gifted child who feels lost without intellectual supplementation of his normal family and school life. Let us call on retired persons of special competence and in good health to return to active life within the community. Let us ask them to help with the children who need extra intellectual stimulus and wise understanding. Let us ask the best qualified of them to serve as advisers to the "sick" family and as special custodians of the culture of the group, so to speak. The community needs them and they need the community.

## CREATIVE EXPRESSION

In the fight for high-level wellness, action to enhance the importance of creative expression in our culture is a must. Creative expression is a most important element in the bridge between the biological nature of man and the spirit of man. The creative spirit resides within every living person. It can be kindled in any man, woman, or child. "What is the creative spirit?" you ask. At one time I defined it as "an expression of self, adventuring into the unknown in search for universal truth."[3] However defined, we need to value it highly and nurture it well, since man's position of dominance in the world stems more di-

rectly from this quality than from all others.

Man finds discovery both absorbing and satisfying. With creative expression comes intense inner satisfaction. At the same time, it permits man to contribute of himself to the social group and thus form bonds with his fellow man of love, trust, and security. Creative expression and love of one's fellows satisfy deep psychological and emotional needs in our inner world and simultaneously are radiated outward to bring us to the fullness of life of which man is capable.

When we learn how to diagnose high-level wellness through objective measures, we shall probably find that a substantial amount of creative expression, altruism, and love in daily life is essential for the approach to a high state of well-being. Through the development and application of these values in daily life, we will achieve self-confidence and faith in ourselves. This in turn will bring growth of self, development toward fuller maturity, and a balanced wellness of body, mind, and spirit.

The goal of high-level wellness for man and society can be acheived, though not easily. The needs are for a clear-cut concept and dedication to it; for money and research; for understanding, courage, and a reassessment of basic values; for a positive orientation toward life and society. We must dare to dream, for "dreams are the seedlings of realities."

---

1. Halbert L. Dunn, "Points of Attack for Raising the Levels of Wellness," *Journal of National Medical Association*, **49**, 1957, 225–235.

2. Halbert L. Dunn, "How Well Is Your Family?," scheduled for publication in an early issue of *Today's Health*.

3. Halbert L. Dunn, "Your World and Mine," in *Essays on Human Relations*, New York: Exposition Press, 1956.

# 21. HOW LAYMEN DEFINE ILLNESS

## *Dorrian Apple Sweetser*

The decision by a person who has something wrong with his health that he is ill and not merely ailing is a turning point in his subsequent behavior. Besides giving him the privileges of the sick role, this decision is also likely to influence what he does about his health.

Most studies of lay views on illness have focused on whether these views coincide with professional ideas of what patients, or prospective patients, should know and do. The usual approach has been to inquire if people are correctly informed of the facts about health, and, if they are not, to explore the reasons. However, for a layman to conclude that he is ill and for a doctor to diagnose him involve quite different processes of decision. There has been little investigation of whether a layman who decides he is ill has based this conclusion, at least in part, on factors which a doctor would not consider to be untrue or imaginary but which rather are irrelevant to a professional judgment about the state of his health.[1] Hence it seems important to find out the conditions under which the layman thinks of himself, or others, as being ill.

## OBJECTIVES

This study was designed to investigate the influence of three conditions on whether laymen would decide that a state of impaired health should be considered as illness: conditions in which the health problem does or does not interfere with usual activities, whether or not it was recent in onset, and whether it is ambiguous — that is, hard for a layman to diagnose. A secondary aim of the study was to ascertain when respondents thought it advisable to see a doctor.

## PROCEDURE

The attempt to achieve these aims was through a process of interviewing sixty persons in a sample which, as will be shown, was selected by a prearranged plan. The interviewing was carried on by graduate students at the Boston University School of Nursing as part of their graduate training. The interviewers read to these persons a series of brief descriptions of individuals with health problems and asked them whether they thought the person depicted in each description was sick, what the illness might be, and what should be done about the health problem. The interview also included questions about the respondent's background, his health practices, and his knowledge of facts about health.

Reprinted by permission of the author and publisher, from *Journal of Health and Human Behavior*, Vol. 1, 1960, pp. 219–225. (The author is indebted to Dr. Norman Berkowitz, Dr. Malcolm Klein, and Miss Mary Malone of the Human Relations Center at Boston University for much helpful criticism of this paper; and to Miss Rose Godbout of the School of Nursing for advice about the interview schedule.)

## THE DESCRIPTIONS OF HEALTH PROBLEMS

In the eight descriptions of persons with health problems which were used in the interview, the three conditions of interference with usual activities, recent onset, and ambiguity were combined in all possible ways. This design allowed replies to all eight items to be utilized in testing the effect of each condition on whether or not respondents considered the persons described to them to be ill.

One description was characterized by all three conditions; three descriptions were each characterized by a pair of conditions; three others were represented by a single condition; and one was depicted as a health problem in which none of the conditions was present. The absence of a condition was made explicit. In other words, a description of a health problem in which interference with usual activities did not occur contained a statement that the person was able to carry out his usual activities. A health problem not of recent onset was described as stable and chronic, as having been present without change for six months or more. And the statement about a health problem which was not ambiguous was framed to represent a familiar ailment such as a bad cold. For example, the health problem which was recent in origin, was not ambiguous, and interfered with usual activities was described as follows: "Here's a man who developed a sort throat and a running nose the day before yesterday. He feels feverish and aches and has a tight feeling in his chest. He doesn't feel like doing anything." The health problem which was ambiguous and not recent in its onset but interfered with usual activities was represented by the statement: "Here's a man who has been feel-ing very tired a lot of the time for the past six months. He gets tired soon after he gets up in the morning. Sometimes he feels dizzy for a few minutes. He doesn't feel like doing as much as he usually does." In the eight items, the sex of the persons described was varied so that two men and two women appear in the four cases in which a condition was present and two men and two women appear in the four in which the condition was absent.

The validity of the concept of ambiguity was tested and found to be satisfactory. An ambiguous health problem had been previously defined as one which would be difficult for a layman to diagnose; and a health problem which was not ambiguous, as one which would be easy for the layman to diagnose. It was found that the proportion of respondents who said that they could not identify the health problem, or who offered two or more different kinds of diagnoses, was higher for each of the four ambiguous items than for any of the unambiguous items. The mean proportion of people who found diagnosis difficult was .55 for ambiguous items and .24 for unambiguous items.

This test of validity does not assume that the lay diagnoses are correct. The only medically valid statement which can be made about the eight items is that the persons depicted are not in the best of health.

Recent onset and interference with usual activities were assumed to have face validity in the items, since they contained phrases such as "the day before yesterday," "for the past six months," "doesn't feel like doing as much as he usually does," and "hasn't interfered with any of her activities." Reliability of the items was tested by investigating whether similar types of respondents would give similar replies. The sample was stratified on age, sex, and education, and then was divided at random into two groups. The frequencies with which the items were identified as illness by the two groups were correlated, and *r* was found to be .87.

The study design assumed that respondents would make a distinction between illness and health problems which they did not consider to be illness. This assumption was validated by the fact that respondents frequently verbalized the process of making this distinction by remarks such as, "He's really sick," or "She's not sick, she's just ailing," or "He's got something wrong with him, but I wouldn't say he's sick."

## THE SAMPLE

The sample consisted of sixty persons, men and women between the ages of 20 and 50 who were living in the Boston metropolitan area. The interviewers were instructed to choose people of specified age and sex, so that the sample would contain an equal number of older and younger men and women. To control variability in social class, interviewers were instructed to limit their selection to persons of given definitions of occupation and education. Relatives and friends of interviewers and persons with training in the health field were ruled out as respondents, in order to minimize the possibility that respondents' reactions would be biased by professional knowledge.

The sample contained almost equal proportions of men and women. Half were 35 years of age or under and half over 35. Half of the sample were professionals, executives, or owners, or the wives of men who held these positions. The remainder, with the exception of four blue-collar workers, were white-collar workers or the wives of white-collar workers. Half were college graduates, one-fifth had had some postgraduate education, and nearly all of the remainder had had at least some high-school education.

## JUDGMENTS ABOUT ILLNESS

The frequencies with which respondents judged the eight descriptions of health problems to be illness are presented in Table 21-1. The range of the number of items judged to be illness by individual respondents was one to eight. No significant differences in the number of judgments were found when respondents were compared on the basis

TABLE 21-1
FREQUENCY OF IDENTIFICATION OF
HEALTH PROBLEMS AS ILLNESS

| Health problem* | Number |
|---|---|
| 1. *Interferes with usual activities, recent onset, ambiguous* | 54 |
| 2. Does not interfere with usual activities, *recent onset, ambiguous* | 40 |
| 3. *Interferes with usual activities, recent onset,* not ambiguous | 52 |
| 4. *Interferes with usual activities,* not of recent onset, *ambiguous* | 39 |
| 5. Does not interfere with usual activities, not of recent onset, *ambiguous* | 22 |
| 6. Does not interfere with usual activities, *recent onset,* not ambiguous | 28 |
| 7. *Interferes with usual activities,* not of recent onset, not ambiguous | 34 |
| 8. Does not interfere with usual activities, not of recent onset, not ambiguous | 25 |

*Conditions present are italicized.

of sex, age, education, occupation, a high or low level of health care, or a high or low amount of knowledge about health.[2]

The effect of interference with usual activities, recent onset, and ambiguity on whether respondents thought the items depicted illness were tested by means of scores assigned to individual respondents. Each respondent was given a score of plus, minus, or zero for his reaction to each condition. He received a score of plus if he judged illness to be present in more of the items in which the condition was present than in the items in which the condition was absent, a score of minus if the reverse were true, and a score of zero if he judged illness to be present as often in items in which the condition was present as in items in which the condition was absent. To illustrate the scoring procedure, a respondent who judged items 1, 2, 4, and 7 in Table 21-1 to be illness would receive a score of plus for his reaction to ambiguity, zero for his reaction to recent onset, and plus for his response to interference with usual activities. The scores of the sample are given in Table 21-2.

The effect of each condition on whether illness was perceived in the health problems was tested by the sign test.[3] In making this test, ties are discarded and only scores indicating differences are used. The frequencies of plus and minus scores for each condition were tested against the null hypothesis that they would be equal in number.

Interference with usual activities and recent onset were found to be significantly associated with the decision that a state of impaired health constituted an illness. Ambiguity was not found to have a significant effect. These findings

### TABLE 21-2
JUDGMENTS OF 60 PERSONS REGARDING VARIOUS HEALTH CONDITIONS AS ILLNESS

| Condition | + | − | 0 | Total |
|---|---|---|---|---|
| Interferes with usual activities* | 40 | 14 | 6 | 60 |
| Recent onset† | 37 | 15 | 8 | 60 |
| Ambiguous‡ | 24 | 22 | 14 | 60 |

*Effect of condition on judgment is significant, $P < .01$. One-tailed test of significance of difference, see reference 3.
†Difference is significant, $P < .01$.
‡Difference not significant.

were retested holding each condition constant and rescoring each respondent's replies to the items. The results were the same as those previously obtained; recent onset was found to have a significant effect on judgment that a health problem was an illness within each of the other two conditions, as was interference with usual activities, while ambiguity had no significant effect. (See Table 21-2.)

## ANALYSIS OF DATA

These findings suggest that, to middle-class Americans, to be ill means to have an ailment of recent origin which interferes with one's usual activities. This idea may be an example of cultural lag, since the idea seems more appropriate to an earlier period when infectious diseases with obvious symptoms were a bigger threat to life than they are today.

At present, chronic illnesses such as heart trouble and cancer are becoming more common, and in their early stages, at least, their symptoms may persist without getting worse and may not interfere with usual activities. In such cases, this conception of illness could cause delay in seeking treatment. However, the best plan for motivating the public to seek early treatment is by no means generally agreed upon among people in the health professions, nor is there general agreement about the value of preventive health examinations for adults.

Cultural lag could explain the origin of the idea that an illness is an ailment of recent onset which interferes with usual activities but could not account for its persistence. Further study is needed to discover the social and psychological functions of the idea. One social function of this idea may be that it is a normative sanction for taking on the role of patient, since it gives laymen a basis on which to decide whether they need the services of a doctor. Psychologically it may be a protection against irrational fears about health, since the idea serves to distinguish health problems which are not illness from those which are, and presumably the former offer less grounds for worry about their consequences than do the latter.

Alternative explanations of the judgments respondents made were explored and rejected by item correlations and cross-tabulations. The alternative explanations investigated were sex of the person described, severity of pain, other kinds of symptoms present, parts of the body affected, and order of presentation of items.

Chi-square tests were made of each of the three sets of scores for differences associated with age, sex, education, occupation, level of health care, and amount of knowledge about health. A significant difference was found between respondents with high and those with low levels of health care in regard to their scores on interference with usual activities.[4] Those with a high level of health care had a disproportionate number of plus scores, and those with a low level of health care had a disproportionate number of zero and minus scores.

This finding suggests that interference with usual activities may be the most important conditions associated in the layman's mind with illness, since respondents who give more attention to their health, that is, who have a higher level of health care, were particularly likely to equate illness with interference with usual activities.

## ADVICE ABOUT HEALTH CARE

Respondents had been asked what they thought the persons depicted in the eight items should do about their health problems. Their recommendations took the form of advice to see a doctor, either at once or after a delay to see if the problem would clear up by itself, or if some home remedy would cure it; to try a home remedy with no other step advised; to do nothing because nothing could be done; or to do nothing because nothing needed to be done. The range of times that respondents advised seeing a doctor was from one to eight. No significant differences in the number of times this was advised were found to be associated with age, sex, education, occupation, level of health care, or amount of knowledge about health.

Whether or not a respondent considered a health problem to be illness had a strong relationship to the kind of advice he offered about it. Eighty-one per cent of the opinions that a health problem was illness were followed by advice to see a doctor, and another 13 per cent were accompanied by advice to wait a bit and then see a doctor if time or a home remedy did not cure the ailment. Advice to see a doctor was given in only 54 per cent of the instances in which respondents thought a health problem was not illness.

The association of the decision that a health problem is an illness with the recommendation to see a doctor lends support to the previous suggestion that the idea of what constitutes a state of illness which has been described in this study functions as a normative sanction for taking on the role of patient. Study is needed of physicians' ideas about the circumstances under which it is advisable for people to seek medical care. The roles of doctor and patient are complementary, and it would be most unusual if ideas on role behavior held by patients were not interlocked with and reinforced by expectations of patients which are held by doctors.

The advice that respondents gave about health problems which they considered illness was further analyzed in order to investigate the relationships between recent onset, interference with usual activities, and ambiguity and the frequency with which respondents recommended seeing a doctor. The same kind of analysis was made of advice about health problems which the respondents did not consider to be illness.

To illustrate the scoring procedure in making these comparisons, the per cent of items describing recent health problems which a respondent regarded as illness and the per cent of recommendations to see a doctor in these instances were noted. The per cent of recommendation to see a doctor in these instances was compared with the per cent of times that the respondent advised seeing a doctor for the treatment of conditions characterizing health problems of long duration which he considered illness. If the former per cent exceeded the latter, he was given a score of plus. If the latter was larger, he was given a score of minus. Ties were represented by zero. The per cent of plus and minus scores was tested by the null hypothesis that they would be equal. The same process was followed to score advice about health problems which they did not consider as illness.

The respondents were more likely to advise a doctor for ambiguous health problems which they considered illness than for unambiguous health problems they judged to be illness. In this comparison, there were 28 plus responses: that is, 28 out of the 60 persons would be more likely to advise seeing a doctor for the former than for the latter set of health problems. In the same comparison, there were 8 minus and 24 zero responses: that is, 8 respondents believed the person with the latter condition was more in need of the doctor, and 24 did not make a difference in the two conditions.[5]

The respondents were less likely to advise seeing a doctor for the treatment of health problems of recent onset which they did not consider illnesses than for health problems of long duration which they did not think were illnesses. In this comparison, only 7 persons — there were 7 plus responses — thought it more advisable to see a doctor for the former set of health problems, while 36 persons — there were 36 minus responses — thought it more important to see a doctor for the latter set, and there were 17 ties.[6]

No significant differences were found when respondents were compared on the basis of age, sex, education, occupation, level of health care, or amount of knowledge about health.

The finding about advice given for ambiguous illnesses may be due to the fact that, if people find it hard to identify an illness, they will feel uncertain of its length and outcome, and this uncertainty gives an added incentive to consulting a doctor. The finding that advice to see a doctor was more often given for health problems of long duration which were not considered illness than for problems of recent onset suggests that respondents have a standard for judging how long it should take for ailments to clear up by themselves.

## SUMMARY

The kind of health problem which respondents considered to be illness were those of recent onset which interfered with usual activities. People with a high level of health care were more sensitive to the condition of interference with usual activities than were people with a low level of health care, which suggests that this condition is the most important one associated in the layman's mind with illness.

Judgment as to whether or not a health problem was illness had a bearing on what respondents thought it was wise to do, since they very often advised seeing a doctor about a health problem which they considered illness and less often gave this advice about health problems which they did not regard as illness. They were particularly likely to advise seeing a doctor about an illness if it was ambiguous, that is, hard to identify, and were particularly likely to advise seeing a doctor about a health problem which they did not think was illness if the problem had been present for some time.

This study has presented evidence that, whatever the number of correct health facts which the participants knew, and regardless of their age, sex, educational or occupational level within the middle class, there were some important nonmedical characteristics of the kind of health problem which they considered to be illness. Once illness was judged to be present, most people thought it advisable to see a doctor, either at once or after a delay. However, when the health problem was not judged to be illness, many thought it all right to do nothing or to try a home remedy.

Much emphasis is given today in public health to early diagnosis and treatment of health problems, particularly by means of preventive health examinations. However, many of the people interviewed think that the time to see a doctor is when you yourself think you are sick, and not before.

The greatest problem arising from these lay views about the circumstances which warrant seeing a doctor is probably in the care of chronic diseases such as heart trouble and cancer. Chronic diseases are increasingly common, and they often have a slow and insidious onset. The symptoms tend to persist and do not always limit activity. Consequently they may not provide much impetus toward seeing a doctor, and yet early diagnosis and treatment are often essential to cure or to the prevention of irreversible damage. This poses a problem in health education which is well known. This study has described some of the reasons why the problem exists.

---

1. Two studies have described configuration facts in lay judgments about health which are different in kind from the configurations of facts in professional judgments. Lena DiCicco and Dorrian Apple, in "Health Needs and Opinions of Older Adults," *Public Health Reports*, 73, 1958, 479–487, presents evidence that their sample defined health as the ability to be active. Elaine and John Cumming,

in *Closed Ranks: An Experiment in Mental Health Education,* Cambridge, Mass.: Harvard University Press, found that laymen used criteria to identify mental illness which were different from the criteria of professionals.

2. Knowledge of health was measured by dichotomizing the sample at the median of the number of correct answers given to a ten-item quiz containing items such as, "A person can get diabetes from eating too many sweet things." As a kind of validity test this measure was correlated with a fairly good four-item Guttman scale based on the quiz; the phi coefficient of correlation was .47, $P < .01$. Persons with a high level of health care were those who said they had their own doctor, their own dentist, and had seen a doctor and a dentist within the past year. Persons with a low level of health care were those to whom one or more of these facts did not apply. Validity of the measure of level of health care was tested by correlation with whether or not respondents had said, in reply to an interview question which preceded questions about their own health care, that they thought regular medical and/or dental checkups were advisable. The phi coefficient of correlation was .48, $P < .01$.

3. Sidney Siegel, *Nonparametric Statistics for the Behavioral Sciences,* New York: McGraw-Hill, 1956, pp. 68–75. The scoring procedure is the equivalent of making a series of pair comparisons. The eight items can be grouped into three sets of four different pairs, the members of a pair being alike except for the presence or absence of one of the conditions and all pairs in a set varying in relation to the same condition. Each pair can be scored *plus* if the item in which the condition is present is judged illness while the other item is not, *minus* if the reverse is true, and *zero* if both or neither item is considered illness. A respondent's score for the set would be *plus* if there were more *plus* scores than *minus* scores for the pairs, *minus* if the reverse were true, and *zero* if there were an equal number of *plus* and *minus* pair scores, or if all pair scores were *zero*.

4. Chi square $= 6.768$; $P < .05$.

5. Two-tailed test, $P < .01$.

6. Two-tailed test, $P < .01$.

# 22. CONSIDERATIONS OF ALTERNATIVE HELP SOURCES

## Philip N. Haese and Richard L. Meile

The subject of this paper[1] is an unanticipated finding in a pilot study designed to ascertain the help sources people say they would turn to in solving the kinds of problems that bring patients to psychiatrists. The unanticipated finding is that persons preferring a psychiatrist as a source of help seldom consider alternative help sources, whereas persons selecting other professional help sources more often say they would consider alternatives. This finding is discussed in the context of current trends in the mental-health enterprise in order to clarify its potential meaning and significance for patients, for those engaged in direct patient services, and for further research.

## METHOD

One hundred adults in a large midwestern city were interviewed in their homes. These persons were selected by a "cluster-quota" method. First, 25 blocks within the city limits were chosen randomly. Then, starting from a fixed point within each block and following a prescribed route, four interviews were completed — two with males and two with females. No more than one person at any one dwelling was interviewed. Callbacks were made only if the interviewer had to return a second time to an area. The sex, age, and educational characteristics of the respondents, along with the occupation of the household head, appear in Table 22-1.

### TABLE 22-1
#### CHARACTERISTICS OF THE SAMPLE

| Characteristics | (N=100) Per cent |
|---|---|
| Sex | |
| Males | 50 |
| Females | 50 |
| Age | |
| 25 or under | 16 |
| 26 to 35 | 29 |
| 36 to 45 | 29 |
| 46 to 55 | 10 |
| 56 or older | 15 |
| Not ascertainable | 1 |
| Education | |
| 8th grade or less | 10 |
| 9th to 11th grade | 15 |
| 12th grade (H.S. grad.) | 38 |
| 1 to 3 yrs. college | 23 |
| 4 or more yrs. college | 14 |
| Occupation of household head | |
| White collar | 43 |
| Professional, technical, and kindred workers | 12 |
| Managers, officials, and proprietors | 17 |
| Clerical and kindred workers | 6 |
| Sales workers | 8 |
| Blue collar | 33 |
| Craftsmen, foremen, and kindred workers | 12 |
| Operatives and laborers | 21 |
| Other | 24 |
| Service workers | 8 |
| Retired | 7 |
| Other (students, etc.) | 9 |

This paper was prepared especially as an original contribution to this book.

TABLE 22-2
PREFERRED SOURCES OF HELP
FOR PSYCHIATRIC PROBLEMS

| Help sources | Problems for which help source preferred (N = 500) | | Persons preferring help source (N = 100) | |
|---|---|---|---|---|
| | No. | Per cent | No. | Per cent |
| Clergyman | 93 | 18.6 | 51 | 51 |
| Self | 87 | 17.4 | 57 | 57 |
| Doctor | 63 | 12.6 | 42 | 42 |
| Family member | 62 | 12.4 | 39 | 39 |
| Psychiatrist | 59 | 11.8 | 37 | 37 |
| Prayer | 34 | 6.8 | 18 | 18 |
| Friend | 19 | 3.8 | 14 | 14 |
| Other help source | 35 | 7.0 | 32 | 32 |
| Don't know | 48 | 9.6 | 31 | 31 |

Within a more extensive interview than reported in this paper, each respondent was presented with five, from a series of 30, hypothetical problems. The 30 problems represent reasons given by a sample of psychiatric patients for seeking the services of a psychiatrist.[2] An attempt was made to distribute these problems randomly across the 100 respondents.[3]

Four questions were asked for each problem: (1) If you (e.g., felt lonesome or lonely) and it were a problem for you, where would you turn to for help? (2) Why is that? (3) What other alternatives would you consider? And (4) Why would you rather turn to (place originally mentioned) rather than to these alternatives? Answers were coded for the help source preferred by the respondent (generally the answer to question 1), alternatives he would consider (generally the answer to question 3), and his reasons for selection or preference (questions 2 and/or 4). This coding then was checked independently by two other persons. The few cases where coders disagreed were resolved.

Other data relevant to this paper are age, sex, education, occupation of household head, and whether or not the respondent said that any of the thirty problems were "true of him."

## RESULTS

Results will be reported in two ways: the number and per cent of problems for which each help source was preferred and the number and per cent of persons exhibiting these preferences.[4] In this way it can be shown that the results do not depend on the responses of a small number of persons. In fact, similar conclusions would be reached from either index.

Moreover, the results will not be subjected to tests of statistical significance. Our purpose here is not to test hypotheses, but merely to present and clarify an unanticipated finding.

The number of times each source of help was preferred is reported in Table 22-2. The psychiatrist ranks third as the preferred source of *professional* help behind the clergyman and nonpsychiatric doctor. The psychiatrist is selected at least once by 37 per cent of the 100 respondents, but he is selected for only 11.8 per cent of the 500 cases. This find-

TABLE 22-3
PREFERENCE FOR PSYCHIATRIST AS SOURCE OF HELP
FOR PSYCHIATRIC PROBLEMS, BY CHARACTERISTICS OF RESPONDENTS

| Characteristics of respondents | Problems for which psychiatrist preferred | | | Persons preferring psychiatrist | | |
|---|---|---|---|---|---|---|
| | No. | Per cent | (N) | No. | Per cent | (N) |
| Sex | | | | | | |
| Male | 26 | 10 | (250) | 17 | 34 | (50) |
| Female | 33 | 13 | (250) | 20 | 40 | (50) |
| Age* | | | | | | |
| 35 and under | 29 | 13 | (225) | 18 | 40 | (45) |
| 36 and over | 30 | 11 | (270) | 19 | 35 | (54) |
| Education | | | | | | |
| 11th grade or less | 13 | 10 | (125) | 6 | 24 | (25) |
| 12th grade (H.S. grad.) | 18 | 9 | (190) | 14 | 37 | (38) |
| 1 or more yrs. college | 28 | 15 | (185) | 17 | 46 | (37) |
| Occupation of household head | | | | | | |
| White collar | 32 | 15 | (215) | 19 | 44 | (43) |
| Blue collar | 14 | 8 | (165) | 10 | 30 | (33) |
| Other | 13 | 11 | (120) | 8 | 33 | (24) |
| Problems | | | | | | |
| None | 20 | 9 | (220) | 15 | 34 | (44) |
| One or more | 39 | 14 | (280) | 22 | 39 | (56) |

*Does not include one case in which age was not ascertainable.

ing is similar to that of Gurin et al., who report that persons who sought professional help for problems sought this help from clergymen, doctors, and psychiatrists in that order of frequency.[5] It also conforms to Woodward's finding that this same order applies "in choosing types of people to supervise a publicly financed program for mental health."[6]

Preference for the psychiatrist by persons with different characteristics is presented in Table 22-3. Both from the point of view of cases and persons the psychiatrist is more often selected by females, persons under 35 years of age, persons with one or more years of college, persons who live in households where the occupation of the head is white collar, and persons who have one or more of the 30 problems. In most cases, however, the differences are very small.

Reasons given for choosing a clergyman, doctor, and psychiatrist are presented in Table 22-4. The psychiatrist, more so than either the clergyman or the doctor, is selected because he is believed to be the appropriate *professional* for dealing with problems of this sort. This also conforms to Gurin et al., who found that among persons seeking help from a psychiatrist, the most frequent reason for their choice was that it was a "help source functionally appropriate for (the) problem," and that this reason was very pronounced among self-referrals.[7]

Table 22-5 shows for each help source the per cent of cases in which the respondent said he would consider an alternative to the preferred help source. Here we see striking differences. Although alternatives were most often considered when a clergyman, doctor, family member, prayer, friend, or

TABLE 22-4
SELECTED* REASONS FOR PREFERRING
CLERGY, DOCTOR, AND PSYCHIATRIST

| Reason for selection or preference | Clergy (N = 93) | | Doctor (N = 63) | | Psychiatrist (N = 59) | |
|---|---|---|---|---|---|---|
| | No. | Per cent | No. | Per cent | No. | Per cent |
| Training appropriate to problem | 31 | 33 | 34 | 54 | 36 | 61 |
| Personal relationship with help source | 8 | 9 | 7 | 11 | 1 | 2 |
| Could confide in help source | 11 | 12 | ... | ... | ... | ... |
| Other reasons and no reason given | 43 | 46 | 22 | 35 | 22 | 37 |

*Only those reasons necessary for the discussion presented in this paper have been tabulated.

other help source was preferred, this is true in only relatively few cases where self or psychiatric help was preferred. This table also shows that this finding probably is not the result of the responses of a relatively few persons. Alternatives were not considered, at least in one of five cases, by 81 per cent of the persons selecting psychiatric help.

Moreover, this phenomenon does not seem to be caused by the acceptance of the psychiatrist in any one group of persons. Table 22-6 shows that, although there are minor variations, the relationship is pronounced in all categories of respondents.

## DISCUSSION

Our findings indicate that the psychiatrist is not the help source that would be utilized most often by persons even if they had the very kind of problems for which patients currently enter psychiatric treatment. Although persons who do select a psychiatrist select him

TABLE 22-5
SELECTION OF HELP SOURCE WITHOUT
ALTERNATIVE BY HELP SOURCE PREFERRED

| Help source preferred | Problems for which no alternative selected | | | Persons selecting help sources without alternative | | |
|---|---|---|---|---|---|---|
| | No. | Per cent | (N) | No. | Per cent | (N) |
| Clergyman | 27 | 29 | (93) | 16 | 20 | (51) |
| Self | 69 | 78 | (87) | 46 | 81 | (57) |
| Doctor | 24 | 38 | (63) | 18 | 43 | (42) |
| Family Member | 21 | 34 | (62) | 13 | 33 | (39) |
| Psychiatrist | 41 | 70 | (59) | 30 | 81 | (37) |
| Prayer | 9 | 26 | (34) | 6 | 33 | (18) |
| Friend | 6 | 32 | (19) | 5 | 36 | (14) |
| Other help source | 13 | 37 | (35) | 13 | 41 | (32) |

TABLE 22-6
SELECTION OF PSYCHIATRIST WITHOUT ALTERNATIVE
BY CHARACTERISTICS OF RESPONDENTS

| Characteristics of respondents | Cases in which psychiatrist is selected without alternative | | |
| --- | --- | --- | --- |
| | No. | Per cent | (N) |
| Sex | | | |
| Male | 17 | 65 | (26) |
| Female | 24 | 73 | (33) |
| Age* | | | |
| 35 and under | 22 | 75 | (29) |
| 36 and over | 19 | 63 | (30) |
| Education | | | |
| 11th grade or less | 10 | 77 | (13) |
| 12th grade (H. S. grad.) | 12 | 67 | (18) |
| 1 or more yrs. college | 19 | 68 | (28) |
| Occupation of household head | | | |
| White collar | 23 | 72 | (32) |
| Blue collar | 9 | 64 | (14) |
| Other | 9 | 69 | (13) |
| Problems | | | |
| None | 15 | 75 | (20) |
| One or more | 26 | 67 | (39) |

*Does not include one case in which age was not ascertainable.

because of his professional expertise in handling these types of problems, it would seem that for most persons considerations other than this are the criteria for selecting professional help.

Our data do not suggest ways of extending the services of the psychiatrist. They do suggest, however, implications for those who do select psychiatric aid. This is especially true for the finding that persons who select psychiatrists rarely select alternative help sources.

At least two explanations for this phenomenon seem possible. One is that the psychiatrist is viewed as an extension of the "self"; that is, a person to whom the prospective patient would be willing to confide those intimate aspects of his life which he normally would not be willing to confide in others. This hypothesis was suggested by the similarity in frequency with which self and psychiatric help was preferred

without consideration of an alternative help source. This hypothesis seems unlikely, however, when the reasons for selecting a psychiatrist are considered. No one selected the psychiatrist because he could confide in him. It is possible, however, that persons might covertly include ease of confiding in a help source under some other reason. The only category of reasons where such an assumption would seem justified is that of knowing the help source personally. The psychiatrist is selected on this basis, however, in only one case, whereas both the doctor and the clergyman are more often selected for this reason.

The second possible explanation for this finding is that the psychiatrist is viewed as a last resort, someone who is turned to only when all other help sources have failed. This hypothesis cannot be rejected from the data in this study. Moreover, it is consistent with

Woodward's interpretation of his data.[8] At any rate, if the psychiatrist is not the last resort, he is, in most cases, the *only* resort. The implications of this fact become clear when viewed against two trends in the current mental-health enterprise.

The first of these trends is mental-health education aimed at increasing the public's acceptance of psychiatric treatment.[9] Such educational efforts assume that knowledge and acceptance of mental illness and psychiatric treatment personnel, techniques, and facilities is important in getting disturbed persons into treatment. This assumption seems justified in view of studies showing large numbers of mentally impaired persons who do not receive psychiatric treatment[10] and other studies showing wide-spread stigma attached to mental illness and psychiatric treatment.[11] Nevertheless, implicit in this mental-health-education trend is the further assumption that treatment will be provided when the person arrives at the psychiatrist. That this assumption is not wholly justified will be seen after an examination of a second trend.

The second trend might be termed "psychiatric conservation." Its source is the scarcity of psychiatrists relative to the numbers of persons needing treatment. Evidence for such a trend is found in numerous research projects aimed at discovering factors that will predict the duration and success of psychiatric treatment.[12] Reports of such projects make plain that, wittingly or unwittingly, many patients are rejected for treatment, either by themselves or by psychiatrists.

In these two trends lies this conflict: although mental-health educators attempt to secure treatment for more persons, "psychiatric conservationists" attempt to find identifiable criteria by which to reject "bad therapy risks."

A problem thus is imposed on prospective psychiatric patients. Those who assume they will find treatment at the most proficient and "only" source of help, the psychiatrist, may find themselves rejected because they are not the best patients, the type of patient best suited to conserve the limited and scarce psychiatric resource.

A direct solution to this dilemma would be to increase the number of psychiatrists and psychiatric facilities. But such an increase probably will not occur in the immediate future.[13] Therefore prospective patients will continue to face their dilemma.

As is true of most research, our data pose more questions than they answer. Further research is indicated in several directions. One such direction would be the determination of the number of alternatives considered and the extent of this consideration by prospective patients at the point of applying for psychiatric treatment. If the essential findings of this study hold up among this group, then still further inquiry could be directed toward the correlation of consideration of alternatives and motivation for therapy.[14] Finally, if such a relationship were found, it would be possible to consider whether or not motivation for therapy could be induced in prospective patients by leading them to consider the pros and cons of alternative help sources.

1. This investigation was supported in part by Public Health Service Grants, MH-00968 and MH-01407, from the National Institute of Mental Health.

2. Research by the authors and others indicates that new admissions to psychiatric treatment conceptualize their difficulties not as "classical" psychiatric symptoms, but as problems in various areas of their lives—economic, physical health, interpersonal, etc. The "problems" presented to the respondents in this study were derived from interviews with 100 psychiatric patients, all of whom were recent admissions to treatment. In these interviews the patients were asked a series of questions to ascertain how they verbalized the problems that brought them to a psychiatrist. Independent coding of these responses by three persons indicated the reliability of this approach. The similarity of our "problem" list to that of at least one other study seemed to indicate some generality of the problem list. Cf. James M. A. Weiss, Lois A. Rommel, and K. Warner Schaie, "The Presenting Problems of Older Patients Referred to a Psychiatric Clinic," *Journal of Geronotology*, **14**, 1959, 477–481; K. Warner Schaie, Lois A. Rommel, and James M. A. Weiss, "Judging the Relative Severity of Psychiatric Out-Patient Complaints," *Journal of Clinical Psychology*, **15**, 1959, 380–388; K. Warner Schaie, Lois R. Chatham, and James M. A. Weiss, "The Multiprofessional Intake Assessment of Older Psychiatric Patients," *Journal of Psychiatric Research*, **1**, 1961, 92-100; James M. A. Weiss and K. Warner Schaie, "The Psychiatric Evaluation Index: Potential Use in Assessment of the Results of Psychotherapy, "*American Journal of Psychotherapy*, **18**, March 1964, Supplement 1, pp. 3-14 and 61-63. A complete list of the problems and the questionnaire used in this study is available from the authors.

3. Each of the 30 problems was not given to an equal number of respondents. Some items were used 15 times, some 18 times, most 16 times. Moreover, the items were not proportionally distributed among the different sample subgroups. Such sophistications were not necessary to achieve the major objectives of the pilot study. Therefore, to evaluate more thoroughly the unanticipated finding presented in this paper, the authors examined the evidence at hand to see whether it was likely that a more adequate sample would significantly change the essential finding. After careful examination of the internal evidence, the authors agreed that if the sample were increased, the probable changes in results either would not change or would more sharply confirm the conclusions. For example, it seemed likely that the proportion of problems for which a psychiatrist was the preferred help source would decrease slightly and the proportion in which the psychiatrist was selected without an alternative help source would remain about the same.

4. The later index could also be stated as the number and per cent of persons preferring a particular help source at least once (and in some cases more than once) in the five cases presented to each respondent.

5. Gerald Gurin, Joseph Veroff and Sheila Field, *Americans View Their Mental Health: A Nationwide Interview Survey*, New York: Basic Books, 1960, p. 307.

6. Julian L. Woodward, "Changing Ideas on Mental Illness and Its Treatment," *American Sociological Review*, **16**, 1951, 452.

7. Gurin, *op. cit.*, p. 316.

8. Woodward states, "It would seem to be one of the psychiatrist's major problems today to break down the "nut doctor" and the "last resort" association in the public mind . . ." *loc. cit.*

9. See, for example, *Mental Health Education: A Critique*, Philadelphia: Pennsylvania Mental Health, Inc., 1960, esp. pp. 21–22; Joint Commission on Mental Illness and Health, *Action for Mental Health*, New York: Basic Books, 1961, esp. pp. 279–280; Earl Ubel, "Public Information—The Why, Where, and to Whom," *Public Information Essential for a Dynamic Mental Health Program: Proceedings of a Technical Assistance Project Conference*, Omaha, Neb.: Community Services Division, Nebraska Psychiatric Institute, 1962, pp. 1–14 (mimeographed); Joanna Nelle, "Mental Health Information and Education Programs for Isolated and Deprived Rural Populations," paper read at the Annual Meeting of the National Association of State Psychiatric Information Specialists, Chicago, June 9, 1965.

10. See, for example, Leo Srole et al., *Mental Health in the Metropolis: The Midtown Manhattan Study,* New York: McGraw-Hill, 1962.

11. See, for example, Elaine Cumming and John Cumming, *Closed Ranks: An Experiment in Mental Health Education,* Cambridge, Mass.: Harvard University Press, 1957; Joint Commission on Mental Illness and Health, *op. cit.,* Chap. III.

12. See, for example, Frank Auld, Jr., and Leonard D. Eron, "Use of Rorschach Scores to Predict Whether Patients Will Continue Psychotherapy," *Journal of Consulting Psychology,* **17,** 1953, 104–109; Frank Auld, Jr., and Jerome K. Myers, "Contributions to a Theory of Selecting Psychotherapy Patients," *Journal of Clinical Psychology,* **10,** 1954, 56–60; Stanley D. Imber et al., "Suggestibility, Social Class, and Acceptance of Psycho-therapy," *Journal of Clinical Psychology,* **12,** 1956, 341–344; Sol L. Garfield and D. C. Affleck, "An Appraisal of Duration of Stay in Out-patient Psychotherapy," *Journal of Nervous and Mental Disease,* **129,** 1959, 492–498.

13. George W. Albee, *Mental Health Manpower Trends,* New York: Basic Books, 1959; Joint Commission on Mental Illness and Health, op. cit., pp. 140–155.

14. Cf. George Katona and Eva Mueller, "A Study of Purchase Decisions," in Lincoln H. Clark (Ed.), *Consumer Behavior: The Dynamics of Consumer Reaction,* New York: New York University Press, 1955, pp. 30–87. Katona and Mueller characterize persons who purchase with minimum deliberation (one criterion of deliberation is number of brands considered) as "indifferent and apathetic."

# 23. THE HOSPITAL AND ITS PATIENTS

## Richard M. Titmuss

For a number of reasons, and I shall mention only one or two, advances of science into the hospital have made it harder to treat the patient as a person. One reason is that more science has meant more division of labor and, inevitably, of course, more professional fragmentation as specialisms have developed and new groups of workers have banded themselves together in professional groups. An increase in the division of labor means that more people with different functions and skills to perform are brought into contact with the patient. Each separate function to be performed, for out-patient as well as in-patient, involves the sick person in a personal contact with more people—more "experts" (for that is how they often appear to the patient). All this happens at a time when the patient, sick perhaps in mind as well as in body, with fears and anxieties about himself and his family, with more questions and uncertainties in a mind disturbed by illness, is less able to cope with the strain of entering into new personal contacts with many strange individuals endowed with all the authority and mystery which surround the hospital and its gift of survival.

As most of us know, to feel ill is to feel unadventurous, to want to retreat from life, to have one's fears removed and one's needs met without effort. Physical illness can play queer tricks with our thoughts and our behavior. This does not mean, as some all too easily suppose, that we are neurotics. In being querulous and ungrateful, demanding and apathetic in turn, we are in fact behaving as ill people. The demands that people make on society are greater when they are ill than when they are well.

Yet the advent of science has made it more difficult, in social and psychological terms, for the hospital as part of society to meet these demands. More science means more division of labor and more experts—more of the mysteries of blood counts, X rays, test meals, investigations, case history taking, and so forth. These, in turn, mean more departmentalism and, all too often, more departmental thinking. As A. N. Whitehead warned us, the fixed person for the fixed duties in a fixed situation is a social menace. He is particularly a menace to the sick person who is more in need, rather than less, for explanation and understanding. But the departmentalism which stems from a division of labor — from a dividing up of services rendered to a patient — is given more to silence than to communication. Silence from those in authority, from doctor, sister, nurse, administrator, clerk, technician, and so on, often means a want of imagination: silence con-

Excerpted by permission of the publisher, from *Essays on the Welfare State*, London: Allen and Unwin, 1958, pp. 124-125.

sents to fear among those who have great need for explanation and reassurance.

What is it that patients complain of more than anything else in relation to the hospital — "No one told me anything" — "Nobody asked me" — "I don't know." How often one comes across people who have been discharged from hospital, bewildered, still anxious and afraid, disillusioned because the medical magic has not apparently or not yet yielded results, ignorant of what the investigations have shown, what the doctors think, what the treatment has been or is to be, and what the outlook is in terms of life and health.

# Epilogue to Part Five

At the turn of the century emphasis was placed on improving environmental factors as a means of controlling the spread of communicable diseases that threatened the total social organization. Mass immunization and improved sanitation have lessened the problem of communicable diseases in the middle and upper classes, but all such diseases remain prevalent among the lower classes. This cultural lag exists because lower-class families tend to be less preoccupied with cleanliness and are less perceptive to signs and symptoms of illness than are middle- and upper-class families. Health workers must continue to be concerned with communicable diseases, for not only do they still exist, but evidence indicates they are again on the increase. This is due partly to the lack of attention they have received in recent years from the health workers and public alike, and partly to fantastic modern transportation which allows their worldwide spread.

Attempts to control other aspects of the environment for health purposes are now prevalent. Industrialization, urbanization, and overpopulation currently concern health workers and much of the general public. The relationship of these facets of life to respiratory diseases, industrial accidents, and air and water pollution are now being examined. Health workers have a responsibility to help prevent as well as to treat the consequences of such problems.

Each health issue reverberates through many aspects of life. Consequently the health worker must play a leading role in the decisions regarding these problems. The potential of overpopulation is one of many such situations. With the decreased death rate and the increase in life expectancy, overpopulation has become a realistic health as well as social problem. In the United States, the population increases by one person every twelve seconds. By the year 2000, it is estimated that the total weight of the world population will outweigh the earth itself. An attempt is being made to curtail this growth by contraceptive devices, both oral and mechanical. But no method of contraception will have a significant impact on population growth until the attitudes and values centered around the family are changed. Increased health and social problems of course will accompany continued population increase.

Individual health problems will become social problems when the condition affects a large enough number of persons to be seen as a potential threat to the social organization. Alcoholism, drug addiction, juvenile delinquency, and homosexuality are major social problems that affect this country. Each of them may be explained from a sociological, psychological, or physiological point of view. For example, alcoholism, from a sociological standpoint, is caused by an inability to escape from a disliked role or by the fact that the individual is expected to play an ambiguous role. From a psychological point of view, alcoholism is due to an unconscious desire to regress to an earlier stage of development. Physiologists have attempted to blame it on nutritional and/or endocrine disorders. Whatever

238

the cause, the estimated number of alcoholics in the United States at present is approximately 5,000,000, and the number continues to rise.

Mental illness is probably the biggest and most costly social problem in this country. If one accepts the psychoanalytic view, about 50 per cent of the population do or will need therapy at some time during their life. More conservative estimates indicate that one of every seven persons will need psychiatric assistance.

The identification of those persons described as mentally ill is probably the best example of the ambiguity and relativity of the terms health and illness. Frequently society dictates who is sick and who is well and defines the role of the caretakers. If the patient is bizarre and a potential threat to himself or others, the psychiatrist or court issues a mandate to isolate and segregate him from the rest of society until he is considered safe. Isolating an individual from society is not new; all persons who are feared or seen as "different" in any given culture have been isolated from the group. In biblical times the leper was placed outside the gates of the city. This approach is still retained with illnesses that are not understood, such as mental illness.

After an individual has been described as mentally ill by either family, friends, coworkers, or the courts, the psychiatrist diagnoses and treats the so-called mentally ill person. Hollingshead and Redlich's study[1] shows differential diagnoses within each social class. More patients were found to be diagnosed and treated as schizophrenic in the lower class while in the upper classes (I and II) more were diagnosed as neurotic. The health worker must be aware of this, for it affects his view and treatment of such patients.

Not only is he responsible for the individual patient, but he must assume a major portion of the health education of communities. This requires a knowledge of community structure, values, and perceptions of health and illness and normality and abnormality. For as Cumming and Cumming[2] found in their study of a Canadian town, where several propositions were used in an educational campaign to change attitudes toward the mentally ill, the community values and fears were not easily altered. The proposition that abnormality and normality are not distinct created so much fear, anxiety, and hostility that meetings were boycotted and the educators shunned. The implication of viewing abnormal and normal behavior on a continuum allowed many individuals to fear that the boundaries of their own "mental wellness" were likely to be shifted, if not destroyed. They envisaged the possibility of being considered mentally ill themselves under such a loose definition: to the either-or type of thinking, if you're not well, then you *must* be sick.

It is imperative that health workers spend time attempting to discover the knowledge, beliefs, and attitudes about illness and treatment in their community. They must also assume a more active part in deciding the types of health information to be disseminated through the mass media. Health workers should by all means avoid the use of medical jargon and cliches, for many times their terminology lends itself to misinterpretation and embarrasses the patient to the point where he cannot ask for clarification.

The health worker also needs to be aware of how society determines his own practices and attitudes. He must be aware that what he considers illogical beliefs or behavior of the patient are, if he looks at the patient's social background, very logical indeed. Failure to communicate or understand can easily result from conflict in the cultural backgrounds and values of patient and professional.

Communication about health and health care assumes many forms. The press, television, and radio have devoted a great deal of time to health since the inauguration of the Physical Fitness Program by the Kennedy Administration. Television programs such as the National Health Surveys[3] not only provide information on health but also help to correct myths and distortions about health and health care. For example, in the total sample tested on nutrition, exercise, immunizations, mental health, alcoholism, and drug addiction, only 69 per cent answered questions on health and health care correctly. Some interesting myths and distortions were exposed. For example, only 34 per cent of the national sample answered the following question correctly: "Is it bad to drink water immediately after strenuous exercise?" Only 33 per cent answered correctly the question: "Should one drink milk after eating fruit?"

The health worker must not only consider what he can contribute to society but also what society can contribute to him. Much has and can be learned from folk medicine. Folk medicine includes beliefs, values, attitudes, and practices regarding cause and treatment of illness. It is primarily based on magic, tradition, and trial and error. Much folk medicine has been incorporated into scientific medicine. For example, the Rauwolfia root was given in India many years ago to persons exhibiting bizarre behavior. The root was refined, called reserpine, and introduced into this country in the 1950's for treatment of mental illness. Scientific medicine in our culture is still influenced by magic and has magical overtones for certain individuals. The "fifty-minute" hour contains many elements of magic. As King points out,[4] the studies which show the interrelationship between physiology and emotions make it appear reasonable that belief in magic can actually lead to disease and even death. Some curses of illness by magic have withstood scientific investigation.

Opinions regarding illness are not always associated with knowledge or education. The amalgamation of pieces of information may in fact result in what we call "pop medicine." Pop medicine may be viewed as a process by which an individual takes isolated bits of accurate information and puts them together in such a fashion that the conclusion is fallacious. An instance: recently a lady sitting in a doctor's office gave the following information to another patient:

I was reading in a magazine that too many X rays can cause cancer. Doctors often give you a lot of X rays. You know nuclear fallout is like X ray. If you have too much exposure to fallout you can get cancer. People who are exposed to fallout can even carry and transmit nuclear rays to others. You know if you have too many X rays, you can transmit rays to others.

Although some of her statements were correct, the conclusion not only was inaccurate but actually terrified one patient who had just completed a series of X rays.

As a result of a composite of accurate and inaccurate information like the foregoing, the decision to seek help may be delayed. Frequently, at the onset of symptoms an individual will attempt a self-diagnosis to explain the symptoms. He will then attempt to fit the illness into his own life style. From his own experiences or those of his associates, he will pick and choose among the variety of treatment modalities. As long as these work or as long as he can find other alternatives and the illness does not seriously interfere with his life style, he does not seek professional medical advice. At the point in time when he can no longer continue with his preferred social role, he will seek, or be forced by others to seek, outside assistance. For some the outside assistance sought may, as indicated earlier, take many forms. If he chooses for help the clergy, faith healers, or chiropractors, he may delay seeking professional medical help because of the different perceptions of illness and causation represented by these groups. Others may postpone seeking help because of fear of dependency, death, punishment, shame or horror. For still others the delay may be due to fear or loss of status, inability to pay for services, refusal to accept charity, or a lack of understanding of the severity of the illness. Although the health worker may be frustrated by this delay, to sanction such behavior further may in fact postpone effective treatment for an indefinite period.

---

1. August B. Hollingshead and F. C. Redlich, "Social Stratification and Psychiatric Disorders," *American Sociological Review*, **18**, 1953, 163–169.

2. Elaine Cumming and John Cumming, *Closed Ranks: An Experiment in Mental Health Education*, Cambridge, Mass.: The Commonwealth Fund, Harvard University Press, 1957.

3. CBS television presentation, January 1966.

4. Stanley H. King, *Perceptions of Illness and Medical Practice*, New York: Russell Sage Foundation, 1962. See Chap. 4.

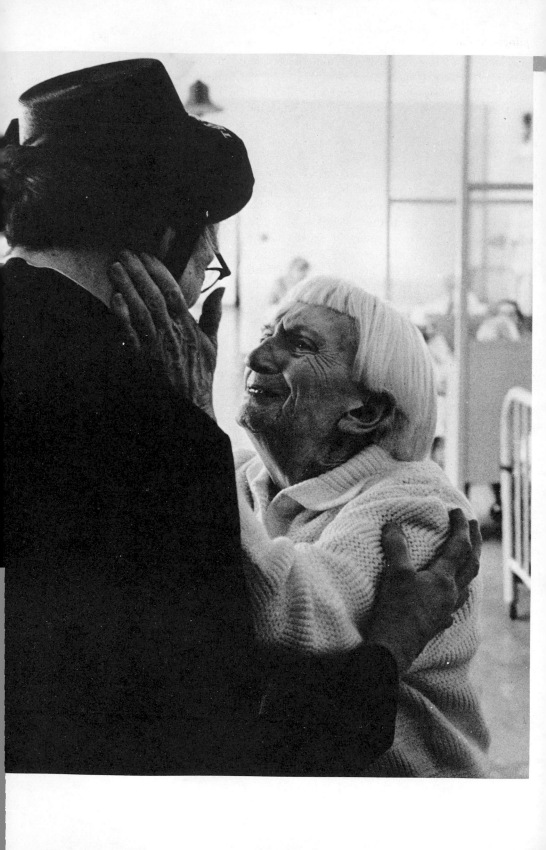

## PART SIX

# On the Path: Patient Problems

No matter how you define it, illness is a psychosocial matter. As we noted earlier, the perceptions, expectations, and reactions to illness vary in relation to a multiplicity of variables. No matter what these differences may be, there are some elements common to all illness, be it physiological, psychological, or both. Perhaps it is these similarities that produce a unifying element in patient care.

From a sociological perspective, illness is a form of deviant behavior in that it is a biological or psychological failure to conform to a specified standard: health. The severity of the nonconformity is interpreted in terms of the degree and direction of the deviation. Under certain circumstances it may be an approved form of behavior, whereas other conditions render it a disapproved form of behavior — for example, appendicitis versus syphilis. What happens to any deviant depends on the tolerance limits of a given group, community, or culture — for example, being drunk New Year's Day versus being drunk on a nonholiday. These tolerance limits vary also with the social conditions surrounding the behavior — for example, the bullet wound in war versus the bullet wound in a street fight. Deviant behavior that exceeds the tolerance limits of a community usually results in public action designed to: (1) protect society, (2) reform or treat the offender, and (3) warn others that the behavior is unacceptable. What exceeds the tolerance limits at one time, however, may not at another.

Under some circumstances certain illnesses may be perceived by the individual, family, community, or even the health team as unacceptable. The length of illness, number of past illnesses, age, social class, social value, and type of illness create a kind of composite view from which such judgments are made. The diagrams on page 244 give indications of some acceptable and unacceptable behaviors.

The perception of acceptable and unacceptable disease entities varies to some extent with the characteristics of the afflicted individual. Let us take an example of three illegitimately pregnant females, one a wealthy socialite, one a lower-class "slum" girl, and the third a registered nurse. When a group of collegiate student nurses were asked to respond to the three girls in terms of the acceptability of the illness, the responses were: (1) "Well, it's okay for the socialite. She has the money and resources to care for the child." (2) "You can't expect anything else from the lower class. They have loose morals." (3) "An R.N.! How awful! But she can't be, she took the Florence Nightingale Pledge!"

From another perspective, the same illness has different implications for those whose life style differs. Consider, for example, the artist, the Arkansas farmer, and the politician, all of whom have compound fractures of the arm. The politician after a short time can resume his position and even campaign. The farmer must make adjustments and secure a helper to farm the land. The artist, however, is totally incapacitated in terms of his work for several months. No assistant can perform his duties.

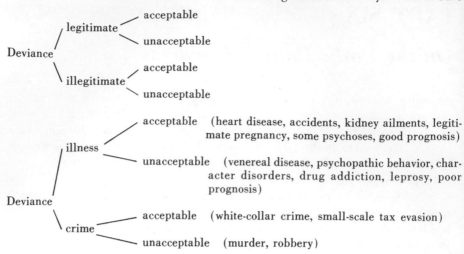

Whether the illness be viewed by the patient as a punishment for sins or, in a relatively sophisticated way, as a biological and/or psychological manifestation, some degree of stress, anxiety, pain, and grief will be present. Although the ways in which the patient, his family, and even the professional staff perceive and handle these problems differ, they present an underlying strain in the care and recovery of all patients. As Parsons indicates, one of the first steps into patienthood is the process of becoming socialized into the role of patient. This process exempts one from performing some previous responsibilities and requires the addition of new ones.

Stress created by changes in roles and responsibilities is, as Selye's study shows, common to some degree in all patients and nonpatients. The increased pace of work or number of patients in a health agency and the demands from patients, the agency, or the profession may increase stress among health workers. Illness and changes in role create stress for the patient.

Illness, in fact may even threaten the self-image. Ideally, medical care requires that the health team be able to regulate the life of the patient in accordance with a treatment modality and rationale. For this to be possible all aspects of the individual's life must be subordinated to the status of a recipient of care and treatment. Being a patient takes precedence over all other roles. Hospitalization or separation from work often is required.

The unfamiliar surroundings of the hospital, the dependence on staff, the indignities of care, and the staff's reaction to the individual may force him to alter his self-concept. This is especially true when the individual perceives illness as weakness and pain as cowardly. For, as Zborowski demonstrates, pain is not simply a matter of physical discomfort. It is perceived and interpreted with a cultural and social context.

Anxiety and stress may be created from fear of loss of function, self-control, part of the body, a loved one, or even death. The perception of illness and pain may create anger, resentment, fear, or even guilt. Fear of loss is at the root of anxiety and somehow must be overcome if recovery is to be achieved. Lack of information which leaves the patient in ignorance may cause him to give way to fantasy and distortion. Anxiety can increase physiological or psychological pain or both. The increase in pain, in turn, may prevent acceptance of treatment because the patient often attempts to avoid pain at all cost. Quint's study and Engel's discussion of grief demonstrate how anxiety and the fear of death or dying become integral parts of the patient's life and problematic for the health professional and family as well. The process of grieving is a natural universal phenomenon for all human beings. Sociological considerations applied to medical situations in the care of patients, in Straus's opinion, however, may alleviate undue stress, anxiety, fear, and grieving.

# 24. ON BECOMING A PATIENT

## Talcott Parsons

For common sense there may be some question of whether "being sick" constitutes a social role at all — isn't it simply a state of fact, a "condition?" Things are not quite so simple as this. The test is the existence of a set of institutionalized expectations and the corresponding sentiments and sanctions.

There seem to be four aspects of the institutionalized expectation system relative to the sick role. First is the exemption from normal social-role responsibilities, which of course is relative to the nature and severity of the illness. This exemption requires legitimation by and to the various alters involved and the physician often serves as a court of appeal as well as a direct legitimatizing agent. It is noteworthy that like all institutionalized patterns the legitimation of being sick enough to avoid obligations cannot only be a right of the sick person but an obligation upon him. People are often resistant to admitting they are sick and it is not uncommon for others to tell them that they *ought* to stay in bed. The word generally has a moral connotation. It goes almost without saying that this legitimation has the social function of protection against "malingering."

The second closely related aspect is the institutionalized definition that the sick person cannot be expected by "pulling himself together" to get well by an act of decision or will. In this sense also he is exempted from responsibility — he is in a condition that must "be taken care of." His "condition" must be changed, not merely his "attitude." Of course the process of recovery may be spontaneous but while the illness lasts he can't "help it." This element in the definition of the state of illness is obviously crucial as a bridge to the acceptance of "help."

The third element is the definition of the state of being ill as itself undesirable with its obligation to want to "get well." The first two elements of legitimation of the sick role thus are conditional in a highly important sense. It is a relative legitimation so long as he is in this unfortunate state which both he and alter hope he can get out of as expeditiously as possible.

Finally, the fourth closely related element is the obligation — in proportion to the severity of the condition, of course — to seek *technically competent* help, namely, in the most usual case, that of a physician, and to *cooperate* with him in the process of trying to get well. It is here, of course, that the role of the sick person as patient becomes articulated with that of the physician in a complementary role structure.

It is evident from the above that the role of motivational factors in illness immensely broadens the scope and increases the importance of the institutionalized role aspect of being sick. For then the problem of social control becomes much more than one of ascertain-

---

Excerpted by permission of the Macmillan Company, from *The Social System*, New York: Free Press of Glencoe, 1964, pp. 436-443, 445-447.

ing facts and drawing lines. The privileges and exemptions of the sick role may become objects of a "secondary gain" which the patient is positively motivated, usually unconsciously, to secure or to retain. The problem, therefore, of the balance of motivations to recover, becomes of first importance. In general motivational balances of great functional significance to the social system are institutionally controlled, and it should, therefore, not be surprising that this is no exception.

A few further points may be made about the specific patterning of the sick role and its relation to social structure. It is, in the first place, a "contingent" role into which anyone, regardless of his status in other respects, may come. It is, furthermore, in the type case temporary. One may say that it is in a certain sense a "negatively achieved" role, through failure to "keep well," though, of course, positive motivations also operate, which by that very token must be motivations to deviance.

It is inherently universalistic in that generalized objective criteria determine whether one is or is not sick, how sick, and with what kind of sickness; its focus is thus classificatory, not relational. It is also functionally specific, confined to the sphere of health and particular "complaints" and disabilities within that sphere. It is furthermore affectively neutral in orientation in that the expected behavior, "trying to get well," is focused on an objective problem, not on the cathectic significance of persons,[1] or orientations to an emotionally disturbing problem, though this may be instrumentally and otherwise involved.

The orientation of the sick role vis-a-vis the physician is also defined as collectively oriented. It is true that the patient has a very obvious self-interest in getting well in most cases, though this point may not always be so simple. But once he has called in a physician the attitude is clearly marked, that he has assumed the obligation to cooperate with that physician in what is regarded as a common task. The obverse of the physician's obligation to be guided by the welfare of the patient is the latter's obligation to "do his part" to the best of his ability. This point is clearly brought out, for example, in the attitudes of the profession toward what is called "shopping around." By that is meant the practice of a patient "checking" the advice of one physician against that of another without telling physician A that he intends to consult physician B, or if he comes back to A that he has done so or who B is. The medical view is that if the patient is not satisfied with the advice his physician gives him he may properly do one of two things: first he may request a consultation, even naming the physician he wishes called in, but in that case it is physician A, not the patient, who must call B in; the patient may not see B independently, and above all not without A's knowledge. The other proper recourse is to terminate the relation with A and become "B's patient." The notable fact here is that a pattern of behavior on the part not only of the physician, but also of the patient, is expected which is in sharp contrast to perfectly legitimate behavior in a commercial relationship. If he is buying a car there is no objection to the customer going to a number of dealers before making up his mind, and there is no obligation for him to inform any one dealer what others he is consulting, to say nothing of approaching the Chevrolet dealer only through the Ford dealer.

The doctor-patient relationship is thus focused on these pattern elements. The patient has a need for technical services because he doesn't — nor do his lay associates, family members, etc. — "know" what is the matter or what to do about it, nor does he control the necessary facilities. The physician is a technical expert who by special training and experience, and by an institutionally validated status, is qualified to "help" the patient in a situation institutionally defined as legitimate in a relative sense but as needing help. The intricacy of the social forces operating on this superficially simple subsystem of social relations will be brought out in the following analysis.

## THE SITUATION OF MEDICAL PRACTICE

### The Situation of the Patient

The first step is to go more in detail into the analysis of relevant aspects of the situation in which the doctor and the patient find themselves. This will provide the setting in which the importance of the broad patterning of both physician's and patient's role can be interpreted, and will enable us to identify a series of mechanisms which, in addition to the physician's deliberate application of his technical knowledge, operate to facilitate his manifest functions in the control of disease, and to promote other, latent functions which are important to the social system.

First, it must be remembered that there is an enormous range of different types of illness, and of degrees of severity. Hence a certain abstraction is inevitable in any such general account as the present one. There is also a range of different types of physician. It will, therefore, be necessary to concentrate on what can be considered certain strategic and typical features of the situation of both.

It will be convenient first to take up the salient features of the situation of the patient and his "lay" associates, particularly members of his family. These may be classified under the three headings of helplessness and need of help, technical incompetence, and emotional involvement.

By institutional definition of the sick role the sick person is helpless and therefore in need of help. If being sick is to be regarded as "deviant" as certainly in important respects it must, is as we have noted distinguished from other deviant roles precisely by the fact that the sick person is not regarded as "responsible" for his condition, "he can't help it." He may, of course, have carelessly exposed himself to danger of accident, but then once injured he cannot, for instance, mend a fractured leg by "will power." The exhortation to "try" has importance at many peripheral points in the handling of illness, but the core definition is that of a "condition" that either has to "right itself" or to be "acted upon," and usually the patient got into that condition through processes which are socially defined as "not his fault."

The urgency of the need of help will vary with the severity of the disability, suffering, and risk of death or serious, lengthy, or permanent disablement. It will also vary inversely with the prospect, as defined in the culture, of spontaneous recovery in terms of certainty and duration. But a sufficient proportion of cases is severe in one or more of these senses, and unlikely to recover spontaneously, at least soon enough, so that the feeling of helplessness and the need of help are very real.

The sick person is, therefore, in a state where he is suffering or disabled or both, and possibly facing risks of worsening, which is socially defined as either "not his fault" or something from which he cannot be expected to extricate himself by his own effort, or generally both. He is also likely to be anxious about his state and the future. This is a very different kind of "need" from that of a person who merely "wants" something that he can be permitted to have if he can "swing" it independently, such as a new car, or even if he "needs something," such as adequate food, if he can reasonably be expected to procure it by his own efforts, as by working for it, and not being lazy or shiftless. In a special sense, the sick person is "entitled" to help.

By the same institutional definition the sick person is not, of course, competent to help himself, or what he can do is, except for trivial illness, not adequate. But in our culture there is a special definition of the kind of help he needs, namely, professional, technically competent help. The nature of this help imposes a further disability or handicap upon him. He is not only generally not in a position to do what needs to be done, but he does not "know" what needs to be done or how to do it. It is not merely that he, being bedridden, cannot go down to the drug store to get what is needed, but that he would, even if well, not be qualified to do what is needed, and to judge what needs to be done. There is, that is to say, a "communication gap."

Only a technically trained person has that qualification. And one of the most serious disabilities of the layman is that he is not qualified to judge technical qualifications, in general or in detail. Two physicians may very well give conflicting diagnoses of the same case, indeed often do. In general the layman is not qualified to choose between them. Nor is he qualified to choose the "best" physician among a panel. If he were fully rational he would have to rely on professional authority, on the advice of the professionally qualified, or on institutional validation.

This disqualification is, of course, not absolute. Laymen do know something in the field, and have some objective bases of judgment. But the evidence is overwhelming that his knowledge is highly limited and that most laymen *think* they know more, and have better bases of judgment than is actually the case. For example, the great majority of laymen think that *their* physician is either the best or one of the few best in his field in the community. It is manifestly impossible for the majority of such judgments to be objectively correct. Another type of evidence is the patterning of choice of physician. A very large proportion of people choose their physicians on the basis of the recommendations of friends or neighbors who "like Dr. X so much," without any sort of inquiry beyond that as to technical qualifications, even as to the medical school from which he holds a degree or the hospital at which he interned.[2] There must be some mechanisms to bridge this "gap." There must be some way of defining the situation to the patient and his family, as to what is "the matter with him" and why, what his prognosis is, what burdens will have to be assumed in recovery. There must be some mechanism for validating the "authority" of the physician, who only in special cases like the military services has any coercive sanctions at his command.

In this connection it should be noted

that the burdens the physician asks his patients and their families to assume on his advice are often very severe. They include suffering — you "have to get worse before you can get better," as for instance in the case of a major surgical operation. They include risk of death, permanent or lengthy disablement, severe financial costs, and various others. In terms of common sense it can always be said that the patient has the obvious interest in getting well and hence should be ready to accept any measures which may prove necessary. But there is always the question, implicit or explicit, "How do I know this will do any good?" The one thing certain seems to be that the layman's answer to this cannot, in the majority of severe and complex cases, i.e., the "strategic" ones, be based primarily on his own rational understanding of the factors involved and a fully rational weighing of them. The difference from the physician in this respect is often a matter of degree, but it is a crucially important difference of degree.

Finally, third, the situation of illness very generally presents the patient and those close to him with complex problems of emotional adjustment. It is, that is to say, a situation of strain. Even if there is no question of a "physic" factor in his condition, suffering, helplessness, disablement, and the risk of death, or sometimes its certainty, constitute fundamental disturbances of the expectations by which men live. They cannot in general be emotionally "accepted" without the accompaniments of strain with which we are familiar and hence without difficult adjustments unless the patient happens to find positive satisfactions in them, in which case there is also a social problem. The significance of this emotional factor is magnified and complicated insofar as defensive and adjustive mechanisms are deeply involved in the pathological condition itself.

The range of possible complexities in this sphere is very great. The problems are, however, structured by the nature of the situation in certain relatively definite ways. Perhaps the most definite point is that for the "normal" person illness, the more so the greater its severity, constitutes a frustration of expectancies of his normal life pattern. He is cut off from his normal spheres of activity, and many of his normal enjoyments. He is often humiliated by his incapacity to function normally. His social relationships are disrupted to a greater or a lesser degree. He may have to bear discomfort or pain which is hard to bear, and he may have to face serious alterations of his prospects for the future, in the extreme but by no means uncommon case the termination of his life.

For the normal person the direction of these alterations is undesirable, they are frustrations. Therefore it is to be expected that two types of reaction should be prominent, a kind of emotional "shock" at the beginning of illness, and anxiety about the future. In both cases there is reason to believe that most normal persons have an unrealistic bias in the direction of confidence that "everything will be all right," that is, they are motivated to underestimate the chances of *their* falling ill, especially seriously ill (the minority of hypochondriacs is the obverse), and if they do they tend to overestimate the chances of a quick and complete recovery. Therefore even the necessary degree of emotional acceptance of the reality is difficult. One very possible reaction is to attempt to deny illness or various aspects of it, to refuse to "give in" to it. Another may be exaggerated self-pity and whining, a complaining demand for more help than is necessary or feasible, especially for incessent personal attention. In any case this factor reinforces the others. It makes it doubly difficult for the patient to have an objective judgment about his situation and what is needed. Whether they pay explicit attention to it in any technical sense or not, what physicians do inevitably influences the emotional states of their patients, and often this may have a most important influence on the state of their cases.

There are two particularly important broad consequences of the features of the situation of the sick person for the problem of the institutional structuring of medical practice. One is that the combination of helplessness, lack of technical competence, and emotional disturbance make him a peculiarly vulnerable object for exploitation. It may be said that the exploitation of the helpless sick is "unthinkable." That happens to be a very strong sentiment in our society, but for the sociologist the existence of this sentiment or that of other mechanisms for the prevention of exploitation must not be taken for granted. There is in fact a very real problem of how, in such a situation, the very possible exploitation is at least minimized.[3]

The other general point is the related one that the situation of the patient is such as to make a high level of rationality of judgment peculiarly difficult. He is therefore open to, and peculiarly liable to, a whole series of ir- and non-rational beliefs and practices. The world over the rational approach to health through applied science is, as we have noted, the exception rather than the rule, and in our society there is, even

today, a very large volume of "superstition" and other non- or irrational beliefs and practices in the health field. This is not to say that the medical profession either has a monopoly of rational knowledge and techniques, or is free of the other type of elements, but the volume of such phenomena outside the framework of regular medical practice is a rough measure of this factor. This set of facts then makes problematical the degree to which the treatment of health problems by applied science has in fact come to be possible. It can by no means be taken for granted as the course which "reasonable men," i.e., the normal citizen of our society, will "naturally" adopt.

The above discussion has been concerned primarily with the sick person himself. But in some cases, e.g., when he is an infant or is in a coma, the patient himself has nothing whatever to say about what is done to him. But short of this, the patient tends to be buttressed by family members and sometimes friends who are not sick. Does this not vitiate the whole argument of the above discussion? Definitely not. It may mitigate the severity of the impact of some of the features of the patient's situation, in fact, it often does. But in the first place laymen, sick or well, are no more technically competent in medical matters in one case than the other. The need of help is also just as strong because the solidarity of the family imposes a very strong pressure on the healthy members to see that the sick one gets the best care possible. It is, indeed, very common if not usual for the pressure of family members to tip the balance in the admission of being sick enough to go to bed or call a doctor, when the patient himself would tend to stand out longer. Furthermore the emotional relationships within the family are of such a character that the illness of one of its members creates somewhat different emotional problems from the patient's own to be sure, but nevertheless often very severe ones, and sometimes more severe, or more difficult for the physician to cope with. It is not, for instance, for nothing that pediatricians habitually mean the mother, not the sick child, when they say "my patient." To anyone schooled in modern psychology the emotional significance of a child's illness for the mother in our society scarcely needs further comment.

Hence we may conclude that the basic problems of the role of the patient himself are shared by the others in his personal circle with whom the physician comes into contact in his practice. Sometimes the role of these others is to facilitate the work of the physician very significantly. But it would be rash to assert that this was true very much more often than the reverse. In any case it is quite clear that the role of family members does not invalidate the significance of the situation of the patient for the character of medical practice, as outlined above.

---

1. This it will appear later is particularly important to the therapeutic process. It is not to be interpreted either that the cathectic significance of persons has no part in the etiology of illness or that cathexis of the physician as an object does not occur—but it is controlled.

2. One physician, a suburban general practitioner, told that in several years of practice only one patient had asked him

from what medical school he had graduated.

3. It is interesting to note that even leftist propaganda against the evils of our capitalistic society, in which exploitation is a major keynote, tends to spare the physician. The American Medical Association tends to be attacked, but in general not the ideal-typical physician. This is significant of the general public reputation for collectivity orientation of the medical profession.

# 25. THE STRESS SYNDROME

## Hans Selye

What is stress? The soldier who sustains wounds in battle, the mother who worries about her soldier son, the gambler who watches the races, the horse and the jockey he bet on: they are all under stress. The beggar who suffers from hunger and the glutton who overeats, the little shopkeeper with his constant fears of bankruptcy and the rich merchant struggling for yet another million: they are also all under stress. Stress is not always due to something bad, nor is it always bad for you.

Stress is the rate at which we live at any moment. All living beings are constantly under stress, and anything — pleasant or unpleasant — that speeds up the intensity of life causes a temporary increase in stress, the wear and tear exerted on the body. A painful blow and a passionate kiss can be equally stressful.

The word "stress" has long been used by laymen to designate tension, fatigue, or exhaustion, but not until recently did physicians begin to realize that stress can be scientifically analyzed and objectively appraised by certain characteristic changes in the structural and chemical composition of the body. At the same time, we learned that stress does not consist merely of damage, but also of adaptation to damage, irrespective of what causes wear and tear.

## DEVELOPMENT OF THE THEORY

It might help to explain the essence of stress as we now understand it in medicine if I briefly relate the circumstances under which I first stumbled upon what I later called the *"stress syndrome."*

I had just completed the preclinical subjects required at that time in medical school as preparation before ever seeing a patient. Then finally came the great day when we were to hear our first lecture in internal medicine and see how a patient should be examined. By way of introduction, we were shown several patients in the earliest stages of various infectious diseases. Each of these patients felt and looked ill, had a coated tongue, complained of fatigue, with more or less diffuse aches and pains in the joints, intestinal disturbances, loss of weight and appetite, and so on. All this was quite evident to me but the professor attached very little significance to any of it. He enumerated only a few "characteristic signs" which might help us in the diagnosis of disease. These I could not see. They were either still absent or at least so inconspicuous that my untrained eye could not distinguish them. Yet we were told that these were the important changes to which we should give all our attention.

The professor explained that, at this early stage, most of the specific, typical diagnostic signs were not yet evident and that, until they appeared, not much could be done. Without them, we could not tell precisely what the patient suffered from and hence it was quite im-

Reprinted by permission of the publisher, from the *American Journal of Nursing*, Vol. 65, 1965, pp. 97–99.

possible to recommend any efficient, specific treatment. I was struck by the fact that the many features of disease which were already manifest, even to me, did not interest our teacher merely because they were "nonspecific"—not characteristic of any one disease.

I realized that we had to find typical disease manifestations in order to identify the particular cause of disease in any one patient. This was obviously essential before we could prescribe any medicines having the specific effect of killing the bacteria or neutralizing the toxins that made these people sick. But what impressed me, the novice, was that apparently only a few signs are actually characteristic of any one disease; most symptoms are apparently quite common to many, or perhaps even to all, diseases.

I wondered why such widely different disease-producing agents—those causing measles, scarlet fever, or tuberculosis, for instance—shared the property of evoking the nonspecific manifestations just mentioned. I also wondered why medicine concentrated all its efforts upon the recognition of individual diseases and the discovery of specific remedies for them, without giving any attention to the much more obvious *syndrome of just being sick.* The patients we had just seen had a syndrome, but it seemed to be one that characterized disease as such, not any one particular disease. Would it be possible, I asked myself, to analyze the mechanism of this ubiquitous syndrome and perhaps even to find drugs which act against the nonspecific factor in disease?

It was not until about 10 years later, however, that I managed to pull all this into the precise language of experimental science. In 1936 at McGill University, we were trying to find a new ovarian hormone in extracts of cattle ovaries. All our extracts, no matter how prepared, produced the same syndrome: an enlargement of the cortex of the adrenal gland, gastrointestinal ulcers, and involution of the lymph nodes and the thymus. At first, I ascribed all these changes to the hypothetical ovarian hormone we were looking for, but it soon turned out that extracts of other organs—in fact, toxic substances of all kinds, cold, heat, X rays, or infections—produced the same changes.

Then I suddenly remembered my classroom impression of the "syndrome of just being sick." In a flash I realized that what I had produced with my impure extracts and other damaging agents was an experimental replica of this condition. This model was then employed in the analysis of the stress syndrome, using the adrenal enlargement, gastrointestinal ulcers, and thymicolymphatic involution as objective indicators of stress. These reproducible and measurable indicators formed the basis for the development of the entire stress concept as we see it today.

## NATURE OF THE SYNDROME

It gradually became evident that *any agent that demands an increased vital activity automatically elicits a nonspecific defense mechanism which raises resistance to stressful agents.*

It should be mentioned that, in physics, stress is the condition existing in elastic material when the strain of an external force acts upon it. Had my English been better at the time, I would have called my phenomenon the "strain syndrome," and that which causes it, "stress." However, I did not realize the difference. By the time I did, the word "stress" had become too generally accepted in medicine to make a change, so I had to invent the term "stressor," now used to describe the agent that causes physiologic stress.

The whole stress syndrome or "general adaptation syndrome" (G. A. S.) evolves in three stages: (1) the "alarm reaction" during which defensive forces are mobilized; (2) the "stage of resistance" which reflects full adaptation to the stressor; and (3) the "stage of exhaustion" which inexorably follows as long as the stressor is severe enough and applied for a sufficient length of time, since the "adaptation energy" or adaptability of a living being is finite.

An important part of the stress defense mechanism is an increased secretion of the so-called adrenocorticotropic hormone (ACTH) by the hypophysis. This, in turn, stimulates the adrenal cortex to produce a group of hormones which I have called the "corticoids." Most important among the latter are the anti-inflammatory "glucocorticoids" such as cortisone, and the pro-inflammatory "mineralocorticoids" such as aldosterone and deoxycorticosterone.

These hormones are essentially useful, but derailments in their production can lead to maladies which I have called "diseases of adaptation," because they are not directly due to any particular pathogen but to a faulty adaptive response to the stress induced by some pathogen. For example, when too much of the anti-inflammatory type of hormone is present, infections or gastrointestinal ulcers develop easily.

## DISEASES OF ADAPTATION

Of course, hormones are not the body's only defense against stress. The production of other chemical compounds and the reactions of the nervous system in response to stress are also of great importance. These mechanisms, too—like the hormone reactions—are subject to error and can thereby precipitate disease. In this sense, certain nervous and emotional disturbances, high blood pressure, and certain types of rheumatic, allergic, cardiovascular, and renal diseases are also diseases of adaptation.

Being the rate of the wear and tear of life, *stress cannot and should not be avoided.* The art is to learn how to live a full life with a minimum of wear and tear. All machines wear out to some extent during use, and the human body is no exception. But the intensity of use is not strictly paralleled by the severity of the wear and tear. A few drops of oil can give much protection to an axle under physical stress, and certain hormones and nervous reactions exert a similar protective influence when the body is under the stress of life.

The secret is not to live less intensely, but more intelligently. Friction and strain beyond its capacity are the worst enemies of the inanimate machine, although an appropriate amount of use helps to keep the rust out. Here, again, the situation is very much the same in the living machine of the human body: the frustrating frictions of fighting the unavoidable and the effort to perform tasks beyond our capacity are the greatest sources of wear and tear, but the stress of using our mind and muscles within the limits of their capacities is healthy, pleasant, and indeed indispensable to keeping fit.

Man's noblest aim is to express himself as fully as possible according to his own lights. Each of us must find his innate stress level and live accordingly. Compulsory inactivity may cause more stress than normal activity. I have always disagreed with those doctors who, for some minor ailment, would send an ambitious business executive to a long and enforced exile in some health resort, to relieve him from stress by absolute inertia. High-strung men often become much more tense when they feel frustrated by not being allowed to pursue their usual interests.

While analyzing stress in my experimental animals, my colleagues, my friends, and myself, I have tried to summarize this philosophy in a little motto. It sounds as trivial as a nursery rhyme but it is based on solid biologic laws—and, at least in my case, it works: "Fight for the highest attainable aim/ But do not put up resistance in vain."

## PROTECTIVE VALUES OF STRESS

When suitably handled, *stress cannot only produce but also prevent disease.* This has been amply substantiated by objective animal experiments. We found, for example, that in the rat, inflammation and allergic reactions can be inhibited by previous exposure to stress. Here, presumably, an increased secretion of anti-inflammatory corticoids is the decisive factor.

More recently, we found that following pretreatment with certain corticoids and sodium salts, it is possible to produce fatal heart accidents in animals by merely exposing them to the stress of forced muscular exercise, cold, or heat. This furnished us with a useful experimental model for the study of sudden cardiac death. Furthermore, we found that if the rats are exposed to stress prior to this sensitizing pretreatment, subsequent exposure to stress causes no cardiac death. Apparently, pretreat-ment with stress offers protection, because only unaccustomed stress triggers cardiac accidents.

Curiously, it does not make any difference which stressor is used for pretreatment; they all offer protection against the production of heart lesions by subsequent exposure to any other stressor. Here, it is evidently not just specific inurement to one agent that counts, but the production of stress by any means. Muscular exercise and cold baths proved to be especially useful protectors because they are well tolerated.

These findings throw some light upon the apparent contradiction in the recommendations of physicians, some of whom warn that muscular exertion can precipitate heart accidents, while others prescribe exercise as a protective measure. Presumably, both schools are right: gradual training protects, while sudden, unaccustomed effort can be harmful.

Further studies with our model showed that heart accidents can be prevented not only by pretreatment with stressors but also by certain potassium and magnesium salts. The protective value of these compounds is now under examination in several clinics. While it is still too early to draw definite conclusions, preliminary results are encouraging.

It may not be inopportune to close a survey such as this with some remarks on medical research in general. This is a crucial time in the history of science, especially in biology and medicine. Nowadays most of the really gifted young men and women become increasingly more attracted to physics, chemistry, space research, and other fields whose breathtaking current progress offers a seductive challenge to the intellectually minded. Yet, in the final analysis, what could be more noble and important than to fight disease, aging, and death?

The American government intends to spend some 20 to 40 billion dollars in order to reach the moon. There may, indeed, be something worth having on the moon; undoubtedly, the first nation to reach another planet will earn much admiration and prestige. And yet—as I have said ever since Operation Sputnik proved to be a success—there is no reason to think that, with an equal investment of money and (more important) talent, a systematic attack on cancer, heart disease, and premature aging would be less likely to succeed than our dreams of interplanetary travel.

I find it very difficult to imagine that any treasure found on another planet could be more important to mankind and more conducive to gratitude and prestige than the cure, say, of cancer or insanity. Even the grandeur of conquering the universe, or the fear that war may break out, or that our world may become overpopulated, seems to pale at the bedside of a patient who will die because we were remiss in our efforts to learn more about disease.

# 26. CULTURAL COMPONENTS IN RESPONSES TO PAIN

## Mark Zborowski

This paper[1] reports on one aspect of a larger study: that concerned with discovering the role of cultural patterns in attitudes toward and reactions to pain which is caused by disease and injury— in other words, responses to spontaneous pain.

### SOME BASIC DISTINCTIONS

In human societies biological processes vital for man's survival acquire social and cultural significance. Intake of food, sexual intercourse, or elimination — physiological phenomena which are universal for the entire living world — become institutions regulated by cultural and social norms, thus fulfilling not only biological functions but social and cultural ones as well. Metabolic and endocrinal changes in the human organism may provoke hunger and sexual desire, but culture and society dictate to man the kind of food he may eat, the social setting for eating, or the adequate partner for mating.

Moreover, the role of cultural and social patterns in human physiological activities is so great that they may in specific situations act against the direct biological needs of the individual, even to the point of endangering his survival. Only a human being may prefer starvation to the breaking of a religious dietary law or may abstain from sexual intercourse because of specific incest regulations. Voluntary fasting and celibacy exist only where food and sex fulfill more than strictly physiological functions.

Thus the understanding of the significance and role of social and cultural patterns in human physiology is necessary to clarify those aspects of human experience which remain puzzling if studied only within the physiological frame of reference.

Pain is basically a physiological phenomenon and as such has been studied by physiologists and neurologists such as Harold Wolff, James Hardy, Helen Goodell, C. S. Lewis, W. K. Livingston, and others. By using the most ingenious methods of investigation they have succeeded in clarifying complex problems of the physiology of pain. Many aspects of perception and reaction to pain were studied in experimental situations involving most careful preparation and complicated equipment. These investigators have come to the conclusion that "from the physiological point of view pain qualifies as a sensation of importance to the self-preservation of the individual."[2] The biological function of pain is to provoke special reactive patterns directed toward avoidance of the noxious stimulus which presents a threat to the individual. In this respect the function of

Reprinted by permission of the author and the American Psychological Association, from the *Journal of Social Issues*, Vol. 8, 1952, pp. 16–30.

pain is basically the same for man as for the rest of the animal world.

However, the physiology of pain and the understanding of the biological function of pain do not explain other aspects of what Wolff, Hardy, and Goodell call the *pain experience*, which includes not only the pain sensation and certain automatic reactive responses but also certain "associated feeling states."[3] It would not explain, for example, the acceptance of intense pain in torture which is part of the initiation rites of many primitive societies, nor will it explain the strong emotional reactions of certain individuals to the slight sting of the hypodermic needle.

In human society pain, like so many other physiological phenomena, acquires social and cultural significance, and, accordingly, certain reactions to pain can be understood in the light of the significance. As Drs. Hardy, Wolff, and Goodell state in their recent book,

. . . [T]he culture in which a man finds himself becomes the conditioning influence in the formation of the individual reaction patterns to pain. . . . A knowledge of group attitudes toward pain is extremely important to an understanding of the individual reaction.[4]

In analyzing pain it is useful to distinguish between self-inflicted, other-inflicted, and spontaneous pain. Self-inflicted pain is defined as deliberately self-inflicted. It is experienced as a result of injuries performed voluntarily upon oneself, e.g., self-mutilation. Usually these injuries have a culturally defined purpose, such as achieving a special status in the society. It can be observed not only in primitive cultures but also in contemporary societies on a higher level of civilization. In Germany, for instance, members of certain student or military organizations would cut their faces with a razor in order to acquire scars which would identify them as members of a distinctive social group. By other-inflicted pain is meant pain inflicted upon the individual in the process of culturally accepted and expected activities (regardless of whether approved or disapproved), such as sports, fights, war, etc. To this category belongs also pain inflicted by the physician in the process of medical treatment. Spontaneous pain usually denotes the pain sensation which results from disease or injury. This term also covers pains of psychogenic nature.

Members of different cultures may assume differing attitudes toward these various types of pain. Two of these attitudes may be described as pain expectancy and pain acceptance. Pain expectancy is anticipation of pain as being unavoidable in a given situation, for instance, in childbirth, in sports activities, or in battle. Pain acceptance is characterized by a willingness to experience pain. This attitude is manifested mostly as an inevitable component of culturally accepted experiences, for instance, as part of initiation rites or part of medical treatment. The following example will help to clarify the differences between pain expectancy and pain acceptance: Labor pain is expected as part of childbirth, but while in one culture, such as in the United States, it is not accepted and therefore various means are used to alleviate it, in some other cultures, for instance in Poland, it is not only expected but also accepted, and consequently nothing or little is done to relieve it. Similarly, cultures which emphasize military achievements expect and accept battle wounds, while cultures which emphasize pacifistic values may expect them but will not accept them.

In the process of investigating cultural attitudes toward pain it is also important to distinguish between pain apprehension and pain anxiety. Pain apprehension reflects the tendency to avoid the pain sensation as such, regardless of whether the pain is spontaneous or inflicted, whether it is accepted or not. Pain anxiety, on the other hand, is a state of anxiety provoked by the pain experience, focused upon various aspects of the causes of pain, the meaning of pain, or its significance for the welfare of the individual.

Moreover, members of various cultures may react differently in terms of their manifest behavior toward various pain experiences, and this behavior is often dictated by the culture which provides specific norms according to the age, sex, and social position of the individual.

The fact that other elements as well as cultural factors are involved in the response to a spontaneous pain should be taken into consideration. These other factors are the pathological aspect of pain, the specific physiological characteristics of the pain experience, such as the intensity, the duration, and the quality of the pain sensation, and, finally, the personality of the individual. Nevertheless, it was felt that in the process of a careful investigation it would be possible to detect the role of the cultural components in the pain experience.

## THE RESEARCH SETTING

In setting up the research we were interested not only in the purely theoretical aspects of the findings in terms of possible contribution to the understanding of the pain experience in general; we also had in mind the practical goal of a contribution to the field of medicine. In the relationship between the doctor and his patient the respective attitudes toward pain may play a crucial role, especially when the doctor feels that the patient exaggerates his pain while the patient feels that the doctor minimizes his suffering. The same may be true, for instance, in a hospital where the members of the medical and nursing staff may have attitudes toward pain different from those held by the patient, or when they expect a certain pattern of behavior according to their cultural background while the patient may manifest a behavior pattern which is acceptable in his culture. These differences may play an important part in the evaluation of the individual pain experience, in dealing with pain at home and in the hospital, in administration of analgesics, etc. Moreover, we expected that this study of pain would offer opportunities to gain insight into related attitudes toward health, disease, medication, hospitalization, medicine in general, etc.

With these aims in mind the project was set up at the Kingsbridge Veterans Hospital, Bronx, New York,[5] where four ethnocultural groups were selected for an intensive study. These groups included patients of Jewish, Italian, Irish, and "Old American" stock. Three groups — Jews, Italians, and Irish — were selected because they were described by medical people as manifesting striking differences in their reaction to pain. Italians and Jews were described as tending to "exaggerate" their pain, while the Irish were often depicted as stoical individuals who are able to take a great deal of pain. The fourth group, the "Old Americans," were chosen because the values and attitudes of this group dominate in the country and are held by many members of the medical profession and by many descendants of the immigrants who, in the process of Americanization, tend to adopt American patterns of behavior. The members of this group can be defined as White, native-born individuals, usually Protestant, whose grandparents, at least, were born in the United States, and who do not identify themselves with any foreign group, either nationally, socially, or culturally.

The Kingsbridge Veterans Hospital was chosen because its population represents roughly the ethnic composition of New York City, thus offering access to a fair sample of the four selected groups, and also because various age groups were represented among the hospitalized veterans of World War I, World War II, and the Korean War. In one major respect this hospital was not adequate, namely, in not offering the opportunity to investigate sex differences in attitude toward pain. This aspect of research will be carried out in a hospital with a large female population.

In setting up this project we were interested mainly in discovering certain regularities in reactions and attitudes toward pain characteristic of the four groups. Therefore the study has a qualitative character, and the efforts of the researchers were not directed toward a collection of material suitable for quantitative analysis. The main techniques used in the collection of the material were interview with patients of the selected groups, observation of their behavior when in pain, and discussion of the individual cases with doctors, nurses, and other people directly or indirectly involved in the pain experience of the individual. In addi-

tion to the interviews with patients, "healthy" members of the respective groups were interviewed on their attitudes toward pain, because in terms of the original hypothesis those attitudes and reactions which are displayed by the patients of the given cultural groups are held by all members of the group regardless of whether or not they are in pain, although in pain these attitudes may come more sharply into focus. In certain cases the researchers have interviewed a member of the patient's immediate family in order to check the report of the patient on his pain experience and in order to find out what are the attitudes and reactions of the family toward the patient's experience.

These interviews, based on a series of open-ended questions, were focused upon the past and present pain experiences of the interviewee. However, many other areas were considered important for the understanding of this experience. For instance, it was felt that complaints of pain may play an important role in manipulating relationships in the family and the larger social environment. It was also felt that in order to understand the specific reactive patterns in controlling pain it is important to know certain aspects of child rearing in the culture, relationships between parents and children, the role of infliction of pain in punishment, the attitudes of various members of the family toward specific expected, accepted pain experiences, and so on. The interviews were recorded on wire and transcribed verbatim for an ultimate detailed analysis. The interviews usually lasted for approximately two hours, the time being limited by the condition of the interviewee and by the amount and quality of his answers. When it was considered necessary an interview was repeated. In most of the cases the study of the interviewee was followed by informal conversations and by observation of his behavior in the hospital.

The information gathered from the interviews was discussed with members of the medical staff, especially in the areas related to the medical aspects of the problem, in order to get their evaluation of the pain experience of the patient. Information as to the personality of the patient was checked against results of psychological testing by members of the psychological staff of the hospital when these were available.

The discussion of the material presented in this paper is based on interviews with 103 respondents, including 87 hospital patients in pain and 16 healthy subjects. According to their ethnocultural background the respondents are distributed as follows: "Old Americans," 26; Italians, 24; Jews, 31; Irish, 11; and others, 11.[6] In addition, there were the collateral interviews and conversations noted above with family members, doctors, nurses, and other members of the hospital staff.

With regard to the pathological causes of pain the majority of the interviewees fall into the group of patients suffering from neurological diseases, mainly herniated discs and spinal lesions. The focusing upon a group of patients suffering from a similar pathology offered the opportunity to investigate reactions and attitudes toward spontaneous pain which is symptomatic of one group of diseases. Nevertheless, a number of patients suffering from other diseases were also interviewed.

This paper is based upon the material collected during the first stage of study. The generalizations are to a great extent tentative formulations on a descriptive level. There has been no attempt as yet to integrate the results with the value system and the cultural pattern of the group, though here and there there will be indications to the effect that they are part of the culture pattern. The discussions will be limited to main regularities within three groups, namely, the Italians, the Jews, and the "Old Americans." Factors related to variations within each group will be discussed after the main prevailing patterns have been presented.

## PAIN AMONG PATIENTS OF JEWISH AND ITALIAN ORIGIN

As already mentioned, the Jews and Italians were selected mainly because interviews with medical experts suggested that they display similar reactions to pain. The investigation of this similarity provided the opportunity to check a rather popular assumption that similar reactions reflect similar attitudes. The differences between the Italian and Jewish culture are great enough to suggest that if the attitudes are related to cultural pattern they will also be different despite the apparent similarity in manifest behavior.

Members of both groups were described as being very emotional in their responses to pain. They were described as tending to exaggerate their pain experience and being very sensitive to pain. Some of the doctors stated that in their opinion Jews and Italians have a lower threshold of pain than members of other ethnic groups, especially members of the so-called Nordic group. This statement seems to indicate a certain confusion as to the concept of the threshold of pain. According to people who have studied the problem of the threshold of pain, for instance Harold

Wolff and his associates, the threshold of pain is more or less the same for all human beings regardless of nationality, sex, or age.

In the course of the investigation the general impressions of doctors were confirmed to a great extent by the interview material and by the observation of the patients' behavior. However, even a superficial study of the interviews has revealed that though reactions to pain appear to be similar, the underlying attitudes toward pain are different in the two groups. While the Italian patients seemed to be mainly concerned with the immediacy of the pain experience and were disturbed by the actual pain sensation which they experienced in a given situation, the concern of patients of Jewish origin was focused mainly upon the symptomatic meaning of pain and upon the significance of pain in relation to their health, welfare and, eventually, for the welfare of the families. The Italian patient expressed in his behavior and in his complaints the discomfort caused by pain as such, and he manifested his emotions with regard to the effects of this pain experience upon his immediate situation in terms of occupation, economic situation, and so on; the Jewish patient expressed primarily his worries and anxieties as to the extent to which the pain indicated a threat to his health. In this connection it is worth mentioning that one of the Jewish words to describe strong pain is *yessurim*, a word which is also used to described worries and anxieties.

Attitudes of Italian and Jewish patients toward pain-relieving drugs can serve as an indication of their attitude toward pain. When in pain the Italian calls for pain relief and is mainly concerned with the analgesic effects of the drugs which are administered to him. Once the pain is relieved the Italian patient easily forgets his sufferings and manifests a happy and joyful disposition. The Jewish patient, however, often is reluctant to accept the drug, and he explains this reluctance in terms of concern about the effects of the drug upon his health in general. He is apprehensive about the habit-forming aspects of the analgesic. Moreover, he feels that the drug relieves his pain only temporarily and does not cure him of the disease which may cause the pain. Nurses and doctors have reported cases in which patients would hide the pill which was given to them to relieve their pain and would prefer to suffer. These reports were confirmed in the interviews with patients. It was also observed that many Jewish patients after being relieved from pain often continued to display the same depressed and worried behavior because they felt that though the pain was currently absent it may recur as long as the disease was not cured completely. From these observations it appears that when one deals with a Jewish and an Italian patient in pain, in the first case it is more important to relieve the anxieties with regard to the sources of pain, while in the second it is more important to relieve the actual pain.

Another indication as to the significance of pain for Jewish and Italian patients is their respective attitudes toward the doctor. The Italian patient seems to display a most confident attitude toward the doctor which is usually reinforced after the doctor has succeeded in relieving pain, whereas the Jewish patient manifests a skeptical attitude, feeling that the fact that the doctor has relieved his pain by some drugs does not mean at all that he is skillful enough to take care of the basic illness. Consequently, even when the pain is relieved, he tends to check the diagnosis and the treatment of one doctor against the opinions of other specialists in the field. Summarizing the difference between the Italian and Jewish attitudes, one can say that the Italian attitude is characterized by a present-oriented apprehension with regard to the actual sensation of pain, and the Jew tends to manifest a future-oriented anxiety as to the symptomatic and general meaning of the pain experience.

It has been stated that the Italians and Jews tend to manifest similar behavior in terms of their reactions to pain. As both cultures allow for free expression of feelings and emotions by words, sounds, and gestures, both the Italians and Jews feel free to talk about their pain, complain about it, and manifest their sufferings by groaning, moaning, crying, etc. They are not ashamed of this expression. They admit willingly that when they are in pain they do complain a great deal, call for help, and expect sympathy and assistance from other members of their immediate social environment, especially from members of their family. When in pain they are reluctant to be alone and prefer the presence and attention of other people. This behavior, which is expected, accepted, and approved by the Italian and Jewish cultures, often conflicts with the patterns of behavior expected from a patient by American or Americanized medical people. Thus they tend to describe the behavior of the Italian and Jewish patient as exaggerated and overemotional. The material suggests that they do tend to minimize the actual pain experiences of the Italian and Jewish patient regardless of whether

they have the objective criteria for evaluating the actual amount of pain which the patient experiences. It seems that the uninhibited display of reaction to pain as manifested by the Jewish and Italian patient provokes distrust in American culture instead of provoking sympathy.

Despite the close similarity between the manifest reactions among Jews and Italians, there seem to be differences in emphasis especially with regard to what the patient achieves by these reactions and as to the specific manifestations of these reactions in the various social settings. For instance, they differ in their behavior at home and in the hospital. The Italian husband, who is aware of his role as an adult male, tends to avoid verbal complaining at home, leaving this type of behavior to the women. In the hospital, where he is less concerned with his role as a male, he tends to be more verbal and more emotional. The Jewish patient, on the contrary, seems to be more calm in the hospital than at home. Traditionally the Jewish male does not emphasize his masculinity through such traits as stoicism, and he does not equate verbal complaints with weakness. Moreover, the Jewish culture allows the patient to be demanding and complaining. Therefore, he tends more to use his pain in order to control interpersonal relationships within the family. Though similar use of pain to manipulate the relationship between members of the family may be present also in some other cultures, it seems that in the Jewish culture this is not disapproved, while in others it is. In the hospital one can also distinguish variations in the reactive patterns among Jews and Italians. Upon his admission to the hospital and in the presence of the doctor the Jewish patient tends to complain, ask for help, be emotional even to the point of crying. However, as soon as he feels that adequate care is given to him he becomes more restrained. This suggests that the display of pain reaction serves less as an indication of the amount of pain experienced than as a means to create an atmosphere and setting in which the pathological causes of pain will be best taken care of. The Italian patient, on the other hand, seems to be less concerned with setting up a favorable situation for treatment. He takes for granted that adequate care will be given to him, and in the presence of the doctor he seems to be somewhat calmer than the Jewish patient. The mere presence of the doctor reassures the Italian patient, while the skepticism of the Jewish patient limits the reassuring role of the physician.

To summarize the description of the reactive patterns of the Jewish and Italian patients, the material suggests that on a semiconscious level the Jewish patient tends to provoke worry and concern in his social environment as to the state of his health and the symptomatic character of his pain, while the Italian tends to provoke sympathy toward his suffering. In one case the function of the pain reaction will be the mobilization of the efforts of the family and the doctors toward a complete cure, while in the second case the function of the reaction will be focused upon the mobilization of effort toward relieving the pain sensation.

On the basis of the discussion of the Jewish and Italian material, two generalizations can be made: (1) *Similar reactions to pain manifested by members of different ethnocultural groups do not necessarily reflect similar attitudes to pain.* (2) *Reactive patterns similar in terms of their manifestations may have different functions and serve different purposes in various cultures.*

## PAIN AMONG PATIENTS OF "OLD AMERICAN" ORIGIN

There is little emphasis on emotional complaining about pain among "Old American" patients. Their complaints about pain can best be described as reporting on pain. In describing his pain, the "Old American" patient tries to find the most appropriate ways of defining the quality of pain, its localization, duration, etc. When examined by the doctor he gives the impression of trying to assume the detached role of an unemotional observer who gives the most efficient description of his state for a correct diagnosis and treatment. The interviewees repeatedly state that there is no point in complaining and groaning and moaning, etc., because "it won't help anybody." However, they readily admit that when pain is unbearable they may react strongly, even to the point of crying, but they tend to do it when they are alone. Withdrawal from society seems to be a frequent reaction to strong pain.

There seem to be different patterns in reacting to pain depending on the situation. One pattern, manifested in the presence of members of the family, friends, etc., consists of attempts to minimize pain, to avoid complaining and provoking pity; when pain becomes too strong there is a tendency to withdraw and express freely such reactions as groaning, moaning, etc. A different pattern is manifested in the presence of people who, on account of their profession, should know the character of the pain experience because they are expected to make the appropriate diagnosis, advise the proper cure, and give the adequate help. The tendency to avoid deviation from certain expected patterns of behavior plays an important role in the reaction to pain. This is also controlled by the desire to seek approval on the part of the social environment, especially in the hospital, where the "Old American" patient tries to avoid being a "nuisance" on the ward. He seems to be, more than any other patient, aware of an ideal pattern of behavior which is identified as "American," and he tends to conform to it. This was characteristically expressed by a patient who answered the question how he reacts to pain by saying, "I react like a good American."

An important element in controlling the pain reaction is the wish of the patient to cooperate with those who are expected to take care of him. The situation is often viewed as a team composed of the patient, the doctor, the nurse, the attendant, etc., and in this team everybody has a function and is supposed to do his share in order to achieve the most successful result. Emotionality is seen as a purposeless and hindering factor in a situation which calls for knowledge, skill, training, and efficiency. It is important to note that this behavior is also expected by American or Americanized members of the medical or nursing staff, and the patients who do not fall into this pattern are viewed as deviants, hypochondriacs, and neurotics.

As in the case of the Jewish patients, the American attitude toward pain can be best defined as a future-oriented anxiety. The "Old American" patient is also concerned with the symptomatic significance of pain which is correlated with a pronounced health consciousness. It seems that the "Old American"

is conscious of various threats to his health which are present in his environment and therefore feels vulnerable and is prone to interpret his pain sensation as a warning signal indicating that something is wrong with his health and therefore must be reported to the physician. With some exceptions, pain is considered bad and unnecessary and therefore must be immediately taken care of. In those situations where pain is expected and accepted, such as in the process of medical treatment or as a result of sports activities, there is less concern with the pain sensation. In general, however, there is a feeling that suffering pain is unnecessary when there are means of relieving it.

Though the attitudes of the Jewish and "Old American" patients can be defined as pain anxiety, they differ greatly. The future-oriented anxiety of the Jewish interviewee is characterized by pessimism or, at best, by skepticism, while the "Old American" patient is rather optimistic in his future orientation. This attitude is fostered by the mechanistic approach to the body and its functions and by the confidence in the skill of the expert which are so frequent in the American culture. The body is often viewed as a machine which has to be well taken care of, be periodically checked for disfunctioning, and eventually, when out of order, be taken to an expert who will "fix" the defect. In the case of pain the expert is the medical man who has the "know-how" because of his training and experience and therefore is entitled to full confidence. An important element in the optimistic outlook is faith in the progress of science. Patients with intractable pain often stated that though at the present moment the doctors do not have the "drug," they will eventually discover it, and they will give the examples of sulfa, penicillin, etc.

The anxieties of a pain-experiencing "Old American" patient are greatly relieved when he feels that something is being done about it in terms of specific activities involved in the treatment. It seems that his security and confidence increases in direct proportion to the number of tests, X rays, examinations, injections, etc., that are given to him. Accordingly, "Old American" patients seem to have a positive attitude toward hospitalization, because the hospital is the adequate institution which is equipped for the necessary treatment. While a Jewish and an Italian patient seem to be disturbed by the impersonal character of the hospital and by the necessity of being treated there instead of at home, the "Old American" patient, on the contrary, prefers the hospital treatment to the home treatment, and neither he nor his family seems to be disturbed by hospitalization.

To summarize the attitude of the "Old American" toward pain, he is disturbed by the symptomatic aspect of pain and is concerned with its incapacitating aspects, but he tends to view the future in rather optimistic colors, having confidence in the science and skill of the professional people who treat his condition.

## SOME SOURCES OF INTRAGROUP VARIATION

In the description of the reactive patterns and attitudes toward pain among patients of Jewish and "Old American" origin, certain regularities have been observed for each particular group regardless of individual differences and variations. This does not mean that each individual in each group manifests the same reactions and attitudes. Individual variations are often due to specific aspects of pain experience, to the character of the disease which causes the pain, or to elements in the personality of the patient. However, there are also other factors that are instrumental in provoking these differences and which can still be traced back to the cultural backgrounds of the individual patients. Such variables as the degree of Americanization of the patient, his socioeconomic background, education, and religiosity may play an important role in shaping individual variations in the reactive patterns. For instance, it was found that the patterns described are manifested most consistently among immigrants, while their descendants tend to differ in terms of adopting American forms of behavior and American attitudes toward the role of the medical expert, medical institutions, and equipment in controlling pain. It is safe to say that the further is the individual from the immigrant generation, the more American is his behavior. This is less true for the attitudes toward pain, which seem to persist to a great extent even among members of the third generation and even though the reactive patterns are radically changed. A Jewish or Italian patient born in this country of American-born parents tends to *behave* like an "Old American" but often expresses *attitudes* similar to those which are expressed by the Jewish or Italian people. They try to appear unemotional and efficient in situations where the immigrant would be excited and disturbed. However, in the process of the interview, if a patient is of Jewish origin he is likely to express attitudes of anxiety as to the meaning of his pain, and if he is an Italian he is likely to be rather unconcerned about the significance of his pain for his future.

The occupational factor plays an important role when pain affects a specific area of the body. For instance, manual workers with herniated discs are more disturbed by their pain than are professional or business people with a similar disease because of the immediate significance of this particular pain for their respective abilities to earn a living. It was also observed that headaches cause more concern among intellectuals than among manual workers.

The educational background of the patient also plays an important role in his attitude with regard to the symptomatic meaning of a pain sensation. The more educated patients are more health conscious and more aware of pain as a possible symptom of a dangerous disease. However, this factor plays a less important role than might be expected. The less educated "Old American" or Jewish patient is still more health conscious than the more educated Italian. On the other hand, the less educated Jew is as much worried about the significance of pain as the more educated one. The education of the patient seems to be an important factor in fostering specific reactive patterns. The more educated patient, who may have more anxiety with regard to illness, may be more reserved in specific reactions to pain than an unsophisticated individual, who feels free to express his feelings and emotions.

## TRANSMISSION OF CULTURAL ATTITUDES TOWARD PAIN

In interpreting the differences which may be attributed to different socio-economic and education backgrounds, there is enough evidence to conclude that these differences appear mainly on the manifest and behavioral level, whereas attitudinal patterns toward pain tend to be more uniform and to be common to most of the members of the group regardless of their specific backgrounds.

These attitudes toward pain and the expected reactive patterns are acquired by the individual members of the society from the earliest childhood along with other cultural attitudes and values which are learned from the parents, parent substitutes, siblings, peer groups, etc. Each culture offers to its members an ideal pattern of attitudes and reactions, which may differ for various subcultures in a given society, and each individual is expected to conform to this ideal pattern. Here the role of the family seems to be of primary importance. Directly and indirectly the family environment affects the individual's ultimate response to pain. In each culture the parents teach the child how to react to pain, and by approval or disapproval they promote specific forms of behavior. This conclusion is amply supported by the interviews. Thus the Jewish and Italian respondents are unanimous in relating how their parents, especially mothers, manifested overprotective and overconcerned attitudes toward the child's health, participation in sports, games, fights, etc. In these families the child is constantly reminded of the advisability of avoiding colds, injuries, fights, and other threatening situations. Crying in complaint is responded to by the parents with sympathy, concern, and help. By their overprotective and worried attitude they foster complaining and tears. The child learns to pay attention to each painful experience and to look for help and sympathy which are readily given to him. In Jewish families, where not only a slight sensation of pain but also each deviation from the child's normal behavior is looked upon as a sign of illness, the child is prone to acquire anxieties with regard to the meaning and significance of these manifestations. The Italian parents do not seem to be concerned with the symptomatic meaning of the child's pains and aches, but instead there is also a great deal of verbal expression of emotions and feelings of sympathy toward the "poor child" who happens to be in discomfort because of illness or because of an injury in play. In these families a child is praised when he avoids physical injuries and is scolded when he does not pay enough attention to bad weather, to drafts, or when he takes part in rough games and fights. The injury and pain are often interpreted to the child as punishment for the wrong behavior, and physical punishment is the usual consequence of misbehavior.

In the "Old American" family the parental attitude is quite different. The child is told not to "run to mother with every little thing." He is told to take pain "like a man," not to be a "sissy," not to cry. The child's participation in physical sports and games is not only approved but is also strongly stimulated. Moreover, the child is taught to expect to be hurt in sports and games and is taught to fight back if he happens to be attacked by other boys. However, it seems that the American parents are conscious of the threats to the child's health, and they teach the child to take immediate care of any injury. When hurt the right thing to do is not to cry and get emotional but to avoid unneces-

sary pain and prevent unpleasant consequences by applying the proper first aid medicine and by calling a doctor.

Often attitudes and behavior fostered in a family conflict with those patterns which are accepted by the larger social environment. This is especially true in the case of children of immigrants. The Italian or Jewish immigrant parents promote patterns which they consider correct, while the peer groups in the street and in the school criticize this behavior and foster a different one. In consequence, the child may acquire the attitudes which are part of his home life but may also adopt behavior patterns which conform to those of his friends.

The direct promotion of certain behavior described as part of the child rearing explains only in part the influence of the general family environment and the specific role of the parents in shaping responses to pain. They are also formed indirectly by observing the behavior of other members of the family and by imitating their responses to pain. Moreover, attitudes toward pain are also influenced by various aspects of parent-child relationship in a culture. The material suggests that differences in attitudes toward pain in Jewish, Italian, and "Old American" families are closely related to the role and image of the father in the respective cultures in terms of his authority and masculinity. Often the father and mother assume different roles in promoting specific patterns of behavior and specific attitudes. For example, it seems that in the "Old American" family it is chiefly the mother who stimulates the child's ability to resist pain, thus emphasizing his masculinity. In the Italian family it seems that the mother is the one who inspires the child's emotionality, while in the Jewish family both parents express attitudes of worry and concern which are transmitted to the children.

Specific deviations from expected reactive and attitudinal patterns can often be understood in terms of a particular structure of the family. This became especially clear from the interviews of two Italian patients and one Jewish patient. All three subjects revealed reactions and attitudes diametrically opposite to those which the investigator would expect on the basis of his experience. In the process of the interview, however, it appeared that one of the Italian patients was adopted by an Italian family, learned of his adoption at the age of fourteen, created a phantasy of being of Anglo-Saxon origin because of his physical appearance, and accordingly began to eradicate everything "Italian" in his personality and behavior. For instance, he denied knowledge of the Italian language despite the fact that he always spoke Italian in the family and even learned to abstain from smiling, because he felt that being happy and joyful is an indication of Italian origin. The other Italian patient lost his family at a very early age because of family disorganization and was brought up in an Irish foster home. The Jewish patient consciously adopted a "non-Jewish" pattern of behavior and attitude because

of strong sibling rivalry. According to the respondent, his brother, a favored son in the immigrant Jewish family, always manifested "typical" Jewish reactions toward disease, and the patient, who strongly disliked the brother and was jealous of him, decided to be "completely different."

## CONCLUSION

This analysis of cultural factors in responses to pain is tentative and incomplete. It is based upon only one year of research which has been devoted exclusively to collection of raw material and formulation of working hypotheses. A detailed analysis of the interviews may call for revisions and reformulations of certain observations described in this paper. Nevertheless, the first objectives of our research have been attained in establishing the importance of the role of cultural factors in an area relatively little explored by the social sciences. We hope that in the course of further research we shall be able to expand our investigation into other areas of the pain problem, such as sex differences in attitudes toward pain, the role of age differences, and the role of religious beliefs in the pain experience. We hope also that the final findings of the study will contribute to the growing field of collaboration between the social sciences and medicine for the better understanding of human problems.

1. This paper is based upon material collected as part of the study "Cultural Components in Attitudes toward Pain," under a grant of the U.S. Public Health Service.

2. James D. Hardy, Harold G. Wolff, and Helen Goodell, *Pain Sensations and Reactions.* Baltimore: Williams and Wilkins, 1952, p. 23.

3. *Ibid.*, p. 204.

4. *Ibid.*, p. 262.

5. I should like to take the opportu-

nity to express my appreciation to Dr. Harold G. Wolff, Professor of Neurology, Cornell University Medical College; Dr. Hiland Flowers, Chief of Neuropsychiatric Service; Dr. Robert Morrow, Chief of Clinical Psychology Section; Dr. Louis Berlin, Chief of Neurology Section; and the Management of the hospital for their cooperation in the setting up of the research at the Kingsbridge Veterans Hospital.

6. Italian respondents are mainly of South Italian origin; the Jewish respondents, with one exception, are all of East European origin. Whenever the Jews are mentioned they are spoken of in terms of the culture they represent and not in terms of their religion.

# 27. MASTECTOMY—SYMBOL OF CURE OR WARNING SIGN?

## Jeanne C. Quint

To physicians, mastectomy is a procedure for the treatment of breast cancer. However, this article concerns mastectomy as a critical experience in the life of a woman. The study reported here was an investigation of adjustment to mastectomy and was limited to a follow-up period of only one year. Obviously, the first year was an important period in the lives of these women. The extent to which death and fear of dying became integral parts of their lives was not anticipated nor were the difficulties they encountered in trying to adjust to the change. For them, the problem of coping with an uncertain future became singularly important.

To discuss the problem of an uncertain future, it is useful to consider mastectomy not as a therapy but as a crucial event. All people undergo experiences which have a great impact on them and which alter their views of themselves. Such experiences can be called "turning points." Mastectomy is a turning point which brings the notion of dying into a woman's personal reality. A woman who undergoes mastectomy must face the fact that she has cancer, a disease associated with death. She has to live with the question, "Did the doctor get it all?" For her, the operation becomes less a symbol of cure than a warning sign.

## METHOD OF STUDY

Data were collected on 21 women who entered a medical center hospital for mastectomy and were seen in their homes at selected intervals during the following year. Included in the study were all women who had mastectomy during the six-month period of hospital field work (except those who had evidence of metastases to areas other than axillary nodes at the time of surgery). As patients, they received medical care supervised either by a private physician or by the medical center resident staff. Participation in the study was voluntary and only one woman chose not to continue after the first home interview.

Data were collected by participant observation, a method in which the observer participates in the daily lives of the people under study over a period of time. This activity permits the observer to see what takes place, listen to what is said, and ask questions for clarification. The field workers were nurses who established contact with these women by taking care of them during their hospital stay. (The field

Reprinted by permission of the author and the American Academy of General Practice, from *GP*, Vol. XXIX, 1964, pp. 119–124. (This study was supported by NIH grant M5495 and was jointly sponsored by the School of Nursing and the Department of Surgery, School of Medicine, University of California, Los Angeles.)

workers shared responsibility with the regular nursing staff, however, so that they would have an opportunity to make and record observations.) The observation was periodic rather than continuous. Home interviews were recorded on tape. This analysis is given in full recognition that the data do not encompass everything that took place during the year but rather are selected samples from the events of that period.

Findings showed that the women in this study met one of two outcomes: they either did not survive the year or began a living pattern marred by concerns about when they might die. Time was foreshortened and they began a search for guidelines in learning to live with an uncertain future.

With wound healing and physical well-being as standards, these women can be separated into three categories: (1) those who faced an uncertain future even though physical recovery appeared excellent; (2) those in whom the incision did not heal or physical discomfort persisted; and (3) those who at some point encountered physical regression and certain death. This article describes the stages through which they passed during the one-year observation period. Discussion begins with those women who appeared to make a satisfactory recovery.

## UNCERTAINTY IN SPITE OF HEALING

The impact did not really hit the patients while they were in the hospital although most of them described a day of depression, usually the third or fourth day after surgery. Although the first look at the incision was "terribly upsetting" to some, most of the women remained remarkably controlled during this period. The first weeks out of the hospital showed a sharp contrast; the women described themselves as "exhausted" or "nervous." Many were surprised that they burst into tears without provocation. As one of them said, "I'm going stir crazy because I can't get it out."

This was an unsettled period characterized by frequent, unexpected physical changes and reactions. The women were keenly aware of these physical signs and showed tremendous preoccupation with the incision itself. Moreover, they tended to label these bodily changes as either "good" or "bad." One woman stated the problem clearly when she said, "I've become very lump conscious." Understandably, these women wanted the physician to assign a specific harmless meaning to these signs and symptoms and most of them sought frequent contact with him during the early weeks. Some physicians met these inquiries with such statements as, "Don't worry, everything is going well" or "The incision looks beautiful." Some women were content with these comments. For others, this response only added to the tension, particularly if discomfort persisted. Eventually they began to look to other sources for clues to their true condition.

A second characteristic of this early posthospitalization period was that families and friends seemed concerned and solicitous. Talk about the surgery itself, however, was generally social. Friends usually asked, "How are you getting along?" and then changed the subject. Family members also kept conversations at a superficial level, perhaps to avoid discussing in detail what the doctor had told them about the patient's condition. One woman described it this way:

They act like they love me more but they're not fooling me. . . . I'm sure in another couple of weeks they'll go back to being their little selves again. . . . In spite of the fact that I'm aware possibly why they're doing this, I like it.

At this time, any mention of cancer or death was made either casually or jokingly.

Healing of the incision and the use of a satisfactory breast substitute initiated a second period. It usually began in the sixth or seventh week and was characterized by a sharp change in behavior. The women experienced a mood upswing as they began to move out into work or social activities. One said, "It gives you a terrific boost." They were less interested in physical signs. A typical comment was, "I'm feeling better." They relied far less on the physician at this time and seldom consulted him about resuming physical activities. A woman who wanted to drive her car simply did not ask her doctor for an opinion. Characteristically, the women evaded talk about the surgery. Most of them denied having thoughts about death at this time. As one of them commented, "I really believe the doctor— that they got it all."

However, the euphoria did not last long. About the fourth month, a period of letdown began. Concern centered on fatigue. As one woman said, "I don't know why I should be so tired." Tasks which once were commonplace became overwhelming but families and friends expected the women to be active again. They found little of the consideration they had received during earlier posthospitalization weeks.

One woman spoke with feeling about the lack of thoughtfulness:

I'm learning not to pay too much attention to what they have to say. I know

which people to talk to and which people not to say anything to and which people to just pretend that nothing ever happened.

Most of the women had already heard stories about other mastectomy patients, primarily tales about those who did not survive.

About the seventh month, the letdown mood gave way to a feeling that one's time on earth was quite uncertain. Frequently, the women referred to others who had had this surgery. Many frankly stated that they associated the stories they heard with themselves.

One woman described a visit with a friend suffering from liver metastases. In her words:

You know how you try to pick them up and don't let them put their fingers on anything real definite. . . . Well, I'm just knocking myself out . . . . I got home and I thought, "Gosh, that might be me."

She said that every time she heard of a woman having this surgery she related the case to herself. She added, "All I can do really is just trust in the doctors. They said they got it and I believe them." It is apparent, however, that she did not rely solely on their words but used other information in making judgments about herself. When sharp, burning pains suddenly appeared in her incision, she said:

The first couple of times it seemed kind of funny . . . it kind of startled me. Then it stopped and I said, "Well, it can't be. You know if the cancer is returning, it's not returning in one spot."

During this period, the patients described situations which clearly indicated that they saw time foreshortened. It was common to hear the statement, "I only hope I'm here." Describing a birthday party her husband had given for her, one woman said, "It might be my last."

By the end of the year, the women seldom discussed this aspect of their lives because they had learned that their families did not like to talk about it. Moreover, they avoided such talk because it stimulated depressing thoughts. However, they could not completely prevent these thoughts because they were accidentally triggered by sudden, unexplainable pains or by stories of women dying of breast cancer. One woman said, "I'm so *conscious* of it, it wears me out." Another commented, "I wish that I could have an association with people who have gotten over it." These women were extremely vulnerable to stories about people with cancer. At the end of the year, they were far less influenced by what the physician said than by what they heard and saw happening to other cancer victims. In spite of the physician's words of hope, they lived with no real certainty of surviving another year.

## UNCERTAINTY COMBINED WITH COMPLICATIONS

It was not surprising to find that the entire year became far more upsetting if the incision did not heal and complications developed. Those hospitalized for wound infection were upset by the wound itself, by inconsistent practices of nursing personnel, and by the loneliness of isolation. Those directed to care for themselves at home were more likley to be upset because they lacked direct access to the physician.

One woman, in desperation, finally phoned the surgeon at his home when he failed to return her call. Here is her description of what happened:

He didn't say a word, you know, just kept silent until I went into my problems and he'd make me feel he wasn't going to encourage me even to talk. I just had the feeling that even though I pay him a good price for his surgery, he still doesn't want to be bothered.

This example illustrates the extent to which these women wanted specific reassurance that everything was fine. The physician, however, could not give them such explicit reassurance. In some instances, he was in an untenable position. No surgeon wants to say, "I'm not sure that we got it all." Under such circumstances, some doctors avoided prolonged discussion with these women. Nevertheless, it is understandable that these frightened women would press their physicians for answers.

Concern about delay in wound healing was increased by some surgeons' erroneous predictions of healing time. In one instance, the wound was still partially open at the end of the year. Yet the woman had been told, "In three months or so, you'll never know this happened to you." Understandably, she was morose during her last interview. For this woman who had seen her mother die of breast cancer, failure to heal was an ominous sign.

Unlike the women who healed without complications, this second group had difficulty identifying physical signs that were symbolic of improvement. In addition, they spent more time seeking reassurance from the doctor. When they met evasive or nonspecific answers, they solicited advice from other physicians. Unfortunately, this maneuver usually brought them contradictory and varied opinions which were disconcerting. Eventually they, too, placed greater trust in the stories they heard about other mastectomy patients.

These women did not describe a period of feeling better but were easily alarmed by all kinds of signs and symptoms throughout the year. Physical complications had delayed the use of a brassiere and breast substitute and had postponed a return to normal social intercourse. Therefore their isolation was prolonged and the strain was increased. These women kept many of their worries to themselves since they found that their families preferred not to discuss such matters. In some instances, family relationships were severed; the tension had become unbearable as the women sought reassurance where none could be offered. At the end of the year, this group was also struggling to achieve some kind of serenity as they faced a future in which each day might bring a warning sign. Moreover, the majority faced the issue alone—not because family members lacked concern but because they could not talk openly about cancer and the possibility of death.

In her final interview, one woman commented,

Well, if anything goes wrong, you say, "Well, they say it's healing; they say they got it all." But you know and I know that everything can look like peaches and cream and not be that way at all. It's a terrifying thought and yet it's something that you must learn to live with because there's nothing else in the world you can do but live with it.

### CERTAINTY OF DEATH

Those women who faced certain death had usually delayed so long in getting care that the cancer was visible externally at the time of surgery. The doctors could not remove the malignancy completely. However, they explained the situation more precisely to family members than to the women themselves. In contrast with the other two groups, these women said they felt well at the time of their first home visit and they did not press the doctors for detailed information about their condition. Although their friends and families were solicitous, there was little talk about the surgery or its possible consequences after the first few weeks.

It was characteristic of this group not to expect recovery although they pretended that all was going well. In spite of the pretense, these women were aware of the warning signs. They played the recovery game with both families and doctors until the time when certain physical signs carried more meaning than the doctors' words in predicting the future. At this point, they openly admitted to the field workers that they knew death was coming. However, they were not this open with their families. They continued to "protect" their families until physical incapacitation forced all to face the reality of the situation. During the final weeks, as pain and discomfort increased, the families began to make decisions for them and placed great reliance on physicians as a relief for their own helplessness.

One woman, whose family combined forces with the doctor to hospitalize her for X-ray therapy, said to the field worker,

You know, actually I'm against all this help. I know it's not going to help. She [her daughter] says, "Well, I keep telling you, they're not trying to prolong your life. They try to make it easier for you."

Unfortunately, the medical treatment for relief of pain sometimes had the reverse effect and occasionally brought moments of intense anguish. For both families and physicians, this was a period of strain, tension, and helplessness. The women themselves were unaware of time in the usual sense and increasingly showed less concern about it. As the pain increased, they wanted the end to come. For them, death was welcome.

## IMPLICATIONS AND COMMENTS

The experiences of these women indicate that little professional help was available for a problem of primary concern. It was not during hospitalization that these patients were ready to talk about their fears but only after they had been at home for a week or more. By then, their families and friends were moving "back to normal" and there was no one to listen. They did not talk to the doctor about the things which most concerned them. Generally, the doctor did not initiate conversation about such topics but focused attention on wound healing and therapeutic regimens.

The importance of the doctor is unquestionable, particularly during the first few months after surgery. To illustrate, one woman was told that she did not have to return to the office for three months after her incision had healed. For her, it was not reassuring to go for that length of time without seeing the surgeon.

Another woman was very concerned about the persistent, sharp pains in her back three months after surgery. Her doctor told her that this was part of healing and that she was "worrying about nothing." Six weeks later, she said,

I don't have any relief from it now. Doctor's doing nothing for it, you know, and I don't know what I'm going to do. I should go back this week, I guess, for a check-up. But he takes a look at me and, see, all the time I have these pains, aches all the time. All he does is take one look at me and says, "Oh, my, it looks fine, good-bye, toodle-oo," and he takes off and you don't see him again. Well, I want him to give me some suggestion or tell me what to do for my arm swelling and this continuous discomfort I have. . . . I don't feel he's doing anything for me and I feel like I'm going right down a rat hole.

The problem of getting definite, supportive answers becomes even more complicated when the woman does not have access to a single doctor but is seen by a succession of residents who have varying amounts of knowledge about her history and, equally important, different ways of discussing it with her. Whether or not he fully recognizes it, the doctor plays a significant part not only in what he says but also in how and when he says it.

These women welcomed someone who would permit them to talk about their real concerns. This was evident in their conversations with the field worker. With her, they were permitted to discuss matters generally forbidden in their everyday social contacts. As they described their lives in transition, one would ask oneself: Is it beneficial or not that everyone avoids using the word *death* and bars these women from discussing their concerns about it? Obviously, families and friends have difficulty because of personal involvement in the situation. Perhaps doctors, whose major concerns are therapy and cure, might also find it difficult to provide such an outlet. Furthermore, few physicians have been trained for this kind of function. One can speculate, however, that someone skilled at listening might make it possible for these women to handle the idea of dying more openly and without the bleak loneliness which now surrounds them.

The findings of this study suggest that the major difficulty a woman faces after mastectomy is learning to "live with death." Yet few people are able to help her come to terms with this change in perspective. What happened to the field workers is ample proof that this task is not to be taken lightly. As they learned, permitting someone else to talk about death forces one to face one's own feelings about death. Moreover, it takes time to develop the ability to be comfortable in such a situation. Most important, this kind of interaction has a poignancy which affects both persons involved and the one who listens needs safeguards to pull him out of the relationship when it threatens to overwhelm him.

There can be little doubt that mastectomy is a critical event in the life of a woman. During the year of observation, these women became progressively isolated with their "disease" and were given few if any outlets for talking about the matters which most concerned them. It became increasingly evident that breast cancer generally carries great fear for women and it is not surprising that most women protect themselves from contacts or conversations which precipitate such thoughts as "Will this happen to me?" A woman with breast cancer lives a lonely life. The data showed that men also avoided talk which might be upsetting. Increased awareness of physical changes in themselves is a major cause of rising tension in these women and this sensitivity is not limited to the first few months after mastectomy.

There is reason to think that other people with cancer share this focus on death and undergo similar difficulties in adjusting to a change in perspective. If dying is a major concern of people with cancer, then perhaps they need an opportunity to deal more openly with it. Surely it is difficult enough to face living on borrowed time without the added problem of conversational isolation during the transition period.

# 28. GRIEF AND GRIEVING

## George L. Engel

Death is an intensely poignant event, one which touches the deepest sources of human anguish, one which each of us yearns to be spared. Yet as nurses and physicians, it is our constant companion. How can we protect ourselves from such repeated personal suffering? One way—and the easiest way—is to develop a shell, to insulate ourselves, to avoid engagement, to make out it does not occur or it is not our concern.

This is what all nurses and doctors do to some degree, a few to the point of callousness. But it is this very human need for self-protective measures that is responsible for the dearth of systematic knowledge, much less scientific study, of the processes of grief and mourning, for it takes courage to undergo the repeated and wrenching impact of the exposure to the grief stricken that a scientific study of grief would demand.[1] There are easier ways to win fame and fortune. Accumulated evidence suggests that the success of the grieving process may be a significant variable regulating the capacity to maintain health.[2]

Grief is so universal a phenomenon among human beings, if not among higher animals as well, that it hardly provokes wonder. It is taken for granted. For it seems only "natural" that one should feel badly upon suffering the loss of a loved one. But why?

Why should it make any difference?

These are outrageous, almost insulting questions, yet the answers which they are likely to provoke are no more than restatements of the fact. "It's natural." "It's human." "Because the deceased is missed." "Because he was loved." "Because what we experienced together can never again be." "It is losing a part of one's self." And so on. All true and yet somehow the essence of the experience is not captured in such phrases. Only the poets, through the ages, have come close to grasping the essential psychological verities of this experience.

Grief fills the room up of my absent child,
Lies in his bed, walks up and down with me,
Puts on his pretty looks, repeats his words,
Remembers me of all his gracious parts,
Stuffs out his vacant garments with his form.
(Shakespeare, *King John*, Act iii, Sc. 4)

Give sorrow words; the grief that does not speak
Whispers the o'er-fraught heart and bids it break.
(Shakespeare, *Macbeth*, Act iv, Sc. 3)

Grief tears his heart, and drives him to and fro.
In all the raging impotence of woe.
(Pope, *The Iliad of Homer*, Book xxii)

Home they brought her warrior dead;
She nor swoon'd nor utter'd cry.

---

Reprinted by permission of the publisher, from the *American Journal of Nursing*, Vol. 64, 1964, pp. 93-98.

All her maidens, watching, said,
She must weep or she will die.
Then they praised him, soft and low,
Call'd him worthy to be loved,
Truest friend and noblest foe;
Yet she neither spoke nor moved.
Stole a maiden from her place,
Lightly to the warrior stept,
Took the face-cloth from the face;
Yet she neither moved nor wept.
Rose a nurse of ninety years,
Set his child upon her knee—
Like summer tempest came her tears—
'Sweet my child, I live for thee.'
(Tennyson, *Songs of the Princess*)

Study of even these few excerpts from literature shows how eloquently poets identify the characteristic features of grief.

1. The smooth, more or less automatic, taken-for-granted aspects of living are interrupted. The grieving person suddenly becomes aware of the innumerable ways in which he was dependent, often quite unconsciously, on the lost object (person) as a source of gratification and as an essential influence for his feeling of well-being and effective functioning, his sense of self, so to speak.

2. The grieving person attempts to refute, to deny, to dispute the reality of the event.

3. The grieving person, in the depth of his feeling of impotence, loss, and helplessness, sends out various behavioral cries for help, to which his fellow men respond. Failure or inability to emit the cry or to elicit a response are fraught with dire implications for recovery.

4. The grieving person attempts to reconstitute in his mind a representation of the lost person to replace that which no longer exists in the real world. This is a difficult and painful process, in which the bitter and the sweet in the end are separated and the mourner ultimately comes to peace with himself and his new state.

5. Both the personal experience of grief and the institutionalized and social rituals of the mourning process serve ultimately to detach the grieving person from the dead and to restore him to his place as a member of the social community.

Further order may be brought into these poetical insights by using the analogy of wound healing. If we define grief as the typical reaction to the loss of a source of psychological gratification, we can compare the experience of the loss to the wound, while the subsequent psychological responses to the loss may be compared to the tissue reaction and the processes of healing.

Whatever one has become accustomed to as a natural and expected part of one's environment — whether it be the presence of a parent, a spouse, a child, a friend, a particular house, the scene of one's happy life experiences, a job, a pet, or even an old shoe — these come to constitute psychological sources of gratification and supply, and their absence is felt as a gap in one's sense of continuity and self-confidence. Functionally, the loss of such a source of gratification is truly a wound.

Successful grief and grieving follow certain more or less predictable steps which permit a judgment that healing is taking place. This healing process can be interfered with by unsound intervention, by failure to provide optimal conditions for healing, or because the individual's resources are not up to the task. But the normal healing processes of grieving cannot be accelerated.

A good grasp of the sequence of events characterizing normal grief and of the meaning of each is essential if one is to help wisely. Further, knowledge of what is normal enables one to identify the pathological.

## SHOCK AND DISBELIEF

The first response on learning of death is often one of shock and disbelief. The survivor may respond with a refusal to accept or comprehend the fact, often crying out, "No!" "It can't be!" Or he may throw himself on the body, attempting to find signs of life or to bring the dead back to life.

This reaction may then be followed by a stunned, numbed feeling in which the grief-stricken person does not permit himself any thoughts or feelings which acknowledge the reality of the death. He may try desperately, but in an automatic fashion, to carry on his ordinary activities, as if nothing had happened, or he may sit motionless and dazed, unable to move. At such times the victim seems out of contact and it may be difficult to gain his attention. This phase may last a few minutes or hours or even days, alternating with flashes of despair and anguish as the reality of the loss briefly penetrates into consciousness.

Sometimes the initial response is overtly an intellectual acceptance of the reality of the loss and an immediate initiation of apparently appropriate activity, such as making arrangements and comforting others. But it is only by not permitting access to consciousness of the full emotional impact of the loss that this can take place. In such an instance the loss is recognized, but its painful character is denied or at least muted.

In general, distinctive of this initial phase are the attempts to protect oneself against the effects of the overwhelming stress by raising the threshold against its recognition or against the painful feeling evoked thereby. Although such responses are more usual and more intense when the death is sudden and unexpected, they may also be observed even when the death has been anticipated.

## DEVELOPING AWARENESS

Within minutes to hours the second stage begins. The reality of the death and its meaning as a loss begin more and more to penetrate consciousness in the form of an acute and increasing awareness of the anguish of the loss, the feeling of something lost, often felt as a painful emptiness in the chest or epigastrium. The environment seems frustrating and empty since it no longer includes the loved person.

Anger may erupt toward persons or circumstances held to be responsible for the death, as the doctor, nurse, hospital, or other family member. The mourner himself may feel he had in some way failed and may berate or even impulsively injure himself. Beating the breast, pounding the head, or thrusting the fist through glass are occasional impulsive, aggressive, and self-destructive acts on the part of the person who is suddenly overwhelmed with grief.

Crying, with tears, is typical of this phase. It is during this period that the greatest degree of anguish or despair, within the limits imposed by cultural patterns, is experienced and expressed. Some cultures demand loud and public lamentation, whereas others expect restraint. Familiarity with such cultural patterns is necessary in evaluating the appropriateness of a grief response. Regardless of such factors, the wish and need to cry is strong and crying seems to fulfill an important function in the work of mourning.

In general, crying seems to involve

both an acknowledgment of the loss and the regression to a more helpless and childlike status. In the latter sense, crying is a communication. The grief-stricken person who cries is the recipient of certain kinds of support and help from the group, although this varies greatly in different cultures. Grief is one situation in which the tears of an adult are generally accepted and understood and the person who is able to cry still feels self-respect and worthfulness and that he is deserving of help.

Some persons suffering a loss want to cry or feel that they should cry, yet are unable to. This type of inhibition of crying must be distinguished from not crying simply because the person who died is not seriously missed, in which case there is no inclination or need to cry, and from the voluntary suppression of crying because of an environmental or cultural demand, in which case the person either "cries inwardly" or waits until he is alone and unobserved before crying. Inability to cry, however, is a more serious matter. It is most likely to occur when the relationship with the dead person had been highly ambivalent and when the survivor is experiencing a good deal of guilt or shame.

## RESTITUTION

Restitution, the work of mourning, is the third stage. The institutionalization of the mourning experience in terms of the various rituals of the funeral help to initiate the recovery processes. First, it involves a gathering together of family and friends who mutually share the loss, although not all to the same degree. At the same time there is acknowledgment of the need for support of the more stricken survivors whose regression is accepted. In this setting, overt or con-

scious expression of aggression is reduced to a minimum.

Many of the rituals of the funeral serve the important function of emphasizing clearly and unequivocally the reality of the death, the denial of which cannot be allowed to go on if recovery from the loss is to take place. The viewing of the body, the lowering of the casket, and the various rituals of different religious beliefs allow for no ambiguity. Further, this experience takes place in a group, permitting ordinarily guarded feelings to be shared and expressed more readily.

In addition, individual religious and spiritual beliefs offer recourse in various ways to the support of a more powerful, beneficent figure or provide the basis for the expectation of some kind of reunion after death and the expiation of guilt. The funeral ceremony also initiates the process of identification with the lost person through the various rituals which symbolize an identity between the mourner and the dead (for example, sackcloth and ashes).

In primitive societies this acting out of the identification is more vivid and literal. In many cultures the funeral ceremony includes a feast or some sort of wake in which is symbolically expressed a triumph over death, a denial of the fear of death or the dead, an attempt to return to life and living.

## RESOLVING THE LOSS

For the mourner, however, the main work of grief goes on intrapsychically, the institutionalization mainly providing sustenance during the period of struggle to achieve this. As the reality of the death becomes accepted, the resolution of the loss involves a number of steps which proceed haltingly and interruptedly.

First, the mourner attempts to deal with the painful void, the awareness of the loss, which is felt also as a defect in the sense of intactness and wholeness of the self. He cannot yet accept a new love object to replace the lost person, although he may passively and transiently accept a more dependent relation with family members and old friends.

In this phase he may be more aware of his own body, experiencing various bodily sensations or pains, in contrast to the earlier period when he may have been quite numb even to great physical hardship. Often such a pain or discomfort is identical with a symptom experienced in the past by the dead person, sometimes during the terminal illness. The mourner suffers in place of the dead person and by so doing not only maintains a tie with the deceased, but also appeases some of his own guilt for any aggressive impulses toward the dead. Normally such symptoms are brief.

For some time the mourner's thoughts are almost exclusively occupied with thoughts of the deceased, first with more emphasis on the personal experience of the loss, later with more emphasis on the person who died. He finds it necessary to bring up, to think over, and to talk about memories of the dead person, a process which goes on slowly and painfully, with great sadness, until there has been erected in the mind an image of the dead person almost devoid of negative or undesirable features.

## IDEALIZATION

Such a process of idealization, however, requires that all negative and hostile feelings toward the deceased be repressed. Such repression may lead to fluctuating guilty, remorseful, and even fearful feelings, with regrets for past acts or fantasies of hostility, inconsiderateness, or unkindness, recollection of some of which may be exaggerated. Sometimes there may be a haunting preoccupation with feelings of responsibility for the death. The various primitive concepts of the dead coming back to haunt or retaliate originate in such guilty feelings.

As the idealization of the dead person proceeds, though, two important changes are being achieved. The recurring thoughts and reminiscences about the deceased serve to establish in the mind a distinct image of the lost person, often buttressed by various external memorials and remembrances. The latter constitute tangible evidences of the more positive aspects of the lost relationship and permit one periodically to renew and relive the gratifications associated in the past with the deceased.

At the same time the mourner consciously and unconsciously begins to take for himself certain admired qualities and attributes of the dead person through the mechanism of identification. This may appear in his adoption of certain mannerisms and in his acknowledged wish to be like the lost person or to carry on his ideals and good deeds. When guilt is present there is a greater tendency for the mourner to take on undesirable traits or even symptoms of the deceased or to exaggerate the need to fulfill the wishes of the deceased.

Many months are required for this process and, as it is accomplished, the survivor's preoccupation with the dead person progressively lessens. Now, reminders of the dead person less often and less intently evoke feelings of sadness and more ambivalent memories can be tolerated with less guilt. As the ties are progressively loosened, the earlier yearnings to be with the dead person, even in death, begin more and more to be replaced by a turning to life. Now, the identification with the ideals, wishes, and aspirations of the lost person provide an impetus to continue in life. These are often expressed as a wish "to be what he would have wanted me to be" or "to carry on for him."

As the psychic dependence on the deceased diminishes, the mourner's interest in new relationships begins to return. Early in the mourning process, this may take the form of interest in and concern with other mourners who share the same loss. By so doing the mourner is able temporarily to reduce his preoccupation with himself and the dead person and instead he feels sorry for and takes care of other mourners. This allows him to reinvest feelings in his other love objects, his spouse, his children, as the case may be, and at the same time to gain some comfort by identifying with the person whom he now comforts and cares for. It also provides some respite from the painful, though necessary, task of dwelling on the loss and the lost object. In family units, different members may facilitate each other's work of mourning by alternating in such roles.[3] Eventually, as the months pass by, the mourner renews his interest in persons and matters not so directly concerned with the loss and with the mourning.

## THE OUTCOME

The successful work of mourning takes a year or more. The clearest evidence of successful healing is the ability to re-

member comfortably and realistically both the pleasures and disappointments of the lost relationship. Many factors influence what the eventual outcome will be. A major determinant is the importance of the lost object as a source of support. The more dependent the relationship, the more difficult will be the task of resolving its loss. The degree of ambivalence toward the deceased is another. When there are persistent, unresolved, hostile feelings, guilt may interfere with the successful work of mourning. The age of the lost object is influential. The loss of a child generally has a more profound effect than the loss of an aged parent. The age of the mourner has its effect, too. The child has less capability of resolving a loss than does an adult. The number and nature of other relationships is still another factor. The person with few meaningful relationships has a more difficult time effecting the detachment from his dependence on the deceased. The mourner is affected by the number and nature of previous grief experiences. Losses tend to be cumulative in their effects. The most recent loss tends to revive that which was unsettled from earlies losses. The degree of preparation for the loss is a factor in that with the death of an aged or incurably sick person, some of the grief work may go on before the death. Finally, the physical and psychological health of the mourner at the time of the loss is important in determining his capacity to deal with the loss at the time it occurs.

## PRACTICAL CONSIDERATIONS

Armed with such systematic knowledge of the grief process, the intuitive and empathic nurse is in a good position to help. While our present knowledge of grief is far too schematic and fragmentary to justify a how-to-do-it manual, clinical experience does provide a few guides useful to nurses. The rationale of these recommendations can be deduced from the preceding material.

*First,* news of death or impending death is best communicated to a family group rather than to an individual alone and should be done in a setting of privacy where the family can behave naturally without the restraints of public display. The perceptive nurse may well identify in advance the family member whose relation vis-a-vis the dying patient is such that he will be able to retain the composure and judgment necessary to help the more stricken survivors. She will alert the doctor of signs of impending death so as to give plenty of time to contact the family and prepare them for the inevitable.

When only one family member is available, the task may fall on the nurse to stay with and comfort the bereaved, at least until the clergyman or a friend can take over. Often the nurse will be aware of the fact that she has been singled out for the role by the lone survivor of the dying patient. It will be well for her to consciously decide in advance whether she is willing and able to accept this responsibility and, if so, to plan how best she can discharge it.

The natural and understandable tendency is to run away from this painful task, to avoid recognizing that one is being singled out to play a crucial role in the unfolding tragedy. The prepared nurse will serve her patient and herself far better than the nurse who allows herself to be caught by surprise. And if she is not up to the task, for whatever reason — and there are many sound reasons why one may not be — her nursing responsibility is best discharged by

recognizing the fact honestly and trying to enlist the aid of someone else.

*Second,* the request to see and take leave of the dying or dead patient should not be denied on the ground that it may be too upsetting or that it will disturb the floor routine. This need to take leave, to ask forgiveness, to touch, kiss, or caress the dying or dead loved one, to take a lock of hair, is of overwhelming importance to some and will not be requested by those for whom it will be disturbing. We forget that dying in the hospital rather than in the home is a recent social change.

Nor should the nurse be deterred in acquiescing to such a request by the fact that the body or deathbed scene are not tidy (though certainly she should try to make them so), or by the anguished outcry that viewing of the deceased may evoke. The latter is part of a necessary psychological response, helpful in facing the reality of the death.

*Third,* when confronted by an angry, bitter, accusatory relative who berates the doctor, the hospital, the nurse, or other family members and accuses them of having neglected, mismanaged, or abused the dying or deceased patient, the nurse must keep two things in mind. Such a person could conceivably be justified in his complaint. But if not, he may be attempting to deal with his own aggression and guilt toward the dying person.

In either event, the nurse will do well to recognize that she serves best by redoubling her efforts to provide the best possible care to the dying person and by avoiding becoming involved in acrimonious dispute. By recognizing that the complaints are not directed to her as a person, that indeed they may be serving an important role in keeping the grieving relative from falling apart psychologically, she will almost certainly be able herself better to tolerate what appear to be entirely unjustified complaints and accusations. This is not the time or circumstance to expect thanks or gratitude, yet she can rest assured that such will be forthcoming later if she has been able to display the necessary tolerance and understanding of this distressing behavior.

*Fourth*, the nurse, knowing that shock and disbelief may be the first response to the news of death, should anticipate that some persons will behave in a grossly disturbed manner. She will require patience, tact, and warm sympathy for the person who refuses to acknowledge the truth of the news as well as for the person who literally collapses or loses control. Understanding that these are ways that people have to protect themselves from the overwhelming should provide her with the confidence that patient, gentle, and feeling reiteration of the reality coupled with the personal demonstration of a wish to help will go far in helping the grief stricken over this difficult strait. Most important is encouraging the bereaved person to cry.

It is not sound to expect the suddenly bereaved person to maintain the social decorum demanded by a busy hospital floor. Rather than attempting to quiet the distraught relatives, out of consideration for other patients, the nurse should actively help the relatives to a place where they can grieve in private. Such behavior on the part of the nurse acknowledges the realistic needs of all and as such stamps her (the nurse) as a feeling as well as sensible person. These are qualities which can be a source of real strength to the bereaved.

*Fifth*, one cannot overemphasize the importance of knowing about and exercising the respect for the cultural, religious, and social customs of the mourners, no matter how strange or even abhorrent they may be to some of us. The institutionalized mourning rituals of peoples, sects, and cultures provide some of the most important external supports for the grief-stricken person, often essential to his ability to tolerate this first period of intense distress. The nurse must be familiar with the timing involved in the rites for the dying characteristic of different religions and see that the necessary steps are taken to assure that those responsible make the necessary provisions.

## GRIEVING PATIENTS

*Sixth*, a good nurse will not overlook the fact that a patient is grieving. Not infrequently people fall ill following a serious loss and because attention is directed toward the more obvious illness the attending physicians and nurses fail to recognize the signs of grief or to elicit the history of the loss.[4] From time to time, one encounters a withdrawn, depressed, often tearful patient and nobody considers the obvious, that he has in the recent past suffered a grievous loss. Not to be overlooked is that the loss may be of a part or a function of the body, as after amputation or loss of vision, as well as after the loss of a loved one.[5]

Even more tragic and less excusable are those instances where survivors of fatal accidents are afforded the best possible medical and surgical care but no one concerns himself with the grief. "Is my husband, my wife, my child alive or dead?" "Can I see him?" "Can I go to the funeral?" all too often are questions which not only are not responded to, are not even allowed to be asked. And all too often physicians and nurses try to suppress by drugs or by avoidance the emerging reactions of grief under the misguided notion that such would interfere with the surgical or medical care. Here, perhaps, is one area most desperately calling for careful study and a more soundly based program of action.

*Seventh*, the grieving infant and child is commonplace. Especially for the child between six months and six years, merely being separated from home and admitted to the hospital is in itself sufficient to elicit a primitive grief response.[6] Consideration of grief in infancy and childhood is beyond the scope of this paper. Suffice it to say that attention to these children is a prime responsibility for the nurse. I have seen remarkable responses when a nurse simply on her own undertook to provide such an infant with the tender loving care so badly needed, even to the extent of carrying the baby about in her arms while performing her other duties.

## THE DYING CHILD

*Finally*, the grief of the parents of the dying child is peculiarly poignant and painful to witness. Here the nurse must exercise great wisdom and compassion if she is to be truly helpful and not get involved in a difficult competitive situation. She must recognize and respect the mother's need to minister to her own child, yet at the same time sensitively perceive when she needs to be relieved.

She must be aware that the mother's attempt to cope may range from tender bedside care to frantic, inappropriate hospital room activity, from exaggerated praise and gratitude for the efforts of doctors and nurses to harsh criticism and complaint, from tearful sentimentality to philosophical resignation.

Because it is so inherent in her psychology as a woman, the nurse is likely to be more emotionally involved in the loss of a child than of an adult patient and she may be upset when the mother's reaction differs from her own or from her expectation of what it should be. An appreciation by the nurse that such behavior on the part of the mother reflects her attempts to cope with her own distress will be helpful in guiding the nurse in her responses. The mother who cannot bear to leave her child's bedside as well as the mother who cannot bear to enter her child's room each may be greatly assisted by the opportunity to share her feelings and thoughts with the nurse who is seen both as another woman and as a professional caretaking person. The assignment of little tasks on the hospital floor can serve the function of letting the mother know she is doing something for her child and at the same time keep her close to her child without being overexposed to the child's suffering.[7]

The nurse frequently is called on to minister to those experiencing grief. A clear understanding of the processes in grief will prove helpful in enabling the nurse to extend herself professionally beyond her status as a humane person.

---

1. Paul Chodoff et al., "Stress, Defenses, and Copying Behavior: Observations in Parents of Children with Malignant Diseases," *American Journal of Psychol-* ogy, **120**, 1964, 743. S. B. Friedman et al., "Behavioral Observations on Parents Anticipating the Death of a Child," *Pediatrics*, **32**, 1963, 610. Erich Linde-

mann, "Symptomatology and Management of Acute Grief," *American Journal of Psychology*, **101**, 1944, 141. G. Wretmark, "A Study of Grief Reactions," *Acta Psychiatrica et Neurologica Scandinavica*, **34**, 1959, Suppl. 292.

2. G. L. Engel, *Psychological Development in Health and Disease*, Philadelphia: Saunders, 1962, Chap. 26. A. H. Schmale, Jr., "Relationship of Separation and Depression to Disease," *Psychosomatic Medicine*, **20**, 1958, 259.

3. W. A. Greene, Jr., "Role of a Vicarious Object in the Adaptation to *Loss*," *Psychosomatic Medicine*, **20**, 1958, 344.

4. Schmale, *loc. cit.*

5. L. M. Caplan and T. P. Hackett, "Emotional Effects of Lower-Limb Amputation in the Aged," *New England Journal of Medicine*, **269**, 1963, 1166.

6. Rene Spitz, "Analytic Depression," *Psychoanalytic Studies of Children*, **1**, 1945, 53.

7. Chodoff, *loc. cit.*; Friedman, *loc. cit.*

*Additional Readings*

J. Bowlby, "Grief and Mourning in Infancy and Early Childhood," *Psychoanalytic Studies of Children*, **15**, 1960, 9–52.

G. L. Engel, "Is Grief a Disease? A Challenge for Medical Research," *Psychosomatic Medicine*, **23**, 1961, 18–22.

Sigmund Freud, "Mourning and Melancholia," in his *Complete Works*, London: Hogarth, 1957, Vol. 14, p. 237.

Peter Marris, *Widows and Their Families*, London: Routledge and Kegan Paul, 1958.

Margaret Mead, "Nursing—Primitive and Civilized," *American Journal of Nursing*, **56**, 1956, 1001–1004.

H. R. Schaffer, "Objective Observations of Personality Development in Early Infancy," *British Journal of Medical Psychology*, **31**, 1958, 174–183.

# 29. SOCIOCULTURAL CONSIDERATIONS IN THE CARE OF PATIENTS

*Robert Straus*

Sociologists and other behavioral scientists working in the health setting are frequently asked for specific examples of observations or questions which represent the potential participation in considerations of medical care. The following observations emerged initially from a symposium shared by an internist, a psychiatrist, and a sociologist concerned with a comprehensive consideration of the hospital management of patients with myocardial infarction.

It is the writer's opinion that many considerations which might be labeled sociological are best applied to medical situations when viewed in the context of their interaction with physiological, biological, psychological, cultural, and environmental determinants of behavior.[1] For this reason and with the hope of stressing the importance of a generic conceptualization, we have intentionally avoided any attempt to distinguish those questions which might be described as peculiar to sociology.

The cardiologist describes myocardial infarction as a condition in which a portion of the heart muscle has been damaged or destroyed. Recovery from the disease requires an opportunity for the damaged area to heal. Often healing can only occur under conditions which make possible absolutely minimal demands on cardiac work. Such conditions are created in part through absolute bed rest and care aided through the use of certain drugs and sometimes by the use of oxygen.[2]

## THE PATIENT'S EMOTIONAL CONDITION

A relationship between the patient's organic and emotional condition has long been recognized.[3] In the presence of myocardial damage the individual's ability to withstand emotional stress is compromised. The relationship between organic damage and stress threshold can have serious implications in the management of myocardial infarction because emotional conditions such as anxiety can in turn have a marked impact on coronary circulation and can greatly increase the amount of cardiac work required to achieve given tasks.[4] Even the work of simple breathing at complete bed rest can involve much greater strain for the anxious patient than for the patient whose mind is at ease. In view of this sensitive relationship between the patient's emotional condition and his cardiac function, it is recognized that his very life may depend upon minimizing factors which produce fear, anxiety, or emotional strain. This is a difficult task at best for the sudden severe pain and other physical manifestations of myocardial infarction are themselves of a frightening nature. Furthermore, for the patient who may realize or suspect the

Reprinted by permission of the author and publisher, from the *Journal of Health and Human Behavior*, Vol. 1, 1960, pp. 119–122.

nature of his disease, knowledge of its grave implications can further increase and intensify a feeling of panic. Against this setting, let us consider some of our sociocultural responses and ask how they may contribute to the emotional-organic response.

## SOCIOCULTURAL RESPONSES TO THE PATIENT

Perhaps the most characteristic response when an individual appears to have suffered a heart attack is to call upon resources in the community geared to dealing with emergencies. The police, the fire department, an ambulance, or all three of these resources may be summoned. Invariably they will arrive with sirens ringing and frequently the manner of emergency personnel bubbles with crisis. Have we ever considered what this emergency response may actually do to the patient? For many who have grown up in our culture, may not the sound of a siren incite fear or excitement? For some, may not the ambulance seem to be a symbol of impending death, especially when as in many communities this vehicle doubles in brass as a funeral coach?

Although there will be many patients whose condition requires transportation which only an ambulance or other emergency vehicle can provide, may not there be many for whom the emotional impact of an emergency ride to the hospital will be more harmful than quiet transportation in a private automobile even though the latter might require some physical exertion?

On arrival at the hospital the patient with myocardial infarction, like all other patients, may be subjected to a new kind of trauma. He is stripped of all symbols of self-identification and finds himself in strange clothes, in a strange bed, in a strange room, faced with relating to a whole army of new and strange people. For some patients the imposition of a complete discontinuity with ordinary activities may be essential to effective therapy. For others, however, the anxiety of separation from familiar surroundings and props may well provoke a dangerous degree of anxiety.

The significance of a particular illness to a patient from a psychosocial point of view and the meaning which experiences resulting from an illness have for a patient are often determined by preexisting beliefs and concepts.

Depending upon his own beliefs and those of his family and friends, the patient may view his illness with undue optimism or equally unwarranted graveness. He may minimize the long-term implications or may be all too ready to accept a life of invalidism. He may have very definite notions about the usual course of disease, and become alarmed when his expectations are not fulfilled, or he may attach particular meaning to certain signs or symptoms and become unduly alarmed when they appear or perhaps when they fail to appear.

In our contemporary culture nearly every patient has been exposed to the various media of mass communication—the newspapers, magazines, radio, television, and to the propaganda of voluntary health organizations. He has been asked to look for certain warning signs which all of these media have stressed. Research is still needed to determine whether the "warning sign" approach to preventive medicine actually facilitates the detection of prodromal signs of disease or whether it may instead forestall detection by increasing anxiety or actually contribute to those illnesses which are complicated by emotional stress.

## PERSONNEL-PATIENT RELATIONS IN THE HOSPITAL

Within the hospital a patient's ability to avoid anxiety depends greatly upon his interpersonal relationships and channels of communication. If hospital personnel who are aware of the gravity of his illness convey this awareness by their voice, their manner, or their touch, may not their very presence invoke anxiety? Or perhaps the noise box so frequently used in hospitals to summon physicians and others in case of emergency, by its very suddenness or the pitch in tone of voice employed, may instill panic in the bedridden patient.

Most hospital patients will share a room with other patients. Much can be done if thought is given to the grouping of patients to minimize trauma or irritation or to maximize compatibility. One might ask whether patients with myocardial infarction should ever be allowed to share a room with other patients who have coronary disease. Is there not a risk that, should one patient experience crisis or death, the trauma of such a situation might invoke deep anxiety or even prove fatal to the other patient?

A recent study has shown that the average hospital patient may come in contact with as many as seventeen different hospital personnel in a single day.[5] These include not only the physician and several nurses, but also a variety of specialized ancillary personnel ranging from laboratory technicians to dietitians, food servers, those who keep records, distribute newspapers, and maintain cleanliness. The very presence of so many strangers in itself may impose a certain amount of emotional strain. In some hospitals where custom calls for moving patients from area to area or room to room in response to administrative requirements, the patient may be asked to relate to a completely new team of ten or seventeen faces with each move. In the management of mycardial infarction, it may well be advisable to consider the impact of this complex system of interpersonal relationships and to make some provisions for simplifying the network of personnel assigned to provide for the patient's needs. We mentioned earlier that anxiety may be increased when the patient is stripped of all symbols of self-identification. When this is the case, stress might be minimized by providing objects and people who signify security. The use of one's own pajamas, the presence of familiar objects of clothing, or a favorite knickknack and the knowledge that dear ones are nearby, can all be important in the planning for comprehensive patient care.

Many patients with myocardial infarction will be obsessed with a feeling of urgency for some task which they feel they must do. For a patient who feels that a letter must be written or a partner advised, may not the physical strain involved in conducting brief business activity involve perhaps less cardiac strain than the chronic worry which would persist should this need be unfulfilled?

Obviously the needs of patients will vary tremendously. For some, the onset of serious illness and resulting hospitalization may bring fulfillment of a long-time search for dependency. Since the initial treatment of myocardial infarction requires imposing a state of dependency upon the patient and maintaining restrictions over a long period of time, there is always danger that a syndrome of overdependency may result. Great sensitivity to the emotional needs of the individual patient will be required during convalescence as the therapist tries to maintain prudent restrictions on overdoing, while encouraging the patient to do what he can for himself.

## INTERPERSONAL RELATIONSHIP OF PHYSICIAN AND PATIENT

The interpersonal relationship between the physician and the patient is an important social situation. If patient care is to be comprehensive and geared to the needs of the individual patient, including his beliefs, values, and personality traits, special skills in communication are required. Every individual, as a result of his own experience, tends to develop certain deaf spots and blind spots which make it difficult for him to really hear or observe phenomena which may literally stare him in the face. It is especially important that physicians and other health personnel develop acuity for hearing and observing both the verbal and nonverbal communications of their patients. It is only recently that techniques have been developed for sharpening these skills, and more recently that importance has been attached to some of the more subtle aspects of communication in the training of health personnel.

We know too that the interpersonal relationship between the physician and the patient is often influenced by many characteristics of a socioeconomic nature. By and large physicians and patients alike feel more comfortable when they are relating to others from similar social strata who share values, beliefs, and attitudes. It has been demonstrated that when physicians have an opportunity to select patients, they will more frequently choose those from social strata similar to their own.[6] It has been found that patients too are more comfortable with physicians who they feel really know and understand their way of life. In order to achieve effective empathy with their patients, it is important that health personnel develop an understanding and a sympathy for differences in cultural, economic, social, and personality characteristics, and for their implications in human response to illness.

## OTHER SOCIOCULTURAL VARIABLES

There are other sociocultural variables which appear important in the hospital management of heart disease, as well as in the management of many other types of health problems. The establishment and enforcement of special diets requires an understanding of the patient's cultural orientation to food. This may be particularly important in the case of certain cultural groups such as the Italian or the Jewish which are sometimes characterized as food oriented because of the great emphasis which is placed upon quality and quantity of food. The importance of family members is another matter which can be highly significant. For example, it has been observed among families from Eastern Kentucky that when one member of the family is ill, the entire family will come to the physician's office or hospital. Provisions for keeping the family nearby or at least for allowing certain members to remain close at hand may have important therapeutic significance for the patient.

In this review of considerations significant to the care of patients with myocardial infarction, we have quite intentionally avoided any attempt to identify sharply those considerations which can be called psychological, sociological, or cultural. Instead, we have tried to pose questions concerning the possible interaction of these factors with physiological and other organic conditions on which the very life of the patient may hang in balance. It is our thesis that the identification and understanding of this interaction process can contribute to a better understanding of human behavior, and together with similar insights developing in the biological sciences and in the fields of clinical medicine, can contribute to a generic understanding of human response to illness and a more comprehensive and effective approach to the practice of medical care.

1. Robert Straus, "A Department of Behavioral Science," *Journal of Medical Education*, 34, 1959, 662–666; Samuel W. Bloom et al., "The Sociologist as a Medical Educator: A Discussion," *American Sociological Review*, 25, 1960, 95–101; Robert Straus, "The Comprehensive Approach to the Problems of Alcoholism," *Quarterly Journal of Studies on Alcohol*, 20, 1959, 669–672.

2. Paul Dudley White, *Heart Disease*, 4th ed., New York: Macmillan, 1951, Chap. 21.

3. E. A. Stead, Jr., J. V. Warren, A. J. Merill, and E. S. Brannon, "The Cardiac Output in Male Subjects as Measured by the Technique of Right Atrial Catheterization. Normal Values with Observations on the Effect of Anxiety and Tilting," *Journal of Clinical Investigation*, 24, 1945, 326–331; F. Mainzer and M. Krause, "The Influence of Fear on the Electrocardiogram," *British Heart Journal*, 2, 1940, 221–230; John B. Hickam, Walter H. Cargill, and Abner Golden, "Cardiovascular Reactions to Emotional Stimuli. Effect on the Cardiac Output, Arteriovenous Oxygen Difference, Arterial Pressure, and Peripheral Resistance," *Journal of Clinical Investigation*, 27, 1948, 290–298.

4. Herbert L. Blumgart, "The Relation of Effort to Attacks of Acute Myocardial Infarction," *Journal of the American Medical Association*, 128, 1945, 775–778; Paul Wood, "Da Costa's Syndrome (or Effort Syndrome)," *British Medical Journal*, 1, 1941, 767–772, 805–811, 845–851.

5. Howard L. Bost and Alan Ross, "Study Relating to the Planning of Progressive Care for Hospital Patients," unpublished, University of Kentucky Medical Center Planning Staff.

6. For example, Leslie Schaffer and Jerome K. Myers, "Psychotherapy and Social Stratification," *Psychiatry*, 17, 1954, 83–93.

# Epilogue to Part Six

After deciding that one is ill and placing oneself in the care of a physician, the decision regarding hospitalization is largely, if not entirely, the responsibility of the doctor. If he fails to communicate adequately with the patient, the latter may derive less benefit from the hospital facilities and the treatment prescribed. The lower-class patient, after deciding to seek help from a physician, is more inclined to place his fate in the doctor's hands. In most instances, either because of ignorance or social distance, he does not push the physician for information, but rather takes the attitude of "he knows what he is doing." To a large extent the patient's social class determines both the availability of care and the type of treatment.

A patient enters the hospital with certain expectations of what is to be done to and for him, and he is immediately confronted with a variety of new situations, events, and people. His feelings about treatment, his condition, and how he should behave become major determinants of the way he will in fact behave. The hospital staff also has certain expectations of its own role. Hospital functions are carried out through its own social structure; that is, every hospital or health agency develops its own division of labor and role relationships. While in the process of fulfilling its functions, the health organization develops its own attitudes, beliefs, and values which eventually become transformed into a kind of subculture. It decides on its goals and the division of labor necessary to achieve these goals. The division of labor places all positions within a formal hierarchy. In terms of hospital goals, some behavior of its constituents may be regulated by explicit policies, while other behavior may or may not be regulated, depending on the effect the behavior has on the hospital's functioning. Each role group within the hospital is expected to behave in a rational, unemotional, and efficient manner in order to carry out the goals of the organization.

The very features of the organization which produce efficiency on the part of the staff may produce problems for the patient. To receive the maximum hospital care, the patient suffers a change in status, removal from home life, reduction in external stimuli, and a potential loss of his self-identity. He must reorganize his life around the demands of the hospital. His waking and sleeping hours, his eating and toilet habits, and his needs and desires must be fitted into the hospital schedule.

The amount of stress and anxiety he experiences will depend on the way he perceives a threatening situation. The manner in which the staff orients him also influences his feelings about his treatment and behavior. During the course of his illness, he needs help in learning to adjust to his immediate situation and to the future implications of his illness.

The degree of the patient's stress and anxiety also depends on the kind and amount of information communicated to him. If a health worker fails to give the patient a diagnosis, his disappointment at this often makes him willing to accept

294

any diagnosis from any source. Family and friends may unwittingly or knowingly attach a diagnosis to his illness which may be completely erroneous, but he may well experience even more anxiety or pain from the misunderstanding. Therefore it is imperative that the staff communicate not only with the patient but also with his family and friends to make sure he receives accurate information which will enable him to participate fully in his care and treatment.

While playing the role of patient, an individual's concerns revolve largely around his immediate experiences. Because the staff members are concerned to a great extent with efficiency and rewards for their own performance, they sometimes make "nonpersons" out of their charges by ignoring the individual's psychosocial aspects.

The staff has its own norms for proper behavior of both patient and family, but for many patients hospitalization is a new experience into which they and their families must be socialized. This process includes not only the question, "How should I act as a patient?" or ". . . as a relative of the patient?" but also "How do I grieve?" Because they do not know how to behave, visitors often unwittingly increase the problems of the patient and staff.

Patients also have a concern regarding time that does not always coincide with that of the staff members who are concerned with the well-being of so many patients that their emphasis is on the present, "today." Although the patient also is concerned with the present, the future implications of his illness are of crucial importance to him. The hospitalized patient needs to restructure time, since old cues for telling time are absent and must be replaced by new ones. The periods between breakfast and lunch and lunch and dinner, which may be passing rapidly for the staff member who is experiencing many kinds of external stimuli, can seem endless to a patient. The length of time between the doctor's visits may conjure up fantasies regarding the meaning of this lapse. "I'm not doing very well; that's why he doesn't come very often." In many situations the physician could prevent hours of anguish if he would give the patient one undivided minute. A simple statement such as "You're progressing well," or "I'm sorry I can't spend more time with you, but I want you to know that you will be fine in a few days," when true, can often do much to allay the patient's fears and feelings of isolation.

If illness is prolonged, the patient gradually becomes more selective regarding from whom he seeks information and accepts treatment. The longer his illness, the more informed he becomes regarding who will give him accurate information and who will perform certain functions for him. He may even develop a strategy for securing information and assistance. He also learns the connotations placed by others upon his illness or the parts of his body that are affected. Unacceptable illnesses such as leprosy or disfigurement will increase his anxiety and produce a sense of stigma. Portions of the body such as breasts, genitals, face, arms, and hands may, under certain circumstances, create psychological and sociological problems for the patient, family, friends, and staff. Many barriers to interaction are related to such stigmatic anomalies. Under certain conditions, such as war, injuries initially may be associated with heroism, but as time passes the heroic aspect fades and isolation increases. Disfiguring or debilitating diseases and injuries, including such things as blindness and deafness, may lead to pity which in turn hampers rehabilitation.

All patients are concerned with discovering ways and means of gaging their progress. In mental hospitals being assigned to an open or closed ward, having privileges such as passes and being allowed to keep personal objects — rings, razors, and matches — give a patient clues to his progress. For the physically ill, some of the cues consist of the reduction in medication, amount of time out of bed, kind of ward assigned, amount and type of food given, and the attitude of the staff.

If the prognosis of the patient is uncertain or poor, new problems are added. The dying patient and his family often must deal with uncertainty, isolation, and physical and/or psychological pain. Many staff members react to the patient on the basis of the diagnosis and prognosis expressed by the physician. Although the ideology of health professionals dictates that they must help the patient to help himself, in practice they and others often isolate the terminally ill patient. This may be due in part to the fact that in our culture dying may be viewed as an unpleasant or unacceptable process. In addition, for those dedicated to sustaining life, the death of a patient may signify failure and evoke guilt feelings. Though the patient is expected to participate in his care, the terminally ill often are deprived of the right to decide their fate. In fact, in many cases their fate is never explicitly stated to them. As a result it is impossible for them to enter into one of the major decisions regarding their life, or eventually to die in dignity.

How can health professionals most effectively expedite a patient's recovery? As we pointed out earlier, one of the most important aspects of care is the acceptance of the individual as a whole person. This requires that the staff be aware of the sociopsychological conditions impinging on the patient and his family. It also requires that the staff be aware of, and accept as valid, a variety of cultural modes of life. Having acknowledged that in fact these differences do exist, the staff must be willing to accept the patient as he is without critical evaluations and ethnocentric value connotations. Time must be taken from the busy schedule of procedural activities to inform patients adequately and accurately and to ascertain how he and his family receive this information. For no matter how staff members may see their own position, they are in effect employed by the patient; therefore they have an obligation to keep the patient and his family informed of the potential consequences of his illness and also to be actively concerned in the ultimate outcome of illness.

## PART SEVEN

# The New Venture: Toward Solutions

The new experiential-living social movement mentioned earlier, of which the problem-solving process is a part, has had a tremendous impact on the roles and functions of health professionals. It also has given impetus to research and publication as a method of resolving problems in the health field. A number of professional schools have incorporated problem-solving techniques and research methods in their basic curriculum. Although these processes are similar, they also have some basic differences in terms of the questions asked and the potential application to practical problems.

All health workers face many problems, some extremely complex, others relatively simple. Frequently the problem posed is new and requires a different approach from any previously encountered. The problem-solving approach provides a means by which the practitioner can cope with new, immediate questions.

Problem solving is primarily a cognitive process through which one gains insight into a given problem and its possible solutions. The process may be relatively simple or complex, with few steps or many, depending on the problem. The organization of the steps shows the way to the solution of the problem. As Mills and Dean point out, there are four major steps in the process: identification of the problem, collection and analysis of data, decision, and evaluation of the decision.

The effectiveness of the problem-solving approach depends on the basic assumption that a problem exists and that appropriate data are available to enable one to reach a decision. After the problem has been identified, several possible solutions are advanced, and one or more are eliminated through reasoning. The final, potential solution then is tried. If it appears to solve the problem by either lessening or eliminating it, the solution has passed the pragmatic test of validity: it works.

The research method differs from problem solving even though all research is intended to solve some kind of problem. The contrary is not true; that is, the problem-solving process does not always involve research. The *primary* purpose of research is not to solve a problem but to make a contribution to general knowledge. It is not concerned with a single situation or any specific problem, but rather with broad underlying problems, recurrent phenomena, and wide application through generalization. Ordinarily research is concerned with three major areas: (1) description, (2) prediction and control, and (3) explanation. It is concerned with defining and outlining the properties of phenomena, with forecasting future occurrences so they may be predicted and controlled, and with describing the relationship of phenomena by explaining how and why certain

events occurred or could have occurred. In this process research also generates
more problems to be explored.

Research is more rigorous, reliable, and discriminatory in its choice of problems
and its techniques for solution than is problem solving. As stated by Goode and
Scates,

> . . . If he questions his explanations, the stage is set for research. If he goes further
> and challenges the methods by which he arrives at his conclusions; if he critically
> and systematically repeats his observations; if he tests the reliability and validity of
> these tools and evaluates his data in other ways; if he scrutinizes the thought processes
> by which he passes from one step of his logic to another; if he gradually refines his
> concept of what he is trying to explain and considers anew the necessary and sufficient
> conditions for proof; if at every step he proceeds with the utmost caution, realizing
> that his purpose is not to arrive at an answer which is personally pleasing, but rather
> one which will stand up under the critical attacks of those who doubt his answer — if
> he can meet these criteria and steadfastly hold to his purpose, then he is doing
> research.[1]

Research always begins with existing theory and ends in its acceptance or
modification or in the development of a new theory. As Folta and Schatzman
point out in their article on research programs, a distinction must be made between theory and fact. "A theory is not a set of facts; rather it is a body of
logically interrelated propositions that assert relations among the properties of
the phenomena under study." Basic research leaves the application of theory to
the problem solver, but Wald and Leonard give an example of how the empirical
approach of developing theories through the systematic study of nursing experience can be expedited.

Every researcher utilizes some model or general conception of the realm in
which he is working. Models are mental pictures of how things are put together
and how they operate. Models and theories are not always the same: a model is
a much broader image of the outline of major phenomena. Models are useful or
not useful, while theories, which are more limited and precise, can be accepted
or proved wrong. Models determine the general realm from which one can choose
theories and variables and thereby limit the world of phenomena. For example,
if one uses the model of organisms causing disease, then several theories regarding which specific organism causes or is related to a specific disease may be
developed. A model, however, does not explain disease entities that are not caused
by organisms. In fact, the exclusive use of this kind of model would blind the
health worker to the possibilities of psychosocial causation.

The researcher is primarily a designer or creator. Frequently he may design
a study which he himself in fact will never carry out. As Stouffer points out, the
time and effort spent in choosing and developing a research design is one of the
most crucial aspects of all research endeavors. The design chosen aids the con-
ductor of research in a decision of techniques of data collection and the kinds of
generalizations that are possible.

There are many techniques for data collection and analysis. It is vital that the
researcher choose these techniques to fit his problem, rather than choosing the
problem to fit the technique. According to Anderson and King, although the
techniques of analysis such as the computer offer new horizons for time-saving

techniques of analysis, their use also creates other problems. The use of computers is a tremendous asset not only to the researcher but also to the problem solver who without the computer would need the assistance of a wide variety of resources and people. Computer programs currently are being used not only for research but also for performing many clerical functions that formerly were the lot of health workers. In addition, at the present time some one hundred separate campuses throughout the United States are interlinked by direct computer systems which will vastly alter the availability of knowledge and information.[2] Computer language has been so designed and perfected that it will be possible for any student on any of the campuses to have immediate access to all materials from the National Library of Medicine, the Medical Literature Analysis and Retrieval System, the Index Medicus, and to materials that are available only on another campus. The potential for such computerized programs does indeed defy the imagination.

1. C. U. Goode and D. E. Scates, *Methods of Research*, New York: Appleton-Century-Crofts, 1954, p. 11.
2. *EDUCOM*, Bulletin of the Inter-University Communications Council, 1, January 1966, 8–10.

# 30. INTRODUCTION TO PROBLEM SOLVING

*Lester C. Mills and Peter M. Dean*

Man has been solving problems since time immemorial, but until recently there has been little conscious effort to teach the process. For the third of a century since the educational method called problem solving was introduced, there has been a steady increase in its use. This has been a slow development, however, possibly because teachers themselves seldom have been taught by this method, especially in their advanced subject-matter courses. At any rate teachers have characteristically given lip service to the value of problem-solving methods, but have been strangely reluctant to employ them.

Evidence has been presented by Anne Roe[1] that the scientist develops from the boy who "found that there was a way in which he, personally, could find things out for himself, and that these could be things which mattered to him. . . . " This process is sometimes designated as *problem solving*, although a variety of other terms and descriptive phrases have been used in the literature of science education. Roe[2] also states that it is not easy to design teaching so that individual thinking is encouraged.

The need for more high-quality scientists is constantly stressed in the press—scientists "who are able to solve problems." Authors of professional texts and various yearbooks concerned with science teaching generally include as a major objective the development of the ability to solve problems. Various science textbooks include chapters or portions of chapters dealing with analyses of scientific methods. The National Science Teachers Association devoted its 1956 national convention to this theme. It is often implied that the student will, as the result of his experience in science education, behave in a "scientific" manner. The usual meaning attached to "scientific" is that the student will be alert to problems, be skillful in making observations and collecting facts, be objective, and be unwilling to jump to conclusions. Problem solving, as the term is used in this [paper], includes these meanings as well as others.

Studies in the psychology of learning seem to support the efficacy of problem solving as a methodology in science education. When a student is learning by solving problems, he is personally involved and he has a definite purpose for his studies. From a long-term view, facts and concepts involved in problem-solving experiences will be remembered and used, for they were encountered in the first place because the student needed to learn them in order to use them.

Excerpted by permission of the publisher, from *Problem-Solving Methods in Science Teaching*, New York: Bureau of Publications, Teachers College, Columbia University, 1960, pp. 1–11, 13.

# WHAT IS PROBLEM SOLVING?

## Problem Solving as a Way of Thinking

Problem solving, as treated in this [paper] is both a way of thinking and a method of teaching. But it is only one of many ways of thinking, and only one of many methods of teaching. As a way of thinking, the process has been investigated by various psychologists and analyzed in their reports. Essentially this type of thinking occurs only *when there is a need for it, when the situation is baffling or unsatisfying, or when the situation presents a difficulty that cannot be met by other means.* Notice that the problem motivates the thinker; the individual must be oriented toward an objective and motivated to attain it. Also a problem may be defined as *a question involving doubt.* Not every problem will initiate the same kind of thinking, and the more difficult problems will not involve the same steps in each case. But, in general, the steps are as follows:

1. A difficulty is recognized.
2. The problem is clarified and defined.
3. A search for clues is made.
4. Various suggestions are made, and are evaluated or tried out.
5. A suggested solution is accepted, or the thinker gives up in defeat.

Perhaps the professional scientist does not consciously go through a series of steps as he conducts his research, although he generally proceeds in logical and reasoned sequences. The scientist has a way of looking at his endeavor that goes beyond the formal steps of scientific methods. He is alert for the unexpected happening, and is able to gain insights while not necessarily following formal methods. There is a greater need for the teacher to be aware of the steps in formal analysis of the work of scientists than for the student to memorize them.

## The Nature of Problems Involving Science

In a sense science creates its problems. Any time the teacher puts together what is known in any area of science, the requirement for the extension of knowledge becomes apparent. The problem is not merely a topic, nor is it merely a question. A genuine problem for a student exists when something, no matter how slight or commonplace in character, puzzles or perplexes him; when something appears to him as unexpected, strange, or disconcerting. It may be "practical" or not. There must seem to be several alternative answers to the problem, and the student must desire to find the best solution.

## Required Conditions for Problem Solving

In the use of problem solving as a method of teaching we must have three conditions:

1. The problem to be solved is adapted to the students' maturity and experience.
2. The students have had analogous previous experience and must possess related information needed for the solution, or they must know how to proceed to get this information.
3. The students are interested in solving the problem.

The individual student is frequently satisfied with a "solution" to a problem if there is merely a reduction of the initial difficulty. This "solution," however, may be of low quality. It may not be the only possible solution, or even the most satisfactory solution. The student should be encouraged to consider all possible solutions in the same manner in which a group of hypotheses would be evaluated.

The quality of a solution depends upon more than just meeting the initial challenge. For instance, the solution should be internally consistent, should promote useful actions or attitudes, and should be acceptable for a reasonable length of time. A solution accepted only verbally as a sort of stopgap measure — such as the rote understandings which are often forgotten before the student leaves the classroom — is of low quality. Solutions involving actions which are readily applied are more successful than solutions which later call forth the comment, "If only we had . . . !" Since scientific problems are generally complex and involve many factors, the effect of high-quality solutions should be to improve our understanding of other aspects of science.

One of the purposes of the science teacher is to help students to develop their problem-solving abilities. Other important objectives include the acquisition of knowledge, accurate concept formation, the understanding of theories and principles, and the development of skills. *The ability to use a problem-solving approach is associated with progress toward achievement of all of these objectives.*

## SCOPE AND CONTENT OF PROBLEM-SOLVING METHODS

Whenever the concerns of students can be identified, problem solving can take place. Recognition of a problem is itself a step in education. *There are, as a matter of fact, a great many potential problem situations in which the problem is never recognized.* One of the concerns of education is to help students develop the ability to locate and define these problems. Students must be guided in determining which problems must or should be dealt with first, and in learning which methods of dealing with problems are most likely to succeed.

### Differentiation by Student Ability

The selection of problems that may be dealt with effectively must depend in considerable measure upon the abilities and previous training of the students. When selection is limited by the short attention span of the young child and his inexperience with resource materials, as in the case of elementary-school pupils, the problems must be simple and easily solved. Success at this level encourages further problem solving. Construction problems solved by careful observation and manual skills have been suggested even for the kindergarten level. As the child becomes more mature and has some facts to reason with, he should be encouraged to use them. Perhaps his best use will be to arrange and rearrange his store of facts into systems which will be needed. Reading experiences occupy a greater part of the education of the child in the intermediate grades. These experiences are drawn into use in problem solving as they develop. The teacher should take advantage of the growth of this ability, as well as of any other special ability the pupil may exhibit.

At every age the child learns to criticize his ideas according to his capabilities. It is not readily apparent to the young learner which ideas and processes possess usefulness for the purpose to be served, or when to relinquish a line of thought or action as hopeless; this doubt is encountered so often that it must be recognized as an integral part of the problem-solving situation. The young child, for instance, abandons plans and materials after trying them in construction. He must be free to remake his construction after he is aided to recognize and express his reasons for wanting to make changes. Thus he becomes directly conscious of being self-critical and of having given up an untenable position.

The student in more advanced courses needs to be able to handle the tools of science in order to test his conclusions. Since some of these tools are costly, dangerous, or unavailable to the student, a certain amount of preliminary self-criticism (fostered and directed by the teacher) is required to avoid attempting a problem beyond the skill of the individual.

The conclusion of a construction task or of an experiment is not the end of the problem-solving situation. The pupil or student ought to develop the practice of reviewing the whole process. Too frequently the finished castle is crushed, the block tower toppled, or the device destroyed before any thought is given to the relative success of the effort. Let the young person step back to see what he has made, and lead him to evaluate his handicraft against what he started out to do. Similarly, the high-school student ought to review problem-solving steps to make sure he has not fallen into error along the way. If possible, he should test his conclusions by actual experience or by comparison with the results of competent authorities. Certainly the tendency to claim that a single example or demonstration has *proved* a conclusion is to be discouraged.

## Relationship to Other Methods

Problem solving is only one way of learning and teaching, and must be related to other methods in actual practice. Different classroom techniques such as lecturing, discussing, demonstrating, and assigning reading and written exercises remain desirable to develop various understandings and skills with which the teacher is concerned. Indeed, discussion may even be necessary in some instances, as the most practical approach to the solution of subproblems. If a group of students discover they need more information about vacuum tubes to complete a project concerned with radios, the whole class may become sufficiently interested to justify a teacher-directed discussion and demonstration. And as part of every teaching situation there is also the need to ask questions and to test programs.

## Practical and Intellectual Problems

Problems of any individual may be divided arbitrarily into the *practical*, in which there is an immediate need to act, and the *intellectual*, in which there is a need to understand or satisfy a curiosity. Among the former are exercises commonly assigned by the teacher such as "Dissect the earthworm to expose its alimentary canal," or "Arrange these two lights and meters so as to measure the resistance of each lamp." The usual written or laboratory test given in school may also be considered of this type. For some students these assignments will not be problems — they will know how to proceed; for others there will be puzzles which may or may not be resolved successfully. In general the solution of the practical problem involves some action associated with learning.

Problems on the intellectual level range from questions easily answered by the teacher to those still unsolved by scientists or society. The young student certainly progresses by exploring his capabilities and investigating his environment. The teacher must be careful to sort through the problems offered by and to the student for those which are within the student's capabilities. Also worthy of consideration, however, are some problems that are "beyond" the student in the sense that the solutions are not yet known. The student may be the one who eventually will find the solution. In any event *an awareness of unsolved problems and the opportunity to reflect upon them is a part of education in problem solving*. It is expected that a change in student behavior or attitude will result from this experience.

## PROBLEM SOLVING IN SCIENCE EDUCATION

### General Limitations

The science teacher operates within limitations imposed by the classroom situation. He is usually restricted to certain subject areas and is expected to help students develop understandings within these areas. In the classroom many concerns about the affairs of everyday life will certainly manifest themselves, some of which the teacher may not wish to consider; for example, questions involving pupil-pupil relationships. However, a selected group of these concerns may profitably be dealt with in, perhaps, a biology course. Since our thoughts and problems are not compartmentalized in terms of bi-

ology, chemistry, or physics, a more valuable learning experience will occur when the resources of many or all of the areas can be drawn upon. This, however, is not always possible within the existing learning situation.

### Individual Differences

The fact that problems are *truly problems* to some but not to all members of a class at any one time leads to certain difficulties. It is at this point that the teacher is encouraged to put into practice what is known about individual differences. Ideally the problem-solving situation permits the teacher to separate the scientifically gifted from less interested students. Some problems of the casual student have already been solved by the gifted, who in turn have progressed to more advanced problems. But problem solving is appropriate for both groups of students, although the complexity of the problems they deal with may differ.

### The Importance of Critical Thinking

Although a part of science education may include analyzing the work of scientists and relating it to various scientific methods, knowledge of the names of the steps involved will not necessarily provide training in scientific thinking. Similarly, learning scientific information and principles, which are repeated on request, will not necessarily train scientists. *Of more importance is the development of a sound approach to critical thinking and a knowledge of how to proceed in arriving at conclusions that are defensible.*

## ANALYSIS OF THE PROCESS

As discussed in this [paper], the problem-solving process may be summarized as follows:

1. A problem is a difficulty or perplexity which is recognized by the individual as one he desires to resolve. Problems that the students are asked to solve must be acceptable to them as their own problems; otherwise the process is not problem solving as here defined.

2. A problem exists when straight-line action is no longer possible. The student must pause and choose between alternatives. If no alternatives appear to be available, he must seek alternatives and choose from among them. The alternatives, however, must be apparent to the problem solver before he can proceed. A teacher might find the solution to a particular problem very obvious, but if the student does not recognize the correct alternative, then as far as he is concerned, it might just as well not exist.

3. A preliminary state of doubt is a definitive characterstic of the problem situation. Obviously a student who feels sure he "knows the answer" to a problem is not going to recognize the problem. On the other hand, such an individual can be involved in a problem if he is shown that his "answer" is not satisfactory.

4. When guiding students in problem solving it is necessary to consider interests and preferences as well as abilities. A teacher might have some difficulty, for instance, in interesting a boy in a problem having to do with cooking.

5. Manipulative aids intended to facilitate the solution of a problem may introduce complications. If a student who wants to see how his voice looks on an oscilloscope is unable to operate the machine, he is faced with a problem. The teacher may be able to utilize this situation to help a student learn a skill which the student was not interested in learning originally, but which became necessary to accomplish his primary purpose.

6. Of fundamental importance is personal discovery by the learner. The joy of discovery may be as real for the student as it was for the scientist who made the original discovery.

7. Success in dealing with a few problems will increase an individual's confidence as he undertakes others; "nothing succeeds like success."

8. The "climate," "atmosphere," or "environment" in which the problem solving goes on is important. This has to do with the motivation of the problem solver as well as the physical setting. If the individual feels that problem solving is "the thing to do," he will be much more likely to attempt it. The nature of the "atmosphere" depends not only on the teacher, but also the rest of the class and the school.

9. Problem-solving processes may be improved through training in accurate observation and in becoming aware of one's biases. Certain of the skills necessary for problem solving can be taught directly, but it is usually necessary to make very specific to the student the relationship between the particular skill and the whole process.

10. Too great complexity may lead to escapist activities such as daydreaming, trouble making, and quasi-solutions. It is essential that the problems selected should be within the capabilities of the students. On the other hand, problems that are too easy are also unlikely to maintain student interest.

11. The ability to work with abstract problems varies from learner to learner. Some children play chess well when they are eight or nine; others never master the abstractions of attack and defense. Some students may be able to solve problems involving theoretical

nuclear physics; others must work with concrete materials. Similarly, some students will be able to solve problems that call for subtle distinctions; other students may never learn to recognize minor differences.

---

1. Anne Roe, *The Making of a Scientist*, New York: Dodd, Mead, 1953, p. 237.

2. *Ibid.*, p. 239.

# 31. EDUCATION IN RESEARCH FOR NURSES

## Jeannette R. Folta and Leonard Schatzman

The academic marketplace has become increasingly like a competitive arena, with academicians being pressured to compete for professional status by means of publication. College and university administrators vie with each other for "top people" in the various fields, persons who are well known, if not preeminent, through their accomplishments in research and/or publication. Evaluations of professional competence, decisions on salary and promotion, and academic survival itself depend progressively more on publication and less on teaching ability or on abilities in the clinical application of knowledge. As with other professions, so too with nursing. This phenomenon has become conditional to the attainment of professional recognition and status. Of course, this trend would pose no problem if the nursing profession were content to hold an exclusively clinical position in the world of health work or if, by some quirk, it was somehow exempt from the research and publications race. Such is not the case, however. The nursing profession has joined the research movement and has sought no special privileges from academic institutions.

## OBSTACLES TO RESEARCH ORIENTATION

If what we are saying is correct, then problems are posed for nursing regarding the preparation and training of students to meet the requirements of scientific research-oriented careers. Compared to social work, and certainly to clinical psychology, nursing has focused less upon basic research and more upon clinical practice. But for a very few training centers, there is very little research orientation in nursing. Undoubtedly part of the problem is that nursing has failed to attract significant numbers of research-oriented persons—a phenomenon probably characteristic of all the health professions, but particularly of nursing. Even when basic research is or becomes an interest, it is usually of a secondary nature. The question then is: how well prepared is nursing to move along at a relatively rapid pace toward its proper place in the world of science, research, and publication?

Research funds are becoming increasingly available to nursing, and nursing journals are growing in size and number, providing the means, models, and media for research expression. In this sense the stage is set. But the pace is relatively slow and will not quicken until a number of obstacles are overcome. One such obstacle is that nursing, including its faculties, is relatively unprepared to conduct research and to instruct others in research technology. For years the discipline has been tied not only to clinical practice, but to educational practices as well.

Reprinted by permission of the authors and McGraw-Hill Book Company, publishers, from the *Journal of Nursing Education*, Vol. 4, 1965, pp. 29–35.

Nurses as teachers seem to have shifted their concern from patients to students, "regarding" one as they would the other. Thus the nursing instructor's energy is absorbed into teaching, supervision, and curriculum development. Much of this is due to the traditional tie between nursing and departments of schools of education—a tie which has done relatively little toward developing research-mindedness. It has, we believe, reinforced the clinical bias rather than enhanced the broader scientific perspective. When research is taught and attempted, it is focused largely upon problems in teaching-learning and problems in comparative clinical studies, and in both cases highly stylized techniques are utilized. As a result many of the best-educated nurses view research, even scientific thinking itself, as a highly organized set of procedures and processes different from clinical practice and content but still relatively fixed and routine. In the meantime, and for these reasons, much of the research on nursing and the training of nurses in research is being conducted by social scientists and psychologists, usually from outside of schools of nursing. This is a growing development and provides one way of ultimately producing a core of nurses who will be able to carry on with the work of developing a research orientation within the profession. Yet unless the research is carefully designed in terms of the special background needs of nurses, the results are not likely to meet the accepted standards of research competence or the needs of the nursing profession.

Many nurses in the higher levels of education are taking or have taken courses in research methodology. This might appear to be the desirable way to achieve sophistication in research, except that the average course, however rich it might be in technical procedure, rarely deals adequately with the logic underlying the operations taught. Under these conditions, independent research is rarely attempted, simply because the researcher does not quite know what he is doing. Unless the data fit a classroom model precisely, action is either blocked or directed toward a search for data that will fit the model. At best, research becomes a series of routine impersonal techniques without much creativity, adventure, or discovery. At worst, the "course work" approach produces boredom and disenchantment with research.

## AVENUES TO RESEARCH IN NURSING

Other avenues are open to nurses in search of an education in research. One of these is the route leading to the doctorate, most usually in the social sciences. This route requires considerable energy, fortitude, and a major reorientation in ways of living and thinking. It is a time-consuming program, not only because of its essential nature, but also because many nurses require additional courses, either as formal prerequisites or because they lack sufficient background. In addition, nurses are not always welcome into such a program. For these and other reasons, the doctorate is attractive mainly to nurses who are relatively young, bright, and highly motivated, and probably somewhat rebellious or disappointed with their lot. The profession must, of course, expect that some of these nurses will not return to nursing, or even to any of the health disciplines.

Still others see possibilities of learning research through on-the-job apprenticeship. This method seems to be unsatisfactory simply because the directors of the various research projects are not likely to offer the nurse a true colleagueship or undertake to educate her. They are much more likely to use her as a data gatherer or data processor. Even under the best of circumstances, the nurse will rarely witness, much less help with, research design, analysis, and writing. Nor does a mere briefing on these procedures constitute an education in research. Consequently a research career via this route may well prove illusory as well as inconclusive and unsatisfactory. Despite the shortcomings in the apprenticeship mode of acquiring research skills, nurses will doubtless continue to use it. It may be all that is available, or given limitations of time and money, all that nurses can afford. We believe, however, that there is another way, one which is feasible and realistic in terms of the needs of both nursing and the health professions generally. This other way is a special program for interested and capable nurses to acquire research skills, a program which can be instituted in most larger schools of nursing. It would be a special program suited to the probable or assumed intellectual strengths and weaknesses of nurses generally. We propose a two- (preferably three-) year program designed as an education in science and research. Our emphasis here is on a "program" instead of on "courses," and on an "education" instead of on "training." The program would capitalize upon skills already acquired by the student in conjunction with her clinical area of specialization. Students would be selected according to capability, imagination, and motivation,

and would be taught and guided on a tutorial level.

## A RESEARCH PROGRAM

At the first stage, the program would include readings, seminars, and didactic instruction in the logic and philosophies of science. There are several philosophical positions, each of which has a kind of world view which implicitly, at least, indicates a way of observing and understanding the world of things, people, and events. The things one looks at, how these are to be examined, and thoughts about them have bearing upon the logic of these operations. The research educator owes it to his students to help them become familiar with these philosophical positions and the operations that logically follow, so that research techniques ultimately learned are related to the systems that produce them in the first place. This ability requires an exposure to a broad historical view of scientific activity in order to relate the various philosophies and the logic of science to the empirical world in which science is practiced. This exposure is necessary in order to avoid viewing philosophies and logical systems as entities unrelated to history. Typically the "methods" course approach assumes implicitly or makes barely explicit the broader logic or rationale for specific techniques being taught, since the major focus is upon mastery of a technology. Research as it is generally now taught in schools of nursing does not involve any discussion of the history of science or the logic of its many techniques. We shall not concern ourselves here with the amount of time necessary for this stage of the program. Whatever period of time seems necessary—

a month or more of full-time work, perhaps—there should be a constant reiteration of the logical basis for all subsequent research operations in connection with the program. In other words, the attention to scientific logic and the philosophy of science is not a course in the program; rather it is a continuing concern of the teacher so that it may eventually be a continuing concern of the student.

Unless the student works from a conceptual structure which is related to a body of knowledge, good scientific work cannot be done. Research should begin with existing theory and result either in its modification or in the development of new theory, for the goal of science is the building of theory. A theory is not a set of facts; rather it is a body of logically interrelated propositions that assert relations among the properties of the phenomena under study. By all means the student must understand that learning theory is distinct from learning fact, for students tend to equate fact with theory. Furthermore, far from simply using theory to examine events, the learner (and researcher) must constantly subject a theory to examination in the light of the events being examined. Clinicians frequently fail to examine or test a theory, but rather concern themselves solely with its application. Implicit here, and as a necessary condition to scientific research, is the development of a critical attitude. For, in fact, the quintessence of the research attitude is a willingness and the ability to modify existing theory or to develop new theory. This is quite different from a concern with the application of theory.

One of the characteristics of scientific work is the art of discovery, the ability to discover. It is necessary to be trained in readiness to perceive new phenomena for this ability to develop. To a certain extent, training and experience will enable a researcher to become aware of the discovery process. Such training will not produce genius, of course, but at least it will assure that the fledgling researcher will be better prepared to think and see creatively.

Education in research must include an abstract content so that the student might become familiar not only with the facts of the field but also with the major scientific problems contained therein. The techniques ultimately learned will be relevant not only to a content but to scientific research problems. Nursing education currently does not clearly distinguish between clinical and basic research, and it tends to lead the learner to a misapprehension of the meaning of research. "Problem solving" is not synonymous with scientific research. Clinical problems are concerned mainly with three modes of approach to any given phenomenon: (1) what needs to be done, (2) what is the best of several alternative actions, and (3) how best to implement the action chosen. These approaches are related to a peculiarity in American educational philosophy, which converts most phenomena into problems requiring solution. This calls for "research" on these solutions and for evaluating and testing. Hence there arises an illusion that the person involved in this kind of work is in fact a scientist.

Having dealt with the logic of scientific method, with ways of handling theory, and with the character of scientific problems, the student must be introduced to the concept of design in research. The stock and trade of the researcher is his ability to design research whether or not he himself collects the data. Starting with a theoretical background which makes specific problems meaningful, the design is a way of identifying as well as of examining issues or questions that beset the researcher. Research design is a process which concerns itself with identifying a basic problem in any given area, with identifying the kind of problem that is researchable, with devising techniques that will shed light on this problem, and with determining when and how these techniques are to be applied at different stages in the development of the research.

Training in technology itself then comes into view. There are many different techniques, each of which is suitable to a specific range of problems. It is unfair to present to students one or more sets of techniques as suitable for any kind of problem, or to let them assume that phenomena not susceptible to these techniques do not pose problems. Education in techniques must flow logically from an education in problem formulation. The research problem should determine the technique, not vice versa. In most research courses, the student typically learns a technique and then tries to find a problem to fit it in order to test the validity of the technique or to prove that he can use it. Doubtless, once a person becomes proficient in a set of techniques, he will characteristically select and deal with things in terms of these techniques. This approach is legitimate, provided the person is sufficiently sophisticated in research to recognize the nature of the selection.

The student must also be prepared to analyze data in order to develop theory. While it may be far too much to expect a student to create theory out of whole cloth, it is not too much to expect a student, in the course of his investigations and analysis, to create concepts out of research experience and data. This may be difficult, even for the best of us, yet can we prepare for a research career with anything less in mind? One new concept can support an existing theory or give it a jolt; two or three new concepts neatly related have the makings of a conceptual structure. Techniques learned are simply tools for such purposes, not ends to be used as demonstrations of personal competence. Research design, patiently taught, yields conditions for concept development. Later, with the data sorted and tentatively examined, we have still other conditions for discovery. When additional data are received, we have opportunity again to examine them, not only in the light of the designed operation—which may yield new concepts— but also in the light of whatever additional perspective and operation becomes available to the intelligent mind. Reality is infinitely complex; therefore the data must be seen by the student as holding potentially much more than was prepared or bargained for. Through such a program, the creative mind may be liberated. We hasten to add that a research training program must provide conditions in which the student can be comfortable with some error, ignorance, and confusion, and at times be able to express freely even the most outlandish ideas. Clearly, the education cannot be simply the mastery of specific technical processes; it must also provide training in thinking processes.

## WRITING FOR PUBLICATION

Finally, there is the matter of writing for publication. Research that is uncommunicated is of little value. As a researcher, one makes an implicit bargain to organize observations and to write them in some publicly acceptable form. Nurses do little writing for publication, and not necessarily because they have little to communicate to some special public. Rather, we suspect, they are lacking in the mechanics and art of writing; thus they regard it as a disagreeable chore. A research training program, therefore, ought to provide some instruction in this aspect of a research career. Such instruction need not be focused upon grammar, but upon the orderly development of ideas relevant to the interest of specific audiences. The student then may be able to not only fulfill one of the requirements of scientific work but at the same time to provide an interested reading public with his findings. We are not certain exactly how this aspect of training can best be accomplished. We are, however, certain that a student must be provided time, encouragement, feedback, and any other condition which is demonstrably conducive to productive written expression.

## CONCLUSION

We have deliberately expressed our views concerning a research training program in relatively abstract terms; consequently we have left implicit many of the specifics of the training we propose, including the acquisition of techniques necessary for careers in research. The program we recommend is built largely around field work techniques, including participant observation, interviewing, and qualitative analysis. Other aspects of research built into such a training program include sampling techniques, the construction, administration, and processing of questionnaires, and quantitative analysis. Rather than describe these features in detail here, we would rather emphasize one special aspect of the instructor-student relationship.

Just as the clinical instructor is thought necessarily to be a good clinician, so too the research instructor must be a good and constant researcher. Within a two- or three-year program there is ample time for both team and individual research. In this way the tutorial system is reinforced and made effective. Also the student learns not only how to work in teams, but is witness and helper to every aspect of research from rough idea to finished writing. In the later stages of the program, the student is able to proceed on her own with a minimum of supervision.

Who should do research anyway? The authors argue that not every clinician, nor even every academician, need do research. For the broad spectrum of nurses, some discussion of scientific work and the logic and philosophy of qualitative and quantitative analysis is sufficient to make them intelligent consumers of research. To expect all nurses to conduct research is both unrealistic and exceedingly burdensome upon the profession, not to say for individual nurses. We would hope, minimally, that every nurse would be able to participate, if briefly, in some aspects of research and engage in an intelligent dialogue about it. Nurses who wish to be clinicians or teachers should be allowed to move in those directions. Nevertheless, if the profession as a whole is to "make its mark" in the scientific world, it must select for special training those few nurses with enough doubt, curiosity, and motivation to become a different kind of nurse.

# 32. TOWARD DEVELOPMENT OF NURSING PRACTICE THEORY

## Florence S. Wald and Robert C. Leonard

How shall nursing develop a scientific body of knowledge basic to nursing practice? Several approaches have been used to develop such knowledge, but all of these approaches have tried to develop nursing knowledge by applying "the basic sciences" to problems of nursing care. The central contention of this paper[1] is that there has been a failure to use the empirical approach of building knowledge directly from systematic study of nursing experience. Therefore we wish to describe the differences between nursing theory as applied theory and nursing theory based on hypotheses developed from an examination of actual clinical nursing practice.

### THE FALLACY OF NURSING AS AN APPLIED SCIENCE

The historical evolution of the nursing profession determined what nurses sought as a scientific base for their practice, and during the first phase of development nursing knowledge has been inextricably linked with the growth of medical knowledge. Medicine began to elaborate its scientific base in the second part of the nineteenth century when clinicians recognized the relationship between tissue changes (microscopic and macroscopic) and the processes of disease. Patho-logists, histologists, bacteriologists, and biochemists systematically studied the relationships between the changes in tissues, the clinical symptoms, and the effects of treatment used. Their findings were used, in turn, by nurses to determine nursing procedures and nursing treatments — techniques for asepsis, treatments for bed sores, management of cardiac patients, infant feedings, to name but a few.

In the early part of the twentieth century nursing also turned to the profession of education for its scientific underpinnings.[2] As a part of this liaison, nursing researchers adopted the methods and aims of educational research, but these methods failed to provide nursing with knowledge basic to its practice. Whatever the merit of this vast body of research for guiding nursing educators, from the outset it proved to be of little use for guiding clinical nursing practice.[3]

In the 1930's and early 1940's nurses turned to another field—industrial management. During these years industry was studying production flow, time and motion, and the utilization of personnel. These studies were viewed as being potentially applicable to nursing because they might provide answers to the problem of the mushrooming hospital complex manned with an increasingly inadequate professional staff.

Reprinted by permission of the authors and publisher, from *Nursing Research*, Vol. 13, 1964, pp. 309–313.

However, the limitations of educational and administrative studies has become increasingly recognized in recent years.[4]

In its recent stage of development, nursing has attempted to develop an alliance between nursing and the physical and social sciences, but the nature of this alliance has remained elusive. For many years nurse educators have urged that social and biological science content be included in the nurse's basic education in order to "integrate" relevant ideas from these disciplines into the basic nursing curriculum. In the 1950's a frantic search for "basic concepts" was begun by individuals and groups.[5] The problems encountered in these "integration" projects, and by this approach in general, may be linked to the difficulty nurses had in finding an answer to three questions: first, "What is nursing?"[6] second, "Which principles from other disciplines appear relevant to nursing as defined?" and third, "Which of these principles prove relevant when tested?"

Nurses have expressed much concern for finding scientific principles applicable to nursing, but they have shown little concern for the selecting out of principles which are not applicable. In the first place, no matter how much acceptance they may have within the other discipline, in the nursing situation such principles may very well prove to be invalid or inappropriate. For example, biological science principles may be invalid when applied to nursing because the nurse deals with people in a social situation—not with animals in a laboratory. A second pitfall is that the nurse may put undue weight on a "general principle" which in reality proves relatively untested and hence unreliable.[7] The proper clinical testing of principles—especially those in the

social sciences—has been retarded by a lack of knowledge about sound clinical experimental designs. But there is an even more fundamental fallacy in establishing principles of nursing practice through the "application" of principles borrowed from so-called "basic" disciplines. This approach assumes that principles for practice actually can be imported from these other disciplines. Alvin Gouldner warns that:

The applied social sciences cannot be fruitfully regarded as springing Athena-like from the furrowed brow of the pure disciplines. Any metaphor which conceives of applied social science as the offspring, and of the basic disciplines as parents, is misleading.[8]

This author goes on to strongly reject "the standard view" that:

The development of the applied social sciences requires no special planning and theoretical analyses...have no distinctive problems and that, with the maturation of the basic disciplines, all that will be required is to transfer their developments, like carrying bones from an old graveyard to a new one.[9]

This is as true for nursing as it is for the other practices.

Nevertheless, nurses have spent the past ten years in a pursuit of nursing knowledge through the untested application of principles from the "pure" disciplines. They have consulted with social scientists, asked social scientists to do research for them, and have undertaken doctoral study in the social sciences. As a result nursing problems are being rephrased as social-science questions rather than questions of practice, and nurses are studying nurses. As Henderson so pungently put it, no other discipline studies the workers rather than the work.[10] Why have nurses studied nurses and not nursing? Since the "pure" scientist, whose help was sought, was trained to pursue his own discipline and was not trained to help others with *their* problems, it might have been expected that he would help nurses to develop his discipline rather than nursing practice.

This approach by the "pure" scientist is justified by viewing nursing strictly as an "applied" discipline, but it has confused the nurses as well as the scientists trying to approach nursing questions. As Gouldner says:

The applied social scientist ... must be trained and prepared to make his own theoretical innovations, [or] ... his work may be in some ways impeded ... by the pure scientist.[11]

In the present state of the behavioral sciences and nursing, we doubt that the integration of relevant basic sciences into clinical nursing is a viable means of building nursing theory. An alternative that has been overlooked is to begin with practical nursing experience and develop concepts from an analysis of that clinical experience, rather than to try to make borrowed concepts fit. This alternative was used by psychoanalysis and, more recently, by social work.[12] In developing its own theories, nursing would become an independent "discipline" in its own right. In freeing themselves from the burden of looking only for applications of the "basic" sciences in their practice, nurses would at the same time take on the responsibility of developing their own science. This calls for the development of nursing practice theory.

## PRACTICE SCIENCE VERSUS DESCRIPTIVE SCIENCE

The important point to be understood is that there is an essential difference between the study of professional practice and the "basic" scientist's practice of his academic discipline.[13] Of course, there are similarities, the practitioner scientist and the basic scientist both are committed to scientific rules of evidence and must observe the same steps of systematic inquiry. Exploratory observations are made, an hypothesis is derived and a way of testing the hypothesis is developed. Both kinds of study involve measurement of the variables and require sound sampling techniques and statistical analysis. Progress in both kinds of science is signaled by the accumulation of ever more general and increasingly well-tested propositions. However, the difference lies in the selection of variables for study and the kind of hypotheses that are entertained. In other words the difference is in the kind of theory they are testing.

The purpose of the practitioner scientist is to systematically study ways to achieve changes. In the case of nursing the aim is to study the way the nurse achieves changes in patients' responses to illness, to hospitalization, to the medical regimen, and changes in the patient's ability to utilize health measures. In other words prescriptions for professional practice must be in cause-and-effect terms. This means that the theories developed by nurse researchers must be causal theories. The "pure" scientist is free to include causal propositions in his theory or to leave them out, although in fact most sciences seem to strive for causal theories. Practice theory is not only limited to causal hypotheses but is further restricted to the use of causal variables that can be manipulated by the practitioner.

As an example of these differences in approach, we can look at the question of pain in human beings. The physiologists ask, "Are there substances in human inflammatory exudate and plasma which are in themselves pain producing: that is, how is this pain caused?"[14] Hardy, Wolff, and Goodell ask, "Do different body areas have dissimilar levels of threshold for the sensation of pricking pain—that is, how is the pain experienced?"[15] Or, to turn to the social scientists, Zborowski looks at people from different ethnic subcultures and asks, "Do people in different cultures respond differently to pain?"[16]

On the other hand, the practitioner asks a different kind of question in approaching the same phenomenon. Gammon and Starr asked, "How can we *relieve* pain? By using counterirritants? Which are the most effective?"[17] Tinterow asks, "Can hypnosis relieve the pain heretofore considered 'intractable'?"[18] Bochnak asks, "Does the request for pain medication really mean the patient has 'pain'? Will the patient be more relieved, with or without medication, if the nurse approaches him in an exploratory, deliberative way?"[19]

It is important to note that the basic disciplines can learn from practice theory. The Tinterow study on hypnosis provides the psychologist with information about how pain is perceived and levels of consciousness. Bochnak's experiment tests sociological hypotheses about dyadic interaction.

The reverse is also true. The developer of practice theory has much to learn from physiological and psychological theories of pain developed by other disciplines. Indeed, this is precisely the path taken by Crowley and other members of the University of California at Los Angeles faculty in assembling all the theories of pain, which they then planned to relate to nursing practice.[20] If this book leaves us dissatisfied, it is not because we doubt the usefulness of attempting to relate these theories from other disciplines to nursing practice.

Rather, the next two steps—the building of a coherent practice theory and its clinical test—have not yet been taken.

## PRACTICE THEORY COMPARED WITH DESCRIPTIVE THEORY

Any scientific theory, whether a theory of practice or not, begins with concepts naming classes of events in nature, and with questions or even hypotheses about how these concepts relate to each other. The concepts and hypotheses may come from anywhere, but we are proposing that for the building of nursing practice theory they should come in part from actual nursing experience[21] and that they must be tested by actual nursing experience.

Research not geared to improving professional practice may be limited to strictly descriptive propositions, but a practice theory must contain causal hypotheses. For example, the anthropologist, William Caudill, in describing the culture of a psychiatric hospital, discovered that the staff and the patients form two separate subcultures and that the two subcultures have a limited amount of communication with one another.[22] This finding is interesting to nurses, and no doubt makes a contribution to anthropology. Yet it does not provide explicit prescriptions for nursing practice. At almost the same time, a nurse, Gwen Tudor Will, looked at the same phenomenon—lack of communication between staff and patients —in a similar situation, a small private psychiatric hospital.[23] Her research could not end with simple description— she went on to ask how the degenerative cycle of "mutual withdrawal" of patient and staff could be broken. She found that the withdrawn, "asocial" patient responded to a different nursing approach. She concluded that if the nurse does not withdraw, but moves toward the patient, the patient's behavior will change and the communication deadlock can be broken. In these two approaches, the social scientist described the existing patterns of organization in the setting, while the nurse manipulated variables to see what effect she would achieve. Because of her purpose as a professional, she was interested not only in what the present situation was like, but also how to change it. Out of this case study came a causal hypothesis about the effect of nursing activity on the patient which can be incorporated into nursing practice theory.[24]

## BARRIERS TO DEVELOPMENT OF RESEARCH IN PRACTICE THEORY

There are a number of particular problems which have impeded nurses in devising theories of practice through research.

### Problems in Preparing the Research Attitude

One characteristic essential to any researcher is independence in thought, yet traditionally the nurse's role has been passive rather than creative. It is usual that the doctor diagnoses and prescribes while the nurse carries out his orders. This pattern of relationship is antithetical to the nurse scientist who must observe for herself and devise ways of acting. Therefore if nurses are to develop as scientists they must learn new patterns of action and establish relationships with their colleagues whether these colleagues be doctor or social scientist or biological scientist. Nurses

once depended on the doctor; they now might depend on these other disciplines rather than using their own powers of observation and their own intellect. While development of nursing practice theory can benefit from a close relationship with scientists, the relationship must be one of mutual give and take, and nurses must strive to develop independence in thought. Traditional subordination to the medical practitioner is probably reinforced by the fact that nursing is almost wholly a woman's profession.

Another issue which makes matters worse is that the subordinate role of nurses is reinforced when they begin to work with the nonpracticing academic disciplines, the so-called "basic disciplines," since these disciplines have a tendency to be snobbish and to regard the practicing professions as "merely" applied fields too deviant from academic standards to be respectable. This makes intelligent collaboration with nurse researchers difficult. Nurses tend to accept this evaluation. Typically they do not see themselves as a potentially rich source of information, of value to nursing as well as to other sciences. After all, nurses have more experience with people in sickness than any other professional group and have their observational skills highly developed.

An attitude essential to research is to question, yet much of the experience of the nurse practitioner works against development of a research attitude. Nurses are pressed to act before they have tested and validated practice. In face of the urgent and constant demand for action, nurse educators have had to recommend nursing practices on the basis of untested assumptions, and our theories tend to be rationalizations for existing practices which become entrenched. Pressure for the nurse to act —not to stop and think—is very real. It comes to the would-be nurse scientist from her colleagues in the hospitals, both nurses and doctors as well as from herself, as she sees the difficult situations which exist in hospitals and which immediately endanger patients' comfort and health. Further, the practitioner is trained to think in absolutes, while in sharp contrast the practitioner researcher must live in eternal uncertainty about those same absolutes by which the practitioner justifies his actions.

Practitioner training stressing that one must not make a mistake encourages a feeling of personal infallibility and cultivates blindess to one's mistakes. Yet it is by analyzing one's mistakes that one learns how to improve practice. This desire for certitude and the concomitant reluctance to examine one's own practice produces basic barriers to learning the research attitude by practitioners. Be they nurses, doctors, and social workers, they have a difficult time accepting the idea of an hypothesis and an even harder time accepting the experimental tests of the hypothetical principles of practice. This is revealed in medicine, for example, in the too frequent neglect of control groups. Practitioners appear to be shocked at the proposition that research can only disprove hypotheses—and that a fact is never "proven."

### The Scientist Must Generalize

Another basic problem we have felt is that nurses are taught to treat patients as individuals. This is good practice, but it means they don't learn to generalize. Therefore it is strange to them to make the empirical generalizations which are a necessary first step in de-

veloping a coherent scientific theory of practice and which research requires.[25] Medical knowledge and research consists of generalizations (about bodily function and malfunction) and similarly nursing knowledge and research must consist of generalizations (about nurse-patient relationships, patient's reactions to illness and treatment, and nurse's reaction to the nursing situation). But however appropriate concentration on the individual case may be for the practitioner, it is impossible for the researchers. If they are to do research, nurses must learn to make this shift in orientation.

### Problems of Skill in Research Methods

Lack of appropriate research methodology is a barrier to the kind of research necessary for developing empirical generalizations upon which to base nursing practice theory. By "methodology" we mean here not only specific technology but the basic metascientific underpinnings that established disciplines have accumulated in their traditions. One problem is simply asking the right kinds of questions. Practicing nurses who know what the problems are do not have, for the reasons just pointed out, the orientation and training necessary to study these problems. To begin with, one must ask researchable questions. It is not sufficient to have a "problem," although that is the beginning. The problem must be stated in a way which permits its scientific investigation. Nurses do not ordinarily learn to ask researchable questions. Thus even when they are sympathetic to research, they tend to set unattainable research objectives. Examples of such questions are: How can nursing be made more effective? Why does the nursing staff have such low morale? What can we do about the nursing shortage? What is the nurse's role? No amount of research can answer such questions as they stand! Before research can begin, we must propose specific answers to these questions. Then research can test these "hypotheses." Our experience suggests that one reason collaborative research with social scientists often answers questions that are mostly of interest to the social scientist is because the nurse has not clarified the problem enough for herself beforehand. And the social scientist does not have the background, nor the interest, to clarify the nursing problem.

In developing clinical nursing research, nurses will often be faced with a choice between precision and acceptability of their findings according to standards developed for other fields and relevance to nursing practice. If nursing theory is to develop, nurses must have the courage to use a rough tool which is more relevant than a widely accepted tool which is not well suited to nursing research. This does not call for lowering standards of rigor, but rather for raising standards of relevance. At the same time, nurses must develop research methods where they do not exist.

## CONCLUSION

We feel that the development of nursing knowledge will be sound and quick once the empirical approach to building knowledge is recognized and used in nursing research. The empirical approach we hold is not only respectable, it is essential.

---

1. This paper was originally presented during a 1963–1964 bimonthly faculty research symposium conducted under a grant from the Division of Nursing Resources, U.S.P.H.S., directed by the senior author and Howard C. Leventhal of the Yale School of Nursing. Members of the philosophy department, William Dickoff and Patricia James, have been generous in giving valuable criticism and encouragement as have other colleagues, both faculty and student. Special acknowledgment is due Donald B. Trow, now Professor of Sociology at Harpur College, for his earlier draft of the sections on generalizing and problem formulation.

2. On the one hand, the link between nursing and education seems difficult to explain. However, it will be remembered that as nurses attempted to attain professional status, the first step they took was to prepare better teachers of nursing. The professional leaders in nursing and the universities to which they turned both believed this could best be accomplished in schools of education, and the school which became most influential in the early years was Teachers College, Columbia University, where a pattern of advanced education was established.

3. Interestingly enough, the educating profession and the nursing profession have an important characteristic in common—both professions strive to create changes in human beings—and therefore they might well study which activities of practice produce these changes and why. It is startling to review research done by both these professions and realize, on the one hand, how little educators have done to study the effect of one particular kind of teaching on student learning as compared with another, and on the other hand, how little nurses have done to study the effect of one particular kind of nursing on patient welfare as compared with another. James B. Conant notes this need for the teaching profession in the chapter on "Theory and Practice in Teaching," in *The Education of American Teachers*, New York: McGraw-Hill, 1963.

4. Virginia A. Henderson, "An Over-

view of Nursing Research," *Nursing Research*, **6**, 1957, 61–71; Rozella M. Schlotfeldt, "Reflections on Nursing Research," *American Journal of Nursing*, **60**, 1960, 492–494; R. Louise McManus, "Nursing Research—Its Evolution," *American Journal of Nursing*, **61**, 1961, 76–79; R. Louise McManus, "Today and Tomorrow in Nursing Research," *American Journal of Nursing*, **61**, 1961, 68–71; L. W. Simmons and Virginia A. Henderson, *Research in Nursing*, New York: Appleton-Century-Crofts, 1964.

5. The group effort has been documented in the West where intermural conferences of various schools have been held under the auspices of WICHE for the purpose of finding content in various fields of nursing. Simmons and Henderson, *op. cit.* Madelyn T. Nordmark and Anne W. Rohweder, *Science Principles Applied to Nursing*, Philadelphia: Lippincott, 1959.

6. The failure to answer this first question results in the kind of confusion about what nursing expects of behavioral science expressed by Eleanor Sheldon in "The Use of Behavioral Sciences in Nursing: An Opinion," *Nursing Research*, **12**, 1963. 150. It should be understood that this is not a research question, but rather a policy issue to be settled by discussion and decision *by nurses.*

7. It is interesting to note that this is as true for social work, law, medicine, or engineering as it is for nursing. Social workers, like nurses, have a "tendency to treat assumptive or hypothetical knowledge as if it had been thoroughly tested and validated." Herbert Bisno, *The Use of Social Science Content in Social Work Education*, working paper for UNESCO meeting, July 1960.

8. A. W. Gouldner, "Explorations in Applied Social Science," *Social Problems*, **3**, 1956, 169–181.

9. *Ibid.*

10. Virginia A. Henderson, "A Research in Nursing Practice—When?" *Nursing Research*, **4**, 1956, 99.

11. Gouldner, *loc cit.*

12. Gouldner points out that "the most successful of the applied psychologies"— psychoanalysis—did *not* start with academic psychology. Freud often stressed

that his theory grew out of his own clinical experience. Gouldner, *loc cit.*

13. This comparison is adapted from Ernest Greenwood's "The Practice of Science and the Science of Practice," in Warren G. Bennis, Kenneth D. Benne, and Robert Chin (Eds.), *The Planning of Change*, New York: Holt, Rinehart, and Winston, 1961, pp. 73–83.

14. Desiree Armstrong et al., "Pain-Producing Substances in Human Inflammatory Exudates and Plasma," *Journal of Physiology*, **135**, 1957, 350–370.

15. J. D. Hardy et al., "Pricking Pain Threshold in Different Body Areas," *Proceedings of the Society for Experimental Biology and Medicine*, **80**, 1952, 425–427.

16. Mark Zborowski, "Cultural Components in Response to Pain," *Journal of Social Issues*, **8**, No. 4, 1952, 16–30.

17. George Gammon and Isaac Starr, "Studies on the Relief of Pain by Counter-Irritation," *Journal of Clinical Investigation*, **20**, 1941, 13–20.

18. M. M. Tinterow, "The Use of Hypnoanalgesia in the Relief of Intractable Pain," *American Surgery*, **26**, 1960, 30–34.

19. Mary Ann Bochnak, "The Effect of an Automatic and Deliberative Process of Nursing Activity on the Relief of Patients' Pain: A Clinical Experiment," unpublished master's thesis, New Haven, Conn.: Yale University School of Nursing, 1961. Mary Ann Bochnak et al., "Comparison of Two Types of Nursing Activity on the Relief of Pain," in *Innovations in Nurse-Patient Relationships: Automatic or Reasoned Nurse Actions*, Clinical Paper No. 6, New York: American Nurses Association, 1962, pp. 5–11.

20. Dorothy M. Crowley, *Pain and Its Alleviation*, Los Angeles: University of California, School of Nursing, 1962.

21. To reiterate, the most popular common and prestigeful source is to borrow them from certain established academic disciplines regarded as "basic" sciences.

22. William Caudill et al., "Social Structure and Interaction Processes on a Psychiatric Ward," *American Journal of Orthopsychiatry*, **22**, 1952, 314–334.

23. Gwen Tudor Will. "A Sociopsychiatric Nursing Approach to Intervention in

a Problem of Mutual Withdrawal on a Mental Hospital Ward," *Psychiatry,* **15,** 1952, 193–217.

24. It should be pointed out that we are not using the word "theory" with the connotation that it contains only "proven facts." Will's hypothesis would need considerably more testing—preferably in well-controlled clinical experimentation—before we should incorporate it into theory with a degree of confidence.

25. Cf. Greenwood, *op. cit.,* pp. 79–80.

# 33. SOME OBSERVATIONS ON STUDY DESIGN

## Samuel A. Stouffer

As a youth I read a series of vigorous essays in the *Century Magazine* by its editor, the late Glenn Frank. His theme was that the natural sciences had remade the face of the earth; now had arrived the age of the social sciences. The same techniques which had worked their miracles in physics, chemistry, and biology should, in competent hands, achieve equally dazzling miracles in economics, political science, and sociology. That was a long time ago. The disconcerting fact is that people are writing essays just like that today. Of course, the last two decades have seen considerable progress in social science—in theory, in technique, and in the accumulation of data. It is true that the number of practitioners is pitifully few; only a few hundred research studies are reported annually in sociology, for example, as compared with more than twenty thousand studies summarized annually in *Biological Abstracts*. But the bright promise of the period when Frank was writing has not been fulfilled.

Two of the most common reasons alleged for slow progress are cogent, indeed.

The data of social science are awfully complex, it is said. And they involve values which sometimes put a strain on the objectivity of the investigator even when they do not incur resistance from the vested interests of our society. However, an important part of the trouble has very little to do with the subject matter of social science as such, but rather is a product of our own bad work habits. That is why this paper on the subject of study design may be relevant. So much has been spoken and written on this topic that I make no pretense to originality. But in the course of a little experience, especially in an effort during the war to apply social psychology to military problems, and in an undertaking to nurture a new program of research in my university, I have encountered some frustrations which perhaps can be examined with profit.

A basic problem — perhaps *the* basic problem — lies deeply imbedded in the thoughtways of our culture. This is the implicit assumption that anybody with a little common sense and a few facts can come up at once with the correct answer on any subject. Thus the newspaper editor or columnist, faced with a column of empty space to fill with readable English in an hour, can speak with finality and authority on any social topic, however complex. He might not attempt to diagnose what is wrong with his sick cat; he would call a veterinarian. But he knows precisely what is wrong with any social institution and the remedies.

In a society which rewards quick and confident answers and does not worry about how the answers are arrived at, the social scientist is hardly to be blamed if he conforms to the norms. Hence much social science is merely rather dull and obscure journalism; a few data and a lot of "interpretation." The fact that the so-called "interpretation" bears little or no relation to the data is often obscured by academic jargon. If the stuff is hard to read, it has a chance of being acclaimed as profound. The rewards are for the answers, however tediously expressed, and not for rigorously marshaled evidence.

In the army no one would think of adopting a new type of weapon without trying it out exhaustively on the firing range. But a new idea about handling personnel fared very differently. The last thing anybody ever thought about was trying out the idea experimentally. I recall several times when we had schemes for running an experimental tryout of an idea in the sociopsychological field. Usually one of two things would happen: the idea would be rejected as stupid without a tryout (it may have been stupid, too) or it would be seized on and applied generally and at once. When the provost marshal wanted us to look into the very low morale of the MP's, our attitude surveys suggested that there was room for very much better selectivity in job assignment. There were routine jobs like guarding prisoners which could be given to the duller MP's, and there were a good many jobs calling for intelligence, discretion, and skill in public relations. We thought that the smarter men might be assigned to these jobs and that the prestige of these jobs would be raised further if a sprinkling of returned veterans with plenty of ribbons and no current assignment could be included among them. We proposed a trial program of a reassignment system in a dozen MP outfits for the purpose of comparing the resulting morale with that in a dozen matched outfits which were left untouched. Did we get anywhere? No. Instead, several of our ideas were put into effect immediately throughout the army without any prior testing at all.

The army cannot be blamed for behavior like that. In social relations it is not the habit in our culture to demand evidence for an idea; plausibility is enough.

To alter the folkways, social science itself must take the initiative. We must be clear in our own minds what proof consists of, and we must, if possible, provide dramatic examples of the advantages of relying on something more than plausibility. And the heart of our problem lies in study design *in advance,* such that the evidence is not capable of a dozen alternative interpretations.

Basically, I think it is essential that we always keep in mind the model of a controlled experiment, even if in practice we may have to deviate from an ideal model. Take the simple accompanying diagram.

|  | Before | After | After — Before |
|---|---|---|---|
| Experimental group | $x_1$ | $x_2$ | $d = x_2 - x_1$ |
| Control group | $x_1'$ | $x_2'$ | $d' = x_2' - x_1'$ |

The test of whether a difference $d$ is attributable to what we think it is attributable to is whether $d$ is significantly larger than $d'$.

We used this model over and over again during the war to measure the effectiveness of orientation films in changing soldiers' attitudes. These experiences are described in Volume III of our *Studies in Social Psychology in World War II.*[1]

One of the troubles with using this careful design was that the effectiveness of a single film when thus measured turned out to be so slight. If, instead of using the complete experimental design, we simply took an unselected sample of men and compared the attitudes of those who said they had seen a film with those who said they had not, we got much more impressive differences. This was more rewarding to us, too, for the management wanted to believe the films were powerful medicine. The gimmick was the selective fallibility of memory. Men who correctly remembered seeing the films were likely to be those most sensitized to their message. Men who were bored or indifferent may have actually seen them but slept through them or just forgot.

Most of the time we are not able or not patient enough to design studies containing all four cells as in the diagram above. Some times we have only the top two cells, as in the accompanying diagram.

$$\boxed{\begin{array}{|c|c|} \hline x_1 & x_2 \\ \hline \end{array}} \quad d = x_2 - x_1$$

In this situation we have two observations of the same individuals or groups taken at different times. This is often a very useful design. In the army, for example, we would take a group of recruits, ascertain their attitudes, and restudy the same men later. From this we could tell whose attitudes changed and in what direction (it was almost always for the worse, which did not endear us to the army!). But exactly what factors in the early training period were most responsible for deterioration of attitudes could only be inferred indirectly. The panel study is usually more in-

formative than a more frequent design, which might be pictured thus:

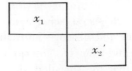

Here at one point in time we have one sample, and at a later point in time we have another sample. We observe that our measure, say, the mean, is greater for the recent sample than for the earlier one. But we are precluded from observing which men or what type of men shifted. Moreover, there is always the disturbing possibility that the populations in our two samples were initially different; hence the differences might not be attributable to conditions taking place in the time interval between the two observations. Thus we would study a group of soldiers in the United States and later ask the same questions of a group of soldiers overseas. Having matched the two groups of men carefully by branch of service, length of time in the army, rank, etc., we hoped that the results of the study would approximate what would be found if the same men could have been studied twice. But this could be no more than a hope. Some important factors could not be adequately controlled, for example, physical conditions. Men who went overseas were intially in better shape on the average than men who had been kept behind; but, if the follow-up study was in the tropics, there was a chance that unfavorable climate already had begun to take its toll. And so it went. How much men overseas changed called for a panel study as a minimum if we were to have much confidence in the findings.

A very common attempt to get the results of a controlled experiment without paying the price is with the design that might be as shown in the accompanying diagram.

This is usually what we get with correlation analysis. We have two or more groups of men whom we study at the same point in time. Thus we have men in the infantry and men in the air corps and compare their attitudes. How much of the difference between $x_2'$ and $x_2$ we can attribute to experience in a given branch of service and how much is a function of attributes of the men selected for each branch we cannot know assuredly. True, we can try to rule out various possibilities by matching; we can compare men from the two branches with the same age and education, for example. But there is all too often a wide-open gate through which other uncontrolled variables can march.

Sometimes, believe it or not, we have only one cell:

When this happens, we do not know much of anything. But we can still fill pages of social-science journals with "brilliant analysis" if we use plausible conjecture in supplying missing cells from our imagination. Thus we may find that the adolescent today has wild ideas and conclude that society is going to the dogs. We fill in the dotted cell representing our own yesterdays with hypothetical data, where $x_1$ represents us and $x_2$ our offspring.

| $x_1$ | $x_2$ |
|---|---|

The tragicomic part is that most of the public, including, I fear, many social scientists, are so acculturated that they ask for no better data.

I do not intend to disparage all research not conforming to the canons of the controlled experiment. I think that we will see more of full experimental design in sociology and social psychology in the future than in the past. But I am well aware of the practical difficulties of its execution, and I know that there are numberless important situations in which it is not feasible at all. What I am arguing for is awareness of the limitations of a design in which crucial cells are missing.

Sometimes by forethought and patchwork we can get approximations which are useful if we are careful to avoid overinterpretation. Let me cite an example:

In Europe during the war the army tested the idea of putting an entire platoon of Negro soldiers into a white infantry outfit. This was done in several companies. The Negroes fought beside white soldiers. After several months we were asked to find out what the white troops thought about the innovation. We found that only 7 per cent of the white soldiers in companies with Negro platoons said that they disliked the idea very much, whereas 62 per cent of the white soldiers in divisions without Negro troops said they would dislike the idea very much if it were tried in their outfits. We have:

|  | Before | After |
|---|---|---|
| Experimental |  | 7% |
| Control |  | 62% |

Now, were these white soldiers who fought beside Negroes men who were naturally more favorable to Negroes than the cross-section of white infantrymen? We did not think so, since, for example, they contained about the same proportion of southerners. The point was of some importance, however, if we were to make the inference that actual experience with Negroes reduced hostility from 62 to 7 per cent. As a second-best substitute, we asked the white soldiers in companies with Negro platoons if they could recall how they felt when the innovation was first proposed. It happens that 67 per cent said they were initially opposed to the idea. Thus we could tentatively fill in a missing cell and conclude that, under the conditions obtaining, there probably had been a marked change in attitude.

Even if this had been a perfectly controlled experiment, there was still plenty of chance to draw erroneous inferences. The conclusions apply only to situations closely approximating those of the study. It happens, for example, that the Negroes involved were men who volunteered to leave rear-area jobs for combat duty. If other Negroes had been involved, the situation might have been different. Moreover, they had white officers. One army colonel who saw this study and whom I expected to ridicule it because he usually opposed innovations, surprised me by offering congratulations. "This proves," he said, "what I have been arguing in all my thirty years in the army — that niggers will do all right if you give 'em white officers!" Moreover, the study applied only to combat experience. Other studies would be needed to justify extending the findings to noncombat or garrison duty. In other words, one lone study, however well designed, can be a very dangerous thing if it is exploited beyond its immediate implications.

Now experiments take time and money, and there is no use denying that we in social science cannot be as prodigal with the replications as the biologist who can run a hundred experiments simultaneously by growing plants in all kinds of soils and conditions. The relative ease of experimentation in much — not all — of natural science goes far to account for the differences in quality of proof demanded by physical and biological sciences, on the one hand, and social scientists, on the other.

Though we cannot always design neat experiments when we want to, we can at least keep the experimental model in front of our eyes and behave cautiously when we fill in missing cells with dotted lines. But there is a further and even more important operation we can perform in the interest of economy. That lies in our choice of the initial problem.

Professor W. F. Ogburn always told his students to apply to a reported research conclusion the test, "How do you know it?" To this wise advice I should like ao add a further question: "What of it?" I suspect that if before designing a study we asked ourselves, more conscientiously than we do, whether or not the study really is important, we would economize our energies for the few studies which are worth the expense and trouble of the kind of design I have been discussing.

Can anything be said about guides for selecting problems? I certainly think so. That is where theory comes in and where we social scientists have gone woefully stray.

Theory has not often been designed with research operations in mind. Theory as we have it in social science serves indispensably as a very broad frame of reference or general orientation. Thus modern theories of culture tell us that it is usually more profitable to focus on the learning process and the content of what is learned rather than on innate or hereditary traits. But they do not provide us with sets of interrelated propositions which can be put in the form: If $x_1$, given $x_2$ and $x_3$, then there is strong probability that we get $x_4$. Most of our propositions of that form, sometimes called "theory," are likely to be ad hoc commonsense observations which are not deductible from more general considerations and which are of the same quality as the observation, "If you stick your hand in a fire and hold it there, you will get burned."

Now in view the the tremendous cost in time and money of the ideal kind of strict empirical research operations, it is obvious that we cannot afford the luxury of conducting them as isolated fact-finding enterprises. Each should seek to be some sort of *experimentum crucis*, and, with rare exceptions, that will only happen if we see its place *beforehand* in a more general scheme of things. Especially we need to look for situations where two equally plausible hypotheses deductible from more general theory lead to the expectation of different consequences. Then, if our evidence supports one and knocks out the other, we have accomplished something.

The best work of this sort in our field is probably being done today in laboratory studies of learning and of perception. I do not know of very good sociological examples. Yet in sociology experiments are possible. One of the most exciting, for example, was that initiated long before the war by Shaw and McKay to see whether cooperative effort by adult role models within a delinquent neighborhood would reduce juvenile delinquency. So many variables are involved in a single study like that

that it is not easy to determine which were crucial. But there was theory behind the study, and the experimental design provided for controlling at least some variables.

It may be that in sociology we will need much more thinking and many more descriptive studies involving random ratlike movements on the part of the researcher before we can even begin to state our problems so that they are in decent shape for fitting into an ideal design. However, I think that we can reduce to some extent the waste motion of the exploratory period if we try to act as if we have some a priori ideas and our eyes on the possible relevance of data to these ideas. This is easier said than done. So many interesting rabbit tracks are likely to be uncovered in the exploratory stages of research that one is tempted to chase rabbits all over the woods and forget what one's initial quarry was.

Exploratory research is of necessity fumbling, but I think that the waste motion can be reduced by the self-denying ordinance of deliberately limiting ourselves to a few variables at a time. Recently two of my colleagues and myself have been doing a little exploratory work on a problem in the general area of social mobility. We started by tabulating some school records of fifty boys in the ninth grade of one junior high school and then having members of our seminar conduct three or four interviews with each boy and his parents. We had all the interviews written up in detail, and we had enough data to fill a book — with rather interesting reading, too. But it was a very wasteful process because there were just too many intriguing ideas. We took a couple of ideas which were deducible from current general theory and tried to make some simple fourfold tables. It was obvious that, with a dozen variables uncontrolled, such tables meant little or nothing. But that lead us to a second step. Now we are trying to collect school records and a short questionnaire on two thousand boys. We will not interview all these boys and their parents in detail. But, with two thousand cases to start with, we hope to take a variable in which we are interested and find fifty boys who are plus on it and fifty who are minus, yet who are approximately alike on a lot of other things. A table based on such matched comparisons should be relatively unambiguous. We can take off from there and interview those selected cases intensively to push further our exploration of the nexus between theory and observation. This, we think, will be economical, though still exploratory. Experimental manipulation is far in the future in our problem, but we do hope we can conclude the first stage with a statement of some hypotheses susceptible to experimental verification.

I am not in the least deprecating exploratory work. But I do think that some orderliness is indicated even in the bright dawn of a youthful enterprise.

One reason why we are not more orderly in our exploratory work is that all too often what is missing is a sharp definition of a given variable, such that, if we wanted to take a number of cases and even throw them into a simple fourfold table, we could.

Suppose we are studying a problem in which one of the variables we are looking for is overprotection or overindulgence of a child by his mother. We have a number of case histories or questionnaires. Now how do we know whether we are sorting them according to this variable or not? The first step,

it would seem, is to have some way of knowing whether we are sorting them along any single continuum, applying the same criteria to each case. But to know this we need to have built into the study the ingredients of a scale. Unless we have some such ingredients in our data, we are defeated from the start. This is why I think the new interest social scientists are taking in scaling techniques is so crucially important to progress. In particular, the latent-structure theory developed by Paul F. Lazarsfeld, which derives Louis Guttman's scale as an important special case, is likely to be exceedingly useful, for it offers criteria by which we can make a small amount of information go a long way in telling us the logical structure of a supposed variable we are eager to identify. The details of Guttman's and Lazarsfeld's work[2] are likely to promote a good deal of attack and controversy. Our hope is that this will stimulate others to think such problems out still better and thus make their work obsolete as rapidly as possible.

Trying to conduct a social-science investigation without good criteria for knowing whether a particular variable may be treated as a single dimension is like trying to fly without a motor in the plane. Students of the history of invention point out that one reason why the airplane, whose properties had been pretty well thought out by Leonardo da Vinci, was so late in development was the unavailability of a lightweight power plant, which had to await the invention of the internal combustion motor. We are learning more and more how to make our lightweight motors in social science, and that augurs well for the future. But much work is ahead of us. In particular, we desperately need better projective techniques and better ways of getting respondents to reveal attitudes which are too emotionally charged to be accessible to direct questioning. Schemes like the latent-structure theory of Lazarsfeld should speed up the process of developing such tests.

I have tried to set forth the model of the controlled experiment as an ideal to keep in the forefront of our minds even when by necessity some cells are missing from our design. I have also tried to suggest that more economy and orderliness are made possible, even in designing the exploratory stages of a piece of research — by using theory in advance to help us decide whether a particular inquiry would be important if we made it; by narrowing down the number of variables; and by making sure that we can classify our data along a particular continuum, even if only provisionally. And a central, brooding hope is that we will have the modesty to recognize the difference between a promising idea and proof.

Oh, how we need that modesty! The public expects us to deal with great problems like international peace, full employment, maximization of industrial efficiency. As pundits we can pronounce on such matters; as citizens we have a duty to be concerned with them; but as social scientists our greatest achievement now will be to provide a few small dramatic examples that hypotheses in our field can be stated operationally and tested crucially. And we will not accomplish that by spending most of our time writing or reading papers like this one. We will accomplish it best by rolling up our sleeves and working at the intricacies of design of studies which, though scientifically strategic, seem to laymen trivial compared with the global concerns of the atomic age. Thereby, and only thereby, I believe, can we some day have the thrilling sense of having contributed to the structure of a social science which is cumulative.

---

1. Carl I. Hovland, Arthur A. Lumsdaine, and Fred D. Sheffield, *Experiments in Mass Communication*, Princeton, N. J.: Princeton University Press, 1949.

2. Samuel A. Stouffer, Louis Guttman, Edward A. Suchman, Paul F. Lazarsfeld, Shirley A. Star, and John A. Clausen, *Measurement and Prediction*, Princeton, N. J.: Princeton University Press, 1949.

# 34. COMPUTER AND SOCIAL SCIENTIST IN INTERACTION

*Gerald A. King and Ronald E. Anderson*

## INTRODUCTION

A social scientist no longer can ignore the computer as a potential member of the research team. If he chooses not to use the computer he generally is called on to justify his decision. If he does plan to use the computer, it is less likely that he will be asked to defend his strategy, even though it may be ill-advised. In this chapter we shall outline a number of the ways in which computers can be employed and some of the ingredients that must enter into decisions regarding computer usage. Certainly the chief elements in these plans derive from the research design, but the use of the computer does influence prior decision making. In view of these considerations we shall suggest how the present and future capabilities of electronic computing devices can be used to achieve optimal integration of the computer into the research process.

## ELEMENTARY COMPUTER CONCEPTS

All large educational centers now have access to general purpose, digital, electronic computers. ("Computer" throughout this chapter will refer only to this type of computer.) Even as far back as 1960 almost all graduate departments of psychology and sociology had per-

sons who employed computers in their research.[1] Yet there are still many behavioral scientists who, though favorably disposed, are not including the computer in their research planning. The first step in planning for optimal utilization of the computer is an understanding of elementary computer concepts.

Basically the computer is a symbol manipulating mechanism. Its manipulations encompass (1) arithmetic calculations, (2) logical decisions, (3) information processing. Standard desk calculators are information processers and arithmetic calculators, but they cannot make logical decisions. The computer can choose between alternatives. Basically this amounts to an ability to respond with "yes" or "no" to questions involving equality. The implications of this capability are difficult to comprehend, for they are far reaching, extending the application of the computer beyond calculation and into the realms of management-control-systems data processing of all kinds. For example, the decision functions can be utilized to rank order a set of numbers, to perform the task of a file clerk, to control inventories, and so on. In addition, the ability to compare configurations of symbols and to proceed with certain operations based on the result of the comparison has opened up the

---

This paper was prepared especially as an original contribution to this book.

fascinating research areas of artificial intelligence and simulation of cognitive processes.[2]

Information is the raw material for computers. The basic unit of information in a computer is a *word*. The *word* is an ordered set of character symbols which occupies one physical location and is always treated as a unit. It may be a decimal number, a string of alphabetic characters, or a series of binary digits. Words are arranged within the computer as the *internal storage* or "memory," which is really a warehouse for words. Each word has an address in this storage so it can be "looked up" and examined by the operating units of the computer. Internal storage is distinct from such storage devices as magnetic tapes, punched cards, disk files, etc., which are referred to as *external storage*. Symbols from external storage must first be placed into internal storage before they can be operated upon.

The computer controls its own activity with an internally *stored program*. The computer *program* is a sequence of instructions, arranged as a series of words and executed one at a time. A program of instructions is written in a *programming language* which is a system of syntactical rules governing the arrangement of well-defined symbols. There are several popular languages, such as *algol*, *cobol*, and *fortran*, which resemble natural languages and are applicable to a wide variety of problems. When a program is written in such a language, it is first punched onto a deck of cards. Before it can be stored in the computer as a controlling device, this program deck must first be translated into more explicit symbols which the computer recognizes as instructions. The translator for this task is a special program, called a *compiler*, with the sole

function of reading programs written in programming languages and converting them into symbols which the machine recognizes as instructions. It should be clear by now that these programs or *software* (in computer jargon *software* refers to programs and *hardware* specifies physical equipment) are extremely important, in fact crucial, to the development of any computer application.

Of course it is necessary to have ways of bringing symbols into and taking them away from the computer's memory. Peripheral equipment — for example, card readers, tape drives, printers — are the primary elements of the channels for getting information into and out of the computer's internal storage. Program instructions can specify explicit operations for these devices. For example, the number "1" specifies the operation "read a card" to the IBM 1401 computer. This particular instruction not only causes the card reader to sense the punched codes from the eighty columns of a card, but those eighty codes are moved into a designated area of the computer storage. A variety of such instructions provide control over each of the input and output devices, allowing the skilled programmer to engage in symbolic interaction with the electronic monster.

## THE COMPUTER IN SOLVING RESEARCH PROBLEMS

If the health scientist has an understanding of computer operations, he will be able to determine whether or not the computer can solve a given data-processing problem. But the role of computer data processing in survey research can be assessed only after considering in detail the steps carried out by survey researchers in the research process. This analysis will provide the foundation for planning the implementation of computerized data processing.

## Computer Applications in the Research Process

*Introduction.* A research problem develops in roughly three stages: conceptualization, research design, and data collection and analysis. Presumably, research decisions flow in that order (and not vice versa) so that the design is chosen on the basis of the researcher's conceptualization, and data analysis is carried out according to the criteria laid down by the methodological decisions. Although limitations of data, data analysis, and methodology perforce set boundaries on the conceptualization, it is generally agreed that hypotheses and concepts should not be chosen merely because of some new development in methodology or the existence of some data. Consequently the starting point for discussion will be the first step in the third stage — that is, drawing the sample — and computer applications will be outlined for each step leading to the interpretation of analyzed data.

*Selecting the sample.* For most research purposes it is desirable to choose the sample on the basis of some set of characteristics. This may take the form of requiring that all members of the sample possess a certain characteristic or the sample may be chosen so that variance on a particular characteristic is maximized. Such sampling is termed "judgment sampling."[3] In some cases the data already collected on a population allows the researcher to manipulate the independent variable by systematic selection of his sample; this may be the only feasible path when only a minute

proportion of the population possesses the particular constellation of characteristics necessary for testing the researcher's propositions; for example, manual workers with college education versus professional workers with less than grade-school education.

Many repositories of data, for example, university administrations and testing centers of large universities, store data for entire populations on magnetic tape, disks, or cards. Through the use of information storage and retrieval programs already available, the researcher can request from the computer, for example, a random sample drawn from all students who have rheumatic heart conditions and a matched pair sample from all students who have no heart pathology such that the normal sample matches the rheumatic heart sample on sex, age, education of mother, occupation of father, and achievement motivation. The output from the computer can be names and addresses on address labels or ID numbers on paper or cards. Clinical records can be pulled or questionnaires sent to the two samples. The same logic can be extended to drawing other types of samples.

*Data collection, coding, and organization.* It is the happy lot of some to have data already available on cards, but it is usually necessary to gather data from records or from subjects in the form of interviews or self-administered questionnaires. Questionnaires can be constructed to provide for accurate responses on the part of the subject and easy tabulation on the part of the analyst. If the information is to be transferred to cards, the questionnaires may have the answer boxes located along the right edge or on a separate sheet in order to eliminate a separate coding step between questionnaire and cards. Structured interviews present essentially the same problems. For a number of years mark-sense cards[4] have been used as answer "sheets" in testing and surveys in order to avoid the keypunching step. More recently optical scanning devices[5] have made it possible to go directly from answer sheet to data analysis, performing the operations of coding, editing, index construction, scaling, and statistical analysis all at one time on the computer. With these devices the use of standard density pens for marking and the construction of a coding program with thorough editing operations guarantee a level of accuracy rarely attained with manual coding and punching.

*Measurement analysis.* Most research projects include a preliminary tabulation of frequency distributions and various descriptive statistics, sometimes referred to as data screening. On the basis of this tabulation, indexes, scales, and other composite measures are constructed. These measures may be screened, as were the original data, for the purpose of choosing category limits before undertaking cross-tabulation or some other statistical procedure. Data-screening runs on computers are probably the easiest operation performed by the analyst. The investigator usually need expend less than fifteen minutes of his time and less than one minute on any of the larger computers in order to screen one thousand cases on as many variables as he wishes. When using optical-scanning devices the data screening can be accomplished at the time the answer sheets are processed.

Survey projects typically include multiple item measures ranging from typologies to psychophysical scales. It will be convenient to divide the production of these measures into three major types: index construction, item analysis, and scaling. Many data-screening programs now available allow the analyst to construct composite measures as additional variables and thus enable him to examine the distribution of the tentative indexes. This operation may be repeated until the user arrives at an index that satisfies his criteria. The computer can punch the individual scores for this index or store them on tape or disk.

For investigators constructing personality scales, the problems of validity and reliability are particularly acute. When several hundred items are included in the item pool from which a dozen scales are to be created, the task of locating valid items and constructing reliable scales would be insuperable without the computer. From an item pool, item-analysis programs construct initial scale assignments on the basis of the user's specifications, compute item-total correlations and reliabilities for the scales, make reassignments and deletions according to criteria set by the user, and iterate[6] until the desired scales are achieved.

An increasing number of survey designs include scaling procedures such as the Guttman scale and Thurstone's successive-intervals scale. Many of these procedures are excessively laborious if manually calculated, but are quite easily computed on any of the larger computers.

*Statistical analysis.* As is true of all other phases of data handling, the testing of hypotheses usually can be accomplished more efficiently on the computer than by a research assistant on the desk calculator or counter-sorter.

Many statistical procedures such as discriminant function analysis are so complicated and time consuming that few researchers attempt to compute them by hand even when their data would permit such analysis. Cross-tabulation of two variables is a relatively simple operation, but it becomes rapidly involved as the number of categories is increased or as controlling variables are added to the analysis. The introduction of controlling variables (subdivision) into the analysis, as used in multivariate cross-tabulation, may be required for other statistical operations. There are two forms in the use of such operations: (1) It is frequently desirable to perform the same statistical operation on each of several subsamples which are homogeneous on the set of controlling variables. (2) For statistics that test multiple samples on a particular variable or set of variables — for example, Mann-Whitney U test, K. V. Wilson multiway nonparametric analysis of variance — it is frequently desired to define the several samples by their positions on a number of variables. In either case the operation is nearly impossible when done manually, and if the controlling variables or the dependent variables are located on different cards (as is the case when the number of variables is greater than can be put on one card), it becomes impossible on the counter-sorter. An increasing number of statistical programs incorporate Boolean sample definition,[7] a feature first suggested by Professor Frank Massey. This option allows the user to compose his subsamples in as complex a fashion as desired at the same time he computes the desired statistics, rather than separately, thus effecting a great savings in time and effort.

## Planning the Implementation of a Computerized Data-Handling System

*Objectives and constraints of the system.* It is useful to start with a conception of the "ideal" system for a specific project. For a thorough knowledge of available technological capabilities enables one to determine "rationally" which aspects of the ideal system can be compromised. At a general level the ideal system would ensure (1) complete reliability, (2) complete control, (3) wide flexibility, and (4) growth potential. These characteristics of the ideal system are unobtainable in their entirety due to technological limitations, cost restrictions, and implementation problems. Reliability is not a serious problem at the hardware level, but it is very much a concern at the software level. Control and flexibility, unfortunately, are often opposing objectives. Programs can be flexibly written to apply generally to many problem situations, but in so doing control may be sacrificed if the amount of data preparation is greatly magnified. Programming limitations are likely to lead to rigidity in system design, since it often is much easier to create a specialized program for a specific processing task. This specialized program is likely to have little growth potential, that is, it may *not* be easily extended to similar processing tasks.

*Specifying the functions to be performed.* In laying out a data-handling system two of the basic design problems are the selection of techniques for storing data and the choice of functions to be performed. Ultimately the goal of the system is the tabulational and statistical analysis of data. But to attain this end, the measurement analysis and the editing functions are vitally important preliminary functions. The editing function is used to trace errors such as (1) logically inconsistent observations[8]— for example, indications that a respondent is both a female and a husband; (2) nonsensical observation codes — for example, "99" as "years of schooling"; and (3) missing information. These errors then can be corrected in some predetermined manner. The measurement analysis function and the statistical-tabulational analysis functions have already been discussed in a previous section.

*Illustrative computer system.* Assuming that these major functions will be performed by computer programs, we can proceed to build our specific system by selecting the most useful storage media. Taking punched cards as the input medium, we can illustrate a system that is frequently used by survey researchers. (See Figure 34-1.) After the

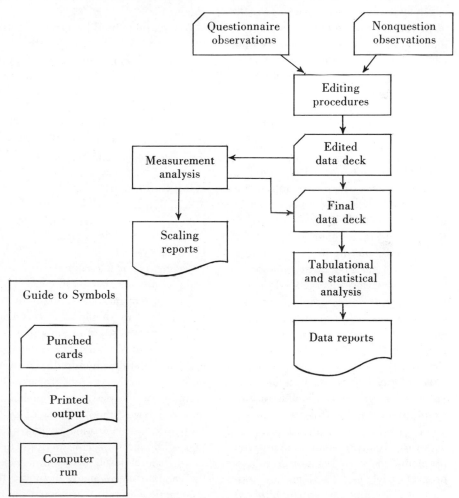

FIGURE 34-1. Process chart of a computerized, survey data-processing system.

empirical observations are transferred to punched cards, these records are edited before they are added to the master deck. Then the measurement and statistical analyses transform the observations of the master deck into meaningful data reports.

The form of data reports is frequently neglected in survey research—often the only meaningful reports are figures on scratch paper. Computer-produced output has not been adequately appreciated as a solution for organizing data summaries. On the other hand, the computer user often is haunted by stacks of computer output which are just as difficult to interpret as rough notes on crumpled scratch paper. Computer programming specifically for well-organized data reports is essential when a large volume of summary data must be interpreted.

*Program availability.* Programmers, academic departments, computation centers, industries, and other organizations accumulate numerous programs. But the field is so young and the referencing and handling problems so large that as yet no systematic solution to library needs has emerged. Moreover, most program bibliographies are not geared to the needs of behavioral scientists. About the only program bibliography that is useful is the "Computer Program Abstracts," published in *Behavioral Science* in each issue since 1960. Each abstract describes a program briefly and indicates how one can secure the programs.

A very promising solution to program problems has been the preparation of program packages. These packages are sets of programs in which, although the programs perform many different operations, the data preparation for using these programs is highly similar. Since the preparation when using general programs often is rather complex, it is extremely valuable to have programs with input and utilization procedures that are consistent with the other programs and that are explicitly described. Although these packages have many other advantages, it is disconcerting that as yet the careful social scientist will find most of these programs inappropriate to his methodology.

Among those used by social scientists the most widely known packages are the Cooley-Lohnes statistical package and the UCLA Biomedical BMD package. Cooley and Lohnes presented their package three years ago[9] and since then Jones[10] has improved its utilization potential with a versatile tape system. Dixon has described the BMD package[11] and has published a user's manual with fairly complete program descriptions.[12]

## Limitations of Computerized Data Processing

*Seduction.* The computer can be a jealous mistress, persuading us to use it in appropriate ways and more frequently than we should. One very common fault is the resort to shotgun analysis. Since it is an easy matter to compute literally hundreds of crosstables, researchers often forsake the planning of analysis in favor of hoping that in a few of the hundreds of tables they will discover some large percentage differences or chi-squares. On a more general level, overconfidence in the computer leads many to bypass the systematic designing necessary for efficient data handling. As a consequence the data may be organized in a manner which, though technically salvable, is clumsy for computer processing. Much original programming can be avoided if the research director attempts to judge the feasibility of the design. Even with an unlimited amount of computer processing, it is obvious that poorly designed research cannot be magically transformed; nevertheless it appears that some researchers enamored of the computer believe that it can.

Investigators often allow the availability of computer programs to dictate the kind of analysis they undertake. If there are programs which compute t tests and analysis of variance, then the researcher will put his data through these routines. Conversely, the lack of immediate availability of programs for particular kinds of statistics frequently leads the researcher to settle for much weaker analysis. Usually, if he searches for them, he will discover the programs needed at some neighboring department or computer installation.

Even when the programs are available, some researchers will hire a programmer to create their own versions. The lure of the computer can be overpowering. Not infrequently one observes the spectacle of the computer being used to perform operations which would be more efficiently performed on some less magnificent machine or by hand.

*Limitations.* Some losses are sustained by researchers using the computer. Many who have worked directly with interview protocols or who have hand-tabulated questionnaire responses have experienced flashes of insight leading to new hypotheses, suggested

explanations, or some brilliantly revised analysis of the data. Unless one deliberately returns to the uncoded data for that purpose. these serendipities may be forfeited. The rapid turnaround on the computer, however, enables the analyst to examine the completed analysis within hours after it was requested —thus the intuitions that suggested the analysis will still be present for interpretation.

Though the hardware of the computer for all practical purposes never makes a mistake (except when the computer goes "down," at which time the mistakes are so large that the garbled output betrays the illness), computer programmers do make errors. And often these errors, which can lead to completely inaccurate reports, are not easily detected by the user. Before programs are selected, the user should insist on documentation proving the reliability of the programs. Since the process of "debugging" programs can be tedious and tricky, many programmers are content to abbreviate this part of the job. *Caveat emptor.*

*Accessibility.* In addition to the lack of physical access to a computer, a number of factors prevent social scientists from using the computer to full advantage. Some of these factors can be blamed on no one, some are clearly the fault of the computer experts, and some can be laid to the ignorance of many social scientists. Misgivings about the use of computers in social science are in many cases well founded. Many analysts have reservations about the applicability of computer methods to qualitative analysis, are unaware of the availability of programs, or overestimate the probable cost.

But the computer is equally as inaccessible to those who wish to take advantage of it but are so completely unfamiliar with how to go about using it that they never make the first steps—and the first steps may be the hardest. All computer installations should have personnel who can introduce greenhorns to the computer and peripheral electronic equipment. Most facilities have "quickie" courses in programming which will advance the user's awareness of the computer's capabilities and methods of processing problems, even though they do not make him an expert programmer. Being introduced to computer terminology is a great advantage for the user in that computer people generally are difficult to communicate with in ordinary English. Esoteric documentation for many programs is much more easily deciphered by the novice than by the uninitiated. Nevertheless, even with some acquaintance with computerese, the suppliant social scientist may despair of fully communicating his problem to a computer expert. The expert oftentimes founders on his lack of comprehension of social-scientific research problems. Research teams have benefitted from the presence of a computer-trained social scientist on their team who can talk to the computer in their stead. Not only can he translate the problem into language understood by the computer or the computer expert, but also he can uncover already existing programs and assess their applicability to the problems at hand. Such a social-scientist computer expert may even solve some of the aforementioned difficulties, since they result largely from communication barriers.

## THE COMPUTER'S INFLUENCE ON METHODOLOGY AND CONCEPTUALIZATION

After considering how the computer can be applied to the solution of some of the problems encountered in survey research, we are led to the conclusion that if the computer can solve these problems so easily, it ought to be possible to tackle the much larger problems that have been laid aside purely because of their magnitude. Increased data-handling capabilities means that there can be greater methodological flexibility, which in turn grants greater freedom in conceptualizing our problems. A great many of our concepts are either-or dichotomies; the new flexibility and efficiency may allow us to use continuous concepts, thus allowing us to gather more rigorous information on a particular process. Of course difficulties in measurement may still prohibit such an extension, but the computer's capabilities also apply to these problems. Many scaling models require very laborious calculations, and texts that describe them often suggest compromises which will give approximate solutions with less effort; much of the gain in using the model thus is forfeited. But with the computer procedures already available, we are free to choose our measurement model without regard to the amount of computation involved.

One of the advantages of the computer is its capacity for processing much larger samples. Albeit justified in its own right, this capacity has other beneficial consequences. An increase in the size of our sample decreases the $\beta$ error in most statistical testing—that is, the probability of accepting a false null hypothesis. When small samples are required, as when hand-tabulating methods are used, the problem of statistical power $(1-\beta)$ becomes acute. In these instances many investigators are hesitant to be satisfied with the less powerful nonparametric statistics even though they may be more appropriate. But with the larger samples accommodated by computer data processing, most nonparametric statistics yield quite acceptably powerful discriminations. In other words, the computer's efficiency permits a research design in which the statistical procedures are selected solely on the basis of the known properties of the variables.

## USING THE COMPUTER IN THE FUTURE

Few dispute that we are in the midst of a computer "revolution." The past decade will be viewed as the period of the explosive proliferation of computers and as a period of technical breakthroughs. There is a growing consensus that the decade ahead of us will be a period of breakthroughs of a different nature; they will be primarily in applications, in "software." It is inevitable that man will find new and improved ways of utilizing his machines.

Already there has been a good deal of speculation about how behavioral scientists will use the computer of the future. Much is expected of the computer as an aid in theory construction,[13] behavioral experiments,[14] content analysis,[15] and classification systems.[16] But in spite of these speculations about pioneering developments in computer application, there have been few speculations about the future impact of computer technology on survey methods.

Although future developments in sur-

vey data processing largely depend on advances in programming systems, considerable progress can and will be made apart from these advances. Greatly improved information handling can be expected as programs or sets of programs combining and extending various operations are written. As flexibility and ease of control are combined in program preparation, more persons will be able to process larger volumes of data across a wider problem scope. The preparation of easily utilized program packages is a promising trend along these lines. At Stanford a behavioral research package is being written which includes a series of editing programs and a large group of statistical analysis programs.[17] The package includes all the common nonparametric statistics in addition to an easily utilized system of file preparation.

Present computer technology necessitates a good deal of organization and preparation in reducing a conceptual question into a set of processing operations. Innovations in programming systems will permit the construction of survey information systems in which the researcher can present his problem to the computer program in nearly ordinary language. For example, one could simply type out *"For organization X, Y, and Z, test the hypothesis that work satisfaction is related to organizational position."* A program would control the operations by finding the relevant data, assembling the appropriate tabulations, and selecting the proper statistical analysis. In addition to a master data file, such a system would require a dictionary file in which sample, variable, and variable category labels are defined in relation to characteristics of the master data file. The dictionary file, replacing the traditional "coding guide" or "code book," could include information about the measurement properties of each variable. Presumably the nature of the analysis would depend on the assumed measurement properties of the variables involved.

It is indeed difficult to anticipate innovations, developments, and applications in this youthful field. But as computer technology progresses and application opportunities open, we believe that adequate utilization of the computer in behavioral research will increasingly depend on the extent to which the problems we have discussed are taken seriously.

1. S. G. Vandenberg et al., "A Survey of Computer Usage in Departments of Psychology and Sociology," *Behavioral Science,* 7, 1962, 108–110.

2. For an excellent summary of the work being done in these areas, see: E. A. Feigenbaum and J. Feldman (Eds.), *Computers and Thought,* New York: Mc-Graw-Hill, 1963. Also of interest is: J. T. Gullahorn and J. E. Gullahorn, "Some Computer Applications in Social Science," *American Sociological Review,* 30, 1965, 353–365; and J. S. Coleman, "Mathematical Models and Computer Simulation," in R. E. L. Faris (Ed.) *Handbook of Modern Sociology,* Chicago: Rand McNally, 1964.

3. Santo F. Camilleri, "Theory, Probability and Induction in Social Research," *American Sociological Review,* 20, 1962, 170–178.

4. A mark-sense card is a regular IBM card that has up to 27 columns of large bubbles with up to 12 in each column. These bubbles can be used as answer boxes, being marked with special electrographic pencils. A specially equipped electronic machine "reads" these marks and punches the card accordingly. These punched cards can then be used in the same machine as any other IBM card.

5. These devices "read" approximately 1000 answer sheets per hour and transmit the information directly to the computer.

6. An iterative procedure is a routine composed of repetitive computations where the output of every step becomes the input to each succeeding step, the process being monitored by controls that cause the termination of the procedure as soon as certain tolerances or other criteria are met.

7. Frank J. Massey, Jr., *The XTAB Series,* Los Angeles: School of Public Health, UCLA, 1962.

8. H. Hyman, in *Survey Design and Analysis,* Glencoe, Ill.: Free Press, 1955, recommends "internal checks" for locating this kind of error. (P. 155ff.)

9. W. W. Cooley and P. R. Lohnes, *Multivariate Procedures for the Behavioral Sciences,* New York: Wiley, 1962.

10. K. J. Jones, "The Multivariate Statistical Analyzer: A Series of Chain-Linked Programs for the 7090/4," from "Computer Program Abstracts," *Behavioral Science,* 10, 1965, 326–327.

11. W. J. Dixon, "Statistical Packages in Biomedical Computation," in R. W. Stacy and B. D. Waxman (Eds.), *Computers in Biomedical Research,* New York: Academic Press, 1965, pp. 47–64.

12. W. J. Dixon (Ed.), "BMD (Biomedical Computer Programs)," Health Sciences Computing Facility, University of California, Los Angeles, 1964.

13. Coleman, *op. cit.*; J. T. Gullahorn and J. E. Gullahorn, "The Computer as a Tool for Theory Development," in D. Hymes (Ed.), *The Use of Computers in Anthropology,* London: Mouton, 1965; Feigenbaum and Feldman, *op. cit.,* esp. P. 2.

14. For example, see D. M. Messick and A. Rapoport, "Computer-Controlled Experiments in Psychology," *Behavioral Science,* 9, 1964, 378–382.

15. D. C. Dunphy et al., "The General Inquirer: Further Developments in a Computer System for Content Analysis of Verbal Data in the Social Sciences," *Behavioral Science,* 10, 1965, 468–480.

16. See Section V, "Classification and Grouping," in Hymes, *op. cit.*

17. Norman H. Nie and D. H. Bent, *Computer Programs for Behavioral Scientists*, forthcoming in 1967.

*Additional Readings*

H. Borko (Ed.), *Computer Applications in the Behavioral Sciences*, Englewood Cliffs, N. J.: Prentice-Hall, 1962.

A. G. Favret, *Introduction to Digital Computer Applications*, New York: Reinhold, 1965.

W. F. Freiberger and W. Prager (Eds.), *Applications of Digital Computers*, New York: Ginn, 1963.

B. F. Green, *Digital Computers in Research*, New York: McGraw-Hill, 1963.

M. Greenberger (Ed.), *Computers and the World of the Future*, Cambridge, Mass.: M.I.T. Press, 1962.

D. Hymes, *The Use of Computers in Anthropology*, London: Mouton, 1965.

K. Janda, *Data Processing: Applications to Political Research*, Evanston, Ill.: Northwestern University Press, 1965.

H. N. Laden and T. R. Gildersleeve, *System Design for Computer Applications*, New York: Wiley, 1963.

R. W. Stacy and B. D. Waxman (Eds.), *Computers in Biomedical Research*, New York: Academic Press, 1965.

# Epilogue to Part Seven

Many of the stresses that confront professionals and patients may be examined utilizing the already developed theoretical framework. Some of these stresses emanate from social movements and change, others from professional and organizational systems; still others are individually oriented. Regardless of their derivation, methods must be developed for their solution. Problem solving and research are processes through which individuals may reach a tentative solution of particular kinds of problems.

The methods of professional education are in a process of change. The health fields provide their students with extremely varied experiences, and the student is expected to transfer, modify, and implement what he learns in one situation so that it will be applicable in another. The problem-solving approach to patient care is encouraged. The learner is expected to identify problems and collect significant data through observation and then synthesize this data into some meaningful whole. This requires a theoretical basis grounded in knowledge of the physical, social, and behavioral sciences. In some instances, however, this new trend has created intraprofessional stress between the "newly" educated and the "traditionally" educated. Their terminology and symbols often differ; hence mutual understanding often is difficult to achieve.

Many professionals have attempted to resolve this conflict among themselves by withdrawing from each other, by blaming, by refusing to share ideas, or even quitting their jobs. But these methods of coping with anxiety are inadequate; they do not solve the problem. These communication problems can better be resolved by the use of the problem-solving method, which requires the knowledge and skills from professionals with different orientations. These groups could then merge to form a different type of professional with a suitable language system and goals, and thereby form a cohesive group. The problem-solving approach to patient and professional problems can increase the individual health worker's autonomy and security, reduce competition, and enhance knowledge.

Utilizing a few concepts from Ruesch's communication theory,[1] health professionals from different orientations can begin to understand each other. One of these concepts is acknowledgment. This may be with or without understanding, but it tells the other individual that you are listening and interested. The next important concept for effective communication is feedback. Everyone in the communication network has a responsibility for asking for clarification of areas that are not understood. The next concept is what Ruesch calls mutual fit (Rogers[2] calls this genuineness). In essence, what these concepts mean is a matching of one's verbal and nonverbal communication. In other words, one says what one means.

Patients are another individual stress that affects health workers. Menzie's study[3] of a London hospital staff demonstrated some of the types of stresses created

344

by patients which affect nurses. The anxieties were created because of strong feelings towards patients — for example, when nurses had contact with patients who were suffering or dying, when patients became overdependent on the nurse, and when the nurse was forced to assume certain responsibilities. Some of the methods that Menzie found that nurses used to cope with these stresses were: splitting up the nurse-patient relationship, depersonalization, detachment or denial of feelings, blaming, performing ritualistic tasks, and avoidance of change. All these methods of coping with stresses are responses to anxiety. Utilizing the problem-solving approach again, the professional identifies the problem of his own anxiety, then he begins to take steps to reduce this anxiety. Peplau[4] gives some concrete ways of coping with anxieties: (1) naming anxiety, which is the identification of the problem; (2) connecting the anxiety and the relief behavior, which includes collecting data around your own behavior; (3) identifying what you expect and what actually happened in the situation; and then (4) considering where in the sequence of events change is possible, which gives you alternatives for action. This problem-solving approach creates an attitude of expecting the unexpected which prevents responding to stressful situations with severe anxiety.

The hospital and most health agencies function under the bureaucratic system. This system was applicable and functional within the Protestant Ethic where the focus was on cleanliness, efficiency, and work orientation. As the Boston studies on role conflict[5] point out, however, nurses are now taught to teach patients as part of their role; still they are not always rewarded for teaching but rather for efficient paper work and so on. This appears to be true in most health agencies. If the rewards for being a good nurse centered around patient care, the nurse would be at the bedside. Utilizing the problem-solving method gives the nurse added strength for change.

A simple element such as identifying where the problem exists adds strength to the health worker who decides he wants to become a change agent. After defining the problem he has to examine such elements as who has the power in the organization to introduce the change, what are the communication patterns in the group, and what consequences will the change have on others in the organization. After he has gone through this particular stage of the problem, he is now confronted with another problem — a personal problem. Does he want to expend the energy necessary to bring about the change? After he has examined the total picture and his own strengths and weaknesses, and decides to continue the project, he is again faced with a problem. How can he get the other people involved in the change? By this time the health worker who has become a change agent realizes some methods that have proven to be ineffectual. Specifically he will not simply introduce the change and try to implement it, neither will he attempt to coerce others into accepting the change, nor will he use his own power by driving his point; but he will involve the people who will be affected by the change in the total process.

There is a final step — the implementers of and users of the problem-solving process for change can expect new stresses. Because this professional has had the courage, knowledge, and skill necessary to step out of the "box," he will be confronted with new stresses and pressures. But knowledge and use of the process may give him strength. This type of process may assist the individual toward self-actualization, freeing him from the bonds of tradition and ritualistic behavior. As Maslow[6] points out, the self-actualizing individual has developed a more problem-centered approach to life stresses, has increased perception, is more accepting of self and others, is more autonomous, and has increased creative ability. As one begins to view life as a series of solvable problems (not in one but in many ways), then one becomes less preoccupied with the "right" answers which in turn can free the individual from tradition and ritualism.

One of the most obvious problems that has been created in work situations is conflict between physicians and nurses. Value systems and personal and professional beliefs and attitudes stemming from the three differing ethical orientations add to the conflicts. These, too, are related in part to the changing roles of men and women and the changing roles of nursing and medicine. If both groups are willing to utilize the problem-solving approach, such conflicts may be elevated from a personal level to an intellectual and behavioral level and then can be resolved.

The patient-professional interpersonal relationship may also contain problems that need solution. The patient problems may be as simplistic as the need for linen change to add to comfort or they may be as complex as the need for psychosocial help to die with dignity. Again, utilizing the same modes of problem-solving just discussed, solutions may be found and patient care enhanced.

The problem-solving approach is most effective for solutions to everyday problems or to problems that affect a single group or agency. When these problems are widespread, they are better handled through research. In the case of patients, although each problem to some extent will be idiosyncratic, their problems as outlined in Part Six are universally recurrent for all ill persons; they therefore lend themselves to research methods. If the health worker and related scientists are to contribute to theories that will bring about the most comprehensive treatment for these recurrent phenomena, they must subject these phenomena to scientific scrutiny through research.

This is by no means an easy task. Indeed, it is fraught with the difficulties of providing sufficient time, finances, and trained personnel. Research may be further complicated by role conflict. The professional who is both a clinician and a researcher is living in a marginal world. The clinical demands frequently make some of Stouffer's designs a virtual impossibility. When confronted with dying or critically ill patients, one may find data collection so demanding as to make it impossible to continue the research. Experimenting with various diagnostic and treatment modalities often must be subordinated to a humanistic approach to patients.

Depending on the particular research problem, the technique of data collection, sample choice, and consequent analytic generalization may have to be modified. If research techniques are not available for the demands of the medical situation, new ones, as Wald and Leonard emphasize, may need to be developed. In any event, unless a sound theory of patient care is developed, practice will continue along traditional, trial-and-error, problem-solving lines.

Although we do not advocate that every clinician be a researcher, nor every researcher a clinician, we do think both groups must develop an appreciation and understanding of the demands of their own orientations. The clinician may need to modify his behavior in the name of research that will, hopefully, add new and useful knowledge, and the scientist must so design his research that clinical practice is not jeopardized.

Research begins with the test of hypotheses derived from a theoretical base, but it must be remembered that the raw data of research itself may generate new theory. Through research that tests theory, one can scientifically scrutinize the problems of inter- and intraprofessional role conflicts, career choices, socialization processes, cultural lag, social change, and patient care. As data accumulate, they too can be conceptualized into new theoretical frameworks which in turn may be tested, accepted or modified, and eventually applied as a theory of patient care.

1. Jurgen Ruesch, *Therapeutic Communication*, New York: Norton, 1961.

2. Carl Rogers, *On Becoming a Person*, Boston: Houghton Mifflin, 1961.

3. Isabel Menzie, "A Report on a Study of the Nursing Service," *Human Relations*, 13, No. 2, 1960.

4. Hildegard Peplau, *Interpersonal Relations in Nursing*, New York: Putnam, 1952.

5. Mary Malone and Norman Berkowitz, "Role and Role Conflict," paper presented at N.L.N. Convention, New York, May 1963.

6. Abraham Maslow, *Toward a Psychology of Being*, Princeton, N. J.: Princeton University Press, 1962.

# *Annotated Bibliography*

## PART ONE

⌐Aasterud, Margaret, "Explanation to the Patient," *Nurs. Forum,* **2**, No. 4, 1963, 36–44.

Explanations given to patients should be based on knowledge of how people react to stress, how anxiety affects a person's ability to communicate, how sociocultural factors influence behavior and the nurse expectations of patient's behavior.

Benedict, Ruth, *Patterns of Culture,* Boston: Houghton Mifflin, 1934.

A comparison of three cultures from a psychoanalytic framework and demonstration that "cultures cannot be compared on an ethical basis, but simply as coexisting and equally valid patterns of life."

Benson, Purnell Handy, *Religion in Contemporary Culture: A Study of Religion through Social Science,* New York: Harper, 1960.

A text in the scientific study of religion discussing the nature, functions, and causes of religion and the relationship of religion to family life and society.

Berkowitz, Norman, and Warren Bennis, "Interaction Patterns in Formal Service Oriented Organizations," *Admin. Sci. Quart.,* **6**, No. 1, 1961, 25–50.

Questionnaire study of nurses in O.P.D. regarding the relationship of status to initiation, transmission of organizational and interpersonal material, frequency and satisfaction of communication.

Bigham, Gloria D., "To Communicate with Negro Patients," *Am. J. Nurs.,* **64**, No. 9, 1964, 113.

This is an article by a Negro nurse writing from the standpoint of a Negro. A nurse and an occasional patient, explaining the subtleties of Negro-white communication, and the role of the white nurse in dealing with Negro patients.

⌐Blair, Peter, *Exchange and Power in Social Life,* New York: Wiley, 1964.

An interactionist approach to the processes in interpersonal relations and social structure.

Bochnak, Mary, Julina Rhymes, and Robert C. Leonard, "The Importance of Communication Skills for Effective Nursing," *Innovations in Nurse-Patient Relationships,* New York: American Nurses Assn., Monograph No. 6, 1962, pp. 5–11.

A discussion of communication between nurses and patients regarding the administration of pain medication.

Brown, Roger, and Ursula Bellugi, "Three Processes in the Child's Acquisition of Syntax," *Harvard Educ. Rev.,* **34**, 1964, 133–151.

349

A good succinct article on the child's development of syntax from utterances of sound to integrative grammatical sentences.

Bullough, Vern L., "Status and Medieval Medicine," *J. Health Hum. Behav.*, **2**, 1961, 204–210.

A suggestion that the separation of medicine from surgery in the Middle Ages was caused by a struggle for control of the medical profession centered around concern for status and need for patients, and is still a situation of status conflict.

Caplovitz, David, *The Poor Pay More: Consumer Practices of Low-Income Families*, New York: Free Press of Glencoe, 1963.

A research study by the Bureau of Applied Social Research of Columbia University on economic practices of the poor including how they spend money for poor value goods, accumulate debts, and get into trouble with the law.

Caudill, W., *Psychiatric Hospital as Small Society*, Cambridge, Mass.: Harvard University Press, 1958.

A description by an anthropologist posing as a patient, of a psychiatric hospital as a closed system resembling a small compact society.

Chombart de Lauwe, Paul, "Introduction: Images of Women in Society," *Int. Soc. Sci. J.*, **14**, 1962, 7–25.

Reveals the image of women held by males and females in various cultures and shows how this image can act to expedite or prevent changes in social structures.

Chrzanowski, Gerard, "Cultural and Pathological Manifestations of Paranoia," *Perspectives Psychiat. Care*, **1**, No. 4, 1963, 34.

This is a study of paranoid personalities leading the author to the conclusion that our culture fosters tendencies to paranoia by encouraging people to strive for uniqueness and individual power in a way that basically leads to isolation, insulation, and profound feelings of loneliness and helplessness.

Conant, James, *Slums and Suburbs: A Commentary on Schools in Metropolitan Areas*, New York: McGraw-Hill, 1961.

Focuses on differences in curriculum, organization, and student job and educational aspirations in city slums versus suburbs.

Davidson, Henry A., "Non-Verbal Communication in a Hospital Setting," *Perspectives Psychiat. Care*, **1**, No. 1, 1963, 12.

Concludes that in working with patients the communication of moods and emotions (nonverbal) with patients and the quality of this communication is more significant than superficial or formal verbal communication.

Dunham, H. Warren, and S. Kirson Weinberg, *The Culture of the State Hospital*, Detroit: Wayne State University Press, 1960.

This study attempts to answer questions confronting psychiatrist and hospital administrator, questions relating to management, treatment, and rehabilitation of patients, and particularly to determine the influence of the culture setting of the hospital upon mental patients.

Dunn, Halbert L., "A Philosophy for Community Development," *Community Development Seminar*, University of North Carolina School of Public Health, May 1963, pp. 5–9.

A comparison of communities to biological models as a way of expressing a philosophy of planning and development.

Dye, Mary C., "Clarifying Patients' Communications," *Am. J. Nurs.*, **63**, No. 8, 1963, 56.

Study of medical-surgical patients demonstrating their difficulty in describing distress adequately enough for the nurse to determine necessary care.

Eldred, Stanley H., "Improving Nurse-Patient Communication," *Am. J. Nurs.*, **60**, No. 11, 1960, 1600–1602.

Advocates the need for understanding and utilizing the processes of non-verbal communication.

Fulton, Robert L., "The Clergyman and the Funeral Director: A Study in Role Conflict," *Soc. Forces*, **39**, 1961, 317–323.

Report of a study of 1990 clergymen's attitudes toward the new role of funeral directors. Findings of the study show that Catholic and Protestant clergymen view their role, the funeral director's role, and the role of funerals differently.

Goffman, Erving, *The Presentation of Self in Everyday Life*, Edinburg: University of Edinburg, Social Sciences Research Center, Monograph No. 2, 1956.

A brilliant piece of work intended as a "sort of handbook" for dissecting the social situations of everyday life, especially ones that occur in buildings and plants.

Hardt, Robert, and Sherwin Feinhandler, "Social Class and Mental Hospitalization Prognosis," *Am. Sociol. Rev.*, **24**, 1959, 829–836.

A study of how the determination of prognosis by physicians is based on and differs with the social class of the patient.

Henry, Jules, *Culture against Man*, New York: Random House, 1963.

An excellent critique of contemporary American culture and its impact on parent-child relations, schools, and old age, as well as the subsequent problems of mental illness, human obsolescence in nursing homes and hospitals.

Hewitt, Helon, and Betty Pesnecker, "Major Blocks to Communicating with Patients," *Am. J. Nurs.*, **64**, No. 7, 1964, 101.

This article demonstrates five categories of verbal errors in dealing with problems of patients, such as changing the subject when a patient is deeply involved with something he is trying to communicate, pressing one's own opinion which gives the impression of moralization, inappropriate reassurance, jumping to conclusions, inappropriate use of facts.

Holland, William R., and Roland G. Tharp, "Highland Maya Psychotherapy," *Am. Anthropol.*, **44**, No. 1, 1964, 41–52.

An examination of Mayan psychotherapy (the persuasive healing method attempting to reintegrate the person into his universe) predicated on a supernatural view, but, like modern therapy, attempts to induce change in attitudes, emotions, and behavior.

Hollingshead, August B., and Frederick C. Redlich, "Social Stratification and Psychiatric Disorders," *Am. Sociol. Rev.*, **18**, 1953, 163–169.

The research reported here grew out of the work of a number of men who, during the last half century, have demonstrated that the social environment in which individuals live is connected in some way, as yet not fully explained, to the development of mental illness.

Hollingshead, August B., and Frederick C. Redlich, *Social Class and Mental Illness: A Community Study*, New York: Wiley, 1958.

This is the final report of one part of a research project carried out by a team of social scientists and psychiatrists into the interrelations between social stratification and mental illness in an urbanized community in New Haven, Conn.

Huber, Helen, "Defining the Role of the Psychiatric Nurse," *J. Ft. Logan Mental Health Center*, **1**, No. 2, 1963, 87–101.

Discusses factors contributing to the lack of definition of a nursing role, developments in nursing role definition, and the value of a nondelineated role. Also discusses need for nursing role in terms of concepts rather than in terms of performed tasks.

Hughes, Everett, "Dilemmas and Contradictions of Status," *Am. J. Sociol.*, **50**, 1945, 353–359.

The problem of perceptions of ideal physicians by lay persons and their inability to judge technical competence.

Hyman, Herbert H., "The Value Systems of Different Classes: A Social Psychological Contribution to the Analysis of Stratification," in Reinhard and Lipset, *Class, Status, and Power*, Glencoe, Ill.: Free Press, 1953.

An analysis of factors that contribute to the lack of social mobility among the lower classes.

Irwin, Orvis, "Infant Speech," *Sci. Am.*, September 1949, 22–24.

A study of infant cries showing patterns of speech which differ among boys and girls.

Johnson, Carmen A., "Nursing and Mexican — American Folk Medicine," *Nurs. Forum*, **3**, No. 2, 1964, 104–112.

Some of the problems that face the health worker with Mexicans are reviewed including the impact of magic and folk medicine and the importance of communicating in the patient's language.

Kleiner, Robert J., and Seymour Parker, "Goal-Striving, Social Status, and Mental Disorder: A Research Review," *Am. Sociol. Rev.*, **28**, No. 14, 1963, 189–203.

A review of "some of the research on the relationship of status position and mobility orientation (i.e., discrepancy between achievement and aspiration) to mental illness."

Kluckhohn, Clyde, *Mirror for Man*, New York: McGraw-Hill, 1949.

A humanistic effort to understand some of our cultural patterns toward the future end that someday "within each society the use of scientific methods in the study of human relations can adjust our culture patterns to these changes brought about by technology and worldwide economic interdependence."

LaBarre, Weston, "The Cultural Basis of Emotions and Gestures," *J. Pers.*, **16**, September 1947, 49–67.
An excellent discussion of the differences of the use of the meaning of emotions and gestures and their cultural origins.

Laffal, Julius, *Pathological and Normal Language*, New York: Atherton Press, 1965.
A psychologist draws from several other disciplines and integrates the findings by developing a general theory of the relationship of language, experience, motivation to the development of normal versus pathological communication.

Leggett, John C., "Uprootedness and Working-Class Consciousness," *Am. J. Sociol.*, **68**, No. 6, 1963, 682–692.
A recent study of Detroit blue-collar workers reveals that workmen born in agrarian regions express a higher degree of working-class consciousness than those reared in industrial settings. This finding runs contrary to Marx's hypothesis on the sources of class consciousness, but is consistent with evidence gathered by several social scientists.

Leighton, Alexander H., and Jane M. Hughes, "Cultures as a Causative of Mental Disorder," *Milbank Mem. Fund Quart.*, **39**, No. 3, 1961, 446–488.
A description of how culture may contribute to or even cause various mental health problems.

Lenneberg, Eric. H., "Language Disorders in Childhood," *Harvard Educ. Rev.*, **34**, No. 2, 1964, 152–177.
A definition and developmental history of several childhood disorders, such as retardation, psychosis, aphasia, and the difficulty of speech acquisition, because of the "expectations" of parents regarding children who are so diagnosed.

Lieberson, Stanley, "Ethnic Groups and the Practice of Medicine," *Am. Sociol. Rev.*, **23**, No. 5, 1958, 542–549.
This paper considers the effect of ethnic origins of physicians on the practice of medicine.

Lipset, Seymour Martin, "Social Stratification and the Analysis of American Society," in Bernard Berelson (Ed.), *The Behavioral Sciences Today*, New York: Basic Books, pp. 188–203.
Early European travelers, struck by U. S. egalitarianism, ". . . also suggested that, precisely as a result of the emphasis on equality and opportunity, Americans were more status conscious than those who lived in the more aristocratic systems of Europe. . . . [T]he lack of a well-defined deference structure linked to a legitimate aristocratic tradition forces well-to-do Americans to emphasize background and symbolism."

Locherby, Florence, *Communication for Nurses*, St. Louis, Mo.: Mosby, 1963.
A simple manual on nurse-patient communication.

Maier, Henry W., "A Child's Cognitive Conquest of Space and Time," *Ind. J. Soc. Res.*, **2**, No. 2, 1961, 31–38.

A summary of Piaget's theories of the development of the concepts of space and time by the young child.

Mamoria, C. B., "Public Health In India," *Ind. J. Soc. Work*, **19**, No. 4, 1959, 291–308.

A synopsis of India's major health problems, their social causes, and a suggestion of ways of increasing public health by community development programs.

*Merrill-Palmer Quart. Behav. Dev.*, **9**, No. 4, 1963.

Entire issue devoted to the contributions and problems of Piaget's theory of language and developmental psychology.

Merton, Robert K., *Social Theory and Social Structure*, rev. ed., Glencoe, Ill.: Free Press, 1957.

Development of a functional analysis and theory of social structure, its latent and manifest consequences for the individual, society, and the social order.

Miller, Walter B., "Cultural Features of an Urban Lower-Class Community," Community Services Branch, U. S. Public Health Service, Washington, D.C., mimeographed, 1958; "Lower-Class Culture as a Generating Milieu of Gang Delinquency," *J. Soc. Issues*, **14**, No. 3, 1958, 5–19; "Implications of Urban Lower-Class Culture for Social Work," *Soc. Serv. Rev.*, **33**, 1959, 219–236.

A detailed description of urban lower-class values, culture, and way of life.

Montague, Ashley, "Culture and Mental Illness," *Am. J. Psychiat.*, **118**, No. 1, 1961, 15.

Discusses the influence of culture on mental illness and the influence of mental illness on culture, and asks the question, "how behaviorally deranged can a society get before it endangers its own survival and that of others?"

Moreno, Jacob L., "Psychiatric Encounters in Soviet Russia," *Int. J. Sociom. Soc.*, **2**, No. 2, 1960, 63–87.

Discussion of the perceptions of psychiatric problems and treatment in Russia.

Opler, Marvin K., *Culture and Mental Health*, New York: Macmillan, 1959.

This is a scholarly selection of work from Margaret Mead, Abram Kardiner, Bingham Dai, and nineteen other distinguished researchers on mental health in various cultures around the world — American Indian, South Pacific, Asia, African, Anglo-American, etc.

Parsons, Talcott, and Edward Shils et al., *Theories of Society*, 2 vols., Glencoe, Ill.: Free Press, 1961.

A comprehensive group of writings by noted theorists on the foundations of theory, differentiation, and variation in social structures, personality and the social system, culture, and social change.

Paynich, Mary Louise, "Cultural Barriers to Nurse Communications," *Am. J. Nurs.*, **64**, No. 2, 1964, 87.

This article relates the problems of a nurse trying to teach members of another culture good health practices when she is faced with an unfamiliar culture and an unfamiliar language.

Piaget, Jean, *The Language and Thought of the Child,* New York: Meridian Press, 1955.
Theoretical discussion of the functions of language, the types and stages of conversation, and the understanding and peculiarities of verbal understanding in children of age groups 4–11.

Quint, Jeanne, "Communication Problems Affecting Patient Care in Hospitals," *J. Am. Med. Assn.,* **195**, January 1966, 36–37.
A discussion of the effect of organizational and personal factors as well as changing roles on communication with patients.

Redfield, Robert, "The Folk Society," *Am. J. Sociol.,* **52**, January 1947, 293–308.
An excellent description of folk society and a demonstration of how knowledge of folk society may contribute to understanding of social disorganization and secularization.

Regler, Lloyd H., and August B. Hollingshead, "Class and Disordered Speech in the Mentally Ill," *J. Health Hum. Behav.,* **2**, No. 3, 1961, 178–184.
A relationship is shown between class status and meaningful communication in a group of persons who went to a psychiatric hospital in San Juan, Puerto Rico, for out-patient care.

Robins, Arthur J., "Psychiatric Institutional Services in India," *Population Rev.,* **12**, No. 1, 1958, 46–62.
A cross-cultural look at the types of services available for psychiatric problems in India.

Rosengren, William R., "Communication, Organization, and Conduct in the 'Therapeutic Milieu,'" *Admin. Sci. Quart.,* **9**, No. 1, 1964, 70–90.
Discussion of differences between organizational structure of custodial type of mental care and the "therapeutic milieu."

Ross, John A., "Social Class and Medical Care," *J. Health Hum. Behav.,* **3**, No. 1, 1962, 35–40.
U. S. National Health Survey data, 1957–1959, covering some 200,000 non-institutionalized civilians, confirm previous studies in showing a direct relationship between class and medical care.

Ruesch, Jurgen, *Disturbed Communication,* New York: Norton, 1957.
A theoretical interpretation of the nature, causes, and potential solutions of problems created by disturbed communication.

Ruesch, Jurgen, *Therapeutic Communication,* New York: Norton, 1961.
A theoretical discussion of the uses of communication as a therapeutic measure in psychiatry.

Schatzman, Leonard, and Anselm Strauss, "Social Class and Modes of Communication," *Am. J. Sociol.,* **60**, No. 4, 1955, 329–338.

A study of lower- and middle-class respondents reveals differences in think-ing processes and ability to take the role of others, to use certain terminology, and to implement communication.

Schoene, Wolfgang, "Medicine as a Factor in Acculturation," *Sociologus*, **8**, No. 2, 1958, 113–125.

Medicine must be classified as a subculture — one that theoretically may be attached to any culture. However, the introduction of hygienic measures on the society level usually sets in motion causal chains whose ramifications tend to affect the most diverse spheres of cultural life and may, if uncontrolled, result in some unwished-for side effects.

Shuval, Judith T., "Social Factors Conditioning Recruitment of Nurses in Israel," *J. Health Hum. Behav.*, **3**, No. 2, 1962, 82–87; "Perceived Role Components of Nursing in Israel," *Am. Sociol. Rev.*, **28**, No. 1, 1963, 37–48.

A description of Israeli nurses' perception of their role.

Skipper, James K., Jr., et al., "What Communication Means to Patients," *Am. J. Nurs.*, **64**, No. 4, 1964, 101.

A survey of 132 patients revealing that patients wish to have explanations from physicians and nurses, as exemplified by: "I can live with anything I can understand."

Skipper, James K., Jr., and Robert C. Leonard, *Social Interaction and Patient Care*, Philadelphia: Lippincott, 1965.

A series of articles on communication theory and patient care.

Smith, Sydney, "The Psychology of Illness," *Nurs. Forum*, **3**, No. 1, 1964, 35–47.

A discusison of the symbolic meaning of illness, its potential threat, and the need for health workers to prepare the patients for illness and treatment.

Sommer, N. Theodore, "The Psychologist and Privileged Communication," *J. Offender Therapy*, December 1962.

Raises issues of "privileged communication" and its meaning to the psychol-ogist, client, and society.

Srole, L., et al., "Mental Health in Metropolis: The Midtown Manhattan Study," in Thomas A. C. Rennie series in *Social Psychiatry*, New York: McGraw-Hill, Vol. 1, 1962.

A contemporary ecological study of the relationships of mental health to geographic areas of the city and class variables.

Steward, Julian H., *Theory of Culture Change: The Methodology of Multilinear Evolution*, Urbana: University of Illinois Press, 1955.

Purpose is the development of "A methodology for determining regularities of form, function, and process which recur cross-culturally among societies found in different cultural areas."

Ujhely, Gertrud, "Discussion of 'Cultural and Pathological Manifestations of Paranoia,'" *Perspectives Psychiat. Care*, **1**, No. 4, 1963, 43.

Applies to the insights of Chrzanowski's theory of paranoia to nursing care adding important insights of her own.

UNESCO, *Int. Soc. Sci. J.*, **14**, No. 1, 1962.

Almost entire issue devoted to series of papers on the images of women in a variety of contemporary cultures.

Volkart, Edmund H., "Man, Disease, and the Social Environment," *Stanford Med. Bull.*, **18**, 1960, 29–33.

In discussing the social environment in relation to disease, the author proposes that medical education should not only make the student aware of the patient in his social environment as a unit of analysis, diagnosis, and therapy but the student should also become aware of his own position in the social environment and the bearing of this on his perception and interpretation of medical events.

Watson, Walter B., and Ernest A. T. Barth, "Questionable Assumptions in the Theory of Social Stratification," *Pac. J. Sociol.*, **7**, No. 1, 1964, 10–16.

Discuss logical deficiencies in the assumption that the family is a solidary unit of class membership. Also question the patriarchal model of family in contemporary society and stratification theory.

Weinberg, S. Kirson, "Mental Healing and Social Change in West Africa," *Soc. Problems*, **2**, No. 3, 1964, 257–270.

Discussion of the effect of social change of types of treatment for mental disorders.

White, Leslie A., "Culturalogical versus Psychological Interpretations of Human Behavior," *Am. Sociol. Rev.*, **12**, December 1947, 686–698.

Discusses similarities and differences in cultural and psychological interpretations of beliefs and behavior.

Williams, Robin M., Jr., *American Society: A Sociological Interpretation*, 2nd ed., New York: Knopf, 1961.

A textbook describing and analyzing social groups and institutions (family, economic, educational, etc.), their value systems, structures, and beliefs.

Wittkower, E. D., and J. Fried, "Some Problems of Transcultural Psychiatry," in Opler (Ed.), *Culture and Mental Health*, New York: Macmillan, 1959, p. 489.

Concludes that "There are no doubt marked differences in the frequency and nature of mental diseases in various cultures, although no methodology has yet been devised to quantify these differences in a statistically valid manner."

## PART TWO

Ackerknecht, Erwin H., "Psychopathology, Primitive Medicine, and Primitive Culture," *Bull. History Med.*, **14**, June 1943, 30–67.

Maintains one of the characteristic traits of our culture is to label phenomena — persons, crowds, cultures, religions — as neurotic, psychotic, and the like which in turn prevents us from seeing value in the "primitive."

Bardis, Panos D., "Synopsis of Theories of Social Change," *Soc. Sci.*, **37**, No. 3, 1962, 181–188.

The most important theories of social change, from those formulated by the ancient Greeks to those of present-day thinkers, are classified into eight major categories with a brief summary of each theory presented together with the works of the main representatives of each school.

Ben-David, Joseph, "Roles and Innovations in Medicine," *Am. J. Sociol.*, **65**, No. 6, 1960, 557–568.

Discusses the characteristics of scientific innovators who are pure researchers and those who are "role hybrid" or research and practicing physicians.

Berry, George Packer, "Medical Education in Transition," *J. Med. Educ.*, **28**, March 1953, 17–42.

An essay on the notion that as the transition continues, behavioral and social sciences will become more important aspects of both the premedical and medical preparation.

Blumer, Herbert, *Collective Behavior*, New York: Wiley, 1957.

A theoretical conception and analysis of forms of collective behavior.

Carter, Richard, *The Doctor Business*, New York: Dolphin (Doubleday), 1958.

This book exposes the commercial side of the doctor's practice and of organized medicine in the United States, revealing the numerous economic pressures operating on the average doctor and presenting the layman an unvarnishd picture of the policies and practices of the American Medical Association, of the availability of health services, of the cost of diagnosis and treatment, and the efficacy of different types of health insurance.

Chladek, Marian, "Nursing Service for Migrant Workers," *Am. J. Nurs.*, **65**, No. 6, 1965, 62.

Concerned with the health problems of migrant workers who are without financial resources and friends and are ineligible for welfare aid.

Coleman, James, and E. Katz, "The Diffusion of an Innovation among Physicians," *Sociometry*, **20**, December 1957, 253–270.

An excellent study of the social processes through which M.D.'s in four cities accepted or rejected a new antibiotic drug for use with patients.

Crane, Edgar, "Immunization — With and Without Use of Counter-Arguments," *Journalism Quart.*, **39**, No. 4, 1962, 445–450.

Recent evidence that a communicator who includes opposition arguments in his presentation can "immunize" his audience against opposition arguments not included raises the question of whether immunization depends on familiarity with any opposition arguments or, perhaps, only on making a decision with the knowledge that an oposition viewpoint exists (and is being rejected).

Cumming, Elaine, "Phase Movement in the Support and Control of the Psychiatric Patient," *J. Health Hum. Behav.*, **3**, No. 4, 1962, 235–241.

Interviews with patients admitted for the first time to a mental hospital reveal that the path to the hospital has four phases: (1) patients receive support from "responsible" members of the web of kinship and friendship; then (2) from the "sociable" members of this web; (3) patients come under the control of members of the network of society's controlling agents who can be thought of as "on the patients' side." (4) Patients come under the control of agents formally charged with the defense of the system.

Cumming, John, "Considerations in Planning Psychiatric Wards in General Hospital," *J. Ft. Logan Mental Health Center*, 1, No. 2, 1963, 59–69.
Review of recommendations of Joint Commission on Mental Illness and Health and the National Association for Mental Health. Discusses problems in financing such programs, which groups of psychiatric patients the service is designed for, what type unit is necessary, use of space and number of staff required.

Dain, Norman, *Concepts of Insanity in the United States — 1789–1865*, New Brunswick, N.J.: Rutgers State University, 1964.
The author explains the changes in psychiatric theory and practice on the one hand, and the apparent lack of change in the fearful and stereotyped public image of insanity on the other.

Davidson, Henry A., "Civil Rights and Mental Hospitals," *Perspectives Psychiat. Care*, 1, No. 4, 1963, 28.
This article discusses the problem of the civil rights of a mental patient both from the angle of the patient and of society.

Dykens, James, Robert Hyde, Louis Orzack, and Richard York, *Strategies of Mental Hospital Change*, Boston: Commonwealth of Massachusetts, Department of Mental Health, 1964.
Report of a project which was superimposed on a state hospital to improve the hospital and its image in the local community.

Field, Mark G., "The Doctor-Patient Relationship and the Perspective of 'Fee-for-Service' and 'Third-Party Medicine,'" *J. Health Hum. Behav.*, 2, Winter 1961, 252–262.
An examination of certain aspects of the doctor-patient relationship as they might be affected by the institutional structure in which this relationship takes place. Comparisons of English, Soviet, and American patterns of medical practice are made with reference to roles played by M.D.'s in varying degrees of commitment to patient and the state, based on professional attitudes and sources of payment.

Friedenberg, Edgar Z., "Neo-Freudianism and Erich Fromm," *Commentary*, 34, No. 4, 1962, 305–313.
An evaluative analysis of the theories of Fromm, his attitudes toward social and political issues, and the differences and similarities between his work and that of Freud.

Gouldner, Alvin W., "Cosmopolitans and Locals: Toward an Analysis of Latent Social Roles—1," *Admin. Sci. Quart.*, 2, December 1957, 281–306.
A theoretical discussion of social influence and interest roles and their implications for the acceptance of change.

Greenblatt, Milton, et al., *From Custodial to Therapeutic Patient Care in Mental*

_Hospitals: Explorations in Social Treatment,_ New York: Russell Sage Foundation, 1955.

Although not yet definitive, an excellent monographic contribution to the sociology of the mental hospital.

Hagendra, S. P., "The Nature and Significance of Ritual," _East. Anthropol.,_ **15**, No. 1, 1962, 2–20.

Discusses ritual as being mythical or metaphysical and hence has differing significance for systems of action.

Hertz, Marguerite, Ira Friedman, Albert Paolino and Gladys Friedman, "Mental Patients and Civil Rights: A Study of Opinions of Mental Patients on Social and Political Issues," _J. Health Hum. Behav.,_ **1**, No. 4, 1960, 251–258.

A study of the influence of specific areas of communication on the opinions of a mentally ill group and on their ability to make decisions on important social and political issues.

Ishiyama, Toaru, et al., "Resolving a Nursing Leadership Crisis," _Am. J. Nurs.,_ **65**, No. 3, 1965, 106.

The authors analyze the reactions of staff when a new director of nursing more interested in people and democratic action than efficiency replaced a director of opposite orientation in an old run-down mental hospital.

Joint Commission on Mental Illness and Health, _Action for Mental Health,_ New York: Science Editions (Wiley), 1961.

An analysis and evaluation of manpower, facilities, and costs of care for the mentally ill and recommendations for a national mental-health program.

Jones, Ernest, _The Life and Work of Sigmund Freud,_ New York: Doubleday, 1963.

A snyoptic biography of Freud including the development of his theories.

Jones, Maxwell, _Therapeutic Community,_ New York: Basic Books, 1953.

A classic on the development of hospitals and units as a "therapeutic community" in which the patient learns to function as he must in returning to his own community.

Jones, Maxwell, _Social Psychiatry,_ Springfield, Ill.: Thomas, 1962.

A presentation of Jones philosophy of mental illness and a theory for psychiatric practice.

Katz, Elihu, and Paul F. Lazarsfeld, _Personal Influence: The Part Played by People in the Flow of Mass Communications,_ Glencoe, Ill.: Free Press, 1955.

An outstanding theoretical contribution to the study of mass communication showing the need to consider "influence" within the context of the group or groups to which individuals belong and identify with.

Kent, Ruth Kimball, "Mental Health Coverage in Six Mass Magazines," _Journalism Quart.,_ **39**, No. 4, 1962, 519–521.

Mental-health articles in the 1960 _Reader's Digest, Life, Look, Ladies Home Journal, McCall's,_ and _Saturday Evening Post_ were analyzed to determine educational value.

King, C. Wendell, *Social Movements in the United States*, New York: Random House, 1956.

An analysis of the nature, motives, problems, career, and consequences of social movements in the United States.

Klapper, Joseph T., *Effects of Mass Communication*, Glencoe, Ill.: Free Press, 1960.

A study summarizing and integrating the findings of published research on the psychological and sociological effects of mass communication.

Korten, David C., "Situational Determinants of Leadership Structure," *J. Conflict Resolution*, **6**, No. 3, 1962, 222–235.

Drawing on R. K. White and R. Lippet's operational definitions of authoritarian and democratic leadership forms, a model is developed of certain situational characteristics that tend to result in each leadership form.

LaPiere, Richard T., *The Freudian Ethic*, New York: Duell, Sloan & Pearce, 1959.

A treatise on the development of the Freudian Ethic in the United States and its permeation throughout the family, work, school, and religious systems of life.

Lee, Alfred McClung, "The Social Dynamics of the Physician's Status," *Psychiatry*, **7**, 1944, 371–377.

A discussion of the assets and liabilities inherent in the great prestige given to M.D.'s.

Leighton, S. H., J. A. Clausen, and R. N. Wilson (Eds.), *Explorations in Social Psychiatry*, New York: Basic Books, 1957.

A series of articles on the mentally ill individual, shared mental illness, and the relationships of mental illness to society.

Lerner, Joseph, "The Role of the Psychologist in the Disability Evaluation of Emotional and Intellectual Impairments under the Social Security Act," *Am. Psychol.*, **18**, No. 5, 1963, 252–256.

Implications for the role of psychologists in evaluation of physical and mental impairments of clients.

Lowry, Ritchie P., "Leadership Interaction, Group Consciousness, and Social Change," *Pac. Sociol. Rev.*, **7**, No. 1, 1964, 22–29.

A series of interrelated hypotheses describing the rise and development of consciousness and identity within a dispossessed leadership group are abstracted from an analysis and criticism of K. Marx's concept of the rise of class consciousness. These are then tested against the findings of a five-year study of leadership interaction in a rapidly changing small community in northern California.

McGee, Reece, *Social Disorganization in America*, San Francisco: Chandler, 1962.

A nonevaluative theoretical approach attempting to outline the positive and negative consequences of individual, group, organizational, and societal change versus disorganization.

Magnussen, Ann, "Who Does What in Defense, in Natural Disaster," *Am. J. Nurs.*, **65**, No. 3, 1965, 118.

An illustrated article showing how every branch of nursing fits into a disaster situation—Red Cross, government, the individual nurse, and nurses' professional groups. The disaster envisaged is war.

Marks, John, Hayden L. Mees, and Edward Summel, "Ideology, Social Change and Violence in a Mental Hospital," *J. Health Hum. Behav.*, **4**, No. 4, 1963, 258.

This discusses breakdown in communications in a disturbed ward of a medium-sized federal mental hospital as a result of what seemed a simple incident, a fight between patients and attendants. Investigation revealed that a change in the hospital philosophy had affected social groups there in the sense that low-status attendants felt disarmed by the changes and resisted them, whereas high-status professionals promoted changes.

Marmor, Judd, Viola W. Bernard, Perry Ottenberg, "Psychodynamics of Group Opposition to Health Programs," *Am. J. Orthopsychiat.*, **30**, 1959, 330–345.

An excellent essay on the types and causes of oppositions to health legislation.

Marx, Melvin, *Theories in Contemporary Psychology*, New York: Macmillan, 1964.

A series of articles on a wide range of theoretical notions of human psychology. Good annotated bibliography.

Merton, Robert K., "Social Structure and Anomie," *Am. Sociol. Rev.*, **3**, 1938, 672–682.

Theoretical demonstration that nonconformity is not rooted in original nature or biological drives, but has roots in certain phases of social structure.

Mongeau, Beatrice, Harvey L. Smith, and Ann C. Maney, "The 'Granny' Midwife: Changing Roles and Functions of a Folk Practitioner," *Am. J. Sociol.*, **66**, 1961, 497–505.

A study showing the effect of social change on the institution of midwifery practiced by old women which still persists in the rural South among the nonwhite population.

Moran, Edith G., "Integration: Pseudo or Genuine?" *Perspectives Psychiat. Care*, **1**, No. 1, 1964, 12.

A discussion of the problems involved in the integration of psychiatric concepts into the basic nursing curriculum, a process that has been in motion since 1954 when the NIMH made funds available to collegiate schools of nursing to encourage this effort.

Mullane, Mary K., "Proposals for the Future of Nursing," *Nurs. Forum*, **1**, No. 4, 1962, 73–84.

The philosophy of nursing education which guided nursing in the past is not appropriate now. Nurses must be prepared and function on councils where goals and services for patients are delineated and evaluated.

Murphy, H.B.M., "Social Change and Mental Health," *Milbank Mem. Fund Quart.*, **39**, No. 3, 1961, 385–445.

An examination of the evidence regarding the effect of social change on mental health in the following types of change: migration from one country to another, migration from one region to another within the same country, the change from war to peace and vice versa, and the adjustment of non-Western peoples to modern Western civilization.

Nelson, Sherman, "The Existential Attitude and the Therapeutic Community," *J. Ft. Logan Mental Health Center*, **1**, No. 2, 1963, 71–85.

Reviews existential attitude, concepts, and orientation. Discusses utilization of existentialism in treatment in a therapeutic psychiatric community.

Norris, Catherine M., "The Trend toward Community Mental Health Centers," *Perspectives Psychiat. Care*, **1**, No. 1, 1963, 36.

Believes that small psychiatric hospitals or psychiatric units in general hospitals, located within the boundaries of the communities to be served, will provide the leadership for community organization in the attack on mental-health problems; that they will provide the resources for expert treatment and consultation and help prepare increased numbers of workers needed in the psychiatric field.

Oaklander, Harold, and Edwin A. Fleishman, "Patterns of Leadership Related to Organizational Stress in Hospital Settings," *Admin. Sci. Quart.*, **8**, No. 4, 1964, 520–532.

Specifically examined are some relationships between the perceptions of the leadership role held by hospital supervisors and the amount of "stress" within their departments and with other units of the organization.

Opler, Marvin K., "Social Psychiatry—Evolutionary, Existentialist, and Transcultural Findings," *Psychosomatics*, **2**, Nov.-Dec. 1961, 35–43.

Author finds that whatever the generic similarities, no two cases are exactly the same, yet they fall into deterministically general patterns in terms of social and cultural variables.

Ostrow, Seymour, "The Medico-Legal Conflict," *Am. J. Nurs.*, **63**, No. 7, 1963, 67–71.

A lawyer discusses the raging conflict between medical and legal authorities regarding drug addiction and care while the addict remains oblivious to the conflict. Contrasts the U. S. system in which M.D.'s "exited with the entrance of the Harrison Act" and the British system in which the law exited and M.D.'s entered into care of addicts.

Owen, Carol, "Feminine Roles and Social Mobility in Women's Weekly Magazines," *Sociol. Rev.*, **10**, No. 3, 1962, 283–296.

Discusses the reality of the roles of women portrayed in nine leading women's weekly magazines and their potential impact on the readers.

Park, Robert E., "Human Nature and Collective Behavior," *Am. J. Sociol.*, **32**, 1927, 733–741.

One of the classic early theories on collective behavior from which most later sociological notions of this phenomenon originated.

Parsons, Talcott, "Toward a Healthy Maturity," *J. Health Hum. Behav.*, **1**, No. 3, 1960, 163–182.
Discusses role of health workers in caring for the older age group whose value in this country is perceived as limited in comparison with youth.

Parsons, Talcott, "Social Change and Medical Organization in the United States: A Sociological Perspective," *Ann. Am. Acad. Polit. Soc. Sci.*, **346**, March 1963, 21–23.
Health is highly valued as a condition of achievement, and the cooperation of the individual in maintaining health is stressed. Against this background the development of "scientific medicine" has impact as part of the trend of industrial society, as well as upon medical education and the organization of medical care around the hospital.

Pryer, Margaret W., Austin W. Flint, and Bernard M. Bass, "Group Effectiveness and Consistency of Leadership," *Sociometry*, **25**, No. 4, 1962, 391–397.
An empirical examination of the significance of the early effectiveness of a leader on his subsequent success in influencing others.

Randall, Ollie A., "The Situation with Nursing Homes," *Am. J. Nurs.*, **65**, No. 11, 1965, 92.
The author finds that nursing homes are too widely considered a business first and a service second, that although nursing care is their main commodity it is usually below minimal standards, and that many nurses who could teach the public what nursing care can and should be are unconcerned or silent.

Roemer, Milton I., "Changing Patterns of Health Service: Their Dependence on a Changing World," *Ann. Am. Acad. Polit. Soc. Sci.*, **346** March 1963, 44–56.
Demonstration on how health services are affected, modified, and changed by world changes such as urbanization, rising cost, increased life expectancy, population growth, and the like.

Rosen, George, "Social Stress and Mental Disease from the Eighteenth Century to the Present: Some Origins of Social Psychiatry," *Milbank Mem. Fund Quart.*, **37**, No. 1, 1959, 5–32.
An historical tracing of the origins and changes in stresses creating mental disease and the subsequent beginnings of social psychiatry.

Rosen, George, "The Evolution of Social Medicine," in Howard E. Freeman et al. (Eds.), *Handbook of Medical Sociology*, Englewood Cliffs, N. J.: Prentice-Hall, 1963, p. 2.
A brief, well-presented exposition of the evolution of medical sociology, tracing the origin of medical sociology from the earliest recognition by philosophers, social reformers, and medical men who felt the health of workers was a social problem.

Roth, Julius A., "Ritual and Magic in the Control of Contagion," *Am. Sociol. Rev.*, **22**, June 1957, 310–314.

An illustration of the action of folkways in the health field in a hospital for tuberculosis.

Russell, William Logie, *The New York Hospital: A History of Psychiatric Service 1771–1936*, New York: Columbia University Press, 1945.

New York Hospital pioneered in both public and private care of mentally ill and is today one of only about a dozen voluntarily supported hospitals in America offering such treatment. This book is an account of treatment at New York Hospital during the years mentioned in the title, using hospital records, tracing the change in psychiatric thought, facilities, and treatment.

Sabshin, Melvin, and Anselm Strauss, "Large State Hospitals: Social Values and Societal Resources," *Archives Gen. Psychiat.* **5**, 1961, 565–577.

A discussion of social values and resources and their subsequent effect on the development and maintenance of large state hospitals.

Sargent, Emilie G., "Health and Welfare of the Aged—Nursing Contributions," *Am. J. Nurs.*, **60**, No. 11, 1960, 1616.

Recommendations of experienced public-health nurses for the 1961 White House Conference on Aging.

Schmadl, June A., "Ritualism in Nursing Practice," *Nurs. Forum*, **3**, No. 4, 1964, 74–84.

Rituals penetrate nursing practice and deprive the nurse of her professional role. Some of these ritualistic maneuvers are "secrecy," "touching," etc. These should be examined in light of the changing role of nurses.

Schmideberg, Melitta, "Editorial: Social Justice and the Therapeutic Professions," *J. Offender Therapy*, **7**, No. 2, 1963, 37–38.

Maintains psychiatry can never take the place of social and legal justice and must recognize this fact before it creates a loss of moral sense in citizens.

Schramm, Wilbur (Ed.), *The Process and Effects of Mass Communication*, Urbana: University of Illinois Press, 1954.

The book gives background materials that can be used to train novices in the field of research and evaluation of mass communication.

Shannon, James A., and Charles V. Kidd, "Federal Support of Research Careers," *Science*, **134**, No. 3488, 1961, 1399–1402.

The central problem of federal research policy is to develop a program to support the "full structure and range of activities necessary to provide a sound scientific program in medical and the related sciences for the indefinite future."

Shepard, Herbert R., and Robert R. Blake, "Changing Behavior through Cognitive Change," *Hum. Organ.*, **21**, No. 2, 1962, 88–96.

Discusses a five-stage methodology for changing behavior of members of groups, organizations, or society.

Smith, Dorothy M., "Myth and Method in Nursing Practice," *Am. J. Nurs.*, **64**, No. 2, 1964, 68.

Maintains the science of communication is more pertinent for ensuring good patient care than is the science of disease or pathology.

Strauss, Anselm, Leonard Schatzman, Rue Bucher, Denuta Ehrlich, and Melvin Sabshin, *Psychiatric Ideologies and Institutions*, New York: Free Press of Glencoe, 1964.

An interactionist approach to the study of organizations which challenges many conventional ideas of the nature of complex organizations and professions.

Turk, Herman, and Thelma Ingles, *Clinic Nursing: Explorations in Role Innovation*, Philadelphia: Davis, 1963.

An excellent study of student doctors, nurses, and patients showing that the lower-class patient receives poor and often unprofessional treatment.

Turner, Ralph, and Lewis M. Killian, *Collective Behavior*, Englewood Cliffs, N. J.: Prentice-Hall, 1957.

A series of readings on the nature and consequences of social movements and other forms of collective behavior.

Vincent, Jewell, "Some Influences of Sigmund Freud on the 1920's in the United States," *South. Quart.*, **2**, No. 2, 1964, 138–149.

An essay on the influence of Freud on the values, beliefs, and functioning of the individual family and society in the 1920's in the United States.

Wax, Murray, and Rosalie Wax, "The Magical World View," *J. Sci. Study Relig.*, **1**, No. 2, 1962, 179–188.

From the standpoint of the magical world, many otherwise inexplicable attitudes of "primitive" peoples become intelligible. The logic of the magical world is retroactive and pragmatic: when an act succeeds, the actor manifested power; when it fails, his power was inadequate.

West, D. J., *The Other Man: A Study of the Social, Legal, and Clinical Aspects of Homosexuality*, New York: Whiteside, Morrow, 1955.

Presents systematically and dispassionately a cross-cultural comparison of ancient civilizations and contemporary societies which leads to the suggestion that homosexual tendencies are normal in the species and occur wherever they are sanctioned.

Winick, Charles, "The Diffusion of an Innovation among Physicians in a Large City," *Sociometry*, **24**, No. 4, 1961, 384–396.

A study of how physicians are influenced to adopt or reject new drugs.

## PART THREE

Becker, Howard S., "Becoming a Marijuana User," *Am. J. Sociol.*, **59**, 1953, 235–242.

This study describes the casual and non-compulsive character of marijuana users who smoke for pleasure and those who smoke for status without pleasure.

Becker, Howard S., and Anselm Strauss, "Careers, Personality, and Adult Socialization," *Am. J. Sociol.*, **62**, 1956, 253–263.

An essay of career choice and development as a process of dynamic adult socialization.

Becker, Howard S., and James Carper, "The Elements of Identification with an Occupation," *Am. Sociol. Rev.*, **21**, 1956, 341–348.

This is a study of the genesis of identification with an occupation in students doing their graduate work in physiology, philosophy, and mechanical engineering.

Becker, Howard, B. Geer, E. Hughes, and A. Strauss, *Boys in White*, Chicago: University of Chicago Press, 1962.

An extensive field study of the socialization process of medical students.

Becker, Howard S. and Blanche Geer, "Medical Education," in Howard E. Freeman et al. (Eds.), *Handbook of Medical Sociology*, Englewood Cliffs, N. J.: Prentice-Hall, 1963.

A discussion of how present medical education affects students' attitudes— their development of a professional self-image, their movement away from idealism to more callous or realistic attitudes to their profession, the interaction between students and faculty, grading and examination practices, etc.—and raises questions for future research on the forces promoting and obstructing change in medical education.

Blau, Peter M., *The Dynamics of Bureaucracy*, rev. ed., Chicago: University of Chicago Press, 1963.

An empirical study of bureaucratic organization with emphasis on the formal and informal mechanisms of control, adaptation, and change.

Bucher, Rue, and Anselm Strauss, "Professions in Process," *Am. J. Sociol.*, **66**, 1961, 325–334.

An approach to professions which focuses on diversity and conflict of interest within a profession and their implications for change.

Bucher, Rue, and Leonard Schatzman, "The Logic of the State Mental Hospital," *Soc. Problems*, **9**, No. 4, 1962, 337–349.

The effects of social change on the conditions of work, classification, and management of patients are discussed.

Bursten, Ben, "The Psychiatric Consultant and the Nurse," *Nurs. Forum*, **2**, No. 4, 1963, 7–23.

The nurse plays an important role in identifying patients who need psychiatric help, in assisting the psychiatrists in implementing therapeutic measures, and in assisting the collection of relevant data about the patient.

Carleton, Pat, "The Socialization Process of Psychiatric Technicians," *J. Ft. Logan Mental Health Center*, **2**, No. 2, 1964, 61–69.

A good discussion of the processes of self-concept evolution during the training of technicians.

Carper, James W., and Howard S. Becker, "Adjustments to Conflicting Expectations in the Development of Identification with an Occupation," *Soc. Forces*, **36**, No. 1, 1957, 51–56.

Group expectations influence the development of an individual's psychosocial identification with an occupation.

Cherescavich, Gertrude, "The Expanding Role of the Professional Nurse in a Hospital," *Nurs. Forum*, **3**, No. 4, 1964, 9–20.

The role of the nurse is changing from a mothering role to a teaching role.

Clark, Peter, and James Wilson, "Incentive Systems: A Theory of Organizations," *Admin. Sci. Quart.*, **6**, No. 2, 1961, 129–166.

Three types of organizations (based on kinds of incentives) are distinguished and hypotheses presented about the characteristic behavior of these types and the correspondence between the types, social change, cooperation, and conflict.

Cleveland, Sidney E., "Personality Patterns Associated with the Professions of Dietician and Nurse," *J. Health Hum. Behav.*, **2**, No. 2, 1961, 113–124.

A study of the characteristics of nurse and dietitian groups which has implications for career choice and adaptation to the occupational role.

Cockerill, Eleanor E., "Medical Social Work," in Russell H. Kurtz (Ed.), *Social Work Year Book 1960*, New York: National Assn. of Social Workers, 1960.

A presentation of the detailed aspects of the role of medical social workers.

Cooley, Charles, *The Two Major Works of Charles H. Cooley*, Glencoe, Ill.: Free Press, 1956.

A theoretical classic on organization, primary groups, communication, sentiment, social class, and institutions.

Corwin, Ronald G., "The Professional Employee: A Study of Conflict in Nursing Roles," *Am. J. Sociol.*, **66**, 1961, 605–615.

A study of 296 graduate and student nurses and their conflict between conceptions of role and the discrepancies between ideal conception and the actual reality experienced at graduation.

Corwin, Ronald G., and Marvin J. Taves, "Nursing and Other Health Professions," in Howard E. Freeman et al. (Eds.), *Handbook of Medical Sociology*, Englewood Cliffs, N. J.: Prentice-Hall, 1963, Chap. 8, pp. 187–209.

A discussion of the struggles of the nursing profession for status, prestige, and identity.

Dailey, Ward, "The Professions and Professional People," *Nurs. Forum*, **1**, No. 1, 1962, 83–89.

The significance of the designation "profession" and the nature of the responsibilities professional people must bear is discussed.

Davis, Fred, and Virginia Olesen, "Initiation into a Women's Profession: Identity Problems in the Status Transition of Coed to Student Nurse," *Sociometry*, **26**, No. 1, 1963, 89–101.

Student nurses experience identity stress because of the difficulty they have integrating the student nurse role with a concurrently emerging identity of adult womanhood.

Davis, Fred, and Virginia L. Olesen, "Baccalaureate Students' Images of Nursing," *Nurs. Res.*, **13**, No. 1, 1964, 8–15.

An attempt to determine the validity of the view that professional education induces among students a greater uniformity and consensus of oulook on their chosen field, and to weigh the relevance of this view for students in a collegiate school of nursing.

Davis, Fred, and Virginia Olesen, "The Career Outlook of Professionally Educated Women," *Psychiatry*, **28**, No. 4, 1965, 334–345.
A study of collegiate, middle-, and upper-middle-class student nurses and their career plans.

Davis, Fred (Ed.), *The Nursing Profession: Five Sociological Essays*, New York: Wiley, 1966.
A controversial series of essays on the paradox of nursing and nurses.

Durkheim, Emile, *The Division of Labor in Society*, Glencoe, Ill.: Free Press, 1933 (1964 reprint).
A classic theory on the development of the division of labor in societies, the function of this division, causes and consequences of specialization in labor.

Ferrari, Louis M., "Some Personality Characteristics of Male Psychiatric Nursing Assistants in One Facility," *Perspectives Psychiat. Care*, **3**, No. 5, 1965, 38.
Study shows the characteristics of the male psychiatric nursing assistants were assertive, self-initiating, motivated, flexible, and controlled.

Field, Mark G. "Structured Strain in the Role of the Soviet Physician," *Am. J. Sociol.*, **58**, No. 5, 1953.
A study of the Soviet physician faced with potential conflict between his role as M. D. and as a member of a political system whose demands differ from the professional dictates.

Fox, Renee C., "Physicians on the Drug Industry Side of the Prescription Blank: Their Dual Commitment to Medical Science and Business," *J. Health Hum. Behav.*, **2**, No. 1, 1961, 3–16.
The M.D.'s themselves must maintain close personal contact with "practicing" M.D.'s, interpret their data on new drugs, and then "translate" these evaluations for management, and finally, guide sales personnel in their relations with practicing M.D.'s.

Furst, E. J., A. W. Raygor, and A. P. Crofoot, "Basic Motivation and Concept of Nursing as Chosen Profession," *J. Psychol.*, **54**, June 1962, 85–100.
This study attempted to prove that the determining factors for career choices were the individual's concept of the vocation and his concept of himself.

Gelber, Ida, "The Addict and His Drugs," *Am. J. Nurs.*, **63**, No. 7, 1963, 52–56.
A brief discussion of history of sedatives, narcotics, and stimulants. Includes discussion on diffculty of early recognition of addict and motivation for withdrawal.

Goode, William J., "Community within a Community: The Professions," *Am. Sociol. Rev.*, **27**, 1957, 194–200.
A commentary on the professions as a subculture or community within a wider social context of community life.

Gray, Robert M., and W. R. Elton Newman, "The Relationship of Medical

Students' Attitudes of Cynicism and Humanitarianism to Performance in Medical School," *J. Health Hum. Behav.*, Summer 1962, 147–151.

Significant though limited differences were found to support the conclusion that students with high cynicism scores perform less satisfactorily in medical school than do comparable students with lower cynicism scores. Students with high humanitarian scores tend to do better than their counterparts with lower humanitarian scores.

Greele, Andrew M., "Influence of the 'Religious Factor' on Career Plans and Occupational Values of College Graduates," *Am. J. Sociol.*, **68**, No. 6, 1963, 658–671.

Catholics were not found to be less inclined to economic rationality (Protestant Ethic) than Protestant.

Gregg, Dorothy, "The Therapeutic Roles of the Nurse," *Perspectives Psychiat. Care*, **1**, No. 1, 1963, 18–24.

A recent perception of the role of the nurse as a functioning therapist in the client-professional situation.

Habenstein, Robert W., "Critique of 'Profession' as a Sociological Category," *Sociol. Quart.*, Autumn 1963, 291–300.

Discussion of profession as a constellation of characteristics—social symbol, function, and ideology—but not as a sociological category.

Hall, Oswald, "The Stages of a Medical Career," *Am. J. Sociol.*, **53**, 1948, 327–336.

The established specialists constitute the inner core of the profession which functions to control appointments to the medical institutions, to exclude or penalize intruders, to distribute patients, and to enforce rules and control competition.

Hall, Oswald, "Types of Medical Careers," *Am. J. Sociol.*, **55**, No. 3, 1949, 243–253.

A descriptive discussion of the multiplicity of the types of medical careers that are possibilities with the physician's role.

Hallowell, Irving A., "Behavioral Evolution and the Emergence of the Self," from *Evolution and Anthropology: A Centennial Appraisal*, 1959.

Darwinism assisted in defining and shaping the problems of modern psychology as well as anthropology by providing the bridge between man and other animals.

Harris Norman C., "Technical Education," *Am. J. Nurs.*, May 1963, 95.

Reorganization of American education to fit the sociological and technological conditions of the present era is proposed.

Hatt, Paul K., "Occupation and Social Stratification," *Am. J. Sociol.*, **55**, 1950, 533–543.

A well-developed scale of occupations by prestige and the relationship of these occupations to social class.

Huber, Helen, "Defining the Role of the Psychiatric Nurse," *J. Ft. Logan Mental Health Center*, **1**, No. 2, 1963, 87–101.

Author identifies the problems that nurses have had in the past in identifying their role. She proposes that nurses determine their own role in light of the needs of society and assume full responsibility for their actions.

Hughes, Everett C., Helen Hughes, and Irwin Deutscher, *Twenty Thousand Nurses Tell Their Story*, Philadelphia: Lippincott, 1958.
A series of studies on a variety of topics are included in this comprehensive report.

Jones, Maxwell, "Psychiatric Nursing Is Out of Tune in the USA," *Am. J. Nurs.*, 1, January 1964, 103.
An attack on the preparation of psychiatric nurses in the United States.

Kriesberg, Louis, and Lathrop V. Beale, "Career Specifications among Medical Students," *J. Health Hum. Behav.*, Fall 1962, 204–212.
Cognitive learning, debts, class standing, and size of original community affect the career plans of medical students.

Kruger, Daniel H., "Professional Standards and Economic Status of Nurses in the United States," *Int. Nurs. Rev.*, 7, December 1960, 43–48.
The low economic status of nurses affects the professional standards, the nursing care, and hampers recruitment.

Kuhn, Manford H., "Self-Attitudes by Age, Sex, and Professional Training," *Sociol. Quart.*, 9, No. 1, 1960, 39–55.
Out of the twenty-statements test on self-attitude, five categories vary in frequency and salience according to age and sex of respondents and according to their professional identification.

Lee, S. C., "The Primary Group as Cooley Defines It," *Sociol. Quart.*, 5, No. 1, 1964, 23–24.
Strictly observing H. Cooley's original primary group concept, many groups regarded as primary in textbooks should be disqualified by virtue of failure in meeting all the defining qualities.

Lewis, Lionel S., and Joseph Lopreato, "Functional Importance and Prestige of Occupations," *Pac. Sociol. Rev.*, 6, No. 2, 1963, 55–59.
Davis' model is an ideal construct that must be adjusted to take into account social values as well as other factors of a sociopsychological character which mediate these values.

Mack, Raymond W., et al., "The Protestant Ethic—Level of Aspiration and Social Mobility: An Empirical Test," *Am. Sociol. Rev.*, 21, 1956, 295–300.
An empirical study to test the hypothesis: "No significant differences will be found either in social mobility patterns or in aspiration level between samples of Protestant and Catholic Americans in several occupations."

Malone, Mary F., "The Dilemma of a Professional in a Bureaucracy," *Nurs. Forum*, 3, No. 4, 1964, 36–60.
There is a basic conflict between the nurse's concept of herself and the concept held by the physician, administrator, and patients in a bureaucratic structure of the hospital.

Mannino, Sandy Francis, "The Professional Man Nurse: Why He Chose Nursing and Other Characteristics of Men in Nursing," *Nurs. Res.*, **12**, No. 3, 1963, 185–190.

The report of a research study on the personal characteristics, attitudes, and perceptions of male nurses.

Martin, Harry W., and Fred E. Katz, "The Professional School as a Molder of Motivations," *J. Health Hum. Behav.*, **2**, No. 2, 1961, 106–112.

The findings of a study of student nurses at the University of Texas Southwestern Medical School indicates career and professionalism in nursing are in line with the traditions of femininity.

Mauksch, Hans O., "Becoming a Nurse: A Selective View," *Ann. Am. Acad. Polit. Soc. Sci.*, **346**, March 1963, 88–98.

The young woman who enters a school of nursing is not only exposed to planned educational experiences but also to informal reality factors which profoundly shape her development. Some of these reality factors include exposure to the human body, superimposed adulthood, and a single-sex, quasi-isolated community.

Merton, Robert K., et al. (Eds.), *The Student Physician*, Cambridge, Mass.: Harvard University Press, 1957.

A Columbia University study of the role of socialization process of student M.D.'s.

Miller, Roger R., "Learning Objectives of Beginning Psychiatric Social Workers," *Soc. Work*, **8**, No. 1, 1963, 44–50.

A type of motivation for learning study of fledgling social workers.

Mills, C. Wright, "The Professional Ideology of Social Pathologists," *Am. J. Sociol.*, **49**, 1942, 165–180.

The attitudes, beliefs, and ideologies of social pathologists regarding their own profession.

Montag, Mildred L., "Technical Education in Nursing," *Am. J. Nurs.*, **63**, No. 5, 1963, 100.

The author concludes that "Technical education in nursing, if it is to follow the pattern of technical education generally, must include in the curriculum courses in general education, courses dealing with the specialized content in nursing, and such courses which are related to and support the specialized content, as the biological, physical, and behavioral sciences."

More, D. M., and Nathan Kohn, Jr., "Some Motives for Entering Dentistry," *Am. J. Sociol.*, **66**, July 1960, 48–63.

Results of a poll of 3578 enrolling dentistry students as to their motives for choosing that profession indicated that autonomy (chance to be one's own boss and choose one's own responsibility), prestige, money, service, and opportunity to use manual skills were all decisive elements in the choice of the profession, with autonomy taking first place.

Mussen, Paul H., John J. Conger, and Jerome Kagan, *Readings in Child*

*Development and Personality*, New York.: Harper and Row, 1965.

A book of readings covering biological factors in early development, early infant-environment interaction, socialization, cognitive development, behavior differentiation, and adolesence.

Nahm, Helen, "Expectations of Students in Graduate Education," *Nurs. Forum,* 1, No. 4, 1962, 19–27.

A before and after study of students in the master's program in nursing at the University of California. The questions asked involved nursing, job expectations, and knowledge gained.

Ort, Robert S., Amasa B. Ford, and Ralph E. Liske, "The Doctor-Patient Relationship as Described by Physicians and Medical Students," *J. Health Hum. Behav.*, 5, No. 1, 1964, 25–33.

The physician's most evident satisfactions arise from personal affiliation and the giving of help and care, whereas his dissatisfactions frequently stem from lack of control and are mainly attributed to the patient.

Pape, Ruth H., "Touristry: A Type of Occupational Mobility," *Soc. Problems,* 11, No. 4, 1964, 336–344.

"Touristry" is a form of traveling dependent on occupation only to the extent that it finances the travel. Nurses, generally young as a group, are influenced in the type of jobs they seek by the freedom from responsibility, access of young men in an area, pay, and working hours.

Parsons, Talcott, "The Professions and Social Structure," *Soc. Forces,* 17, May 1939, 457–467.

An essay on the important features of our society and its dependence on the smooth operation of the professions.

Parsons, Talcott, "Illness and the Role of the Physician: A Sociological Perspective," *Am. J. Orthopsychiat.*, 21, 1951, 452–460.

A sociological notion of the role of M. D. in the treatment of the patient.

Piotrowski, Jerzy, "Attitudes toward Work by Women," *Int. Soc. Sci. J.*, 14, No. 1, 1962, 80–91.

A comparative study of the attitudes of working and non-working women and their husband's attitudes toward working wives in postwar Poland.

Quarantelli, Enrico, "The Career Choice Patterns of Dental Students," *J. Health Hum. Behav.*, 2, No. 2, 1961, 124–131.

A study of the relationship of personal and social characteristics of student dentists to their professional career choices.

Quinney, Earl R., "Occupational Structure and Criminal Behavior: Prescription Violation by Retail Pharmacists," *Soc. Problems,* 11, No. 2, 1963, 179–185.

A research study testing a theory of role conflict (professional versus business) and its relation to prescription violation by pharmacists.

Reissman, Leonard, and Ralph V. Platou, "The Motivation and Socialization of Medical Students," *J. Health Hum. Behav.*, 1, No. 3, 1960, 174–182.

A study and analysis of the motivation and socialization process of M. D. students showing three general student types.

Rorbaugh, Lewis N., "Doctoral Programs for the Professions: A University Responsibility," *Nurs. Forum*, 1, No. 4, 1962, 35–40.
    Universities have the same responsibilities for doctoral programs for the professions as they have for the arts and sciences. Nursing should take its rightful position in the family of scholars within the framework of universities.

Rosen, George, "Changing Attitudes of the Medical Profession to Specialization," *Bull. History Med.*, 12, July 1942, 343–354.
    Demonstrates the dilemma of physicians whose specialization was viewed by colleagues as "quackery" and the economic factor that gave strength to the move toward specialization.

Rushing, William, *The Psychiatric Professions: Power, Conflict, and Adaptation in a Psychiatric Hospital Staff*, Chapel Hill: University of North Carolina Press, 1964.
    The major theme of this book is that mental hospitals of the therapeutic variety, being relatively new, are organizations in the process of institutionalization.

Sanders, Marion K., "Social Work: A Profession Chasing Its Tail," *Harper's Magazine*, 214, March 1957, 56–62.
    An essay on the dependence of social work on psychoanalytic theory rather than the development of its own theory.

Schatzman, Leonard, and Rue Bucher, "Negotiating a Division of Labor among Professionals in the State Mental Hospital," *Psychiatry*, 27, No. 3, 1964, 266–277.
    A study of how psychiatric professionals decide among themselves how they will perform tasks to meet treatment and their own professional requirements.

Sewell, William H., "Some Recent Developments in Socialization Theory and Research," *Ann. Am. Acad. Polit. Soc. Sci.*, 349, September 1963, 163–181.
    Discussion of developments in theory and methodological advances of early and late socialization utilizing the role approach, social class, and social structure.

Skipper, James K., Jr., "Functional Significance of the Nurse Role: An Evaluation," *J. Health Hum. Behav.*, 3, No. 1, 1962, 41–45.
    This report of an empirical test of I. Thorner's thesis, which suggests that a set of shared expectations is held by nurses, proves to be oversimplified and needs modification.

Smith, Phil M., *Influence of Wage Rates on Nurse Mobility*, Chicago: University of Chicago Press, 1962.
    Even though salary ranks high as a factor in job selection, this study shows other factors are equally important.

Stephens, Roberta R., "In the Middle of the Muddle," *Nurs. Forum*, **3**, No. 4, 1964, 29–35.

A nurse is expected to be a team leader, interpreter, coordinator, technician, keeper of supplies, comforter, and buffer in today's complexity of nursing practice.

Stevenson, Neva, "Curriculum Development in Practical Nurse Education," *Am. J. Nurs.*, **64**, No. 12, 1964, 81.

Concurrent study of theory and practice, and experience with the mentally ill are some of the trends in practical nurse education.

Trail, Ira D., "Registered Nurse Students in Baccalaureate Programs," *Nurs. Forum*, **1**, No. 4, 1962, 29–33.

The registered nurse in a collegiate program faces many problems which require teachers who provide stimulation, acceptance, and interest.

Tryon, Robert C., "Psychology in Flux: The Academic, Professional Bipolarity," *Am. Psychol.*, **18**, No. 3, 1963, 134–143.

A treatise on the conflict between academic versus professional goals, values, and beliefs in psychology.

Wilensky, Harold L., "The Professionalization of Everyone?," *Am. J. Sociol.*, **70**, No. 2, 1964, 137–158.

Describes stages and obstacles that characterize occupational groups which aspire to gain professional status.

Williams, Margaret A., "The Myths and Assumptions about Team Nursing," *Nurs. Forum*, **3**, No. 4, 1964, 61–73.

A discussion of how teams can most effectively operate in reality to assure optimal patient care.

Yeager, Wayne, Wilson T. Sowder, and Albert V. Hardy, "The Mental Health Worker: A New Public Health Professional," *Am. J. Public Health*, **52**, October 1962, 1625–1630.

Faced with the problem of providing extensive community mental-health services, Florida developed a new category and role called mental-health workers and then evaluated this new "profession."

Zander, A., A. R. Cohen, and E. Stotland, *Role Relations in the Mental Health Professions*, Ann Arbor: University of Michigan Press, 1957.

Primarily a psychological study and interpretation of role relations of psychiatrists, social workers, and nurses in a mental-health agency.

## PART FOUR

Allport, Gordon, *Patterns of Growth in Personality*, New York: Holt, Rinehart & Winston, 1961.

An elementary exposition of personality development for the student with little or no background in psychology.

Barber, Ray, *Marriage and the Family*, 2nd ed., New York: McGraw-Hill, 1953.

A sociological textbook covering basic information on mate selection, family structure and function, etc.

Braverman, Charles, and Barbara Day, "A Test of the Theory of Complementary Needs as Applied to Couples during Courtship," *Am. Sociol. Rev.*, **21**, 1956, 602–605.

A study of sixty college couples concludes that the findings do not support the theory of complementary needs recently advanced by Robert F. Winch et al. "It is unlikely that any theory of mate selection which is stated in terms of a uniform direction of relationship between needs in general will be substantiated."

Burgess, Ernest W., and Harvey J. Locke, *The Family from Institution to Companionship*, New York: American, 1953.

A scholarly, comprehensive, scientific account of family behavior with rich case histories written in sociological terms.

Cahill, Imogene, "The Mother from the Slum Neighborhood," Conference on Maternal and Child Nursing, *Current Concepts in Nursing Care*, Pamphlet No. 1, 1964, pp. 1–12.

The V.N.A. in New York City discovered that parents classes were attended mainly by the upper and middle class. Consequently a study of lower-class mothers was made to provide answers to their lack of attendance and possible solutions for their needs.

Chance, Erika, *Families in Treatment*, New York: Basic Books, 1959.

The major thesis of this book is that a combination of clinical and research descriptions of families in treatment contributes more to our understanding than the separate use of either.

Coale, Ansley J., and C. Y. Tye, "The Significance of Age Patterns of Fertility in High Fertility Populations," *Milbank Mem. Fund Quart.*, **39**, No. 4, 1961, 631–646.

A study of Malthus' theory that delayed marriage is a factor in demographic transition, population growth, and birth rate.

Cumming, John H., "The Family and Mental Disorder: An Incomplete Essay," *Milbank Mem. Fund Quart.*, **39**, No. 2, 1961, 185–228.

A framework for looking at the family using T. Parsons' theories of socialization showing the relationship of socialization, life-cycle problems, and mental health.

Devereux, Edward C., Jr., Urie Bronfenbrenner, and George J. Suci, "Patterns of Parent Behavior in the United States of America and the Federal Republic of Germany: A Cross-National Comparison," *Int. Soc. Sci. J.*, **14**, No. 3, 1962, 488–506.

Recent studies of child-rearing trends in the United States have indicated a shift toward: (1) greater permissiveness, (2) freer expression of affection, (3) increased reliance on "psychological" techniques of discipline as against such direct methods as spanking, and (4) an increase in the relative importance of the mother vis-a-vis the father as the principal agent of both discipline and support in the family. The present study presents detailed comparison of current child-rearing practices in matched samples of German and U. S. families.

Downey, Kenneth J., "Parental Interest in the Institutionalized, Severely Mentally Retarded Child," *Soc. Problems,* 11, No. 2, 1963, 186–193.
An empirical study of why some parents demonstrate greater interest in institutionalized mentally retarded children than others shows that the younger parents and the higher educated parents show least interest.

Dunn, Halbert L., "A Positive View of Aging Asks Much of Education," *School Life,* U. S. Department of Health, Education, and Welfare, January 1964, 2–6.
A view that education for aging needs to begin early in life with a plan for maturity.

Duvall, E. M., "Conceptions of Parenthood," *Am. J. Sociol.,* 52, No. 3, 1946, 193–203.
A discussion of married couples' perceptions of what parenthood will and does consist of in terms of attitudes, roles, and problems.

Dynes, Russell R., et al., "Levels of Occupational Aspiration: Some Aspects of Family Experience as a Variable," *Am. Sociol. Rev.,* 21, 1956, 212–215.
A study of the relationship between aspirational level and interpersonal experiences which tend to support some current assumptions in psychoanalytic literature: that unsatisfactory interpersonal relationships in the family are significantly related to high aspirational levels and satisfactory relationships related to lower aspirational levels.

Erickson, M. C., "Child Rearing and Social Class," *Am. J. Sociol.,* 52, No. 3, 1946, 190–192.
A comparison of the attitudes and practices of child rearing by the five social classes in the United States.

Fischer, Ann, "The Importance of Sibling Position in the Choice of Careers in Pediatric Nursing," *J. Health Hum. Behav.,* 3, No. 4, 1962, 283–288.
The hypothesis that oldest daughters are more likely to become nurses than daughters in other sibling positions was tested on a sample of 109 student nurses in Boston in 1957.

Frazier, E. F., *Negro Family in the United States,* Chicago: University of Chicago Press, 1939.
A social scientific description of family patterns and role relationships in Negro families during the depression.

Freeman, Victor, et al., "Family Group Counseling as Differentiated from Other 'Family Therapies,'" *Int. J. Group Psychotherapy,* 13, No. 2, 1963, 167–175.
A proposal of family counseling as a focus on group interaction rather than individual intrapsychic processes.

Freeman, Victor, "Differentiation of 'Unit' Family Therapy Approaches Prominent in the United States," *Int. J. Soc. Psychol.,* Congress Issue 1964, pp. 35–46.
A definition of family therapy and a comparison of the treatment approach of several prominent therapists. Includes a good but brief bibliography.

Glick, Paul C., "The Family Cycle," *Am. Sociol. Rev.*, **12**, 1947, 165–174.

Statistics on the various stage of the family cycle in the United States with comparisons between those conditions existing in 1890 and those in 1940 as to median age of first marriage, birth of first child, birth of last child, marriage of first and last children, death of husband or wife, changes in family characteristics, in residence, and in economic characteristics.

Goode, William J., "Theoretical Importance of Love," *Am. Sociol. Rev.*, **24**, 1959, 38–47.

A good discussion of the role of "love" in marriage, child rearing, and family life.

Goode, William J., "Marital Satisfaction and Instability: A Cross-Cultural Class Analysis of Divorce Rates," *Int. Soc. Sci. J.*, **14**, No. 3, 1962, 507–526.

A discussion of the ideological biases which have produced a static situation in marital stability and instability research, followed by an examination of the relationship between divorce rates and class position.

Greenblum, Joseph, "The Control of Sick-Care Functions in the Hospitalization of a Child: Family Versus Hospital," *J. Health Hum. Behav.*, **2**, No. 1, 1961, 32–38.

The hypothesis that parents are less willing to transfer control of the primary (socioemotional) components than the instrumental (medical care) components of sick-care is examined showing that the length of hospitalization and uncertainty of prognosis are related to parental transfer of control to health workers.

Hall, Calvin S., and Gardner Lindzey, *Theories of Personality*, New York: Wiley, 1957.

A survey and comprehensive summary of the existing theories of personality development.

Hall, Elizabeth, and Sylvia Bruce, "Maternal and Child-Health Nursing," *Current Concepts in Nursing Care*, Conference on Maternal and Child Nursing, Ross Laboratories, 1964 pamphlet.

An excellent discussion on the problems of parenthood, the effect of children's illness, and some possible solutions for health professionals.

Herzog, Elizabeth, "Unmarried Mothers: Some Questions to Be Answered and Some Answers to Be Questioned," *Child Welf.*, **41**, No. 8, 1962, 339–350.

An essay on the issues raised in illegitimacy and some possible solutions to some problems.

Hobart, Charles, and Lauralee Lindholm, "The Theory of Complementary Needs: A Re-Examination," *Pac. Sociol. Rev.*, **6**, No. 6, 1963, 73–79.

Report of research study testing Winch's theory. Findings do *not* support theory of complementary needs but rather tend in the direction that similarity is more important than complementary in mate selection process.

Kaplan, Oscar J. (Ed.), *Mental Disorders in Later Life*, Stanford, Calif.: Stanford University Press, 1956.

A multidisciplinary approach to the study of disordered behavior among the aged.

Kardiner, Abraham, "Explorations in Negro Personality," in Marvin Opler (Ed.), *Cultural and Mental Health,* New York: Macmillan, 1959, p. 413.

An essay concerned with the questions: (1) Does social discrimination affect personality? (2) What is the best way of finding out in a reliable manner what these effects are?

Kirkpatrick, Clifford, *The Family: As Process and Institution,* New York: Ronald, 1955.

A sociological text describing the family functions and processes and the family as an institution replete with stability and change.

LaBarre, Weston, "The Patient and His Families," *Casework Papers,* New York: Family Service Assn. of America, 1958, pp. 61–71.

Demonstrates the problems occurring when adult men with power and responsibility must submit without question to the authority and decisions of the doctor.

Landis, Judson T., "A Comparison of Children from Divorced and Non-Divorced Unhappy Marriages," *Fam. Life Coordin.,* 11, No. 3, 1962, 61–65.

A study of 3000 subjects to determine the association between parental marital happiness as viewed by the respondents, and the respondents relationships with parents, dating maturation, and self-conceptions.

Lewis, Oscar, *Five Families,* New York: Basic Books, 1959.

A cross-cultural comparison of family structure, beliefs, and roles.

Meadow, Lloyd, and Ruth B. Edelson, "Age and Marital Status and Their Relationship to Success in Practical Nursing," *Nurs. Outlook,* 11, April 1963, 289–290.

A study of 244 student practical nurses showing that older, married students are slightly better risks.

Meissner, W. W., "Thinking about the Family-Psychiatric Aspects," *Fam. Process,* 3, No. 1, 1964, 1–40.

An appraisal of current theories and findings in family-oriented psychiatric care.

Miller, D. R., and G. E. Swanson, *The Changing American Parent,* New York: Wiley, 1958.

A theoretical discussion of the social changes affecting families in contemporary society.

Miller, Sally, "A Study in Family Dynamics," *Perspectives Psychiat. Care,* 1, No. 2, 1963, 9.

A study of one family in detail to demonstrate the difficulties in dealing with the interwoven problems of individual, interpersonal, and sociocultural factors.

Myers, Jerome, and Bertram H. Roberts, *Family and Class Dynamics in Mental Illness,* New York: Science Editions (Wiley), 1959.

A report of a study on the relationship of family structure and class to the development of mental illness.

Nagi, Saad Z., and Donovan L. Clark, "Factors in Marital Adjustment after Disability," *J. Marr. Fam.*, **26**, No. 2, 1964, 215.

A presentation of findings of a survey and delineating factors associated with adjustments in marital status after disability.

Nash, D. H., and P. Berger, "The Child, the Family, and the 'Religious Revival' in Suburbia," *J. Sci. Study Relig.*, **2**, No. 1, 1962, 85–93.

To explore the reasons why Americans have been committing themselves increasingly to organized religion, a sample of recent joiners was interviewed.

National Center for Health Statistics, U. S. Department of Health, Education, and Welfare, *Measurement of Personal Health Expenditures*, Washington, D. C.: U. S. Government Printing Office, Public Health Service Publication, No. 1000, Series 2, No. 2, June 1963, 59pp.

An NORC study measuring the validity of responses of subjects on questions of medical and dental expenses.

National Center for Health Statistics, U. S. Department of Health, Education, and Welfare, *Family Income in Relation to Selected Health Characteristics*, Washington, D. C.: U. S. Government Printing Office, Public Health Service Publication, No. 1000, Series 10, No. 2, July 1963, 50 pp.

Information from nationwide yearly interviews conducted for the U. S. National Health Survey in approximately 38,000 households comprising 125,000 persons was examined to analyze three types of health characteristics: (1) disability data that measure the overall effects of chronic and acute illness on the population; (2) hospital-discharge data that measure the effect of illness on the utilization of health facilities; and (3) persons-injured data that gage the impact of accidents and other unforeseen events on the individual.

Parsons, Talcott, and Renee Fox, "Illness, Therapy and the Modern Urban Family," *J. Soc. Issues*, **8**, No. 4, 1952.

An essay on the relationship of various illnesses and therapies and their impact on urban families.

Parsons, Talcott, and Robert Bales, *Family, Socialization and Interaction Process*, Glencoe, Ill.: Free Press, 1955.

A collection of papers on the American family as a social system with role differentiation, the socialization of the child, and the organization of personality. Maintains the family is not in a state of disorganization but rather one of change.

Pollak, Otto, "Social Determinants of Family Behavior," *Soc. Work*, **8**, No. 3, 1963, 95–107.

The effects of illness, power structure, normlessness, and attitudes on family behavior are analyzed.

Queen, Stuart, Robert Habenstein, and John Adams, *The Family in Various Cultures*, Philadelphia: Lippincott, 1961.

A comparison of family systems in twelve different cultures and a tracing of the historical origins of family traits in contemporary United States.

Riese, Hertha, *Heal the Hurt Child*, Chicago: University of Chicago Press, 1962.

A description of a program of combined education and psychotherapy for the extremely deprived child.

Rodgers, Roy, "Some Factors Associated with Homogeneous Role Patterns in Family Cycle Careers," *Pac. J. Sociol.*, **7**, No. 1, 1964, 38–48.

Reports a study of the relationships between size of family, spacing of children, and similarity of role patterns in the family life cycle. Relates findings to a potential theory of family problems and relationships.

Rollins, James M., "Two Empirical Tests of a Parsonian Theory of Family Authority Patterns," *Fam. Life Coordin.*, **12**, Nos. 1–2, 1963, 5–79.

A study testing a theory of family *authority* patterns derived from a portion of the general theoretical system of T. Parsons.

Rossi, Peter H., *Why Families Move: A Study in the Social Psychology of Urban Residential Mobility*, Glencoe, Ill.: Free Press, 1955.

A comprehensive study through depth interviews of the sociopsychological processes accompanying change of residence.

Rutledge, Aaron L., and Dorothy E. Barrier, "Should the Marriage Counselor Ever Recommend Divorce?" *Marr. Fam. Living*, **25**, No. 3, 1963, 319–325.

A discussion of the role of social workers and family counselors, concluding that they should never recommend divorce.

Schiller, Johannes, and Robert Leik, "Symbolic Interaction and Family Role Adjustment," *Pac. Sociol. Rev.*, **6**, No. 1, 1963, 30–36.

Discusses the relationship of value commitment in interaction and changes in family roles. Develops postulates for testing regarding role adjustment in families and the interaction between man and wife.

Schwartz, Charlotte Green, "Perspectives on Deviance — Wives' Definitions of Their Husband's Mental Illness," *Psychiatry*, **20**, 1957, 275–291.

A study of wives' perceptions of their husband's behavior and their definition of mental illness.

Smart, Susan S., "Social Class Differences in Parent Behavior in a Natural Setting," *J. Marr. Fam.*, **26**, No. 2, 1964, 223.

A study of parents and children at two beaches investigating the socioeconomic differences in the relationships and behavior of both parents and their offspring.

Speck, Ross V., "Family Therapy in the Home," *J. Marr. Fam.*, **26**, No. 1, 1964, 72–76.

An essay on the potential for family therapy in the home rather than in a more formal setting.

Spitz, Rene A., *The First Year of Life*, New York: International Universities Press, 1965.

A detailed description of interchange between mothers and their children and their subsequent normal or deviant development.

Talmon, Garber Y., "Social Change and Family Structure," *Int. Soc. Sci J.*, **14**, No. 3, 1962, 468–487.

An analysis of the effects of quick and radical social change in Israel on patterns of family organization and on the relationship between the family and the community.

Templeton, Joe A., "The Influence of Family Size on Some Aspects of Teen-Agers' Attitudes, Behavior, and Perceptions of Home Life," *Fam. Life Coordin.*, **11**, No. 3, 1962, 51–57.

A questionnaire study of 10,000 junior and senior high-school students' attitudes, beliefs, behavior, and aspirations and the relationship of these variables to family size.

Tibbits, Clark, *Aging in the Modern World*, Ann Arbor: University of Michigan Press, 1957.

A book of readings on middle age, the process of aging, adult family relations, opportunities and responsibilities of retirement.

Tuckman, Jacob, and Helen Connon, "Attempted Suicide in Adolescents," *Am. J. Psychol.*, **119**, September 1962, 228–232.

A comprehensive study of the backgrounds, circumstances, and means used by 100 consecutive attempted suicides by adolescents.

UNESCO, *Int. Soc. Sci. J.*, **14**, No. 3, 1962.

Issue devoted primarily to changes in American, German, Japanese, and Russian family structure and child-rearing practices.

Vincent, Clark E., "The Family in Health and Illness: Some Neglected Areas," *Ann. Am. Acad. Polit. Soc. Sci.*, **346**, March 1963, 109–116.

An excellent article demonstrating the need to consider many heretofore neglected areas of family relationships and their relation to health and illness.

Waxler, Nancy E., and Elliot G. Mishler, "Hospitalization of Psychiatric Patients: Physician-Centered and Family-Centered Influence Patterns," *J. Health Hum. Behav.*, **4**, No. 4, 1963, 250–257.

T. Parsons and others have tended to emphasize the normative basis of a particular type of M.D.-patient relationship in which the patient relinquished his rights and the physician took full responsibility for treatment decisions and the patient's fate. Intensive interviews with wives, mothers, and referring physicians of a small sample of male patients referred to two psychiatric hospitals, suggest that there is a second normative power pattern — the family-centered relationship — in which responsibility for the treatment decision is located within the family.

Winder, C. L., and Lucy Rau, "Parental Attitudes Associated with Social Deviance in Preadolescent Boys," *J. Abnorm. Soc. Psychol.*, **64**, No. 6, 1962, 418–424.

A psychological study of the relationship between personality characteristics of preadolescent boys and parental attitudes.

## PART FIVE

Apple, Dorrian (Ed.), *Sociological Studies of Health and Sickness*, New York: McGraw-Hill, 1960.

An excellent selection of papers under the four general headings, "The Recognition of Need for Health Care," "The Patients' Points of View," "Psychosocial Processes in Illness," and "The Organization of Hospitals."

Babcock, Charlotte G., "Food and Its Emotional Significance,' *J. Am. Diet. Assn.*, **24**, May 1948, 390–393.
    The significance of food as an indicator of trust and liking is fully discussed.

Bieber, Irving, et al., *Homosexuality: A Psychoanalytic Study*, New York: Basic Books, 1962.
    A systematic study of 106 male homosexuals and 100 male heterosexuals in psychoanalytic treatment.

Blankenship, L. Vaughn, and Ray H. Elling, "Organizational Support and Community Power Structure: The Hospital," *J. Health Hum. Behav.*, **3**, No. 4, 1962, 257–268.
    A case study of relationships between four general hospitals and the community influence on these hospitals.

Bredemeier, Harry, and Jackson Toby, *Social Problems in America: Casualties and Costs in an Acquisitive Society*, New York: Wiley, 1960.
    An excellent conceptual framework on the costs and casualties from those who fail to meet social standards and those who follow them.

Breed, Warren, "Occupational Mobility and Suicide among White Males," *Am. Sociol. Rev.*, **28**, No. 2, 1963, 179–188.
    A report of a study of 103 white males who committed suicide and their class mobility and work situations.

Brigante, Thomas R., "Some Defensive and Offensive Patterns of the Psychologically Sophisticated," *J. Health Hum. Behav.*, **1**, Summer 1960, 101–107.
    Focuses on some of the ways in which mental-health workers and others use professional knowledge and psychological jargon to avoid self-understanding and to express unacceptable feelings toward others.

Cannon, Walter B., " 'Voodoo' Death," *Am. Anthropol.*, **44**, April 1942, 169–181.
    Reports by anthropologists, missionaries, and M.D.'s concerning death due to magic with no known physical cause.

Clausen, John, and Marian Yarrow, "Paths to the Mental Hospital," *J. Soc. Issues*, **11**, 1955, 25–32.
    A discussion of the variety of ways and circumstances under which individuals become mental-hospital patients.

Crawford, Fred R., Glen W. Rollins, and Robert L. Sutherland, "Variations in the Evaluation of the Mentally Ill," *J. Health Hum. Behav.*, **1**, No. 3, 1960, 211–219.
    A report of a limited study on attitudes and behaviors toward the mentally ill. Positive attitudes toward the mentally ill did not necessarily mean positive action toward released mental patients.

Cumming, Elaine, and John Cumming, *Closed Ranks: An Experiment in Mental*

*Health Education,* Cambridge, Mass.: Harvard University Press, 1957.

An analysis of a community mental-health education program and why it failed.

Cussler, Margaret, and Mary L. de Gwe, *Twist the Cup and the Lip,* New York: Twayne, 1952.

A study of the significance of food and drink for the healthy and the ill.

Davis, John W., "Is Philosophy a Sickness or a Therapy?" *Antioch Rev.,* **23,** No. 1, 1963, 5–22.

Philosophers have been in general agreement that theirs is one of the disciplines equipped to solve the problem of the meaninglessness of individual lives. Some point out, however, that rather than being a therapy, philosophy is itself a sickness.

Dovenmohle, Robert H., "Health and Aging," *J. Health Hum. Behav.,* **1,** No. 4, 1960, 273–278.

A summary of physical and psychiatric findings of a multidisciplinary study of 260 community volunteers over the age of 60, and 78 psychiatrically hospitalized subjects over 60, focusing on physical, psychiatric, psychological, and social functioning in their interrelationships.

Dunham, Warren H., "Social Structures and Mental Disorders: Competing Hypotheses of Explanation," *Milbank Mem. Fund Quart.,* **39,** No. 2, 1961, 259–311.

Various and often contradictory hypotheses to explain significant rate differentials of mental illness are discussed.

Dunn, Halbert L., "What High-Level Wellness Means," *Canadian J. Pub. Health,* **50,** No. 11, 1959, 447–457.

A definition of wellness differentiating it from "good health." Outlines the needs of man and ways of achieving optimal levels of wellness as a dynamic condition.

Eichenlaub, John E., "Cliches That Confuse the Patient," *Med. Econ.,* **34,** December 1957, 242–256.

An essay highlighting problems of the use of cliches and abbreviations by M.D.'s for patients who may be too embarrassed to ask for clarification.

Elling, Ray, and Sandor Halebsky, "Organizational Differentiation and Support: A Conceptual Framework," *Admin. Sci. Quart.,* **6,** No. 2, 1961, 185–209.

A study of the problem of support furnished to achieve goals in voluntary private hospitals as compared to government and community hospitals.

Enterline, Philip E., "Cause of Death Responsible for Recent Increases in Sex Mortality Differentials in the United States," *Milbank Mem. Fund Quart.,* **39,** No. 2, 1961, 312–325.

A comparison of the rate and causes of male and female deaths from 1920–1958.

Etzioni, Amitai, *Modern Organization,* Englewood Cliffs, N. J.: Prentice-Hall, 1964.

An introductory text in the study of organizational behavior.

Fabing, Howard D., "On Going Berserk: A Neuro-Chemical Inquiry," *Am. J. Psychol.*, **113**, November 1956, 409–415.
    A review of the effect of toxic mushrooms on a number of social groups.

Faris, Robert E. L., and H. Warren Dunham, *Mental Disorders in Urban Areas: An Ecological Study of Schizophrenia and Other Psychoses*, New York: Hafner, 1939 (reprinted in 1960).
    A classic ecological study demonstrating the high incidence of schizophrenia in the crowded slums and manic depressive and neuroses in the suburbs.

Finney, Joseph, "What Is Sickness?" *Merrill-Palmer Quart.*, **9**, No. 3, 1963, 205–228.
    An excellent discussion of the competing views on the question whether psychoneuroses and personality disorders can properly be called sickness.

Fischer, Ann, and J. L. Fischer, "Culture and Epidemiology: A Theoretical Investigation of Kuru," *J. Health Hum. Behav.*, **2**, No. 1, 1961, 16–25.
    Small societies offer special opportunities for the use of anthropology in the study of medical problems. The study of Kuru, a disease of the central nervous system found in a New Guinea group, was used as an example.

Ford, Donald H., and Hugh B. Urban, *Systems of Psychotherapy: A Comparative Study*, New York: Wiley, 1963.
    A systematic comparison analysis of ten divergent theories of therapy.

Freeman, Howard E., and Gene G. Kassebaum, "Relationship of Education and Knowledge to Opinions about Mental Illness," *Ment. Hyg.*, **44**, 1960, 43.
    Authors presented data that did not support the assumption that opinions regarding mental illness were linked to knowledge.

Freidson, Eliot (Ed.), *The Hospital in Modern Society*, New York: Free Press of Glencoe, 1963.
    A collection of papers on the role of the hospital in contemporary society.

Fromm, Erich, *The Sane Society*, New York: Rinehart, 1955.
    This book represents a continuation of Fromm's search for a new synthesis of Freud and Marx in the study of social character, accepting Freud's assumption that human nature and society can have contradictory demands that may cause a society to be sick and Marx's concept of alienation of man under capitalism.

Gibbs, Jack P., and Walter T. Martin, "Mortality Rates and Participation in Sustenance Activities: An Ecological Analysis," *J. Health Hum. Behav.*, **3**, No. 1, 1962, 112.
    An empirical study concerned with the variation in participation patterns associated with variation in mortality rates.

Goffman, Erving, *Asylums*, New York: Anchor (Doubleday), 1961.
    A series of essays on the characteristics of total institutions, the career of mental patients, and the medical model of care.

Goffman, Erving, *Stigma: Notes on the Management of Spoiled Identity*, Englewood Cliffs, N. J.: Prentice-Hall, 1963.

A theory that in order for interaction to proceed smoothly, the several participants must have a socially accredited identity acceptable to others. The mutual acceptance of identities forms the basis of the "working consensus" on which the interaction is based.

Goldstein, Bernard, Lawrence G. Northwood, and Rhoda Goldstein, "Medicine in Industry: Problems of Administrators and Practitioners," *J. Health Hum. Behav.*, **1**, No. 4, 1960, 259–268.

A study focusing on problems arising out of the institutional arrangements within which the industrial medical function is performed, the norms of the social system of the firm, and the problems of status for industrial doctors and nurses.

Greenblat, Milton, et al., *The Patient and the Mental Hospital*, Glencoe, Ill.: Free Press, 1957.

A series of articles on the organization and implications of the mental hospital, its personnel, and patients.

Gruenburg, Ernest M., "The Epidemiology of Mental Disease," *Sci. Am.*, March 1954, 38–42.

Epidemiology is interested in the pattern of disease occurrence, in the factors that determine the pattern, and particularly in how the factors can be modified to eliminate the disease from the population.

Gurin, Gerald, Joseph Veroff, and Sheila Field, *Americans View Their Mental Health*, New York: Basic Books, 1960.

A study of 2460 respondents' views on their own adjustment, what to do, and where to go when trouble strikes.

Hirsch, Joseph, "Suicide," *Ment. Hyg.*, **43**, 1959, 516.

A statistical study of suicide by country, sex, age, and racial group.

Jaco, E. G., *Social Epidemiology of Mental Disorders*, New York: Russell Sage Foundation, 1960.

A theoretical sociological explanation of the epidemiology of mental illness.

Kane, John J., *Social Problems: A Situational Value Approach*, New York: Russell Sage Foundation, 1962.

A consideration of the theoretical orientation to problems of population, health, gerontology, crime, alcoholism, suicide, minority groups, and social institutions.

King, Stanley H., *Perceptions of Illness and Medical Practice*, New York: Russell Sage Foundation, 1962.

A textbook for physicians demonstrating how some findings of behavioral science are applicable to the practice of medicine.

Kinsey, Alfred C., et al., *Sexual Behavior in the Human Female*, Philadelphia: Saunders, 1953.

An extensive study of the values, beliefs, vocabulary, knowledge, and sex activities engaged in by a large voluntary sample of American women.

Klarman, Herbert E., "Characteristics of Patients in Short-Term Hospitals in

New York City," *J. Health Hum. Behav.*, **3**, No. 1, 1962, 46–52.

A study of the length of hospitalization and type of care given according to ethnic status, age, and source of payment.

Koos, Earl L., *The Health of Regionville*, New York: Columbia University Press, 1954.

A study of three social classes, beliefs, and practices of health.

Koos, Earl L., " 'Metropolis'—What City People Think of Their Medical Services," *Am. J. Pub. Health*, **45**, December 1955, 1551–1557.

The majority of respondents in this study indicated an unfavorable reaction to hospital care though they were unable to identify exactly why they held this opinion.

Larson, Richard F., "Clerical and Psychiatric Conceptions of the Clergyman's Role in the Therapeutic Setting," *Soc. Problems*, **11**, No. 4, 1964, 419–427.

A study of the differences in perception between the clergy and psychiatrists regarding the role of the clergy in therapy.

Mechanic, David, "Some Factors in Identifying and Defining Mental Illness," *Ment. Hyg.*, **46**, 1962, 66.

A theoretical descriptive model of the processes by which persons within a community are adjudged to be mentally ill.

Merton, Robert, and Robert Nisbet, *Contemporary Social Problems: An Introduction to the Sociology of Deviant Behavior and Social Disorganization*, New York: Harcourt, Brace & World, 1961.

A series of readings comparing problems of complex industrial society with other types of societies. Focuses on individual deviant behavior and social disorganization.

Middleton, John, "Prejudices and Opinions of Mental Hospital Employees Regarding Mental Illness," *Am. J. Psychol.*, **110**, August 1953, 133–138.

Research study of auxiliary personnel which demonstrates that many believe mental illness is either hereditary or caused by masturbation or immorality.

Mishler, Elliott G., and Norman A. Scotch, "Socio-Cultural Factors in the Epidemiology of Schizophrenia," *Psychiatry*, **26**, No. 4, 1963, 315–351.

A critical review and analysis of socio-cultural studies of the incidence of schizophrenia.

Opler, Morris E., "The Cultural Definition of Illness in Village India," *Hum. Org.*, **22**, No. 1, 1963, 32–35.

A description of the differences in perceptions and definitions of illness in an Indian subculture.

Park, Robert E., "Human Migration and the Marginal Man," *Am. J. Sociol.*, **33**, 1928, 881–893.

A discussion of the relationship of movement (migration) and the development of the "marginal" man.

Parsons, Talcott, "Age and Sex in the Social Structure of the U.S.," *Am. Sociol. Rev.*, **7**, October 1942, 604–616.

A discussion of the value of youth in America, isolation of the elderly, blending of sex roles, and attitudes of the youth groups.

Paterson, Ralston, "Why do Cancer Patients Delay?" *Canadian Med. Assn. J.*, **73**, December 1955, 931–940.

States fear, shame, and horror are associated with delay in seeking prompt care.

Pfautz, Harold W., and Gita Wilder, "The Ecology of a Mental Hospital," *J. Health Hum. Behav.*, **3**, No. 2, 1962, 67–72.

The social psychological implications of the observed differences are discussed: the public image of the hospital, communication with the hospital, and therapeutic potential of the staff.

Raphael, Edna E., "Community Structure and Acceptance of Psychiatric Aid," *Am. J. Sociol.*, **69**, No. 4, 1964, 340–358.

Shows that differences in use of psychiatric services may be the consequences of diffusion of a social innovation rather than the incidence or prevalence rate of mental illness.

Roemer, Milton I., "The Distribution of Hospital Beds Needed in a Region," *J. Health Hum. Behav.*, **1**, No. 2, 1960, 94–101.

A study of the areas where hospitals under the Hill-Burton Act should be built in order to best meet needs of city and country people alike.

Roemer, Milton I., "On Paying the Doctor and the Implications of Different Methods," *J. Health Hum. Behav.*, **3**, No. 1, 1962, 4–14.

In organized programs of medical care there are three principal ways of paying M.D.'s: fee-for-service, capitation, and salary. The mechanism of each method is defined and the apparent consequences analyzed in terms of: (1) quantity of medical care provided, (2) quality of care, (3) costs, (4) administrative and (5) the larger policies of the medical care field.

Romano, John, "Patients' Attitudes and Behavior in Ward Round Teaching," *J. Am. Med. Assn.*, **117**, August 1946, 664–667.

A study of fifty hospitalized patients' definitions and comprehension of sixty terms and abbreviations most used in bedside teaching rounds.

Rothaus, Paul, and Robert Morton, "Problem-Centered Versus Mental Illness Self-Descriptions," *J. Health Hum. Behav.*, **3**, Fall 1962, 198–203.

Several arguments are offered which question the value of the concept of mental illness as a framework for programs that offer help to distressed persons.

Samora, Julian, Lyle Saunders, and Richard F. Larson, "Medical Vocabulary Knowledge among Hospital Patients," *J. Health Hum. Behav.*, **2**, No. 2, 1961, 83–92.

A test of patients' knowledge of fifty common nontechnical terms used frequently by M. D.'s showing that most do not understand the terms.

Schnore, Leo F., "Statistical Indicators of Medical Care: An Historical Note," *J. Health Hum. Behav.*, **3**, No. 2, 1962, 133–135.

Statistical data presented on the number of physicians, nurses, and hospitals.

Shulman, Sam, and Anne M. Smith, "The Concept of 'Health' among Spanish-Speaking Villagers of New Mexico and Colorado," *J. Health Hum. Behav.*, **4**, No. 4, 1963, 226–234.

A study of health behavior of Spanish-speaking villagers in New Mexico and Colorado showing their criteria for health and illness.

Stoeckle, John D., and Gerald E. Davidson, "Communicating Aggrieved Feelings in the Patient's Initial Visit to a Medical Clinic," *J. Health Hum. Behav.*, **4**, No. 3, 1963, 199.

It is suggested that the expression of aggrieved feeling by medical patients to physicians is associated with a deficiency in available persons among the patient's intimate relationships with whom to share his feelings.

Talbert, Robert H., "Ecological Variations in Dental Health in a Metropolitan Community," *J. Health Hum. Behav.*, **3**, No. 2, 1962, 128–132.

An attempt to determine the dental health according to socioeconomic status.

Titchener, James L., et al., "Problem of Delay in Seeking Surgical Care," *J. Am. Med. Assn.*, **160**, April 1956, 1187–1193.

Study of 200 randomly selected surgical patients showed many delay for fear of punishment or retribution from significant others, fear of dependency, shame, or fear of death.

Wax, Murray, "On Public Dissatisfaction with the Medical Profession: Personal Observations," *J. Health Hum. Behav.*, **3**, No. 2, 1962, 152–156.

An essay on some differences between the public view of health and one medical view.

Williams, Griffith W., "Illness and Personality," *Am. J. Nurs.*, **63**, No. 6, 1963, 85.

The article poses the question, "What is the impact of the role of being a patient on the development and expression of personality?"

Williams, Josephine J., "Patients and Prejudice: Lay Attitudes toward Women Physicians," *Am. J. Sociol.*, **51**, January 1946, 283–287.

A study of 100 middle-class women and one class of medical students and their perceptions and feelings toward women M.D.'s.

Wilson, Robert N., "The Social Structure of a General Hospital," *Ann. Am. Acad. Polit. Soc. Sci.*, **346**, March 1963, 67–76.

An essay on the complex organizational structure of a modern general hospital.

Wooden, Howard E., "The Hospital's Purpose Is the Patient, But . . . ," *Mod. Hosp.*, **92**, January 1959, 90–96.

States "the raison d'etre of most hospitals is care of patients but a number of other functions as teaching, research, custody and control, and operation and business functions are often primary and patients secondary."

## PART SIX

Andersen, Ronald M., and Robert L. Eichhorn, "Correlates of Labor Efficiency

among Older Farmers in Poor Health," *Rur. Sociol.*, **29**, No. 2, 1964, 181–193.
    A study of 397 farmers in poor health demonstrates that variables other than health are related to labor efficiency and inefficiency.

Baker, Joan M., and Karen C. Sorensen, "A Patient's Concern with Death," *Am. J. Nurs.*, **63**, No. 7, 1963, 90–92.
    A "how to" recognize and handle the needs of the patient who wants to talk about impending death.

Bates, Frederick LeRoy, and Rodney F. White, "Differential Perceptions of Authority in Hospitals," *J. Health Hum. Behav.*, **2**, No. 4, 1961, 262–267.
    A study of the hospital administrators, M.D.'s, and nursing supervisors in thirteen hospitals, demonstrating differences in their perception of authority in others.

Beecher, Henry K., *Measurement of Subjective Responses*, London: Oxford University Press, 1959.
    Comparison of observations on wounded soldiers and civilian postoperative surgery patients in terms of the differences in perception of pain and necessity for drugs.

Becker, Howard S., *The Other Side: Perspectives on Deviance*, New York: Free Press of Glencoe, 1965.
    An excellent book of readings on the place of deviants in society, the relationship of deviants and conformists, and the role of deviants in society.

Berkowitz, Norman H., Mary F. Malone, and Malcolm W. Klein, "Patient Care as a Criterion Problem," *J. Health Hum. Behav.*, **3**, Fall 1962, 171–175.
    An examination of the concept of patient care in 53 clinics regarding the suitability of the current view that patient care is unitary.

Brigante, Thomas R., "Some Defensive and Offensive Patterns of the Psychologically Sophisticated," *J. Health Hum. Behav.*, **1**, Summer 1960, 101–107.
    Focuses on ways in which mental-health workers and others use professional knowledge and psychological jargon to avoid self-understanding and to express unacceptable feelings toward others in a "safe, partially sanctioned way."

Brown, Esther Lucile, "Meeting Patients' Psychosocial Needs in the General Hospital," *Ann. Am. Acad. Polit. Soc. Sci.*, **346**, March 1963, 117–125.
    An essay on the concerns of patients other than their physical condition, and the need to consider these other psychosocial and cultural concerns.

Buck, McKenzie, "Adjustments during Recovery from Stroke," *Am. J. Nurs.*, **64**, No. 10, 1964, 92.
    A personal diary of an M. D. stricken with "stroke" reporting his insights and difficulties.

Carstairs, G. M., "The Social Limits of Eccentricity: England," in Marvin K. Opler (Ed.), New York: *Culture and Mental Health*, MacMillan, 1959, p. 373.
    Raises the question to what degree our contemporary urban society can tolerate the presence of socially withdrawn and even conspicuously abnormal

persons in its midst without succumbing to the temptaion to shut them away from sight again.

Chernus, Jack, "Let Them Die with Dignity," *Coronet,* September 1964, 57–61.
An M. D. speaks out his views on telling the hopelessly ill their diagnosis and then helping them to die in psychological peace.

Clinard, Marshall, *Sociology of Deviant Behavior,* New York: Rinehart, 1958.
Excellent material on the definition, nature, and kinds of deviant behavior, as well as sources of attitudes and kinds of control of such behavior.

Cohen, Jacob, and E. L. Struening, "Opinions about Mental Illness in the Personnel of Two Large Mental Hospitals," *J. Abnorm. Soc. Psychol.,* **64,** No. 5, 1962, 349–360.
Likert-type opinion items relevant to the mentally ill were administered to employees to measure opinions and attitudes of mental-health workers to mental illness.

Cooper, W. Clark, Philip E. Enterline, and Eloise T. Worden, "Estimating Occupational Disease Hazards through Medical Care Plans," *Pub. Health Rep.* **77,** December 1962, 1065–1070.
Study of physicians' billing forms as potential record resource for epidemiological data needed to determine prevalence and causal relationship between illness and the occupational environment.

Cousteau, Jacques Y., with Frederic Dumas, *The Silent World,* New York: Harper, 1953.
A study by a great skin diver of the changes in environment and the problems of self in an isolated environment.

Crumb, Frederick K., "A Resonance of Agony," *Perspectives Psychiat. Care,* **1,** No. 6, 1963, 16–18.
An excellent subjective account of feelings generated in staff work with depressed patients day in and day out.

Davis, Fred, "Definitions of Time and Recovery in Paralytic Polio Convalescence," *Am. J. Sociol.,* **61,** May 1956, 582–587.
In a study of polio patients, the researcher finds that the hospital tries to loosen effective ties with home and family by increasing dependency of the patient, thereby making the process of recovery perceived differently in terms of time dimension.

Diller, Leonard, "Psychology of Disabled Children," *Am. J. Nurs.,* **64,** No. 7, 1964, 131.
The report of a psychologist in a rehabilitation institute for children discusses the reliability of psychological tests and how realistic children are about the nature of their disability, its cause, and rehabilitation goals.

Dodge, Joan S., "Nurses' Sense of Adequacy and Attitudes toward Keeping Patients Informed," *J. Health Hum. Behav.,* **2,** No. 3, 1961, 213–216.
Study shows that nurses who are "psychologically stronger" and who have

a feeling of personal adequacy express the importance of communicating to the patient.

Eichhorn, Robert L., and Ronald M. Andersen, "Changes in Personal Adjustment to Perceived and Medically Established Heart Disease: A Panel Study," *J. Health Hum. Behav.*, **3**, No. 4, 1962, 242–248.
    A panel study of adjustive behavior of farmers with heart disease demonstrating that changes in health precautions and information about disease were most closely related to the subject's perception of whether or not he has "disease."

Elling, Ray, Ruth Whittemore, and Morris Green, "Patient Participation in a Pediatric Program," *J. Health Hum. Behav.*, **1**, No. 3, 1960, 183–191.
    A study showing that reflexive self-concept of mothers rather than social class is significantly related to participation in health programs for their children.

Erikson, Kai T. "Patient Role and Social Uncertainty—A Dilemma of the Mentally Ill," *Psychiatry*, **20**, 1957, 263–274.
    A study of the socialization of mental patients in hospitals during periods of social uncertainty and ambiguity.

Fletcher, Joseph, "The Patient's Right to Die," *Harper's Magazine*, **22**, October 1960, 139–143.
    An essay on the meaning of the medical profession's prolongation of life when it no longer seems necessary.

Fox, Renee C., *Experiment Perilous*, Glencoe, Ill.: Free Press, 1959.
    An excellent study of patients and physicians faced with poor prognoses and uncertain experimental treatment modalities.

Freeman, Howard E., and Ozzie G. Simmons, *The Mental Patient Comes Home*, New York: Wiley, 1963.
    This book is a comprehensive examination of the posthospital experience of some 649 mental patients followed up during the year after hospitalization.

Freidson, Eliot, "Client Control and Medical Practice," *Am. J. Sociol.*, **65**, January 1960, 374–382.
    A study of lay culture referrals and professional referrals of patients to M.D.'s and the effect of the referral on the control of both patients and their physicians.

Fulton, Robert, *Death and Identity*, New York: Wiley, 1965.
    A series of studies of grief, the impact of bereavement on personality, and attitudes toward death among various populations.

Funkenstein, Daniel, "The Physiology of Fear and Anger," *Sci. Am.*, May 1965, 2–6.
    A study of autonomic nervous system and the adrenal gland reaction to fear and anger.

Gies, Gilbert, and Robert Fulton, "Death and Social Values," *Ind. J. Soc. Res.*, **3**, No. 2, 1962, 7–14.

Traces the development of social values regarding death, reviews relevant studies, and indicates areas to be explored.

Glaser, Barney, and Anselm L. Strauss, "The Social Loss of Dying Patients," *Am. J. Nurs.*, **64**, No. 6, 1964, 6–8.

A discussion of the social value placed on a dying patient by nurses, patients, and others, and the impact of this social loss.

Glaser, Barney, and Anselm L. Strauss, "Awareness Contexts and Social Interaction," *Am. Sociol. Rev.*, **29**, No. 5, 1964, 669–679.

A study of dying patients, their awareness of illness and prognosis, and its relationship to social interaction.

Glaser, Barney G., and Anselm L. Strauss, "Temporal Aspects of Dying as a Non-Scheduled Status Passage," *Am. J. Sociol.*, **71**, July 1965, 48.

Conceptualizes dying as a nonscheduled status passage and considers problems of how the people invovled handle its timing. The analysis focuses on temporal aspects of the central issues of (1) legitimating *when* the passage occurs, (2) announcing the passage to others, and (3) coordinating the passage.

Goffman, Erving, "On the Characteristics of Total Institutions," *Proc. Sympos. Prev. Soc. Psychiat.*, Washington, D. C.: Walter Reed Army Institute of Research, April 1957, pp. 15–17.

A conceptual comparison of mental hospitals and military organizations describing the characteristics of these institutions.

Goffman, Erving, "The Moral Career of the Mental Patient," *Psychiatry*, **22**, No. 2, 1959, 123–142.

A theoretical essay of the socialization of mental patients.

Groth, M. S. W., Hirman Gordon, and Frank Dietrich, "The Problem of Unvisited Patients in a Mental Hospital," *Ment. Hyg.*, **44**, 1960, 210.

A discussion of the characteristics, problems, and distribution of unvisited patients.

Hale, Shirley L., and Julia H. Richardson, "Terminating the Nurse-Patient Relationship," *Am. J. Nurs.*, **63**, No. 9, 1963, 116.

An article on terminating nurse-patient relationships after a good relationship has been built up between patient and nurse in a psychiatric hospital.

Heinaelmann, Fred, "Factors in Prophylaxis Behavior in Treating Rheumatic Fever: An Exploratory Study," *J. Health Hum. Behav.*, **3**, No. 2, 1962, 73–81.

A comprehensive study of personal and social factors involved in attitudes and behavior of patients toward prophylaxis for rheumatic fever.

Hershey, Nathan, "Obtaining Consent for the Use of Body Tissues," *Am. J. Nurs.*, **63**, No. 8, 1963, 105.

A discussion of practices of various states providing for donation of bodies and body parts for medical purposes.

Hertz, Robert, *Death and the Right Hand* (trans. by Rodney and Claudia Needham), Glencoe, Ill.: Free Press, 1960.

A classical work by one of Durkheim's students which examines the concepts of soul, fate, mortuary rites, and the symbolism of right and left in a foreign culture.

Higgins, Robin, "The Concept of Maladjustment: Its Social Consequences," *Hum. Rel.*, **16**, No. 1, 1963, 61–73.
An analysis of some aspects of "levels of wellness" and the social services provided for young deviants.

Hines, Joseph S., "Social Distance to Three Types of Hospitals," *J. Health Hum. Behav.*, **2**, No. 3, 1961, 210–213.
A report on a study of responses to three types of patients: a surgical patient, a tuberculosis patient, and a mentally ill patient. Study shows more reluctance to visit or send cards to the mentally ill.

Hirschberg, Gerald, et al., *Rehabilitation*, Philadelphia: Lippincott, 1964.
A good manual for the care of the disabled, handicapped, and geriatric patients.

Jaco, E. G., "The Social Isolation Hypothesis and Schizophrenia," *Am. Sociol. Rev.*, **19**, No. 5, 1954, 567–577.
An essay on the reality of the hypothesis that social isolation is related to schizophrenia.

Jacobson, Margaret M., and Robert F. Eichhorn, "How Farm Families Cope with Heart Disease: A Study of Problems and Resources," *J. Marr. Fam.*, **26**, No. 2, 1964, 166–173.
A research study on the impact of heart disease in the husband-father on the farm, the ways in which families handled the problem, and factors that influenced their response to the situation.

Jaspers, Karl, "The Patient Faces His Illness," *Perspectives Psychiat. Care*, **3**, No. 1, 1965, 24.
This chapter from the book *General Psychopathology*, translated by J. Hoenig and Marian W. Hamilton and published by University of Chicago Press in 1963, is a very perceptive essay in which he concludes at one point: "In the last resort it is a person's character that determines what the illness makes of him."

Jeffris, Jane, "The Best Healing Device," *Am. J. Nurs.*, **64**, No. 9, 1964, 74.
A story of the perceptions of a nurse who is a polio quadriplegic regarding the care given and care needed for such patients.

Levine, Gene N., "Anxiety about Illness: Psychological and Social Bases," *J. Health Hum. Behav.*, **3**, Spring 1962, 30–34.
An empirical study conducted in 1959 with a quota-controlled sample of 2970 persons in thirty counties across the country to determine their attitudes toward various grave illnesses and the voluntary health and welfare organizations combatting them.

Levine, Jacob, "Responses to Humor," *Sci. Am.*, February 1956, 31–35.
A study of the Freudian notion that people laugh when they momentarily gratify forbidden impulses.

Lindemann, Erich, "Symptomatology and Management of Acute Grief," *Am. J. Psychol.*, **101**, September 1944, 141–148.

A study of the families of the Coconut Grove Fire of Boston and the effects of their inability to express sorrow and hence to carry out grief.

Litman, Theodor James, "The Influence of Self Conception and Life Orientation Factors in the Rehabilitation of the Orthopedically Disabled," *J. Health Hum. Behav.*, **3**, No. 4, 1962, 249–256.

An intensive study of 100 assessing the influence of social and psychological variables on the rehabilitation of the physically disabled.

Lowenthal, Marjorie Fiske, and Paul L. Berkman, "The Problem of Rating Psychiatric Disability in a Study of Normal and Abnormal Aging," *J. Health Hum. Behav.*, **5**, No. 2, 1964, 40–44.

Two questions are discussed: (1) Are there psychiatrically disturbed elderly people being maintained in the community, and, if so, how do they differ from those who arrive on a psychiatric ward? (2) Are there normal aging symptoms which everyone develops if he lives long enough and which at the same time are not necessarily harbingers of pathological disability?

Macgregor, Frances Cooke, "Some Psychosocial Problems Associated with Facial Deformities," *Am. Sociol. Rev.*, **16**, October 1951, 629–638.

A report of many kinds of disfigurement and disability and how they alter or limit perception.

Mechanic, David, and Edmund Volkart, "Illness Behavior and Medical Diagnoses," *J. Health Hum. Behav.*, **1**, No. 2, 1960, 86–94.

Data are presented indicating relationship of various types of diagnoses to the tendency to adopt the sick role and the degree of perceived stress.

Mechanic, David, "Religion, Religiosity, and Illness Behavior," *Hum. Org.*, **22**, No. 3, 1963, 202–208.

A study of patterns of illness behavior among different ethnic and religious groups.

Melzack, Ronald, "The Perception of Pain," *Sci. Am.*, February 1961, 41–49.

Discusses the physiology and culturology of pain and gives evidence that pain is not a fixed response to a hurtful stimulus but rather its perception is modified by past experiences, expectations, and our culture.

Miller, Keat S., and Ira Iscoe, "The Concept of Crisis," *Hum. Org.*, **22**, No. 3, 1963, 195–201.

A review of the concept of emotional crisis as it has been employed by sociologists, psychiatrists, and related professions.

Murphey, Bradford J., "Psychological Management of the Patient with Incurable Cancer," *Geriatrics*, **8**, March 1953, 130–134.

A study of how M.D.'s unwittingly may contribute to patient fear through his reactions to his own inability to cure the disease.

Nicholl, Margaret, "A Patient with Cancer of the Tongue," *Am. J. Nurs.*, **63**, No. 9, 1963, 132.

The patient becomes the teacher and helps the young student nurse to find ways of coping with her own anxiety while helping the patient who had undergone disfiguring surgery.

Nimbkar, Smt Kamala, "Employment Potential of the Physically Handicapped," *Int. J. Soc. Work*, **20**, March 1960, 94–97.

A paper presented to the eleventh National Indian Conference of Social Welfare demonstrating the high work potential of the physically handicapped.

Norris, Catherine, "Greetings from the Lonely Crowd," *Nurs. Forum*, **1**, No. 1, 1961–62, 73–82.

An analysis of current "get-well" cards as messages to the ill, their relationship to patients, and patient's experiences as members of the "ill" society.

Oseenberg, Richard J., "The Experience of Deviance in the Patient Role: A Study of Class Differences," *J. Health Hum. Behav.*, **3**, No. 4, 1962, 277–282.

Interviews of hospital patients to evaluate social factors regarding varied reactions to hospitalization and to help clarify the relationship between the deviance of illness and the "sick role."

Parsons, Talcott, "Toward a Healthy Maturity," *J. Health Hum. Behav.*, **1**, No. 3, 1960, 163–173.

The author indicates the close connection between illness, disability, and aging, and the implications for health care of older people stemming from a view of illness as a form of deviant behavior, one which provides for the individual "perhaps the most important single escape hatch from the pressure to achieve."

Quint, Jeanne C., "Nursing Service and the Care of Dying Patients: Some Speculations," *Nurs. Sci.*, **2**, No. 6, 1964, 432–443.

Some problems that confront patients who are dying and nurses who care for dying patients.

Quint, Jeanne, "Institutionalized Practices of Information Control," *Psychiatry*, **28**, No. 2, 1965, 119–132.

States that to have cancer is to bear a stigma, hence health workers devise tactics for controlling social interaction between people with differing amounts of information about the disease.

Redlich, Frederick C., "The Patient's Language: An Investigation into the Use of Medical Terms," *Yale J. Biol., Med.*, **17**, January 1945, 427–453.

A study of patients in a neuropsychiatric unit concluding that understanding medical terminology is somewhat dependent on motivation and perception of the patient but that most do not understand M.D.'s and their language.

Rosengren, William R., "The Sick Role during Pregnancy: A Note on Research in Progress," *J. Health Hum. Behav.*, **3**, No. 3, 1962, 213–218.

A study of pregnant women testing Parsons' sick-role concept and the behavior of these women with their M.D.'s.

Samora, Julian, Lyle Saunders, and Richard F. Larson, "Medical Vocabulary Knowledge among Hospital Patients," *J. Health Hum. Behav.*, **2**, Summer 1961, 83–92.

A test of a variety of ethnic lower-class respondents concluding that most information given to these patients by professional staff was not clearly understood even by patients of average or better education.

Samora, Julian, Lyle Saunders, and Richard F. Larson, "Knowledge about Specific Diseases in Four Selected Samples," *J. Health Hum. Behav.*, **3**, No. 3, 1962, 176–184.

A study of laymen's health knowledge regarding etiology, symptoms, and treatment of several common diseases.

Shea, Frank, and Elizabeth Hurley, "Hopelessness and Helplessness," *Perspectives Psychiat. Care*, **2**, No. 1, 1964, 32.

An essay on how to deal with feelings of hopelessness which result in an inability to mobilize energy and effort on the part of the patient.

Smith, Margo, "Ego Support for the Child Patient," *Am. J. Nurs.*, **63**, No. 10, 1963, 90.

An illustrated article with practical suggestions to pediatric nurses on helping the young child in a hospital understand what is happening to him, and giving him emotional support in this frightening situation.

Turner, Charlotte, and Robert F. Mahoney, "After Hospitalization," *Am. J. Nurs.*, **64**, No. 9, 1964, 137.

This article relates how nurses in one large hospital worked together to increase the quality and quantity of their referrals to community agencies.

Ullman, Montague, "Disorders of Body Image after Stroke," *Am. J. Nurs.*, **64**, No. 10, 1964, 89.

An article dealing with the fact that many patients ignore the changes in their appearance, behavior, and even their illness after a stroke.

Von Mering, Otto, and Stanley H. King, *Remotivating the Mental Patient*, New York: Russell Sage Foundation, 1957.

A description of changing patterns of patient care on different types of wards in state hospitals.

Wahl, C. W., "The Fear of Death," *Bull. Menninger Clin.*, No. 6, November 1958, 214–223.

An excellent essay on the rational and irrational fears around death.

Whatley, Charles D., Jr., "Status, Role, and Vocational Continuity of Discharged Mental Patients," *J. Health Hum. Behav.*, **4**, No. 2, 1963, 105–112.

A study of the relationships of status to the continuity or discontinuity of work life after discharge from mental hospitals.

*PART SEVEN*

Abdellah, Faye, and Eugene Levine, *Better Patient Care through Nursing Research*, New York: Macmillan, 1965.

A theoretical treatment of the kinds and value of nursing research that will promote patient care.

Arndt, Clara, "Some Views on Teaching and Research in Nursing Service Administration," *J. Nurs. Educ.*, 4, No. 1, 1965, 9.

The author emphasizes the need for more effective administration and nursing research where "individuals must develop abilities to think, to exercise judgment, to adjust, and to learn independently in a world of constant flux."

Beigel, Hugo G. (Ed.), *Advances in Sex Research*, New York: Harper and Row, 1963.

A survey of sex research and analysis of the advances made in increasing knowledge about sex attitudes, beliefs, and behavior.

Bensman, Joseph, and Arthur Vidich, "Social Theory in Field Research," *Am. J. Sociol.*, 65, No. 6, 1960, 577–584.

Discussion of the relationship of theory as a model in research and the problems of using theory heuristically.

Berelson, Bernard, and Gary A. Steiner, *Human Behavior: An Inventory of Scientific Findings*, New York: Harcourt, Brace and World, 1964.

An extensive review of the discoveries of behavioral and social scientists regarding human behavior.

Bowman, Claude C., "Cultural Ideology and Heterosexual Reality: A Preface to Sociological Research," *Am. Sociol. Rev.*, 14, No. 5, 1949, 624–632.

An analysis of the relationship of cultural ideology and perception to actual heterosexual behavior.

Brownell, William A., "Problem Solving," Chap. 12 in *The Psychology of Learning*, Forty-first Yearbook of the National Society for the Study of Education, Part II, Chicago: University of Chicago Press, 1942.

Problem solving is defined and research in problem solving is discussed. Eleven practical suggestions for developing ability in problem solving are presented.

Buck, Rodger L., "Training Social Scientists for Medical Research and Teaching," *J. Health Hum. Behav.*, 1, No. 1, 1960, 53–55.

A proposal for training programs for medical social scientists.

De Sainz, Doris, "The Public Health Nurse as Research Interviewer," *Nurs. Outlook*, 10, 1962, 514–516.

A discussion of how the public-health nurse may act as a research interviewer in a natural setting.

Dohrenwend, Barbara Snell, and Stephen A. Richardson, "Field Methods and Techniques: A Use for Leading Questions in Research Interviewing," *Hum. Org.*, 23, No. 1, 1964, 76–84.

A suggestion that, with proper precautions, leading questions may provide a useful tool for collecting information beyond that requested.

Dunham, H. Warren, *Sociological Theory and Mental Disorder*, Detroit: Wayne State University Press, 1959.

The author examines three basic questions: Are there significant variations in the incidence of mental disorder and of specific mental disorders, over a

period of years, in different social classes and in different geographical locali-
ties? Is there a relationship between the personality type of a mental case before
his breakdown, and the type of disturbance or particular symptoms he develops? Does the cultural organization of a society influence the incidence of
mental disorder in that society?

Durkheim, Emile, *The Rules of Sociological Method*, Glencoe, Ill.: Free Press,
1938.
   A classic in rules for observation, distinguishing between normal and abnormal, classifying data, and doing research analysis.

Elinson, Jack, "Methods of Sociomedical Research," in Howard E. Freeman et
al., *Handbook of Medical Sociology*, Englewood Cliffs, N. J.: Prentice-Hall,
1963, Chap. 18, pp. 449–471.
   Discussion of methodology in sociomedical research; brief descriptions of
nominal scale, ordinal scale, interval scale; touches briefly on concepts of
validity, reliability, and technique of experiment, and concludes that "sensitivity to the problems of method has resulted in improved and more sophisticated research techniques in both medical and behavorial sciences."

Feibleman, James K., "The Nature of the Hypothesis," *Nurs. Forum*, 1, No. 1,
1961-1962, 47–60.
   Discusses the character and classification, discovery and criteria for good
hypothesis.

Green, Arnold W., "Sociological Analysis of Horney and Fromm," *Am. J. Sociol.*,
51, No. 6, 1946, 533–540.
   A systematic sociological analysis of two foremost psychiatric theories.

Hamovitch, Maurice B., "Research Interviewing in Terminal Illness," *Soc. Work*,
8, No. 2, 1963, 4–9.
   A description of experiences with the use of research interviews of different
kinds in a study program concerned with a traumatic situation—the terminal
illness of a child.

Hangartner, Rev. Carl A., "The Responsibilities of Universities and Colleges for
the Educational Preparation of Professional Nurses," *J. Nurs. Educ.*, 4, No. 1,
1965, 19.
   A plea for nursing schools to increase academic requirements, intellectual
challenges, and instructor preparation.

Hassenplug, Lulu Wolf, "Preparation of the Nurse Practitioner," *J. Nurs. Educ.*, 4,
No. 1, 1965. 29.
   A thoughtful discussion of the "quiet revolution" now going on in nursing
education; the reconsideration and revision of baccalaureate programs; the
encouragement of research activities.

Highley, Betty, "Antepartal Nursing Intervention," *Nurs. Forum*, 2, No. 4, 1963,
62–80.
   A descriptive study of one case where primary preventive nursing intervention was employed. These interventions included assisting the mother in

dealing with guilt and grief over the death of the first born and assisting the mother in accepting the unplanned and unwanted newborn.

Holmer, Paul L., "Scientific Language and the Language of Religion," *J. Sci. Study Relig.*, **1**, No. 1, 1961. 42–55.

A discussion of the need for delineation of both language systems.

Howland, Daniel, and Wanda E. McDowell, "The Measurement of Patient Care: A Conceptual Framework," *Nurs. Res.*, **13**, No. 1, 1964, 4–7.

A theoretical model based on cybernetics to outline the patient-care process in the hospital.

Kandel, Denise B., and Richard H. Williams, *Psychiatric Rehabilitation: Some Problems and Research*, New York: Atherton, 1964.

An analysis of research as a social process and the problems of professional rivalry and hostility between various categories of professional workers, resistance encountered by researchers from hospitals, agencies, patients and their families, lack of clear concepts on the part of researchers as to their roles, discouragement of researchers at lack of immediate results, etc.

Kaplan, Abraham, *The Conduct of Inquiry*, San Francisco: Chandler, 1964.

An excellent book on scientific independence and autonomy of scientific inquiry showing how disciplines may and should borrow techniques, concepts, laws, data, models, and theories from one another.

King, Lester, "Is Medicine an Exact Science?" *Philos. Sci.*, **19**, 1952, 131–140.

Raises the issue of whether or not medicine qualifies as a science.

Komorita, Nori I., "Nursing Diagnosis," *Am. J. Nurs.*, **63**, No. 12, 1963, 83.

Answers questions regarding the definition of nursing diagnosis, how it is made, what it accomplishes and how it differs from M.D. diagnosis.

Krauss, Irving, "An Approach to Evaluating the Effectiveness of a Public Health Program," *J. Health Hum. Behav.*, **3**, No. 2, 1962, 141–146.

A framework is proposed for assessing and evaluating the effectiveness of planned public-health programs.

Lastrucci, Carlo, *The Scientific Approach: Basic Principles of the Scientific Method*, Cambridge, Mass.: Schenkman, 1963.

A good basic text on science, research methods, processes, and scientific analysis.

Lazarsfeld, Paul, and Morris Rosenberg (Eds.), *The Language of Social Research: A Reader in the Methodology of Social Research*, Glencoe, Ill.: Free Press, 1957.

A series of good readings on concepts and indices, multivariate analysis, change and the philosophy of social science research.

Lefton, Mark, et al., "Decision-Making in a Mental Hospital: Real, Perceived, and Ideal," *Am. Sociol. Rev.*, **24**, No. 6, 1959, 822–829.

An analyses of the differences between real, perceived, and ideal decisions made in a mental hospital.

Loevinger, Jane, "Conflict of Commitment in Clinical Research," *Am. Psychol.*, May 1963.

A discussion of the problems in research when the researcher has both a clinician and research orientation and commitment.

Luski, Margaret B., *Interdisciplinary Team Research Methods and Problems*, National Training Laboratories, 1958.

A comprehensive rendering of the assets and problems, as well as methods, for multidisciplinary research.

McEwen, William, *The Problem of Social-Scientific Knowledge*, Totowa, N.J.: Bedminster, 1963.

A philosopher suggests an epistemological pattern of inquiry, research methodology, and postulates of systems, probability, causality, coherence, hypothesis testing, and law-like generalizations about behavioral process.

Mereness, Dorothy, "Preparing the Nurse Researcher," *Am. J. Nurs.*, **9**, September 1964, 78.

This is a plea for education in nursing which will attract students with a genuine interest in science, which will prepare students to enter masters' programs without having to make up deficiencies, and which will not produce guilt in the student who prefers research instead of direct care of patients.

Meyer, Burton, and Loretta Heidgerken, *Introduction to Research in Nursing*, Philadelphia: Lippincott, 1962.

A textbook on research, its methods and techniques.

*Nursing Outlook*, **13**, No. 5, 1965.

The entire issue is devoted to research attitudes, interpreting statistics and a variety of research methods applicable to differing health problems and situations.

Overall, John E., and Donald R. Gorham, "A Pattern Probability Model for the Classification of Psychiatric Patients," *Behav. Sci.*, **8**, No. 2, 1963, 109–116.

This research was undertaken to provide quantitative definitions of psychiatric diagnostic types, to specify objective decision rules for diagnosis, and to program a computer to classify patients.

Parloff, Morris B., and Joseph H. Handlon, "The Influence of Criticalness on Creative Problem-Solving in Dyads," *Psychiatry*, **27**, No. 1, 1964, 17–27.

A study of the relationship of critical judgment and freedom to creativity and production in problem solving.

Peplau, Hildegard, *Interpersonal Relations in Nursing*, New York: Putnam, 1952.

A classic theoretical discussion of interpersonal relations in nursing which has many implications for all health workers.

Perry, Stewart, "Observations on the Social Processes in Psychiatric Research," *Behav. Sci.*, **1**, No. 4, 1956, 290–302.

An essay on personal observations of the kinds of social processes that transpire in research in psychiatric settings.

Perry, Stewart, and Lyman C. Wynne, "Role Conflict, Role Definition, and Social

Change in a Clinical Research Organization," *Soc. Forces*, **38**, No. 1, 1959, 62–65.

Discussion of "built-in" conflicts in research hospitals where staff must act as clinicians as well as researchers.

Ray, William W., *An Introduction to Experimental Design*, New York: Macmillan, 1960.

A rather sophisticated book for graduate students, yet a clear treatment of the ideas and principles of research design and statistical analysis for experimental method of research.

Reader, George G., "Medical Care," *J. Health Hum. Behav.*, **3**, No. 1, 1962, 3.

A special issue on medical care with papers representing various methods of social-science research and the relationship to medicine.

Reif, F., "The Competitive World of the Pure Scientist," *Science*, **134**, 1961, pp. 1957–1962.

An analysis of the functions and dysfunctions of competition among scientists.

Ruesch, Jurgen, "Research and Training in Social Psychiatry in the U.S." *Int. J. Soc. Psych.*, **7**, 1961, 87–96.

A discussion of the strengths and weaknesses of research and training in social psychiatry.

Schwartz, Doris, "Toward More Precise Evaluation of Patients' Needs," *Nurs. Outlook*, **13**, No. 5, 1965, 42–44.

The author proposes a patient evaluation schedule to assess patient needs and plan patient care by use of problem solving.

Sellitz, Claire, Marie Jahoda, Morton Deutsch, and Stuart Cook, *Research Methods in Social Relations*, rev. one-vol. ed., New York: Holt, Rinehart & Winston, 1961.

An undergraduate text on the research processes, formulation, designs, methods, and analysis.

Shapiro, Sam, and Raymond Fink, "Methodological Considerations of Studying Patterns of Medical Care Related to Mental Illness," *Milbank Mem. Fund Quart.*, **4**, October 1963, 371–399.

A pilot study examined methodological problems in studying the role of the family M.D. in providing medical care for patients who, in his judgment, have a mental, emotional, or psychological condition.

Sharp, Lawrence J., "The Behavioral Scientist in Nursing Research," *Nurs. Res.*, **13**, No. 4, 1964, 327.

Author discusses the problems involved in the collaboration of behavioral scientists with nurses in nursing and nursing research and raises questions of status differences, role differences, and subcultural differences.

Sheldon, Eleanor Bernert, "A Report on an Experimental Program in Nursing Research," *Nurs. Res.*, **13**, No. 1, 1964, 16–19.

A brief description of the assumptions and progress of a scientifically oriented post-master's research program.

Simmons, Ozzie G., and James A. Davis, "Interdisciplinary Collaboration in Mental Illness Research," *Am. J. Sociol.*, **63**, No. 3, 1957, 297–303.

A discussion of need for and problems of interdisciplinary approach to mental-health research.

Solon, Jerry Alan, Cecil G. Sheps, Sidney S. Lee, and Joseph P. Barbano, "Patterns of Medical Care: Validity of Interview Information on Use of Hospital Clinics," *J. Health Hum. Behav.*, **3**, No. 1, 1962, 21–29.

An extensive study concentrating on patients' patterns of obtaining medical care in clinics revealed high validity of interview data and actual use of clinics.

Stankiewicz, Barbara, "Guides to Nursing Intervention in Projective Patterns of Suspicious Patients," *Perspectives Psychiat. Care*, **2**, No. 1, 1964, 39.

The author gives five principles for use in handling patients with patterns of suspicious behavior: (1) they need to learn to trust themselves, (2) they need to be able to trust others, (3) they need to test reality, (4) they need to experience success in groups, and (5) they need outlets for anger and aggressive drives.

Turner, George C., "Problem-Solving — A Changing Concept," *Sci. Teacher*, **24**, No. 339, 1957, 350–351.

There is no set order of steps to be followed in solving problems. The individual sometimes moves from analyzing a situation to a conclusion without stating definite problems or hypotheses.

Vidich, Arthur J., Joseph Bensman, and Maurice R. Stein (Eds.), *Reflections on Community Studies*, New York: Wiley, 1964.

A series of highly personal accounts of their own experiences by sociologists who have written "classics" studies in community settings.

Vinter, Robert, "Analysis of Treatment Organization," *Soc. Work*, **8**, No. 3, 1963, 3–15.

The major operational features of complex organizations, whose primary tasks are to change persons identified as deviant, are outlined.

Wiener, Philip, *Readings in Philosophy of Science*, New York: Scribner, 1953.

A series of readings on science, its concepts, methods, problems, analyses, and syntheses.

Williams, Richard H., "The Strategy of Sociomedical Research," in Howard E. Freeman et al. (Eds.), *Handbook of Medical Sociology*, Englewood Cliffs, N.J.: Prentice-Hall, 1963, pp. 423–447.

This essay is directed at identifying the institutional and other arrangements for doing sociomedical research, characteristic problems of working in medical settings, sources of support for sociomedical research, and discussion of the soundness of these sources.

## ADDITIONAL READINGS

Arrington, George Ernest, Jr., and Gabriel Hilkovitz, "Man and His Environment: A New Course of Study at the Medical College of Virginia," *J. Med. Educ.*, **39**, No. 7, 1964, 704.

A description of a new course in social-science concepts introduced to "develop feelings for human beings and respect for the individual."

Bandman, Elsie, et al., "The Patient-Relations Nurse Coordinator," *Am. J. Nurs.*, **64**, No. 9, 1964, 133.

Explaining the role of the coordinator, this article proceeds on the assumption that the patient's welfare is the concern of everyone; therefore the coordinator as the spokesman and agent for the patient should have access to everyone and a mandate to cut across departmental lines.

Becker, Ernest, "Social Science and Psychiatry: The Coming Challenge," *Antioch Rev.*, **23**, No. 3, 1963, 353–366.

A sociological analysis of menopausal depression is made to demonstrate how the social scientist can contribute to the understanding of the etiology and explanation of psychiatric problems.

Belknap, Ivan, *Human Problems of a State Mental Hospital*, New York: McGraw-Hill, 1956.

A study of the variety of kinds of human "everyday" problems of state hospitals.

Bettelheim, Bruno, *The Informed Heart*, Glencoe, Ill.: Free Press, 1961.

This book asks and tries to answer the questions: to which degree can the environment influence and shape man, his life, and his personality, and to which degree can it not; how and to which degree can environment be used to shape life and personality; and how must personality be developed so as to stand up in any environment or, if need be, to change environment for the better.

Boulding, Kenneth E., "After Civilization What?" *Bull. Atom. Sci.*, **18**, 1962, 2–6.

An exploration of the problems and trends toward post civilization.

Brown, Esther Lucile, *Newer Dimensions of Patient Care*, New York: Russell Sage Foundation, 1961.

Discusses the use of the physical and social environment of general hospitals for therapeutic purposes.

Buck, Rodger L., "Behavioral Scientists in Schools of Medicine," *J. Health Hum. Behav.*, **2**, No. 1, 1961, 59–64.

A study of the nature of appointments of social scientists to medical schools; the departmental affiliation, teaching and research roles performed and degrees held by these social scientists.

Chisolm, G. B., "The Psychiatry of Enduring Peace," in M. B. Cohen (Ed.), *Advances in Psychiatry*, New York: Norton, 1959.

Advocates preventive roles for psychiatry rather than treatment; leaves treatment to others.

Clausen, John A., "Social Factors in Disease," *Ann. Am. Acad. Polit. Soc. Sci.*, **346**, March 1963, 138–148.

A discussion of the effects of social order, social definitions, and life styles on health and illness.

Cumming, Elaine, and John Cumming, *Closed Ranks: An Experiment in Mental Health Education,* Cambridge, Mass.: Harvard University Press, 1957.

A demonstration of an attempt to change attitudes regarding mental illness in a Canadian city and the city's subsequent "closing ranks" on the researchers.

Cumming, Elaine, and John Cumming, "The Organization of the Large Mental Hospital: Hindsights and Current Issues," *Hum. Org.,* **21**, No. 2, 1962, 97–106.

A discussion on ways in which such hospitals have been organized and re-organized and the issues remaining to be solved.

Dumas, Rhetaugh Graves, "Psychological Preparation for Surgery," *Am. J. Nurs.,* **63**, No. 8, 1963, 52–55.

The theory of Orlando (*The Dynamic Nurse-Patient Relationship,* Putnam, 1961) is tested to determine the effect of special nursing care of the preoperative patient, with emphasis on the psychological aspects, showing how this care reduces incidence of postoperative complications.

Engel, George, *Psychological Development in Health and Illness,* Philadelphia: Saunders, 1962.

A good textbook for health workers on psychological concepts and methods of dealing with these concepts in patient care.

Gabel, J., "Sociology and Psychiatry: Existential Analysis and Marxism in Psychiatry," *Ann. Sociol.* (France), 1961, 229–246.

A discussion of the uses of existential and Marxism philosophy in psychiatric definitions and treatment.

Jaco, E. Gartley (Ed.), *Patients, Physicians and Illness,* Glencoe, Ill.: Free Press, 1958.

An extensive series of articles by M.D.'s and scientists arranged as a sourcebook.

Katz, Alfred, and Jean S. Felton, *Health and the Community,* New York: Free Press of Glencoe, 1965.

A book of readings on the major programs, issues, and achievements in public-health practice.

King, Stanley H., "Social Psychological Factors in Illness," in Howard E, Freeman et al. (Eds.), *Handbook of Medical Sociology,* Englewood Cliffs, N.J.: Prentice-Hall, 1963, p. 99.

This essay demonstrates that "illness is not solely a biological and physical phenomenon, but an event that occurs in a social context and reflects the intimate association of the person with other human beings."

Lefton, Mark, Shirley Angrist, Simon Dinitz, and Benjamin Pasamanick, "Social Class, Expectations, and Performance of Mental Patients," *Am. J. Sociol.,* **68**, July 1962, 79–87.

A study of sixty-two married female patients indicates that the role of social class and expectations as meaningful concepts in the study of mentally ill patients "awaits the formulation of an adequate frame of reference," and that this frame of reference must recognize the interaction of sociological and psychiatric variables and provide the means by which the relative importance of each may be tested.

Macgregor, Frances Cooke, *Social Sciences in Nursing*, New York: Russell Sage Foundation, 1960.

Describes a course for undergraduate nurses using several subcultural patient cases to demonstrate the use of social science.

McIntire, Charles, "The Importance of the Study of Medical Sociology," *Bull. Am. Acad. Med.*, **1**, 425–434.

Author finds that medical sociology has a twofold aspect: it is the science of the social phenomena of the physicians themselves, as a class apart and separate; and the science that investigates the laws regulating the relations between the medical profession and society as a whole, treating of the structure of both, how present conditions came about, what progress civilization has effected, and everything related to the subject.

Mandell, Arnold J., and Mary P. Mandell, "What Can Nursing Learn from the Behavioral Sciences?," *Am. J. Nurs.*, **63**, No. 6, 1963, 104–106.

These authors, experts in their fields, discuss a few aspects of behavior that might help the nurse in understanding the patient.

Monteiro, Lois A., "Notes on Patient Teaching — A Neglected Area," *Nurs. Forum*, **3**, No. 1, 1964, 26–33.

The nurse as a teacher is involved in interpreting to patients and families scientific facts basic to the maintenance and promotion of health. The teaching can be very formal or incidental.

Moore, Wilbert E., and Melvin M. Tumin, "Some Social Functions of Ignorance," *Am. Sociol. Rev.*, **14**, No. 6, 1949, 788–795.

A sociological analysis of the positive functions of ignorance.

Polak, Paul, "Generalization Gradients and A Continuum of Social-Psychiatric Therapies," *J. Ft. Logan Mental Health Center*, **2**, No. 1, 1964, 1–10.

Disagrees with notion that "insights" gained in psychotherapy result in behavior change and that the new learning is transferred to "real" life after discharge. Discusses need for psychiatric programs to be as close to patients' "real" life as possible for maximum therapeutic effect.

Roney, James G., Jr., "An Anthropologist Looks at Medicine," *Pa. Med. J.*, **63**, July 1960, 1000–1004.

Author finds that since health and medical systems are a part of our present world competition, if we do not voluntarily solve our problems, it is conceivable that, in the interest of survival, the federal government may solve it for us.

Roney, James G., Jr., "Social Sciences in the Teaching of Public Health," *J. Health Hum. Behav.*, **1**, No. 1, 1960, 47–52.

Discussion of the contributions of social science to public health in program development, operation, administration, and in epidemiological studies.

Ruhlman, Rose, and Toaru Ishiyama, "Remedy for the Forgotten Back Ward," *Am. J. Nurs.*, **64**, No. 7, 1964, 109.

A study of the factors accounting for high-accident frequency on a "vegetated" back ward.

Sanua, Victor, "Sociocultural Factors in Responses to Stressful Life Situations: The Behavior of Aged Amputees as an Example," *J. Health Hum. Behav.*, **1**, No. 1, 1960, 17–24.

An exploratory study designed to test the hypothesis that there are sociocultural components in patients' reactions to stress situations and disabilities.

Scheff,, Thomas J., "Control over Policy by Attendants in a Mental Hospital," *J. Health Hum. Behav.*, **2**, No. 2, 1961, 93–105.

A study of how attendants can and do control M.D.'s, patients, and organizational policy in mental hospitals.

Schwartz, Morris S., Emmy Lanning Shockley, et al., *The Nurse and the Mental Patient: A Study in Interpersonal Relations*, New York: Russell Sage Foundation, 1956.

A summation of experiences in working in disturbed patient wards and the observed dynamics of interpersonal relations on the ward.

Shryock, Richard Harrison, *Medicine and Society in America: 1660–1860*, Ithaca, N. Y.: Cornell University Press, 1962.

An historical rendering of the medical profesison, medical thought and practice, health and disease, and the change in society which affect medicine.

Simmons, Leo W., and Harold G. Wolff, *Social Science in Medicine*, New York: Russell Sage Foundation, 1954.

A presentation of the importance of social and cultural factors in disease and care.

Skipper, James K., Jr., et al., "Some Possible Consequences of Limited Communication between Patients and Hospital Functionaries," *J. Health Hum. Behav.*, **5**, No. 1, 1964, 34–39.

A review of the meaning and functions of communication to hospitalized patients and some barriers to that communication.

Stainbrook, Edward, "Man and His Changing Environment: Health and Disease and the Changing Social and Cultural Environment of Man," *Am. J. Pub. Health*, **51**, 1961, 1005–1013.

An excellent article on trends, social class, culture, role, socialization, and the necessity to utilize these concepts in the care of the sick.

Steiger, William A., Francis H. Hoffman, Victor A. Hansen, and Herman Niebuhr, "A Definition of Comprehensive Medicine," *J. Health Hum. Behav.*, **1**, No. 2, 1960, 83–85.

A definition of comprehensive medicine as taught at Temple University stating that its most significant feature is that it is patient oriented rather than disease oriented.

Straus, Robert, "A Role for Behavioral Science in a University Medical Center," *J. Am. Acad. Polit. Soc. Sci.*, **346**, March 1963, 99–108.

A description of the roles for social scientists in planning, activation, teaching, and research in a new medical center at University of Kentucky.

Straus, Robert, and John A. Clausen, "Health, Society and Social Science," *J. Am. Acad. Polit. Soc. Sci.*, **346**, March 1963, 1–8.

A discussion of the holistic approach to medical science and comprehensive health care.

Susser, M. W., and W. Watson, *Sociology in Medicine*, New York: Oxford University Press, 1962.

A good book on the relationship of culture, class, mobility, family, and socialization, to health, the economy, and social support.

Thomas, Betty J., "Clues to Patient's Behavior," *Am. J. Nurs.*, **63**, No. 7, 1963, 100–102.

A discussive article on the application of psychiatric nursing principles to medical-surgical behavior.

Willie, Charles V., "Sociology in Medicine," *N. Y. St. J. Med.*, **61**, May 1961, 1715–1720.

Author defines the goals of medical sociology as the creation of information that will help persons in the health professions to determine, within their range of knowledge and specialty, the care and services most suitable for a patient and a community.

Wilson, Robert N., "Patient Practitioner Relationships," in Howard E. Freeman et al. (Eds.), *Handbook of Medical Sociology*, Englewood Cliffs, N.J.: Prentice-Hall, 1963, pp. 273–295

An exposition of the reciprocal relationship of doctor and patient; the contradiction of the one-to-one relationship in an increasingly specialized and social milieu; the increasing dependence of patient upon medical team effort rather than the arts of one individual healer.

Wolford, Helen G., "Complemental Nursing Care and Practice," *Nurs. Forum*, **3**, No. 1, 1964, 8–20.

A developmental approach to a new role for nurses as an independent practitioner who follows the patient through an entire critical episode through various agencies. A new approach to continuity of patient care.

Young, Donald R., "Behavioral Science Application in the Professions," in Bernard Berelson (Ed.), *The Behavioral Sciences Today*, New York: Basic Books, 1963, pp. 222–233.

A discussion of ways in which the health professionals and social scientists benefit from improved liaisons with those of applied and theoretical orientations.

# Name Index